Mennonite Church USA

2003 Directory

J. Ron Byler, editor
James E. Horsch, publishing editor
Doris Mendel Schmidt, congregational editor
Deb Ratzlaff, ministerial editor
Kathryn Rodgers, agency editor
Cindy Snider, churchwide editor
Merrill R. Miller, designer
Karen Bachman, database consultant
Terry Graber, publishing consultant

Faith & Life
Resources

A Division of Mennonite Publishing House
Newton, Kansas
Scottdale, Pennsylvania
Waterloo, Ontario
Winnipeg, Manitoba

Mennonite
Church
USA

MENNONITE CHURCH USA 2003 DIRECTORY
Copyright © 2003 by Faith & Life Resources, Scottdale, Pa. 15683
   Published simultaneously in Canada by Faith & Life Resources, Waterloo, Ont. N2L 6H7
International Standard Book Number: 0-8361-9233-8 (Squareback)
International Standard Book Number: 0-8361-9234-6(Spiral)
International Standard Serial Number: 1527-1722
Printed in the United States of America
Book and cover design: Merrill R. Miller
To order or request information,
Please call 1-800-245-7894 or 1-800-743-2484
Website: www.mph.org

Welcome!

Relationships are the mortar that holds together the various parts of Mennonite Church USA—congregations, area conferences, churchwide agencies, and related organizations.

This book helps us build our relationships as a new church. From these relationships come many ministries through the combined efforts of many people in many places, following God's leading.

You will note that this book comes to you in a different form than what you have seen in previous years. As a part of the reorganizing of Mennonite Publishing House, responsibility for the *Mennonite Church USA 2003 Directory* has shifted to Executive Board staff.

Collaborating with area conferences and Mennonite Publishing House, Executive Board staff has produced a new, condensed directory for Mennonite Church USA. This collaboration is symbolic of the many ways we are all called to work together in shaping our new church.

I think you will find this directory to be an essential resource for effective communication within the many parts of the church that will help build understanding and strong relationships.

As you use this directory, breathe a prayer of gratitude for the leaders and workers listed on its pages.

Blessings to you,

Jim Schrag
Executive Director
Mennonite Church USA Executive Board

Mennonite Church USA

Vision

Vision: Healing and Hope

God calls us
to be followers of Jesus Christ
and, by the power
of the Holy Spirit,
to grow as communities
of grace, joy, and peace,
so that God's healing and hope
flow through us to the world.

Priorities

To follow Jesus Christ more faithfully we are called to:
- enrich our prayer, worship, and study of the Scriptures.
- offer all that we are and have to God.

To grow as communities of grace, joy, and peace we want to:
- call and nurture congregational leaders for ministry in a changing environment.
- practice love, forgiveness, and hospitality that affirm our diversity and heal our brokenness.

To live as people of healing and hope we are committed to:
- invite others to faith in Jesus Christ.
- seek God's peace in our homes, work, neighborhoods, and the world.

Statement adopted 1995 by the Conference of Mennonites in Canada, General Conference Mennonite Church, and Mennonite Church denominational assemblies. The statement was reaffirmed by Mennonite Church Canada and Mennonite Church USA.

Contents

**Want to know where to find an agency or organization?
Use the index in Section Three of this directory.**

Welcome from Jim Schrag 3

Mennonite Church USA Vision 4

Special Days and Church Year 2003 8

Abbreviations 10

Editor's note 11

Section 1: Churchwide agencies 13

           Map 30

           Table: Mennonite Church USA congregations and members 32

Section 2: Conferences and congregations 33

Section 3: Organizational index 119

Section 4: Mennonite World Conference 189

Section 5: Sister denominations 197

Section 6: Ministers 203

Section 7: Congregations by location 265

Table: Mennonite Church USA congregations and members by state .... .280

Churchwide Organizational chart 282

Mennonite Directory Advertisers .... .284

Quickfind 285

Special days and the church year 2003

The following listing includes days that are observed by a significant number of Mennonite Church USA and Mennonite Church Canada congregations. Note that these days are in *italic* typeface. Church agencies that support these observances are indicated in parentheses after the name of the day. The seasons of the church year are also carried.

A Mennonite Church USA calendar that lists dates of area conference, churchwide agency, and other events is maintained by Mennonite Church USA Executive Board, Elkhart, Indiana.

Contact by telephone 574-294-7523, fax 574-293-1892, e-mail info@MennoniteUSA.org, or web www.MennoniteChurchUSA.org/calendar

A Mennonite Church Canada event listing is maintained by the Mennonite Church Canada General Board, Winnipeg, Manitoba. Contact by telephone 204-888-6781, fax 204-831-5675, e-mail office@mennonitechurch.ca, or web www.mennonitechurch.ca/events.

Contact these national offices about these dates in your planning.

JANUARY
6 Epiphany, Season of Epiphany begins. Season is January 6 – March 2.
19 *Many Peoples Sunday* (EB-Office of Cross Cultural Ministries & Mennonite Church Canada Witness) – 3rd Sunday
21 Birthday of Anabaptism, 1525
26 *Mennonite World Fellowship Sunday* (MWC) – 4th Sunday

FEBRUARY
2 *Church Education Sunday* (Mennonite Education Agency & Christian Formation Council) – 1st Sunday

MARCH
2 Transfiguration – Last Sunday after Epiphany
2 *Disability Awareness Sunday* (MMA & MHS) – 1st Sunday
5 Ash Wednesday
7 World Day of Prayer – 1st Friday
9 First Sunday in Season of Lent. Season is March 9 – April 13

APRIL
13 Palm/Passion Sunday, Holy Week begins
17 Maundy Thursday
18 Good Friday
20 Easter Sunday, Season of Easter begins. Season is April 20 – June 1.
27 *Evangelism & Church Planting Sunday* (Mennonite Mission Network & Mennonite Church Canada Witness) – 1st Sunday after Easter

MAY
4 *Stewardship Sunday* (MMA & Christian Formation Council) – 1st Sunday
11 *Christian Family Sunday* (EB Office of Congregational Life & Christian Formation Council) – 2nd Sunday
29 Ascension Day – Thursday, 40 days after Easter

JUNE
8 Pentecost Sunday
8 Season after Pentecost begins. Season is June 8 – November 23

JULY

3-8 Mennonite Church USA Assembly, Atlanta, Georgia

6 *Christian Citizenship Sunday* (EB Office of Congregational Life & Christian Formation Council) – 1st Sunday

AUGUST

11-17 Mennonite World Conference, Bulawago, Zimbabwe

31 *Publishing Sunday* (MPH) – last Sunday

SEPTEMBER

21 *Mutual Aid Sunday* (MMA & Christian Formation Council) – 3rd Sunday

28 *Congregational Life Sunday* EB Office of Congregational Life & Christian Formation Council) – 4th Sunday

OCTOBER

5 Worldwide Communion Sunday – 1st Sunday

19 *Ministers Sunday* (EB Office of Ministerial Leadership & Christian Formation Council) – 3rd Sunday

26 *Mennonite Heritage Sunday* (EB Historical Committee & Christian Formation Council) – last Sunday

NOVEMBER

Missions Month (Mennonite Mission Network & Mennonite Church Canada Witness)

9 *Peace Sunday* (EB Office of Congregational Life & Mennonite Church Canada Witness) – Sunday before the 11th

16 Bible Sunday

30 First Sunday of Advent. Season is November 30 – December 21.

DECEMBER

25 Christmas Day

28 Season of Christmas begins. Season is December 28 – January 4.

Dates in the Church Year, 2003-2016

Year	Sundays after Epiphany	Ash Wed. Lent begins	Easter Sunday	Ascension Day	Pentecost Sunday	Sundays after Pentecost	Season of Advent begins
2003	8	March 5	April 20	May 29	June 8	24	Nov. 30
2004	7	Feb. 25	April 11	May 20	May 30	25	Nov. 28
2005	5	Feb. 9	March 27	May 5	May 15	27	Nov. 27
2006	8	March 1	April 16	May 25	June 4	25	Dec. 3
2007	7	Feb. 21	April 8	May 17	May 27	26	Dec. 2
2008	4	Feb. 6	March 23	May 1	May 11	28	Nov. 30
2009	7	Feb. 25	April 12	May 21	May 31	25	Nov. 29
2010	6	Feb. 17	April 4	May 13	May 23	26	Nov. 28
2011	9	March 9	April 24	June 2	June 12	23	Nov. 27
2012	7	Feb. 22	April 8	May 17	May 27	26	Dec. 2
2013	5	Feb. 13	March 31	May 9	May 19	27	Dec. 1
2014	8	March 5	April 20	May 29	June 8	24	Nov. 30
2015	6	Feb. 18	April 5	May 14	May 24	26	Nov. 29
2016	5	Feb. 10	March 27	May 5	May 15	27	Nov. 27

Notes

The Season of Advent begins with the Sunday nearest November 30. Ash Wednesday is the Wednesday before the sixth Sunday before Easter. Ascension Day is on the Thursday after the sixth Sunday after Easter. Pentecost Sunday is the seventh Sunday after Easter.

Abbreviations

AAMA   African-American Mennonite Association
ACC   Atlantic Coast Conference of the Mennonite Church
AIMM   Africa Inter-Mennonite Mission
AMBS   Associated Mennonite Biblical Seminary
ALL   Allegheny Mennonite Conference
BIC   Brethren in Christ
CAL   Center for Anabaptist Leadership (Southern California)
CAM   Chicago Area Mennonites
CDC   Central District Conference
CIM   Council of International Anabaptist Ministries
CM   Conservative Mennonite Conference
COB   Church of the Brethren
CP   Central Plains Mennonite Conference
CPT   Christian Peacemaker Teams
DC   Washington DC Area Mennonite Workers
EDC   Eastern District Conference
EMS   Eastern Mennonite Seminary
EMU   Eastern Mennonite University
FRC   Franconia Mennonite Conference
FRK   Franklin Mennonite Conference
GC   Goshen College
GS   Gulf States Mennonite Conference
HMONG   Hmong Ministries
IMH   Iglesia Menonita Hispana
IL   Illinois Mennonite Conference
IM   Indiana-Michigan Mennonite Conference
KB   Kingdom Builders (Philadelphia Mennonite Council)
LAN   Lancaster Mennonite Conference
LAO   Lao Mennonite Ministries
MC USA Mennonite Church USA
MCC   Mennonite Central Committee
MDS   Mennonite Disaster Service
MEA   Mennonite Education Agency

MEDA   Mennonite Economic Development Associates
MILC   Mennonite Indian Leaders Council
MM   Mennonite Men
MMA   Mennonite Mutual Aid
MPH   Mennonite Publishing House
MUM   Mennonite Urban Ministry of Denver
MW   Mennonite Women
MWC   Mennonite World Conference
NC   North Central Mennonite Conference
NYC   New York City Council of Mennonite Churches
NY   New York Mennonite Conference
OH   Ohio Conference of the Mennonite Church
PNW   Pacific Northwest Mennonite Conference
PSW   Pacific Southwest Mennonite Conference
RM   Rocky Mountain Mennonite Conference
SC   South Central Mennonite Conference
SE   Southeast Mennonite Conference
UNMC   United Native Ministries Council
VA   Virginia Mennonite Conference
VIET   North American Vietnamese Mennonite Fellowship
WDC   Western District Conference

OTHER ABBREVIATIONS
Ch   Church
Chr   Christian
Comm   Community
Cong   Congregation
Fell   Fellowship
Menn   Mennonite

Editor's note

It takes a team . . .

The new *Mennonite Church USA 2003 Directory* is the result of a team effort.

The Mennonite Church USA Executive Board has joined with area conferences and Mennonite Publishing House to produce this new directory. Each of our conferences has worked with their congregations to gather congregational, conference, and ministerial data. Many others have also played key roles in the *Directory*'s development.

Together, we've produced a resource we hope all parts of Mennonite Church USA—congregations, conferences and agencies—will find useful on a day-to-day basis.

You'll find some new features in this directory:

A fully alphabetized agency section (section 3) will help you quickly find any agency relating to Mennonite Church USA.

An expanded denominational section will give you more background on our sister denominations and church groups (section 5).

The quickfind in the back of the book has been expanded to include e-mail addresses and web pages.

The information in the ministerial and congregational sections has been integrated.

I hope you'll appreciate these changes and the new look for the *Directory*, but I'll quickly admit that it is still a work in progress. We'll be making more changes in future years, so let us know what works well for you and what changes or additions you would find helpful in the future. One new feature we are already working on is a user-friendly web version of this directory.

The year 2002 marked the official birth of Mennonite Church USA. I hope this *Directory* will help shape our work together as we seek to follow God's call for Mennonite Church USA and as we continue on our journey to become a missional church.

J. Ron Byler, editor
RonB@MennoniteUSA.org
Mennonite Church USA 2003 Directory

**Mennonite
Church**
USA

Executive Board

Churchwide Agencies

1

Mennonite Church USA Executive Board

OFFICES
info@MennoniteUSA.org,
www.MennoniteUSA.org
Toll-free 1-866-866-2872 for all staff
Great Plains office: 722 Main St, PO Box 347, Newton KS 67114-0347, 316-283-5100, fax 316-283-0454
Great Lakes office: 500 S Main St, PO Box 1245, Elkhart IN 46515-1245, 574-294-7523, fax 574-293-1892

To e-mail any staff person of the Mennonite Church USA Executive Board, use first name and first initial of last name @MennoniteUSA.org

BOARD
Ervin Stutzman (stutzerv@emu.edu), moderator, 1315 Harmony Dr, Harrisonburg VA 22802, 540-432-4261; D. Duane Oswald, moderator-elect; Ruth Naylor, secretary; James M. Harder and Roy Williams, at-large members; B. Elaine Bryant; Cleon Claassen; Leslie Francisco III; Susan Gingerich; Pat Hershberger; Edith Landis; Olivette McGhee; Harold N. Miller; Sue E. Miller; Shoua Moua; Jane Hoober Peifer; Lois Thieszen Preheim; Edwin Rempel; Nancy Rodriguez-Lora; Sharon Waltner

Office of Executive Director
Executive@MennoniteUSA.org

STAFF
Jim Schrag, executive director (Great Plains)
J. Ron Byler, associate executive director (Great Lakes)
Shelley Buller, executive assistant (Great Plains)
Kathryn Rodgers, executive assistant (Great Lakes)

INFORMATION
The Office of the Executive Director facilitates the work of the Executive Board, Constituency Leaders Council and the delegate body, building networks of leaders from all parts of the church. Included in the Executive Director's office are the functions of Peace Advocate and Historical Committee.

PEACE ADVOCATE
Peace@MennoniteUSA.org,
www.MennoniteUSA.org
330-683-6844, fax 330-683-6844
PO Box 173, Orrville OH 44667-0173

Staff
Susan Mark Landis, peace advocate (Orrville, Ohio)
Kathy Harshbarger, peace advocate assistant (Great Lakes)

Information

The Peace Advocate leads and organizes prophetic witness and peace and justice advocacy on behalf of Mennonite Church USA. See also Peace and Justice Support Network in section 3.

HISTORICAL COMMITTEE

Goshen Archives: 1700 S Main St, Goshen IN 46526-4794, 574-535-7477, fax 574-535-7756, archives@goshen.edu/mcarchives, www.goshen.edu/mcarchives

North Newton Archives: 300 E 27th St, North Newton KS 67117-0531, 316-284-5304, fax 316-284-5843, mla@bethelks.edu, www.bethelks.edu/services/mla

Staff

John Sharp, director (Goshen)
Cathy Hochstetler, assistant archivist (Goshen);
James Lynch, assistant archivist (North Newton);
Ruth Schrock, archives assistant (Goshen);
Dennis Stoesz, archivist (Goshen);
John D. Thiesen, archivist (North Newton)

Information

The purpose of the Historical Committee is to help the church—individuals, congregations, conferences and agencies—to preserve its records and discover the significance of Mennonite history for daily life, work, and the church's mission in the world. (See Historical Organizations in Section 3 for local agencies.)

Office of Administration

Administration@MennoniteUSA.org

STAFF

Ted Stuckey, director (Great Plains)
Karen Bachman, IT technician (Great Plains); Larry Becker, IT and building manager (Great Plains); Carol Epp, administrative assistant (Great Lakes); Karen Kaufman, administrative assistant (Great Plains); Marilyn Loganbill, assistant treasurer (Great Plains); Deb Ratzlaff, receptionist (Great Plains); Lela Mae Sawatzky, receptionist (Great Plains); Doris Schmidt, receptionist (Great Plains); Robin Schrag, con-

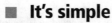

troller (Great Plains); Jarrett Stucky, assistant to the director (Great Plains)

INFORMATION
The Office of Administration provides for finances, asset management, accounting, and auditing. (See also separate listing for Church Extension Services in section 3.)

Office of Communications
Communications@MennoniteUSA.org

STAFF
Cindy Snider, director (Great Plains)
Ken Gingerich, graphic design coordinator (Great Lakes); Alex Naula, web designer (Goshen, Ind.); Laurie Oswald, news service director (Great Plains); Doris Schmidt, Mennonite Church USA Directory assistant (Great Plains); Jo-Ann Schmidt, administrative assistant (Great Plains)

INFORMATION
The Office of Communications articulates the church's identity, communicates news, and provides a public voice to others.

Office of Congregational Life
CongregationalLife@MennoniteUSA.org

STAFF
Marlene Kropf, director (Great Lakes)
Evon Castro, administrative assistant (Great Lakes); Ken Hawkley, assistant director, Discipling Ministry (18050 Marlin Lane, Homewood IL 60430-1929); Linford and Mary Etta King, assistant directors, Community Life Ministry (311 N Lime St, Lancaster PA 17602); Steve Ropp, youth minister (601 E Taylor St, Bloomington IL 61701-5346); Noel Santiago, assistant director, Witness and Peace Ministry (771 Route 113, Souderton PA 18964)

INFORMATION
The Office of Congregational Life equips congregational leaders for ministry.

Office of Convention Planning
ConventionPlanning@MennoniteUSA.org

STAFF
Jorge Vallejos, director (Great Lakes)
Sue Conrad, assistant director (Great Lakes); Carol Epp, administrative assistant (Great Lakes); Lana Miller, assistant director (Great Lakes); Louise Showalter, administrative assistant (Great Lakes)

INFORMATION
The Office of Convention Planning provides staff and organizational planning for the biennial assembly of Mennonite Church USA. This assembly includes conventions for all ages including adults, young adults, youth, junior high youth, and children.

Office of Cross-Cultural Relations

Cross-Cultural@MennoniteUSA.org
2311 Tower Place, Hampton VA 23666
Toll-free 1-866-866-2872 and 757-826-0241,
fax 757-825-8771

STAFF
Kenyetta Aduma, director (Hampton VA)
Ammeral Johnson, administrative assistant
(Hampton VA)

INFORMATION
The Office of Cross-Cultural Relations serves the
needs of persons of color and promotes their
participation in the wider church.

Office of Ministerial Leadership

MinisterialLeadership@MennoniteUSA.org

STAFF
Keith Harder, co-director and denominational
minister (Great Plains)
Dale Stoltzfus, co-director and denominational
minister (270 Ivy Terrace, Lancaster PA
17601)
Diane Zaerr Brenneman, denominational minis-
ter (1061 480th St SW, Parnell IA 52325);
Gilberto Flores, denominational minister (Great
Plains)
Kathy Harshbarger, administrative assistant
(Great Lakes)
Deb Ratzlaff, administrative assistant (Great
Plains)
Steve Ropp, youth minister (601 E Taylor St,
Bloomington IL 61701-5346)

INFORMATION
The Office of Ministerial Leadership supports
conference ministers and pastors in their leadership roles.

EXECUTIVE BOARD PUBLICATIONS
Equipping (10 issues per year) Melanie
Mueller, editor; Mennonite Church USA bulletin
inserts, Cindy Snider, editor; *Mennonite Church
USA Directory*, J. Ron Byler, editor; *Mennonite
Historical Bulletin* (quarterly), John E. Sharp,
editor; *Mennonite Life* (online quarterly), John
D. Thiesen, James C. Juhnke, and Raylene Hinz-
Penner, editors

Committee/Council

LEADERSHIP DISCERNMENT COMMITTEE
The Leadership Discernment Committee is
charged by the Delegate Assembly to discern
persons to serve on the boards of churchwide
agencies and to bring a slate of nominees to the
Delegate Assembly for their affirmation.

Members
Mark Weidner, chair (mweidner@ambs.edu),
3003 Benham Ave, Elkhart IN 46517 (574-295-
3726); Sarah Arn; Lara Hall Blosser; Rose
Covington; Ivorie G. Lowe; Lloyd Miller; Ruth A.
Suter; Bill Zuercher

CONSTITUENCY LEADERS COUNCIL (CLC)
Leaders from each area conference and recognized group meet together at least twice each
year to provide counsel and advice to the
Mennonite Church USA Executive Board and to
engage in conference-to-conference dialogue.
Representatives are listed in sections 2 and 3
with each conference and recognized group.

Officers/Staff
D. Duane Oswald, chair (doswald@avante-
health.com), 1111 E Herndon Ave, Suite 308,
Fresno CA 93720 (559-431-9410); Janeen B.
Johnson, vice chair; Bill Zuercher, recording
secretary; Jim Schrag, staff

We are called
to teach this faith
to our children and our
children's children. Deut. 4:9

Mennonite Education Agency

An agency
of
**Mennonite
Church**
USA

(866) 866-2872
info@mea.mennonite.net

The mission of the Mennonite Education Agency is to strengthen the life, witness, and identity of the Mennonite Church USA through education.

MEA is committed to serving the educational needs of the church from early childhood through seminary – developing vision, dismantling racism, facilitating cooperation and collaboration, providing advocacy and support services, and building relationships and accountability between schools and the church.

Mennonite Education Agency

OFFICE
info@mea.mennonite.net
www.mcusa.mennonite.net/agency_mea
Toll-free 1-866-866-2872 and 574-642-3164,
    fax 574-642-4863
63846 County Road 35, suite 1, Goshen IN
46528-9621

STAFF
Carlos Romero, executive director
    (carlosr@mea.mennonite.net)
Jennie Kauffman, office manager
    (jenniek@mea.mennonite.net)
Ruth Schrock, administrative assistant
    (ruths@mea.mennonite.net)
Lisa Heinz, associate director (finance focus)
    (lisah@mea.mennonite.net)
J. David Yoder, associate director (elementary and
    secondary focus) (jdavidyoder@aol.com)
To be named: associate director (communica-
    tion focus)

INFORMATION
The mission of the Mennonite Education Agency
is to strengthen the life, witness, and identity of
Mennonite Church USA through education.

The Education Integration Committee envisions
a Mennonite Church USA that is characterized
by a passionate commitment to the lordship of
Jesus Christ in all aspects of corporate and personal life; a deep and abiding dedication to the
distinctive Anabaptist/Mennonite expression of
Christian faith as summarized in the Confession
of Faith in a Mennonite Perspective; the assur-
ance that this faith expression must be antiracist,
including persons "from every nation, from all
tribes and peoples and languages" (Rev. 7:9);
the conviction that we are called to teach this
faith to our children and children's children
(Deut. 4:9); and the certainty that church
schools play a critical role in this process.

Mennonite Education Agency relates to the
Mennonite Elementary Education Council,
Mennonite Secondary Education Council,
Associated Mennonite Biblical Seminary, Bethel
College, Bluffton College, Eastern Mennonite
University, Goshen College, and Hesston College.
(See "Schools" in section 3 for information on
secondary and elementary schools, as well as
separate listings for each college and seminary.)

Enrollments (fall 2001) of MEEC schools were
5,252 total; MSEC schools (grades 9-13) were
3,390 total (2,154 Mennonite and other
Anabaptist); MC USA colleges (Bethel, Bluffton,
EMU, GC, HC): full-time undergraduate were
3,519 total (1,651 Mennonites), 3,666 full-
time-equivalent (FTE), 192 degree-completion
students, 335 graduate students; MC USA seminaries (AMBS, EMS): full-time were 115 total,
61 MC USA/MC Canada, 76 Mennonites, 180
part-time, 164 FTE.

BOARD
Rosalind E. Andreas, chair
(randreas@zoo.uvm.edu), 113 Ridge Top Lane,
Essex Junction VT 05452, 802-879-0012; Ed
Diller, vice chair; James L. Rosenberger, secre-
tary; Jesus M. Cruz, treasurer; Terri J. Plank
Brenneman; Anne Hege; Susan Schultz Huxman;
Paul Johnson; Franzie L. Loepp; John Stahl Wert;
Connie F. Stauffer

FUND FOR PEOPLEHOOD EDUCATION REFERENCE COMMITTEE
Jesus M. Cruz, chair
(cmj_52@yahoo.com), 441 Surrey Dr,
Lancaster, PA 17602, 717-581-7816; Tim Jost

INVESTMENT COMMITTEE
Phillip J. Rich, chair (pjrich@bright.net), 1201
Lindau St, Archbold, OH 43502, 419-446-2215;
Jesus M. Cruz; Carl B. Harman; Lowell G. Herr;
Fred Liechty, Bob Peters; R. Clair Sauder;
Thomas R. Bishop; Abram H. Clymer; Jeff
Miller; Ronald E. Piper; James L. Histand;
R. Wendell Sauder; Willis Sommer

Mennonite Elementary Education Council

The Mennonite Elementary Education Council is organized to interpret, coordinate, and promote the work of Mennonite elementary schools, both among the schools and their sponsoring groups and throughout Mennonite Church USA.

John S. Weber (Kraybill Mennonite School), chair (weberjj@desupernet.net), 598 Kraybill Church Rd, Mount Joy PA 17552, 717-653-5236; Ken Hartzler (Belleville Mennonite School), 717-935-2184; Joyce Taylor (Central Christian Learning Center), 330-857-2686; Ib Thomson (Chicago Mennonite Learning Center), 773-735-9304; Conrad Showalter (Clinton Christian School), 574-642-3940; Susan Yoder (Conestoga Christian School), 610-286-0353; David L. Sauder (Ephrata Mennonite School), 717-738-4266; Melvin L. Weaver (Gehmans Mennonite School), 717-484-4222; Paul E. Isaacs (Greenwood Mennonite School), 302-349-4131; Tom Burnett (Hinkletown Mennonite School), 717-354-6705; Andrew R. Meiser (Juniata Mennonite School), 717-463-2898; Matthew R. McMullen (Lake Center Christian School), 330-877-2049; Dave King (Lancaster Mennonite School), 717-299-0436; Dwilyn Beiler (Linville Hill Mennonite School), 717-442-4447; Kay Predmore (Lititz Area Mennonite), 717-626-9551; David M. Helmus (Locust Grove Mennonite School), 717-394-7107; Crist Peachey (Manheim Christian Day School), 717-665-4300; Ken Platt (Mt. Pleasant Christian School), 757-482-9557; Neal J. Eckert (New Covenant Christian School), 717-274-2423; Robert D. Rutt (Penn View Christian School), 215-723-1196; Alma Geosits (Quakertown Christian School), 215-536-6970; Jean Martin (Sarasota Christian School), 941-371-6481; Susan Yoder Ackerman (Warwick River Christian School), 757-877-2941; Elvin Kennel (West Fallowfield Christian School), 610-593-5011

Mennonite Secondary Education Council

The Mennonite Secondary Education Council consists of the chief administrator of each participating high school.

J. Richard Thomas (Lancaster Mennonite High School), chair (lmh@redrose.net), 2176 Lincoln Hwy E, Lancaster PA 17602, 717-299-0436; Margarita Kolthoff (Academia Menonita), 787-783-1295; Ken Hartzler (Belleville Mennonite School), 717-935-2184; Allan Dueck (Bethany Christian Schools), 574-534-2567; Frederic A. Miller (Central Christian School), 330-857-7311; Elaine A. Moyer (Christopher Dock Mennonite High School), 215-362-2675; Susan Yoder (Conestoga Christian School), 610-286-0353; J. David Yoder (Eastern Mennonite High School), 540-432-4500; Marlan Kaufman (Freeman Academy), 605-925-4237; Wilbur D. Yoder (Iowa Mennonite School), 319-656-2073; Matthew R. McMullen (Lake Center Christian School), 330-877-2049; Neal J. Eckert (New Covenant Christian School), 717-274-2423; Barbara Moses (Philadelphia Mennonite High School), 215-769-5363; Terry Schellenberg (Rockway Mennonite Collegiate), 519-743-5209; Eugene Miller (Sarasota Christian School), 941-371-6481; Conrad Swartzentruber (Shalom Christian Academy), 717-375-2223; Victor Winter (United Mennonite Educational Institute), 519-326-7448; Eric D. Martin (Western Mennonite High School), 503-363-2000

CHURCHWIDE AGENCIES

1

Mennonite Mission Network

OFFICES

info@MennoniteMission.net,
www.MennoniteMission.net
Toll-free 1-866-866-2872

Great Lakes Office: 500 S Main St, PO Box
370, Elkhart IN 46515-0370, 574-294-8669,
fax 574-294-8669

Great Plains Office: 722 Main St, PO Box
347, Newton KS 67114-0347, 316-283-
5100, fax 316-283-0454

Mennonite Media Office: 1251 Virginia Ave,
Harrisonburg VA 22802-2497, 540-434-
6701, fax 540-434-5556,
info@MennoMedia.org

To e-mail any staff person of Mennonite Mission
Network, use first name and first initial of last
name @MennoniteMission.net.

EXECUTIVE STAFF

Stanley W. Green, executive director/CEO
(StanleyG@MennoniteMission.net)
Erwin Rempel, associate executive director and
senior executive for the division of Mission
Network Services
(ErwinR@MennoniteMission.net)
Barbara Eichorn, corporate secretary
(BarbaraE@MennoniteMission.net)
James R. Krabill, senior executive, Global
Ministries (JamesK@MennoniteMission.net)
Peter Graber, senior executive, Missional
Church Advancement
(PeterG@MennoniteMission.net)

INFORMATION

Mennonite Mission Network, a program agency
of Mennonite Church USA, exists to lead, mobi-
lize and equip the church to participate in holistic witness to Jesus Christ in a broken world. We
envision every congregation and all parts of the
church being fully engaged in God's mission—

across the street, all through the marketplaces
and around the world. The Mission Network
supports ministries in 54 countries, 31 U.S.
states, and six Canadian provinces. Mennonite
Mission Network succeeds the former
Commission on Home Ministries and the
Commission on Overseas Mission (General
Conference Mennonite Church) and Mennonite
Board of Missions (Mennonite Church).

Mennonite Mission Network has four core
ministries: (1) engage people and cultures with
the gospel of Jesus Christ, (2) start missional
congregations, (3) cultivate missional congregations, and (4) foster a missional identity in the
church. Mennonite Mission Network has more
than 165 long-term workers and facilitates
annual assignments for more than 2,000 short-
term volunteers.

Mennonite Mission Network has three divi-
sions and 15 departments: **Global Ministries**
(Africa; East Asia; Europe; Latin America;
Service, Learning and Discipleship; West Asia;
Middle East), James R. Krabill, senior executive;
Missional Church Advancement (Church
Relations and Partnership Formation;
Communications; Development; Leadership
Development; Missional Church Development)
Peter Graber, senior executive; **Mission
Network Services** (Finance, Human
Resources, Information Technology), Erwin
Rempel, senior executive. In addition,
Mennonite Media promotes an Anabaptist
understanding in secular media and creates
resources to assist congregations in their min-
istry.

Mennonite Mission Network operates a variety of mission initiatives and service programs
in North America and beyond, including:
Anabaptist Biblical Training Institute, a leadership training program for Spanish-speak-
ing lay people (Gilberto Flores, director)
City on a Hill, providing church planting and
ministry grants to urban locations (Marty
Bender, administrator)
Group Venture, linking groups to options for

service and spiritual reflection in North America (Del Hershberger, administrator)

Mennonite Voluntary Service, providing one- or two-year opportunities for individuals to live out their faith through service in communities across North America (Scott Siemens and Tonia Stutzman, administrators)

Prayer partner ministry, inviting people to commit to regular prayer for mission (Marietta Sawatzky, facilitator)

RAD (Reaching and Discipling) for young adults (18-30) in team-based discipleship training and outreach in Asia, Europe, Latin America, or North America (Bob Sprunger, administrator)

Second Mile: A Peace Journey for Congregations, an educational tool for congregations who want to proclaim Christ's peace in a broken world (Leo Hartshorn, Rep.)

Service Adventure, promoting service, learning, and spiritual growth for post-high-school students in nine U.S. communities (Chris Kahila, administrator)

SOOP (Service Opportunities for Older People), short-term service opportunities for adults age 50 and older (Arloa Bontrager, administrator)

Third Way Café, an Internet ministry produced by Mennonite Media

Youth Venture, a one- to three-week short-term mission experience for teens (ages 14-20) in North America or internationally (Del Hershberger, administrator)

Mennonite Mission Network has 10 operating partnerships involving congregations, area conferences and other groups organized to accomplish specific mission objectives. Another seven are in some stage of exploration.

Dagestan (Russia) is a partnership with the Friends of the Tabasaran (based in west-central Ohio) to support Christian leadership among the Tabasaran people and build long-term relationships; Joe Henson, facilitator.

DEO (Discipleship Encounter Outreach) is an initiative involving Mennonite Mission Network, Hesston (Kan.) College, Bethel (Kan.) College, Western District and South Central Conference to equip young people to become whole-life disciples of Jesus Christ; Ritch Hochstetler, director.

DOOR (Discovering Opportunities for Outreach and Reflection) Network establishes centers where those who are interested in urban Anabaptist missions are prepared for leadership roles; partners in Denver, Chicago, Miami, Buffalo, San Antonio, and other urban sites; Glenn Balzer, facilitator.

Ecuador is a partnership with the Colombian Mennonite Church and Central Plains Mennonite Conference to provide support and companionship to the indigenous church and people of Ecuador.

Great Lakes Discipleship Center equips young adults to become lifelong, radical disciples of Jesus Christ. Mission Network partners include congregations from the Great Lakes region, Illinois Mennonite Conference, Indiana-Michigan Mennonite Conference, Ohio Mennonite Conference, and the Evangelical Mennonite Church; Brad Bame, facilitator.

Mongolia is a coalition of Ohio congregations (Mongolia Support Group) that support ministry through Joint Christian Services International in Mongolia; Burt Parks, facilitator.

Northwest Ohio Partners in Mission supports long-term mission efforts, particularly through workers in Bolivia and the Dominican Republic; Roger Rupp and Mike Wyse, facilitators.

Patagonia develops new churches and renews existing churches in Patagonia (southern Argentina) and Illinois by building relationships and sharing resources. Mission Network partners include the Argentine Mennonite Church (IEMA), Arm in Arm (a support group from Illinois) and Mennonite Churches in Patagonia (IMPA); Delbert and Frieda Erb, facilitators.

CHURCHWIDE AGENCIES

1

Senegal mobilizes a movement to Christ among the Wolof people of Senegal, leading to the planting of churches. Mission Network partners include Africa Inter-Mennonite Mission and Friends of the Wolof; Earl Roth, facilitator.

South Africa/New Zion is a leadership and people exchange focused on church planting in South Africa and Virginia conference. Mission Network partners include New Zion Church movement based in Pietermaritzburg, South Africa, Calvary Community Church in Hampton, Va., and Virginia Mennonite Board of Missions.

BOARD

Lee Schmucker, chair (LeeSchmuckerMMN@aol.com), 9404 W Wyncroft, Wichita KS 67205, 316-721-2443; N. Leroy Kauffman, vice chair; Linda Blades; Herman D. Bontrager; Tesfatsion Dalellew; Roma J. Eicher; Heidi Regier Kreider; Chuwang Pam; Alice Ruth Ramseyer; Steve Cheramie

Risingsun; Tonya Ramer Wenger; Leonard C. Wiebe; David D. Yoder

PUBLICATIONS

Beyond Ourselves (quarterly) Tom Price, editor; *InterMission* (regular e-mail newsletter); *Links@Mennomedia* (contemporary media newsletter 3x year), Melodie M. Davis, editor; *Missio Dei* (booklet series inviting reflection and dialogue on mission issues), James R. Krabill, editor; Mission Network news (weekly e-mail of news releases from Mennonite Mission Network), Charles T. Jones, editor; *Mustard Seeds* (quarterly for mission partners who provide regular support for four Mission Network projects annually); *Prayer Vine* (monthly guide of daily prayer requests available in print or by e-mail), Marietta Sawatzky, editor; *Urban Connections* (inter-Anabaptist newsletter published 3x a year), Regina Shands Stoltzfus, editor; *x-Tending God's Mission* (quarterly), Stanley W. Green, editor

Building
for the
future
of Mennonite Church USA
and Mennonite Church Canada

Mennonite Publishing House

Faith & Life Resources

Herald Press

Provident Bookstores

Visit us at www.mph.org

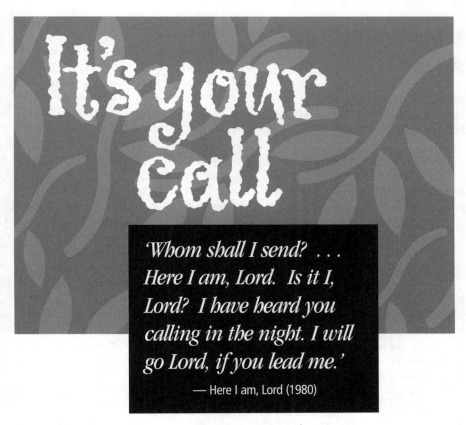

It's your call

> 'Whom shall I send? . . .
> Here I am, Lord. Is it I,
> Lord? I have heard you
> calling in the night. I will
> go Lord, if you lead me.'
> — Here I am, Lord (1980)

Missional, *schmissional*
It's all about how you respond

Throughout history, Christians have found new words to describe their responsibility to God: proclaiming "Jesus is Lord," being Christ-centered, having an Anabaptist vision or asking WWJD. The latest is "missional church." The bottom line is this: Each of us is invited to align our purposes with those of God. The most important thing isn't how we describe it, but how we respond. For help deciding how, contact us today.

Toll-free: 866-866-2872
www.MennoniteMission.net

Mennonite
Mission
Network
The mission agency of Mennonite Church USA

MMA Stewardship Agency

MENNONITE MUTUAL AID

mma@mma-online.org, www.mma-online.org
800-348-7468 and 574-533-9511, fax 574-533-5264
1110 N Main St, PO Box 483, Goshen IN 46527

EXECUTIVE STAFF

Howard Brenneman, president and CEO,
 Howard.Brenneman@mma-online.org
Mel Claassen, chief financial officer,
 Mel.Claassen@mma-online.org
Eunice Culp, vice president, human resources,
 Eunice.Culp@mma-online.org
Rod Diller, senior vice president, trust services
 and Mennonite Foundation,
 Rod.Diller@mma-online.org
Ron Dueck, vice president, group business
 development, Ron.Dueck@mma-online.org
Steve Garboden, senior vice president, adminis-
 trative services and health services,
 Steve.Garboden@mma-online.org
Barth Hague, vice president, marketing services,
 Barth.Hague@mma-online.org
John Liechty, senior vice president, financial
 services, John.Liechty@mma-online.org
Steve Martin, senior vice president, corporate
 marketing, Steve.Martin@mma-online.org
Roger Nafziger, vice president, education and
 development, Roger.Nafziger@mma-online.org
Vyron Schmidt, vice president, fraternal benefits,
 Vyron.Schmidt@mma-online.org
Barb Slagel, vice president, information technol-
 ogy and chief information officer,
 Barb.Slagel@mma-online.org
Karl Sommers, vice president, corporate plan-
 ning, Karl.Sommers@mma-online.org
Jeff Swartzentruber, executive director of
 Mennonite Foundation,
 Jeff.Swartzentruber@mma-online.org

INFORMATION

MMA was founded in 1945. Its mission is to lead Anabaptists toward greater practice of biblical principles of holistic stewardship.

MMA's Board of Directors is elected or appointed from Mennonite Church USA and Mennonite Brethren Church. The organization is composed of 12 active legal entities that handle its administrative services and operate its programs.

MMA offers expertise and assistance to Mennonites and other Anabaptists in pursuing stewardship solutions through its diversified insurance and financial services as well as charitable programs and educational resources.

Insurance includes health, life, long-term care, and disability income coverage, with plans for individuals and groups.

Financial services include mutual funds, annuities, trust services and estate consultation, Mennonite Retirement Trust, staff pension plan for congregations and church institutions, and investment management for individuals and institutions. MMA provides mortgages and other financing for institutions and congregations. All investments are guided by stewardship investing principles.

Mennonite Foundation provides planned charitable giving for individuals and planned giving and investment advisory services for institutions. Mennonite Foundation offers seminars and other educational events and serves members of Mennonite Church USA and other Mennonite and Anabaptist-related groups.

MMA's fraternal benefits include capital development for congregations, matching grants, educational resources, stewardship ministries, and programs in mental illness and disabilities. Fraternal benefits are made possible because part of MMA is a fraternal benefit association, and money that would otherwise be paid in taxes is instead channeled to members and churches. Fraternal benefits do not increase members' premiums or fees.

REGIONAL VICE PRESIDENTS — SALES

Glen Kauffman, 1675-A Virginia Ave, Harrisonburg VA 22802, 540-434-3666; Phil Mason, Ole Town Square, 371 N Old Hwy 81, PO Box 909, Hesston KS 67062, 620-327-4043; Roy Bergey, 1110 N Main St, PO Box 483, Goshen IN 46527-0483, 574-533-9511; David Gautsche, 1110 N Main St, PO Box 483, Goshen IN 46527-0483, 574-533-9411; Leon Hoover, 201 E Oregon Rd, Ste 103, Lititz PA 17543, 717-560-6800; Stanley Schrock, 2224 N Fine St, Suite 101, Fresno CA 93727, 559-458-7205

CHURCH RELATIONS MANAGERS

Lois Bontrager, 5358 Kidron Rd, PO Box 266, Kidron OH 44636, 800-986-9988; Barbara Borntrager, 1675-A Virginia Ave, Harrisonburg, VA 22802, 800-442-7930; Steve Bustos, 1110 N Main St, PO Box 483, Goshen IN 46527-0483, 800-348-7468; Mark Fly, 569 Yoder Rd, PO Box 163, Harleysville PA 19438, 800-332-4141; Beverlee Keck, 14839 Calpella St, LaMirada CA 90638-3004, 800-276-1586; Bob Larson, 1100

N Meridian St, Apt 42, Newberg OR 97132-1187, 800-888-6053; Jan LaRue, 17350 N Estrella Vista Dr, Surprise AZ 85374, 800-686-9450; Brad Miller, 1110 N Main St, PO Box 483, Goshen IN 46527-0483, 800-348-7468; James Miller, 201 E Oregon Rd, Ste 103, Lititz PA 17543, 800-494-6622; Marvin Penner, 371 N Old Hwy 81, PO Box 909, Hesston KS 67062-0909, 877-467-7294; H. James Smith, 1110 N Main St, PO Box 483, Goshen IN 46527-0483, 800-348-7468; Juan Wall, 2224 N Fine St, Ste 101, Fresno CA 93727, 800-643-3747

MENNONITE FOUNDATION REGIONAL REPRESENTATIVES

John Buckwalter, 201 E Oregon Rd, Ste 103, Lititz PA 17543, 800-494-6622; Marion Beyeler, 5358 Kidron Rd, PO Box 266, Kidron OH 44636, 800-986-9988; Stan Brown, 9111 W 21st St N #5, Wichita KS 67205-1809, 316-841-5777; Marlin Hershey, 201 E Oregon Rd, Ste 103, Lititz PA 17543, 800-494-6622; John Hess-Yoder, J.D., West Professional Plaza, 8655 SW

Citizens Dr, Ste 102, PO Box 1010, Wilsonville OR 97070, 800-888-6053; Todd Holsopple, 1110 N Main St, PO Box 483, Goshen IN 46527, 800-348-7468; Steve Hunsberger, 569 Yoder Rd, PO Box 163, Harleysville PA 19438, 800-332-4141; Suzanne Kennedy, 1675-A Virginia Ave, Harrisonburg VA 22802, 800-442-7930; Arlin Lapp, 569 Yoder Rd, PO Box 163, Harleysville PA 19438, 800-332-4141; Greg Miller, 1110 N Main St, PO Box 483, Goshen IN 46527, 800-348-7468; Mike Miller, Ole Town Square, 371 N Old Hwy 81, PO Box 909, Hesston KS 67062, 877-467-7294

BOARD

Bruce Harder, chair (hbc7@qwestnet), 2555 NE 28th St, Portland OR 97212, 503-284-1653; Carol Suter, vice chair; John L. Burkey; Carol L. Duerksen; Ken Enns; David Faber; Natalie A. Francisco; Richard Friesen; Brad Gabel; Kathleen Grieser; Henry Landes; Dave von Gunten; Arlan R. Yoder; Gene E. Yoder; LaVern Yutzy

Mennonite Medical Association

MMA is a group of over 600 Mennonite physicians, dentists and medical/dental students from around the world.

The Association was formed to

- Encourage, guide, and assist Mennonite students in their pursuit of medical and dental careers.
- Practice, uphold, and promote the highest standards and ethics of the medical and dental professions.
- Publish a quarterly journal, the *Mennonite Health Journal*.
- Support and maintain the Anabaptist Center for Healthcare Ethics.
- Hold annual conventions with Mennonite Nurses Association
- Provide funding for Student Elective Term, an opportunity for students to serve in a developing country.

Jep Hostetler, Executive Secretary; Joyce Hostetler, Administrative Assistant
193 E. Frambes, Columbus, OH 43201-1409
MMA@mennmed.org or **Tel/FAX 614-299-8922**

It's your mission

"See, I am making all things new." — Revelation 21:5

"From the past will come the future . . ."

— In the bulb there is a flower

Where's my CHM? COM? MBM? Has anything really changed?

We've heard both kinds of questions at Mennonite Mission Network. We've reassured some that the worldwide ministries of the former mission agencies continue in more than 50 countries. The same is true for familiar North American programs — from Mennonite Voluntary Service and City on a Hill to Mennonite Media and Service Adventure. Transformation is about becoming something new, yet any new creation retains the DNA of its predecessors. At the same time, continuity doesn't preclude becoming a new creation any more than having the same physical features precludes being born again.

Toll-free: 866-866-2872
www.MennoniteMission.net

Mennonite
Mission
Network
The mission agency of Mennonite Church USA

Mennonite Publishing House

MPH is a joint ministry of Mennonite Church Canada and Mennonite Church USA.

OFFICES

Scottdale (info@mph.org, www.mph.org)
724-887-8500, fax 724-887-3111
616 Walnut Ave, Scottdale PA 15683-1999
Newton (flr@mph.org)
316-283-5100, fax 316 283-0454
718 Main St, PO Box 347, Newton KS 67114-0347
Waterloo (hpcan@mph.org)
519-747-5722, fax 519 747-5721
490 Dutton Dr, Waterloo ON N2L 6H7
Winnipeg (flr@mph.org)
204-888-6781, fax 204 831-5675
600 Shaftesbury Blvd, Winnipeg MB R3P 0M4

ORDER FULFILLMENT

Faith & Life Resources—church literature, flr@mph.org, 800-743-2484
Herald Press—trade books, hp@mph.org, 800-245-7894
Provident Bookstores, pbsorder@mph.org, 800-759-4447

EXECUTIVE STAFF

Phil Bontrager, acting CEO (philb@mph.org)
Lisa Burkhart, executive assistant (lburk@mph.org)
Levi Miller, director, Herald Press and Faith & Life Resources (levi@mph.org)
Ken Reinford, director, Provident Bookstores (reinford@mph.org)
Jack Scott, director, Marketing and Development (jscott@mph.org)

Executive office

Phil Bontrager, publisher; Jack Scott, marketing and development; Chris Ronallo, controller; Dan Mark Hertzler, integrated systems; Jonathan Fox, maintenance; Kermit Roth, management information services; Janet Berg, shipping & receiving

Faith & Life Resources

Levi Miller, director; Cynthia Linscheid, manager church sales and marketing; Alma Unrau, customer service; Sandra Johnson, design; Michelle Quinn, proofreader; Debbie Cameron and Lisa Burkhart, administrative assistants; and Editors, see Publications listing that follows.

Herald Press

Levi Miller, director; Sarah Kehrberg, editor; Patricia Weaver, marketing; Jonathan Sutherland, manager, Waterloo, Ont. depot; Merrill R. Miller, design; Pat Bailey, administrative assistant

Provident Bookstores

Ken Reinford, director

INFORMATION

Mennonite Publishing House was founded in 1908 and Faith & Life Press in 1860, with a merger into one publishing entity as Mennonite Publishing House, Inc. in 2001. Governance is by the MPH Board of Directors.

The purpose and function of Mennonite Publishing House is to *equip the church to experience and share (communicate) the gospel*. MPH is comprised of three business units: (1) Faith & Life Resources—congregational publishing; (2) Herald Press—trade publishing; (3) Provident Bookstores—retail sales.

BOARD

Ron Sawatsky, chair (ronsawat@earthlink.net), 224 Harvard Court, Souderton PA 18964, 215-721-2092; Ervin Stutzman, vice chair; James Harder, secretary-treasurer; Bruno Friesen; Henry Krause; Joy Kroeger; Ruth Naylor; Duane Oswald; Sam Steiner; Roy Williams

PUBLICATIONS

Adult Bible Study (quarterly), Byron Rempel-Burkholder, editor (ByronRB@mph.org); *On the Line* (monthly), Mary C. Meyer, editor (mary@mph.org); *Purpose* (weekly), James E. Horsch, editor (horsch@mph.org); *Rejoice!* (quarterly), Byron Rempel-Burkholder, editor (ByronRB@mph.org); *Story Friends* (monthly), Susan Reith Swan, editor (Debbie@mph.org); *WITH* (eight issues per year), Carol Duerksen, editor (debbie@mph.org).

Other publications include Fast Lane Bible Studies; Generation Why Bible Studies; Good Ground Bible Studies; *Hymnal: A Worship Book*; Hymnal Subscription Service; Jubilee: God's Good News; Mennonite Bulletin Services; Second Mile: A Peace Journey for Congregations; Then and Now Herald Bible School Series; and resources related to denominational focus, church membership, peace and justice, stewardship, and Anabaptist heritage.

PROVIDENT BOOKSTORE LOCATIONS AND MANAGERS

Toll-free: 800-759-4447
pbs@mph.org, www.providentbookstores.com
Berne (pbsberne@mph.org)
   260-589-2135, fax 260-589-3925
   159 W Main Street, Berne IN 46711
   Jilaine Graber, manager
Bloomington (pbsblm@mph.org)
   309-662-1432, fax 309-662-4642
   1500 E Empire St, Bloomington IL 61701
   Christina Litwiller, manager

Goshen (pbsgosh@mph.org),
   574-533-9521, fax 219-533-9550
   119 E Lincoln Ave, Goshen IN 46528
   Jeryl Weaver, manager
Lancaster (pbslanc@mph.org)
   717-397-3517, fax 717-397-8299
   Lancaster Shopping Center, 1625 Lititz Pike, Lancaster PA 17601
   Ken Reinford, manager
Branches:
   Ephrata (nhumbert@mph.org), 717-733-2098, fax 717-733-2330, 1065 Sharp Ave, Ephrata PA 17522, Nate Humbert, manager;
   New Holland (nhumbert@mph.org), 717-354-5258, fax 717-354-4656, 16 S Tower Rd, New Holland PA 17557, Nate Humbert, manager
Newton (pbsnewton@mph.org)
   316-283-2210, fax 316-283-0454
   724 Main St, PO Box 347, Newton KS 67114-0347
   Janine Arnold, manager
Wooster (pbsohio@mph.org),
   330-345-4117, fax 330-345-4578
   3721 Burbank Rd, Wooster OH 44691
   Mary Jo Kapper, manager
Souderton (pbssoud@mph.org)
   215-723-4397, fax 215-721-1610
   Souderton Center, 773 Rt 113, Souderton PA 18964
   Doug Landis, manager

Locations of Mennonite Church USA offices and institutions and top 20 states of denominational membership

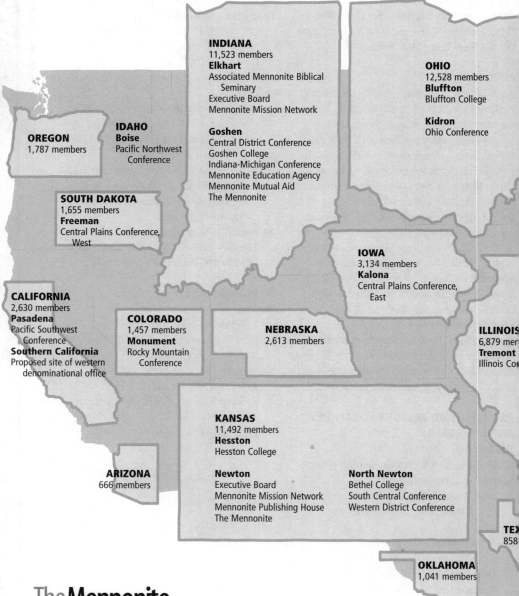

INDIANA
11,523 members
Elkhart
Associated Mennonite Biblical
    Seminary
Executive Board
Mennonite Mission Network

Goshen
Central District Conference
Goshen College
Indiana-Michigan Conference
Mennonite Education Agency
Mennonite Mutual Aid
The Mennonite

OHIO
12,528 members
Bluffton
Bluffton College

Kidron
Ohio Conference

OREGON
1,787 members

IDAHO
Boise
Pacific Northwest
    Conference

SOUTH DAKOTA
1,655 members
Freeman
Central Plains Conference,
    West

IOWA
3,134 members
Kalona
Central Plains Conference,
East

CALIFORNIA
2,630 members
Pasadena
Pacific Southwest
    Conference
Southern California
Proposed site of western
    denominational office

COLORADO
1,457 members
Monument
Rocky Mountain
Conference

NEBRASKA
2,613 members

ILLINOIS
6,879 mer
Tremont
Illinois Co

ARIZONA
666 members

KANSAS
11,492 members
Hesston
Hesston College

Newton
Executive Board
Mennonite Mission Network
Mennonite Publishing House
The Mennonite

North Newton
Bethel College
South Central Conference
Western District Conference

TE
858

OKLAHOMA
1,041 members

TheMennonite

Reprinted and updated with permission from The Mennonite.

*Three congregations who were members of the former General Conference but not of a GC district
    conference have two years to join a Mennonite Church USA affiliated area conference
** 12 South American congregations were members of the former General Conference

WISCONSIN
Exeland
North Central Conference

MINNESOTA
1,008
members

MICHIGAN
1,687
members

NEW YORK
2,346 members
Martinsburg
New York Conference

PENNSYLVANIA
35,962 members

Scottdale
Mennonite Publishing House

Somerset
Allegheny Conference

Lancaster
Lancaster Conference

Chambersburg
Franklin Conference

Morgantown
Atlantic Coast Conference

Souderton
Eastern District Conference
Franconia Conference

Philadelphia
Proposed site of eastern
denominational office

MARYLAND
1,299 members

VIRGINIA
7,811 members
Harrisonburg
Eastern Mennonite University
Eastern Mennonite Seminary
Mennonite Mission Network
Mennonite Media
Virginia Conference

MISSISSIPPI
Philadelphia
Gulf States Conference

FLORIDA
2,345 members
Sarasota
Southeast Conference

MENNONITE CHURCH USA MEMBERSHIP		
Area conference	**Congs.**	**Members**
Unaffiliated*	3	42
Allegheny	35	3,290
Atlantic Coast	35	4,635
Central District	57	7,577
Central Plains	58	8,150
Eastern District	17	2,477
Franconia	44	6,926
Franklin	14	1,180
Gulf States	14	668
Illinois	43	6,278
Indiana-Michigan	92	10,836
Lancaster	203	18,529
New York	17	1,383
North Central	13	513
Ohio	77	11,103
Pacific Northwest	33	2,833
Pacific Southwest	42	3,296
Rocky Mountain	20	1,465
South Central	49	4,283
Southeast	29	2,451
Virginia	65	8,631
Western District	71	11,571
South America**	12	3,719
minus dual-member		
adjustment	51	7,864
Total membership	**992**	**113,972**

Mennonite Church USA
Congregations and Members

For dually affiliated congregations, the "inclusive" columns include all members and all congregations in both area conferences. The "exclusive" columns attribute half of the members and congregations to each conference to give a realistic total tally.

Conference	Number of congs. (inclusive)	# of congs. (exclusive)	# of members (inclusive)	# of members (exclusive)
Unaffiliated [1]	3	3	42	42
Allegheny	35	35	3,290	3,290
Atlantic Coast	35	35	4,635	4,610
Central District	57	42	7,577	6,343
Central Plains	58	58	8,150	8,150
Eastern District	17	17	2,477	2,453
Franconia	44	44	6,926	6,926
Franklin	14	14	1,180	1,180
Gulf States	14	14	668	668
Illinois	43	36	6,278	5,681
Ind.-Michigan	92	87	10,836	10,616
Lancaster	203	203	18,529	18,529
New York	17	17	1,383	1,383
North Central	13	13	513	513
Ohio	77	73	11,103	10,686
Pacific NW	33	33	2,833	2,833
Pacific SW	42	42	3,296	3,296
Rocky Mtn	20	18	1,465	1,328
South Central	49	41	4,283	3,606
Southeast	29	29	2,451	2,451
Virginia	65	65	8,631	8,631
Western District	71	61	11,571	10,757
South America [2]	12	12	3,719	3,719
TOTAL		**992**		**113,972**

(1) These three congregations, formerly members of the General Conference but not of a GC area conference and not dually affiliated with an MC area conference, have two years to join an area conference affiliated with Mennonite Church USA.

(2) Congregations in South America who were members of the former General Conference are included in Mennonite Church USA numbers. The status of these congregations will be addressed during the next year.

Conferences and congregations

2

Mennonite Church USA includes 21 area conferences. Each of these conferences and its affiliated congregations is included in this section.

At the beginning of this section is a list of three congregations that were formerly members of the General Conference but not a GC area conference and not dually affiliated with an MC area conference. Congregations from South America that were formerly members of the General Conference are listed at the end of this conference section.

The chart on the previous page, "Mennonite Church USA Congregations and Members," summarizes membership in Mennonite Church USA area conferences and congregations.

See listing of abbreviations of area conferences, recognized groups, church agencies and denominations on page 10 in the front of the Directory.

A DESCRIPTION OF EACH ITEM INCLUDED IN THE CONGREGATIONAL ENTRY IS AS FOLLOWS:

Name	**(ID number)**	**(Affiliation/s)**	**Membership**
Bethel Menn Community Ch	(3602)	(DA, AC, GCMC, NYC)	28

Mailing address
PO Box 5593, Chicago IL 60680

Telephone, fax, e-mail, web
312-922-5333, fax 312-421-2551, gibor@megsinet.net

Location of meetingplace (if different from mailing address)
1434 S Laflind

Name(s) of pastoral team member(s), title
Tony Bianchi, pastor

FOR EXAMPLE
Bethel Menn Community Ch (11825) (IL, CAM, AAMA) 40
PO Box 5593, Chicago IL 60680
312-922-5333, fax 312-421-2511, gibor@megsinet.net
1434 S Laflind
   Tony Bianchi, Pastor

Conference Unaffiliated

(These former General Conference congregations have until February 2004 to join an MC USA area conference.)

Congregations

Atlanta Menn Fell (10291) **19**
℅ Susan Gascho, Menn Hospitality House, 683 Grant St, Atlanta GA 30315
404-622-2300, gascho606@aol.com
St Paul's U Methodist Church, 501 Grant St SE
   Susan Gascho, Pastor

Richmond Menn Fell (10042) **18**
7612 Wanymala Rd, Richmond VA 23229-4239
804-627-5338, jesing@lycos.com,
http://richmond.va.us.mennonite.net
   Jon Singletary, Pastor

Zion Menn Ch (6845) **5**
PO Box 682, Canton OK 73724

Allegheny Mennonite Conference

OFFICE
officeamc@cs.com
814-443-2007, fax 814-445-3418
111 E Main St, PO Box 12, Somerset PA 15501

STAFF
Kathy Holsopple, administrator assistant
(officeamc@cs.com)
Kurt Horst, conference minister
(kurtamc@cs.com)
Joy Cotchen, youth minister
(jcotchenamc@cs.com)

GENERAL INFORMATION
Year founded: 1876
Members: 3,290
Congregations: 35
Ministers: 70
CLC reps: Kurt Horst, Lawrence Brenneman, and
Donna Mast
Annual Conference: July 17-20, 2003

EXECUTIVE COMMITTEE
Lawrence Brenneman, moderator, RR 6 Box
6636, Keyser WV 26726, 304-788-0277; Gloria
Rosenberger, moderator-elect; Mary Beth Lind,
Jim Rosenberger, Charles Shenk, Jeanne
Smucker, Enos Tice

PUBLICATION
Conference News (Monthly), Donna Mast, editor (kingview@westol.com), 1007 Kingview Rd,
Scottdale PA 15683, 724-887-9451

COMMISSIONS
Finance and Stewardship Commission. Jim
Rosenberger, chair (jlr@stat.psu.edu), 464
E Foster Ave, State College PA 16801, 814-
234-2167; Roger Oswald, Tony Kanagy
Missions Commission. Jeanne Smucker, chair
(jmrsmucker@aol.com), 1054 Black Forest
Rd, Pittsburgh PA 15235, 412-731-0876;
Ken Litwiller, Steve Kriss III
Faith, Life, and Procedures Commission.
Enos Tice, chair (enostice@gcnet.net), 117
Mineral St, Salisbury PA 15558, 814-662-
4331; Trish Yoder, Melvin Blough
Leadership Commission. Charles Shenk,
chair (shenk@allusa.net), 206 Newcomer
Dr, Scottdale PA 15683, 724-887-7641;
Steven Heatwole, Judy Nord, Steve Sauder
Mission and Service Commission. Jeanne
Smucker, chair (jmrsmucker@aol.com),
1054 Black Forest Rd, Pittsburgh PA 15235,
412-731-0876; Ken Litwiller, Steve Kriss III
Youth Cabinet. Joy Cotchen, youth minister,
staff (jcotchenamc@cs.com), PO Box 12,
Somerset PA 15501, 814-443-2007; Becky
Horst, chair; Bill Brubaker, adult advisor;
Jesse Blasko, George Heinlein, Adam Lloyd,
Anna Mast, Bret Miller, Sarah Ramer, Marcy
Spory, Nathan Stehouwer

OTHER CONFERENCE AGENCY AND REPS
Mission and Service Projects
International Guest House, 1441 Kennedy St
NW, Washington DC 20011, 202-726-5808;
Annabelle Kratz, board chair
Mennonite Urban Corps—Pittsburgh. 5615
Stanton Ave, Pittsburgh PA 15206, 412-362-
2268
Offenders Ministry, Don Speigle, minister,
5689 Somerset Pike, Boswell PA 15531,
814-629-5947
VS Projects, Philippi Service Adventure Unit, 26
Beech St, Philippi WV 26416, 304-457-4652

Congregations

Barrville Menn Ch (10140) (ALL) **81**
48 Barrville Mountain Rd, Reedsville PA 17084
717-935-2583

Blough Menn Ch (10157) (ALL) **102**
794 Woodstown Hwy, Hollsopple PA 15935
814-479-7535, bloughchurch@hotmail.com,
http://www.hows.net/15935BMC
    Leon Hostetler, Contact Person

Boyer Menn Ch (10165) (ALL) 71
RR 1 Box 73, Mifflinburg PA 17844
570-966-2392
Oak Dr, Rt 2, Middleburg
   Samuel J. Yoder, Pastor

Canan Station Menn Ch (10173) (ALL) 70
RR 2 Box 455, Burns Ave, Altoona PA 16601
814-695-0341
   Daryl Dawson, Pastor

Carpenter Park Menn Ch (10181) (ALL) 185
2662 Carpenters Park Rd, Davidsville PA 15928
814-288-3264, fax 814-288-4624,
carpenterparkchurch@netzero.net
   Todd Brenneman, Pastor

Cornerstone Fell Menn Ch (29942) (ALL) 35
24 Devon Dr, Hollidaysburg PA 16648
814-695-8935, RevJJJ@aol.com,
http://www.hows.net/16648CMF
YWCA, 224 Union Ave, Altoona
   Jeff J. Jones, Pastor

Crossroads Community Ch (10488) (ALL) 43
1259 Scalp Ave, Johnstown PA 15904-3137
814-266-5000, NRothccc@aol.com
Just west of Rt 219 & Scalp Ave Interchange
   Nelson R. Roth, Pastor

First Menn Ch (10215) (ALL) 46
705 Somerset St, Johnstown PA 15901
814-535-1688

Glade Menn Ch (10231) (ALL) 105
5011 Accident Bittinger Rd, Accident MD 21520
301-245-4285, fax 301-245-4285, gladechurch@juno.com,
http://www.forministry.com/21520gmc

Gortner Union Ch (22632) (ALL, COB) 31
PO Box 464, Oakland MD 21550
301-334-7969, ssauder@pennswoods.net
4391 Mason School Rd
   Steve Sauder, Pastor

Hyattsville Menn Ch (10223) (ALL, DC) 135
4217 East-West Hwy, Hyattsville MD 20782
301-927-7327, fax 301-596-9498, melschmidt@msn.com,
http://www.ence.umd.edu/~klbrubak/hyat/hyat.html
   Melvin D. Schmidt, Pastor
   Cynthia Lapp, Pastor for Music and Arts

Kaufman Menn Ch (10256) (ALL) 121
916 Miller Picking Rd, Davidsville PA 15928
814-479-7813, Kmcmenno@yahoo.com,
http://www.hows.net/15935KMC
Miller Picking Rd, 1/2 mile east of Rt 403 N
   Don Hamsher, Pastor

Kingview Menn Ch (10264) (ALL) 134
1007 Kingview Rd, Scottdale PA 15683
724-887-9451, kingviewch@juno.com
   Conrad Mast, Co-Pastor
   Donna Mast, Co-Pastor

Living Way Fell (11434) (ALL) 0
931 Soap Hollow Rd, Hollsopple PA 15935-8417
814-288-5763

Manbeck Menn Ch (10280) (ALL) 47
RR 1, Beaver Springs PA 17812
570-658-5333
Stage Rd

Maple Grove Menn Ch (21931) (ALL) 284
PO Box 955, Belleville PA 17004
717-935-9900, mgmcbe@acsworld.com
115 Maple Grove Rd

Martinsburg Menn Ch (10298) (ALL) 105
300 E Spring St, Martinsburg PA 16662
814-793-4211, mmc@wmsburgpa.com,
http://www.martinsburg.pa.us.mennonite.net
   Jeff Shull, Pastor

Masontown Menn Ch (10306) (ALL) 91
PO Box 683, Masontown PA 15461
724-583-7464
Smithfield-Masontown Rd

Meadow Mountain Menn Ch (10322) (ALL) 53
6302 Bittinger Rd, Swanton MD 21561
301-245-4030, revfrederick@hotmail.com
6117 Bittinger Rd
   Duane Frederick, Pastor

Menn Ch of Scottdale (10413) (ALL) 140
801 Market St, Scottdale PA 15683
724-887-7470, fax 724-887-7470, scottmc@westol.com,
http://www.forministry.com/15323mcos
   Charles E. Shenk, Interim Pastor

Mill Run Chapel (10330) (ALL) 62
RR 6 Box 1424, Altoona PA 16601
814-942-4003

**Morgantown Ch of the Brethren (27300) (ALL,
COB)** 95
464 Virginia Ave, Morgantown WV 26505
304-292-5616
   Cameron Blake Kaufman-Frey, Pastor

New Life Menn Ch (10740) (ALL) 14
604 Listie Rd, PO Box 7, Listie PA 15549
814-288-5617, rls173@aol.com
Listie Rd
   Ron Spory, Pastor

Oak Grove Menn Ch (10348) (ALL) 56
PO Box 368, Grantsville MD 21536
301-895-4054, fax 301-895-4054, tcfetterly@earthlink.net,
http://www.acountryvillage.com
188 Zehner Rd
   Tim Fetterly, Pastor

Otelia Menn Ch (10355) (ALL) 47
RR 2 Box 147, Mount Union PA 17066
814-543-7269, fax 814-543-7269, davidcjr@juno.com
RD 1 Rt 103

Philippi Menn Ch (26500) (ALL) **20**
216 S Main St, Philippi WV 26416
304-457-2602

Pinto Menn Ch (10363) (ALL) **157**
PO Box 44, Pinto MD 21556
304-726-4386, lthersh1@prodigy.net
13822 Pinto Rd SW
    Philip Dayton, Pastor
    Lester T. Hershey, Associate Pastor
    Paul T. Livengood, Associate Pastor

Pittsburgh Menn Ch (10371) (ALL) **36**
4005 Murray Ave, Pittsburgh PA 15217
412-421-8007, fax 412-421-8007, lukehurst@aol.com

Red Run Menn Ch (10397) (ALL) **31**
15122 Mt Savage Rd NW, Mt Savage MD 21545
301-264-3039
670 Meyersdale Rd (5 miles east of Grantsville)
    Carlos Reyes, Pastor

Rockville Menn Ch (10405) (ALL) **127**
319 Rockville Rd, Belleville PA 17004
717-935-2796, rockmchr@juno.com

Springs Menn Ch (10439) (ALL) **322**
PO Box 127, Springs PA 15562
814-662-4201, springsmc@mapisp.com
1686 Springs Rd
    Steven Jay Heatwole, Pastor

Stahl Menn Ch (10447) (ALL) **112**
1201 Soap Hollow Rd, Johnstown PA 15905
814-288-5523, kaufmanrm@hotmail.com,
http://www.stahlchurch.pa.us.mennonite.net
    Marvin L. Kaufman, Pastor
    Joy Cotchen, Youth Pastor

Thomas Menn Ch (10454) (ALL) **131**
112 Swank Rd, Hollsopple PA 15935
814-479-2127

Tressler Menn Ch (10462) (ALL) **130**
PO Box N, Greenwood DE 19950
302-349-4128, lowpegbechtel@juno.com
Owens Station, Rt 16 E
    Lowell B. Bechtel, Pastor

University Menn Ch (10470) (ALL) **71**
318 S Atherton St, State College PA 16801
814-234-2039, umc@vicon.net,
http://www.vicon.net/~aroth/umc.html

CONFERENCES AND
CONGREGATIONS

2

Atlantic Coast Conference

OFFICE
atlanticcoast@juno.com
610-286-7517 and 800-238-0126
Mailing address: PO Box 737, Morgantown PA
19543-0737
Office location: 2791 Best Rd, Morgantown PA

STAFF
Miriam Martin, conference administrator
(atlanticcoast@juno.com)
Warren L. Tyson, conference minister
(wltyson@yahoo.com)
Merv R. Stoltzfus, conference youth minister
(woodray@aol.com)
Brian Martin, director, Baltimore Discipleship
Center (brian.cheryl@juno.com)

GENERAL INFORMATION
Year founded: 1978
Members: 4,635
Congregations: 35
Ministers: 86
CLC reps: Miriam Martin, LeRoy Petersheim,
Warren Tyson
Annual delegate session: (4th weekend in
October) October 25, 2003

EXECUTIVE COMMITTEE
Edgar Stoesz, moderator
(edgarstoesz@juno.com), 929 Broad St, Akron
PA 17501; James Wenger, moderator-elect;
Nilson Assis, treasurer; Etta Esch, Rick Umble,
Mary Grace Shenk

PUBLICATION
ACC Currents (Bimonthly), Lois E. Whisler, edi-
tor (lwhisler@supernet.com), 10 Panther Dr,
Hanover PA 17331

COMMITTEES
Missions. Nolan K. Good, chair
(ngood21871@aol.com), 7278 Mennonite
Church Rd, Westover MD 21871; Eileen
Graybill, David Horning, Brian Martin, Doris
and Wilmer Martin, Kathy Smucker, Rick
Umble
Finance and Stewardship. Nilson Assis,
chair (nilsassis@aol.com), 105 Eric Ave,
Shillington PA 19607; Robert Bear, Ken Herr,
Lloyd Kuhns, Miriam Martin, Leon Miller,
Ray Ranck
Ministerial Leadership. Calvin L. Yoder,
chair (calyoder@yahoo.com), 100 Quarry
Rd, Leola PA 17540; Jose M. Ortiz, LeRoy
Petersheim, Nancy Sauder, Donna L. Shenk,
Warren Tyson, Lois Whisler, Nelson Yoder
Peace and Justice Task Force. Pat Yoder,
chair (npyoder1@juno.com), 5948 Michele
Dr, Narvon PA 17555; L. Jason Baer, Arlene
Baer, Jim Dunst, Julie Dunst, Miriam Martin,
Jean Senseing, Justin Shenk, Larry Shirk, Jeff
Stoltzfus, J. Richard Thomas
Gifts Discernment. Sue King, John Goldfus,
Nevin and Suetta Grove, Sharon Stoltzfus
Youth. Bill Blank, chair, 160 McHenry,
Parkesburg PA 19365; Kristen Herr, Anne
Hertzler, Michael Layton, Dwight Rohrer,
Candace Stoltzfus, Merv R. Stoltzfus

OTHER CONFERENCE AGENCY AND REPS
Mennonite Women. Flo Harnish, chair
(fharnish@redrose.net), 117 Valley View Dr,
Ephrata PA 17522; Etta Esch, Nina Kauffman
Harnish, Amy Herr, Jean Sensenig, Mae
Shenk, Rosemary Shenk, Elaine Shirk, Ruth
Smucker, Jan Stoltzfus

Congregations

Akron Menn Ch (15651) (ACC) **444**
1311 Diamond St, Akron PA 17501
717-859-1488, fax 717-859-3942, amc@akronmench.org,
http://www.akronmench.org
　　James S. Amstutz, Lead Pastor
　　Dawn Yoder Harms, Pastor

Andrews Bridge Christian Fell (11428) (ACC) . .**23**
1873 Georgetown Rd, Christiana PA 17509
717-529-2553, abcf@epix.net
Georgetown Rd
　　Ray Marvin, Pastor

Ark Bible Chapel (15669) (ACC) **55**
88 Woodchoppertown Rd, Boyertown PA 19512
610-987-0429, kglick@juno.com,
http://www.forministry.com/19512abc
　　Karl G. Glick, Pastor

Bethany Grace Fell (15735) (ACC) **215**
400 Reading Rd, East Earl PA 17519
717-445-6644, fax 717-445-0285, bethanymc1@juno.com
　　Leon R. Shirk, Pastor
　　David K. Stoltzfus, Associate Pastor
　　Todd E. Henley, Youth Pastor

Bethel Menn Ch (15743) (ACC) **84**
2335 Biglerville Rd, Gettysburg PA 17325
717-677-8057
　　Ezra M. Tice, Pastor

Birch Grove Menn Ch (15792) (ACC) **33**
321 Broad St, Port Allegany PA 16743
814-642-9275
Two-Mile Rd, RD 2
　　Neil Binder, Pastor

Black Oak Menn Ch (15800) (ACC) **31**
2247 Stoneybreak Rd, Warfordsburg PA 17267
877-263-6105, pastor@blackoakmennonite.org,
http://www.blackoakmennonite.org
　　Richard E. Rutherford Jr, Pastor

Cedar Grove Menn Ch (15834) (ACC) **200**
13343 Williamsport Pike, Greencastle PA 17225
717-597-3681, fax 717-597-1943, cnmstrite@comcast.net
　　Clarence B. Strite, Interim Pastor

**Community Menn Ch of Lancaster (27441)
(ACC)** **186**
328 W Orange St, Lancaster PA 17603
717-392-7567, cmcl@mennonite.net,
http://cmcl.pa.us.mennonite.net
　　Pamela R. Dintaman, Co-Pastor
　　Katherine Jameson Pitts, Co-Pastor

Conestoga Menn Ch (15875) (ACC) **235**
2769 Main St, Morgantown PA 19543
610-286-9124, fax 610-913-0441,
conestogamc1@juno.com
On Rt 23
　　Alvin B. Horning, Pastor
　　Nelson S. Yoder, Associate Pastor
　　Glenn Leaman, Licensed Deacon

Ephesians Menn Ch (23762) (ACC, NYC, IMH) . .**10**
9 Kew Gardens Rd Apt 102, Jamaica NY 11415
718-261-4752
128 W 16th St, Manhattan
　　Salomon Arias, Pastor

First Menn Ch (15958) (ACC, NYC, IMH) **17**
PO Box 278, Brooklyn NY 11206
718-253-7267, fax 718-253-7267, arpac@aol.com
23 Marcus Garvey Blvd, Brooklyn
　　Reinaldo (Ray) Pacheco, Pastor
　　Moises Sanchez, Assistant Pastor

Forest Hills Menn Ch (16287) (ACC) **332**
100 Quarry Rd, Leola PA 17540
717-656-6227, fax 717-656-8607,
http://www.foresthillschurch.org
　　Calvin L. Yoder, Pastor
　　Shawn D. Moyer, Youth and Young Adult Pastor
　　Evanna Hess, Minister of Nurture and Service

**Friendship Community Ch (16253) (ACC, NYC,
AAMA)** **35**
2281-83 Southern Blvd, Bronx NY 10460
718-933-3915, fax 718-329-0441, FCC2283@juno.com
　　Kenneth Lee Thompson, Pastor

Hebron Menn Ch (23572) (ACC) **53**
13315 Highlane St, Hagerstown MD 21742
301-797-3697, h-mgshenk@juno.com,
http://www.netministeries.org/see/churches/ch05423
　　Harold A. Shenk, Co-Pastor
　　Mary Grace Shenk, Co-Pastor

Holly Grove Menn Ch (16089) (ACC) **174**
7333 Mennonite Church Rd, Westover MD 21871
410-957-3463, hollygmc@juno.com
　　Nathan T. Stucky, Youth Pastor

Hope Community Ch (10039) (ACC) **120**
31 Lobachsville Rd, Fleetwood PA 19522
610-641-8961, pastorjim@hopecomm.org,
http://www.hopecomm.org
　　James K. Beachy, Pastor

Hope Community Fell (11579) (ACC) **62**
224 Hall St, Phoenixville PA 19460
610-327-3109, CLLoyd98@juno.com
　　Gary E. Lloyd, Pastor

Hopewell Menn—Reading (25999) (ACC) **125**
45 S 6th St, Reading PA 19602
610-373-3907, fax 610-373-1604,
hopewellreading@juno.com
6th & Cherry
　　Kendrick J. Scandrett, Pastor

Iglesia Evangelica Menonita Eben-Ezer (28589) (ACC, NYC, IMH) 14
PO Box 1266, Bronx NY 10451
718-798-1794, fax 718-538-9288
1126 Sherman Ave, Bronx
  Jorge Nin, Director of Church Council

Immanuel Community Ch (26468) (ACC, NYC, OD) 109
15020 Barclay Ave, Flushing NY 11355
718-460-2063, fax 718-353-4266, immanuel7@juno.com
  Judy Ebersole, Pastor
  Mark D. Perri, Pastor
  Conrad Sauers, Pastor

Manhattan Menn Fell (3602) (ACC, NYC) 28
314 E 19th St, New York NY 10003
212-673-7970, fax 212-673-7970, mel@childrenofiraq,
http://www.manhattanmennonite.org
221 E 15th St

Maple Grove Menn Ch of Atglen (16188) (ACC) 239
PO Box 480, Atglen PA 19310
610-593-6658, fax 610-593-6658, mgchurch@juno.com
549 Swan Rd
  Enno Jurisson, Pastor
  Bill D. Blank, Associate Pastor

Media Menn Ch (16238) (ACC) 100
PO Box 70, Oxford PA 19363-0070
610-593-2140
5th St & Media Rd
  Richard Umble, Interim Pastor

Menn Congregation of Boston (16246) (ACC, EDC) 49
155 Powder House Blvd, Somerville MA 02144
617-868-7784, biedrzycki@mindspring.com
Clarendon Hill Presbyterian Church

Neffsville Menn Ch (16360) (ACC) 566
2371 Lititz Pike, Lancaster PA 17601-3653
717-569-0012, fax 717-569-2417, neffmc@redrose.net,
http://www.stoprestpray.org
  Linford D. King, Pastor
  Dwight Rohrer, Youth Pastor
  Arthur P. Dyck, Minister of Music

New Life Christian Fell (29249) (ACC) 50
7401 Bernville Rd, Bernville PA 19506
610-488-1235, fax 610-488-1235,
newlifebernville@juno.com
  Marquel Ortiz, Pastor

North Baltimore Menn Ch (27920) (ACC) 52
4615 Roland Ave, Baltimore MD 21210
410-542-0988, fax 410-542-0989, Jaswenger@aol.com,
http://www.forministry.com/21210nbmc
  James Rodney Wenger, Pastor

Ocean City Menn Christian Fell (26476) (ACC) .33
11811 Ocean Gtwy, Ocean City MD 21842
410-213-0821
  P. Melville Nafziger, Interim Pastor

Oley Menn Ch (16436) (ACC) 76
PO Box 394, Oley PA 19547
610-967-3899, fax 610-967-3899, davewinb@aol.com
1571 Memorial Highway
  David W. Bartow, Interim Pastor

Quarryville Community Fell (11104) (ACC) 24
15 E Third St, Quarryville PA 17566
717-786-6842
  Michael D. Hall, Pastor

Ridgeview Menn Ch (16576) (ACC) 409
3723 Ridge Rd, Gordonville PA 17529
717-768-3143, fax 717-768-0569,
ridgeviewchurch@juno.com
  John H. Denlinger, Pastor
  Ray Lapp, Associate Pastor

Rockville Menn Ch (16600) (ACC) 225
210 Cupola Rd, Honey Brook PA 19344
610-273-9577, Rockville@pkfamily.com
  Amos K. Stoltzfus Jr, Pastor
  Eugene Smucker, Assistant Pastor

Sandy Hill Menn Ch (16642) (ACC) 166
420 S Sandy Hill Rd, Coatesville PA 19320
610-857-3959, fax 610-857-4364, shmc@ccis.net,
http://www.sandyhill.pa.us.mennonite.net

Zion Menn Ch—Birdsboro (16865) (ACC) 61
582 Zion Rd, Birdsboro PA 19508
610-856-7417, noah.edie@juno.com
  Noah S. Stoltzfus, Pastor
  Marc Hamer, Assistant Pastor

Central District Conference

OFFICE
cdcoffice@hoosierlink.net
574-534-1485; fax 574-534-8654
1015 Division St, Goshen IN 46528

STAFF
Lloyd Miller, conference minister
(cdcllm@hoosierlink.net)
Lavon Welty, associate conference minister east
(OH, MI) (lavon@wcoil.com)
Wayne Hochstetler, associate conference minister west (IL, WI)
(ilconmin@mindspring.com)
Robert Yoder, conference minister for youth and young adults east (IN, MI, OH)
(bob@im.mennonite.net)
Emma Hartman, administrative assistant
(cdcoffice@hoosierlink.net)

GENERAL INFORMATION
Year founded: 1957
Members: 7,577
Congregations: 57
Ministers: 171
CLC reps: Janeen Bertsche Johnson, Lloyd Miller, Mary Lehman Yoder
Annual Conference: March 6-8, 2003

BOARD OF DIRECTORS
Kevin Farmwald, president
(farmwald@adelphia.net), PO Box 250,
Sugarcreek OH 44681, 330-852-2894; John
Hockman, treasurer; June Thomsen, secretary;
Millard Moser, Mick Sommers

PUBLICATIONS
FOCUS (Monthly) and *The Reporter* (Quarterly)

COMMITTEES
Camp Friedenswald. Joe Graber, chair
(jgraber@adamswell.com), 2377E 400S,

Berne IN 46711, 260-589-8664; Wilbur
Bauman, Kate Gundy, Daryl Martin, Jan
Sohar, Marlene Suter, Jane Troyer, Mary
Lehman Yoder
Education and Nurture. Lois Kaufmann-
Hunsberger, chair (terryandlo@yahoo.com),
914 E Rudisell Blvd, Ft Wayne IN 46806,
260-744-0411; Gwen Gustafson-Zook, Betty
Jeschke, Anita Rediger, John Schrock
Evangelism and Church Development.
Pauline Kennel, chair (lpkennel@msn.com),
888 S Roselle Rd, Schaumburg IL 60193,
847-895-3654; Verle Brubaker, Sheryl Dyck,
Jeanette King, Russell Leinbach, Barry
Schmell
Historical. Ann Hilty, chair
(hiltya@bluffton.edu), 239 College Rd,
Bluffton OH 45817, 419-358-3365;
Margaret Baker, John Heyerly, Gordon Oyer
Ministerial. Robert Ramseyer, chair
(ramseyer@wcoil.net), 107 Magnolia Ln,
Bluffton OH 45817, 419-358-0835; Kathy
Neufeld Dunn, Lois Kaufmann, Phil Waite,
staff
Peace, Service, and Justice. Hilary Bertsche,
John A. Bertsche, Phil Eicher, Elizabeth
Holdeman, Kurt Ritchie
Program. Cindy Ropp, chair
(crropp@juno.com), 601 E Taylor,
Bloomington IL 61701, 309-829-7428;
Gerald Biesecker-Mast, Christine
Schumacher
Stewardship and Finance. John Hockman,
chair (hockman@kuntrynet.com), PO Box
297, Topeka IN 46571, 260-593-2389; Rich
Gerig, Emma Hartman, Lawrence Matthews,
James Mohr

OTHER CONFERENCE AGENCY AND REPS
Mennonite Women. Gail Shetler, president
(bgshetler@yahoo.com), 506 Revere Dr,
Goshen IN 46526, 574-534-5446; Naomi
Baumgartner, Helen Claassen, Jan Croyle,
Rosalie Grove, Gladene Hershberger,
LaVerne Petersen

Congregations

Agora Christian Fell (11103) (CDC, OH) 0
400 W Broad St, Columbus OH 43215
614-280-1212, fax 614-280-0312, agoracf@aol.com
Rebecca J. Bartholomew, Co-Pastor
Richard Bartholomew Jr, Co-Pastor

Ames Menn Ch (23424) (CDC) 6
PO Box 1752, Ames IA 50010-1752
515-233-6384,
allanbeatty@murraystate.alumniconnections.com
233 Walnut Ave Rd, Ste B

Ann Arbor Menn Ch (13508) (CDC, IM) 7
1455 Kelly Green Dr, Ann Arbor MI 48103-2614
734-996-9815
Arrowwood Community Center, 2566 Arrowwood
Chibuzor Vincent Ozor, Pastor

Assembly Menn Ch (22582) (CDC, IM) 127
1201 S 11th St, Goshen IN 46526
574-534-4190, assemblymenn@juno.com,
http://assembly.in.us.mennonite.net
Corner of 11th & New York
Lois Johns Kaufmann, Co-Pastor
Karl Schirch Shelly, Co-Pastor
Mary Lehman Yoder, Co-Pastor

Bethel Menn Ch (2125) (CDC) 40
18443 Illinois Rt 9, Pekin IL 61554
309-346-2726

Boynton Menn Ch (2160) (CDC) 72
PO Box 531, 326 Jefferson St, Hopedale IL 61747
309-449-5503, boynton@bwsys.net
RR 122 & Jefferson
Kurt Litwiller, Pastor
Abraham Cremeens, Associate Pastor

Calvary Menn Ch (2190) (CDC) 359
112 E Adams St, Washington IL 61571
309-444-2722, fax 309-444-7009, calmen@mtco.com
115 E Jefferson St
Verle Alden Brubaker, Pastor

Carlock Menn Ch (2195) (CDC) 65
217 E Washington, PO Box 189, Carlock IL 61725-0189
309-376-2781
Ralph Wayne Foote, Pastor

Christ Community Menn Ch (29397) (CDC, IL, CAM) 30
888 S Roselle Rd, Schaumburg IL 60193-3965
847-895-3654, fax 847-895-3654,
john_bushi@yahoo.com, http://www.ccmc-mennonite.org
Pauline Kennel, Pastor
John Bushi, Minister of Evangelism
Leroy Eldon Kennel, Minister of the Word
Janice Kennel Ropp, Minister of Counseling

Cincinnati Menn Fell (23325) (CDC, OH) 66
3046 Minot Ave, Cincinnati OH 45209
513-871-0035, cmfoffice@juno.com
4229 Brownway Ave
Pauline Ann Nofziger, Pastor

Columbus Menn Ch (16378) (CDC, OH) 197
35 Oakland Park Ave, Columbus OH 43214
614-784-8957, fax 614-784-9002,
cmc@columbusmennonite.org,
http://www.columbusmennonite.org
Joyce M. Wyse, Interim Pastor

Comins Menn Ch (2205) (CDC) 96
4263 N First St W, PO Box 60, Comins MI 48619-0060
989-848-2909, cominsmennonite@yahoo.com,
http://www.geocities.com/cominsmennonite
Robert Martz, Pastor

Community Menn Ch (28332) (CDC, IL, CAM, AAMA) 75
16200 Kedzie Ave, Markham IL 60426
708-333-1358, fax 708-333-1684,
chuckneufeld@compuserve.com,
http://community.mennonite.com
Chuck T. Neufeld, Pastor
Bonnie Beth Neufeld, Co-Pastor
Horace McMillon, Associate Pastor

Dover Christian Fell (10709) (CDC, OH) 35
206 W 3rd St, Dover OH 44622-2904
330-364-8590, fax 330-364-8590, jpollock@bright.net
Al Mast, Interim Pastor

Eighth Street Menn Ch (2270) (CDC) 242
602 S 8th St, Goshen IN 46526-4019
574-533-6720, fax 574-533-8324, eighthst@bnin.net,
http://www.bnin.net/~eighthst
Elmer A. Wall, Interim Pastor
Brenda Sawatzky Paetkau, Associate Pastor

Evanston Menn Ch (11890) (CDC, IL, CAM) 27
736 Dobson St, Evanston IL 60202
847-864-3954, fax 847-492-1458, mcb9476@aol.com
Mitchell C. Brown, Pastor

Faith Menn Ch (10127) (CDC, IM) 35
1201 S 11th St, Goshen IN 46526
574-534-1173, gustazook@aol.com
Teresa Dutchersmith, Pastor
Gwen Ann Gustafson-Zook, Pastor

First Menn Ch (2344) (CDC) 1125
566 W Main St, PO Box 111, Berne IN 46711
260-589-3108, fax 260-589-2846,
craig@firstmennonite.org, http://www.firstmennonite.org
G. Craig Maven, Pastor
Nathan Tatman, Youth Pastor
Ray Keim, Pastor of Congregational Care
Harold Walden Nussbaum, Minister of Visitation
Marie Nussbaum, Minister of Visitation
Dennis Gene Schmidt, Pastor of Christian Education

First Menn Ch (2347) (CDC) 521
101 S Jackson St, Bluffton OH 45817-1294
419-358-5766, fax 419-358-1616, FMC@bluffton.edu
Corner of Jackson & Church
   Dorothy Nickel Friesen, Pastor
   John L. Schrock, Associate Pastor

First Menn Ch (2359) (CDC, AAMA, CAM) 35
1477 W 73rd St, Chicago IL 60636
   John H. Burke, Pastor

First Menn Ch (2401) (CDC) 88
900 W Market St, Nappanee IN 46550-1800
574-773-7294, fmc99@kconline.com,
http://www.churches.kconline.com/fmc99
   Mark William Stahl, Pastor

First Menn Ch (2324) (CDC) 160
113 W Main St, PO Box 250, Sugarcreek OH 44681
330-852-2822, farmwald@adelphia.net
NW Corner of Main & Broadway
   Kevin Dale Farmwald, Pastor

First Menn Ch (2333) (CDC) 106
405 Trease Rd, Wadsworth OH 44281
330-334-1863, fax 330-334-3283, jraecroyle@cs.com,
http://www.firstmennonite.com
   James R. Mohr, Pastor

**First Menn Ch of Champaign-Urbana (11924)
(CDC, IL)** 126
902 W Springfield Ave, Urbana IL 61801
217-367-5353, fax 217-367-2716, ljwilson@net66.com,
http://www.prairienet.org/mennonite
   Larry J. Wilson, Pastor
   Cynthia Massanari Breeze, Associate Pastor

**Florence Church of the Brethren (11315) (CDC,
COB)** 0
17975 Centreville-Constantine Rd, Constantine MI 49042
269-435-7732, fax 269-435-5800,
amy.kurtritchie@juno.com
   Amy Suzanne Gall Ritchie, Co-Pastor

Grace Community Ch (2400) (CDC, CAM) 42
4155 S Rockwell St, Chicago IL 60632
773-247-4782
   June E. Thomsen, Pastor

Grace Menn Ch (2420) (CDC) 329
504 E Main St, PO Box 387, Pandora OH 45877
419-384-3038, gracemennonite@q1.net
   John Michael Dey, Pastor
   David Thomas Maurer, Minister of Youth and Christian
     Education

Hively Avenue Menn Ch (2455) (CDC) 99
800 E Hively Ave, Elkhart IN 46517-2564
574-294-3423, fax 574-294-4022, hivelymeno@aol.com,
http://hivelyavenue.in.us.mennonite.net
   Michael Kent Sommers, Pastor

**Iglesia Menonita Comunidad de Fe (2207) (CDC,
CAM, IMH)** 20
134 S Braintree Ct, Schaumburg IL 60193-1309
847-534-7242
4155 S Rockwell
   Gilberto Gaytan, Pastor

Joy Fell Menn Ch (27391) (CDC, IL, AAMA) 30
2918 W Montana St, Peoria IL 61605
309-674-0529
   Phillip Maclin, Pastor

Jubilee Menn Ch (11111) (CDC, OH) 45
PO Box 428, Bellefontaine OH 43311
937-592-8101, jubilee@2access.net,
http://www.jubileemennonite.com
   Friendly Senior Center
   Tim Lehman, Pastor

Lafayette Menn Fell (26021) (CDC, IM) 8
PO Box 355, Lafayette IN 47902-0355
765-743-4876, hovde@dcwi.com,
http://livingfaith.in.us.mennonite.net
102 N. Chauncy (First United Methodist), West Lafayette
   David Hovde, Contact Person

Lima Menn Ch (16402) (CDC, OH) 80
1318 N Main St, Lima OH 45801
419-222-2120, limamc@bright.net

Living Love Ministries (11096) (CDC, IL, AV) . . .75
PO Box 5473, Peoria IL 61601
309-676-2772
707 NE Perry Ave
   Maria Hatfield, Pastor
   Walter Smeltzer, Associate Pastor

Madison Menn Ch (10078) (CDC, IL) 111
PO Box 44522, Madison WI 53744-4522
608-276-7680, mmc@madison-mennonite.org,
http://www.madison-mennonite.org
1501 Gilbert Rd
   Tonya Ramer Wenger, Pastor

**Maple Avenue Menn Ch (23697)
(CDC, IL, CAM)** 39
346 Maple Ave, Waukesha WI 53186
262-547-6937, bfons@webtv.net
   Clarice Kratz, Co-Pastor
   Lawrence M. Kratz, Co-Pastor

Maplewood Menn Ch (2530) (CDC) 182
4129 Maplecrest Rd, Fort Wayne IN 46815-5326
260-485-8512, fax 260-486-2831,
maplemenno@juno.com,
http://www.forministry.com/46815mmc
   Barry Lee Schmell, Pastor
   Roger Hartman, Youth Pastor

Meadows Menn Ch (2540) (CDC) 133
24955 Church St, Chenoa IL 61726
309-747-2744, meadowsc@gridcom.net.
Meadows
   John Ernest Heyerly, Pastor

**CONFERENCES AND
CONGREGATIONS**

2

Menn Ch of Normal (11833) (CDC, IL) 284
805 S Cottage Ave, Normal IL 61761
309-452-6622, fax 309-452-0478, normal.mennonite@
verizon.net, http://www.normalmennonite.com
    Tim E. Schrag, Pastor
    Jane Thorley Roeschley, Associate Pastor
    Steve A. Ropp, Youth Pastor

Morning Star Ch (29652) (CDC, IM) 24
2000 S Hoyt Ave, Muncie IN 47302
765-287-0021
    Gladys Maina, Pastor
    Simon Mungai, Associate Pastor

MSU Menn Fell (12757) (CDC, IM) 40
PO Box 6068, East Lansing MI 48826
517-482-9961, msumennofell@juno.com,
http://msu.mi.us.mennonite.net
Alumni Memorial Chapel, MSU Campus
    June Mears-Driedger, Pastor

North Danvers Menn Ch (2620) (CDC) 134
5517 E 1950 North Rd, Danvers IL 61732-9240
309-963-4554, rbucher@frontiernet.net
5517 E 1950 North Rd
    Richard Wayne Bucher, Pastor

**North Suburban Menn Ch (27557)
(CDC, IL, CAM)** 24
1500 W Hawley St, Mundelein IL 60060-1508
847-566-8386, fax 847-475-1006
    David Kerner, Pastor

Oak Grove Menn Ch (16428) (CDC, OH) 410
7843 Smucker Rd, Smithville OH 44677
330-669-2697, fax 330-669-2617, ogsmthvll@aol.com,
http://www.oakgrovemc.org
    Norma B. Duerksen, Pastor

Oak Park Menn Ch (24653) (CDC, IL, CAM) 58
PO Box 3091, Oak Park IL 60303
773-343-4251, PWaite6116@aol.com
425 Central Park Ave
    Phil Waite, Pastor

Paoli Menn Fell (22624) (CDC, IM) 59
2589 N CR 100 W, Paoli IN 47454
812-723-2414, fax 812-723-3515, mininger@blueriver.net
    Mary Mininger, Co-Pastor
    Philip A. Mininger, Co-Pastor

Pleasant Oaks Menn Ch (2645) (CDC) 152
13307 CR 16, PO Box 447, Middlebury IN 46540
574-825-2784, robinpleaoaks@juno.com
    Robin La Rue, Pastor

Plow Creek Menn Ch (22335) (CDC, IL) 31
19183 Plow Creek Unit #2, Tiskilwa IL 61368
815-646-6600, fax 815-646-6600, lereha@ilstu.edu,
http://www.plowcreek.org
1925 E 880 N
    Richard Gordon Foss, Lay Minister
    Lynn Reha, Pastoral Elder
    Louise Stahnke, Pastoral Elder

Prairieview Menn Ch (12138) (CDC, IL) 221
13013 N 400 Rd E, PO Box 369, Flanagan IL 61740
815-796-4298
    Douglas D. King, Pastor

Salem Menn Ch (2680) (CDC) 192
3363 Zuercher Rd, PO Box 7, Kidron OH 44636
330-857-4131, fax 330-857-4196, salemex@raex.com
    Darrell Lee Ediger, Pastor
    Kevin S. Himes, Minister of Music

**Shalom Community Ch (23242)
(CDC, IM, COB)** 45
PO Box 8080, Ann Arbor MI 48107-8080
734-761-7366, fax 734-761-7366,
shalomcommunitychurch@yahoo.com,
http://www.shalomcommunitychurch.mi.us.mennonite.net
2670 Sequoia Pkwy Rd
    Paul Versluis, Pastor

Silverwood Menn Ch (2715) (CDC) 228
1712 W Clinton St, Goshen IN 46526
574-533-1922, fax 574-533-4069, silverwd@maplenet.net
    Kenneth Bontreger, Senior Pastor
    Jonathan Corbin, Associate Pastor

Southside Fell (12930) (CDC, IM) 95
140 W Mishawaka Rd, Elkhart IN 46517
574-293-2825, ssfellow@juno.com
AMBS Chapel, 3003 Benham Ave
    Rhoda M. Schrag, Pastor

St John Menn Ch (2670) (CDC) 407
15988 Rd 4, Pandora OH 45877
419-384-3680, fax 419-384-3640, raddisguy@wcoil.com
    Rennie W. Burrus, Pastor
    Bradlee T. Bame, Associate Pastor
    Steve Scott, Director of Children and Family Ministries

St Louis Menn Fell (24182) (CDC, IL) 64
1443 Ross Ave, St Louis MO 63146-4563
314-878-2832, jubaer@dgpurdy.com, http://www.slmf.org

Topeka Menn Ch (2775) (CDC) 134
206 E Lake St, PO Box 156, Topeka IN 46571
260-593-2389, hockman@kuntrynet.com
    John Edward Hockman, Pastor

Trenton Menn Ch (2779) (CDC) 142
2 E Main St, PO Box 19, Trenton OH 45067
513-988-0313, rharbaum@cinci.rr.com
    Glenn H. Martin, Pastor

Central Plains Mennonite Conference

OFFICE
cpmcsd@gwtc.net
605-925-4463; fax 605-925-7293
121 E Third St, PO Box 101, Freeman SD 57029

STAFF
Ed Kauffman, conference minister
(edkauffman@gwtc.net)
Tim Detweiler, east regional minister
(tdetweiler@hotmail.com)
Sharon Kennel, west regional minister
Sharon Wyse Miller, missions minister
(swmission@lisco.com)
Shana Peachey Boshart, youth minister
(shana@netins.net)
Duane Miller, financial officer
(swdkm@lisco.com)
Monica Friesen, office manager
(cpmcsd@gwtc.net)

GENERAL INFORMATION
Year founded: 2000
Members: 8,150
Congregations: 58
Ministers: 98
CLC reps: Bill Hochstetler, Ed Kauffman,
Sharon Kennel
Annual Meeting: June 19-22, 2003, Henderson
NE
Conference historian: Barb Troyer
Conference archivist: LaNae Waltner

CONFERENCE COUNCIL
Bill Hochstetler, moderator
(WSH@ShuttleworthLaw.com), 755 Elliot Ct,
Iowa City IA 52246, 319-358-2520; S. Roy
Kaufman, assistant moderator; Atlee Yoder, sec-
retary; Lois Thieszen Preheim, treasurer; Sid
Burkey, Carol Janzen, Nyle Kauffman, George
O'Reilly, Amy Spencer, Rodney Unruh, Martha
Yoder

PUBLICATION
Scattered Seeds (6/year), Jane Yoder-Short, edi-
tor (yodshort@avalon.net), 1705 Angle Rd SW,
Kalona, IA 52247, 319-683-2547

COMMITTEES
Congregational Ministries. Rodney Unruh,
chair (reunruh@att.net), 214 E 29th St,
Sioux Falls SD 57105, 605-338-7906;
Lynette Block, David Brunner, Peg Burkey,
Mary Lou Farmer, Dawn Stahl
Outreach and Service. Amy Spencer, chair
(edit@kctc.net), 805 5th St, PO Box 513,
Kalona IA 52247, 319-656-3916; Patricia
Barron, Glenn Boese, Felipe Cantu, Noreen
Gingerich, Doyle Roth, Marlene Thieszen,
Norm Unternahrer
Pastoral Leadership. George O'Reilly, chair
(bethelchurchmtlakemn@earthlink.net),
1217 9th Ave, Mountain Lake MN 56159,
507-427-2002; David Boshart, Rosie Epp,
Arthur Kennel, Marlin Kym, Pam Gerig
Unruh
Discernment. S. Roy Kaufman, chair
(lorokauf@gwtc.net), 28103 443rd Ave,
Freeman SD 57029, 605-925-7106; Glenda
Maury, Patrick Preheim, Frank Yoder

OTHER CONFERENCE AGENCY AND REPS
Mennonite Women. Marcene Ratzlaff, chair,
PO Box 22, Henderson NE 68371, 402-723-
4670; Esther Buller, Anette Eisenbeis, Dee
Goertzen, Mary Litwiller, Judy Yoder

Mennonite Men. Robert W. Friesen, chair, PO
Box 706, Henderson NE 68371, 402-723-
4736; Duane Adrian, Scott Erb, Steve Graber,
Harold Hofer, Wilbur Litwiller, Randy Roth,
Royce Roth

CONFERENCES AND CONGREGATIONS

2

Congregations

Ashland Christian Fell (4025) (CP, MILC) 9
PO Box 819, Colstrip MT 59323-0819
406-784-6130
Old Mission Rd, Ashland
    Doug Bishop, Pastor

Beemer Menn Ch (13144) (CP) 138
327 Sherman St, PO Box 421, Beemer NE 68716
402-528-7255, beemermenno@gpcom.net
    Jarvis Hochstedler, Pastor

Bellwood Menn Ch (13151) (CP) 218
520 B St, PO Box 66, Milford NE 68405
402-761-2709, fax 402-761-3095, bell606@juno.com
    Marlin Kym, Pastor
    Betta Kym, Assistant Pastor

Beth-El Menn Ch (13169) (CP) 152
115 N F St, PO Box 96, Milford NE 68405
402-761-3278, bethelmilford@alltel.net

Bethany Menn Ch (4055) (CP) 222
509 S Juniper St, PO Box 396, Freeman SD 57029
605-925-7402, fax 605-925-7202, bethanym@gwtc.net,
http://www.gwtc.net/~bethanym
    Randall LaMont Tschetter, Pastor

Bethel Menn Ch (4120) (CP) 458
301 N 9th St, PO Box 542, Mountain Lake MN 56159
507-427-3075, bethelchurchmtlakemn@earthlink.net
    George Christopher O'Reilly II, Pastor

Bethel Menn Ch (13177) (CP) 183
3185 Wayland Rd, PO Box 96, Wayland IA 52654
319-256-8531, fax 319-256-8531, pslabaugh@farmtel.net,
http://bethel.ia.us.mennonite.net
    Phil L. Slabaugh, Pastor

Bethel Menn Ch (4130) (CP) 59
HC 30 Box 2071, Wolf Point MT 59201
406-392-5215, mspenner@nemontel.net
18 mi north on Hwy 250
    Marvin Wesley Penner, Pastor

Bethesda Menn Ch (4135) (CP) 1152
930 16th St, PO Box 130, Henderson NE 68371-0130
402-723-4562, fax 402-723-4567,
bethesda@mainstaycomm.net,
http://www.mainstaycomm.net/bethesda
    Weldon R. Martens, Pastor
    George K. Kaufman, Associate Pastor
    Joel R. Schroeder, Youth Pastor

Cedar Falls Menn Ch (24935) (CP) 37
215 West 9th St, Cedar Falls IA 50613
319-277-5611, cfmcjds@cedarnet.org
    Jennifer Davis Sensenig, Pastor

Daytonville Community Ch (13201) (CP) 9
300 13th St, Wellman IA 52356
319-646-2246
    Ezra W. Shenk, Pastor

Des Moines Menn Ch (13219) (CP) 73
4001 56th St, Des Moines IA 50310
515-276-2379, fax 515-276-2379, desmenno@aol.com
Corner of 56th & Madison
    Randall J. Roth, Pastor
    Ha Baccam, Associate Pastor

East Union Menn Ch (13243) (CP) 239
PO Box 760, Kalona IA 52247
319-656-2590, eucares@kctc.net,
http://pages.prodigy.net/enos-mohawk/web/index.html
5615 Gable Ave SW
    Walter Jay Miller, Pastor

Eicher Emmanuel Menn Ch (2265) (CP) 60
2670 330th St, Wayland IA 52654
319-256-2098, eichermennonitechurch@farmtel.net
    Melvin J. Koehn, Pastor

Emmanuel Menn Ch (4275) (CP) 128
18507 405th Ave, Doland SD 57436
605-266-2588, gwiebe@willinet.net
    Gordon Wayne Wiebe, Pastor

Emmanuel Menn Ch (11125) (CP) 53
4715 Laura Lane, Shoreview MN 55126
651-766-9759, fax 651-766-9759, emmauel@visi.com,
http://www.emc.MennoLink.org
1501 Hendon St, St Paul
    Mathew Swora, Pastor

Evangelical Menn Ch (13250) (CP) 52
PO Box 1397, Fort Dodge IA 50501
515-576-0022
1633 N 29th St

Faith Menn Ch (23127) (CP) 109
2720 E 22nd St, Minneapolis MN 55406
612-375-9483, faithmc@juno.com,
http://www.dkmicro.com/fmc
    Patty Jo Friesen, Pastor
    Patrick Preheim, Pastor

First Menn Ch (13268) (CP) 91
7300 Holdrege St, Lincoln NE 68505
402-467-1526, fax 402-466-9397, ratzlaff@alltel.net
    Steve C. Ratzlaff, Pastor

First Menn Ch (4397) (CP) 142
305 N 7th St, PO Box 473, Mountain Lake MN 56159
507-427-2237, seekfrst@rconnect.com
    E. Elaine Kauffman, Pastor

First Menn Ch of Iowa City (13276) (CP) 289
405 Myrtle Ave, Iowa City IA 52246
319-338-0302, fax 319-688-5091, 1stmenno@avalon.net,
http://www.firstofiowacity.ia.us.mennonite.net
    S. Ken Beidler, Pastor
    Margaret Richer Smith, Pastor
    Robert Smith, Pastor

Friedensberg Bible Ch (4350) (CP) 52
40602 307th St, Avon SD 57315-5825
605-286-3621, fax 605-286-3892
30996 406 Ave

Good Shepherd Community Ch (4375) (CP) . . .60
2100 W Ralph Rogers Rd, Sioux Falls SD 57108-2643
605-336-9189, fax 605-336-9189, jefturner@juno.com,
http://www.goodshepherdsf.org
  Jeffrey A. Turner, Pastor

Hilltop Community Ch (13136) (CP, CAL) 32
128 Morrison Ave, Jackson MN 56143-1354
507-847-2609
115 S Hwy
  Edward J. Wenger, Pastor

Hutterthal Menn Ch (4490) (CP) 233
Drawer A, Freeman SD 57029
605-925-7186, irfri@gwtc.net
27473 437th Ave, Freeman
  Ivan D. Friesen, Co-Pastor
  Rachel Friesen, Co-Pastor

Julesburg Menn Ch (13300) (CP) 65
320 W 7th St, PO Box 52, Julesburg CO 80737
970-474-2580
Corner of 8th & Elm
  Arthur J. Roth, Pastor

Kalona Menn Ch (13318) (CP) 342
902 6th St, PO Box 819, Kalona IA 52247
319-656-2736, kmscott@kctc.net
  Mick Murray, Pastor
  Scott Swartzendruber, Pastor

Lame Deer Menn Ch (4635) (CP, MILC) 45
PO Box 232, Lame Deer MT 59043
406-477-8388
  Joe Walks Along Sr, Pastor

Lao Christian Fell (4496) (CP, LAO) 35
PO Box 145, Mt Lake MN 56159-0145
507-427-3834

Lower Deer Creek Menn Ch (13334) (CP) 241
1408 540th St SW, Kalona IA 52247
319-656-3336, fax 319-656-2029, ldc@kctc.net,
http://lowerdeercreek.ia.us.mennonite.net
  Donald A. Patterson, Pastor

Manson Menn Ch (13342) (CP) 124
PO Box 627, Manson IA 50563
712-469-3387, manson.menno@juno.com
1310 8th St
  Curtis Kuhns, Pastor

Milford Menn Ch (13367) (CP) 149
920 3rd St, PO Box EE, Milford NE 68405
402-761-2244, fax 402-761-2269, mmc761@alltel.net
  Lewis W. Miller, Pastor

Muscatine Menn Ch (13375) (CP, IMH) 0
122 Evergreen Ln., Fruitland IA 52749
563-264-5544
  Cruz Rada, Pastor

Neu Hutterthal Menn Ch (4610) (CP) 88
PO Box 19, Bridgewater SD 57319
605-729-2745
Rural Bridgewater
  Kenneth Loren Ontjes, Pastor

New Hope Menn Ch (10992) (CP) 12
4441 N 80th St, Omaha NE 68134
402-573-6072, fax 402-573-6084 (call first),
NewHopeOmaha@aol.com
St Luke United Methodist Church, 11810 Burke St
  Susan E. Janzen, Pastor

Northside Christian Family Center (24166) (CP, AAMA) 12
PO Box 19298, Omaha NE 68119-0298
402-453-7429, fax 402-451-1312
4102 Florence Blvd
  Owen Taylor, Pastor

Peace Menn Ch (28787) (CP) 21
2700 Division St, Burlington IA 52601
319-753-1325, fax 319-753-9333, peacemenno@lisco.com
  Sharon Wyse Miller, Pastor

Pleasant View Menn Ch (13425) (CP) 98
1101 N Lucas St, Mount Pleasant IA 52641
319-385-8562, pvmenno1@interlinklc.net
  Marc Hershberger, Pastor

Pulaski Menn Ch (2650) (CP) 125
202 West St, PO Box 98, Pulaski IA 52584
641-675-3329, fax 641-675-3334, jefflud@netins.net,
http://www.netins.net/showcase/pulaskimenno
  Jeffery A. Ludwig, Pastor

Rochester Menn Ch (4667) (CP) 22
2119 15th Ave NW, Rochester MN 55901-1569
507-529-7910, fax 507-288-7361, brunnerd@prodigy.net
Assisi Heights, 1001 14th St NW
  David D. Brunner, Pastor

Salem Menn Ch (4675) (CP) 404
28103 443rd Ave, Freeman SD 57029-5840
605-925-4553, southchurch@gwtc.net
  S. Roy Kaufman, Pastor
  Stacey Kramer, Associate Pastor

Salem Menn Ch (13433) (CP) 195
PO Box 165, Shickley NE 68436
402-627-4155, dee@inebraska.com
820 Rd V
  Wilton Detweiler, Pastor

Salem-Zion Menn Ch (4690) (CP) 369
27844 443rd Ave, PO Box 67, Freeman SD 57029
605-925-7410, fax 605-925-7410
  Robert L. Engbrecht, Pastor

Sermon on the Mount Menn Ch (24018) (CP) . .29
1512 E Mulberry St, Sioux Falls SD 57103
605-357-9125, smmc@juno.com,
http://sermononthemount-mennonite.org
  Rosella E. Epp, Pastor

2 CONFERENCES AND CONGREGATIONS

St Paul Menn Fell (28555) (CP) **22**
622 Bidwell St, St Paul MN 55107
612-291-0647
125 W Stevens St

Sugar Creek Menn Ch (13441) (CP) **330**
1209 Franklin Ave, Wayland IA 52654
319-256-8811, fax 319-256-6061,
sugarcreekmc@farmtel.net
  Roger Alan Farmer, Pastor

Swiss Menn Ch (4755) (CP) **23**
PO Box 135, Alsen ND 58311
701-256-5174, wadholm@utma.com
520 3rd Ave
  Richard Wadholm, Pastor

**Templo Alabanza Menonita (13284) (CP,
IMH)** **53**
613 3rd St, Moline IL 61265
309-797-3808
  Felipe Cantu, Pastor

United Hmong Menn Ch (4480) (CP, HMONG) . .**42**
1115 Greenbrier St, St Paul MN 55106-2540
651-772-8375, fax 651-771-2898,
tongpaihang@yahoo.com
  Tong Hang, Pastor

Washington Menn Ch (13458) (CP) **139**
815 E Polk St, Washington IA 52353
319-653-6041, wash.mennonite@juno.com,
http://washington.ia.us.mennonite.net
  Timothy R. Detweiler, Pastor
  Grant Nebel, Associate Pastor

Wayland Menn Ch (2815) (CP) **200**
104 Second St, PO Box 67, Wayland IA 52654
319-256-2743, fax 319-256-7003,
waylandmcusa@farmtel.net

Wellman Menn Ch (13466) (CP) **132**
1215 8th Ave, PO Box 122, Wellman IA 52356
319-646-2532, wmchurch@netins.net
  Robert Lee Hartzler, Interim Pastor

West Union Menn Ch (13474) (CP) **305**
3253 305th St, Parnell IA 52325
319-646-6004, wunion@netins.net
  David W. Boshart, Pastor
  Helen Yoder, Staff Deacon

White Chapel Menn Ch (15594) (CP) **18**
106 White Chapel Rd, Glendive MT 59330
nevpeter@midrivers.com
  Neville John Peterson, Pastor

**White River Cheyenne Menn Ch (4171)
(CP, MILC)** **57**
PO Box 50, Busby MT 59016
406-592-3643, willisnadine@juno.com
  Mennonite Church Rd
  Willis Herman Busenitz, Pastor

Wood River Menn Ch (13482) (CP) **99**
14988 West Husker Hwy, Wood River NE 68883
308-583-2087, dentonj@kdsi.net
  Cloy Roth, Pastor

Zion Menn Ch (4855) (CP) **70**
PO Box 186, Bridgewater SD 57319
605-729-2301, mpleopold@unitelsd.com
950 N Rd Main
  Matt Leopold, Pastor

Zion Menn Ch (2860) (CP) **129**
504 University St, Box 83, Donnellson IA 52625
319-835-9124, fax 319-835-0124, logesbjl@interlinklc.net
720 Park St
  Richard Alvin Bentzinger, Pastor

MENNONITE CHURCH
USA 2003 DIRECTORY
2

Eastern District Conference

OFFICE
info@fmc-online.org; www.mrn.org
215-723-5513, fax 215-723-1211
771 Rte 113, Souderton PA 18964

STAFF
Warren L. Tyson, conference minister
(wltyson@yahoo.com), PO Box 785,
Brownstown PA 17508, 610-286-7517,
fax 610-286-6860
YPU Leadership Team (formerly conference
youth minister, to be appointed)

GENERAL INFORMATION
Year founded: 1847
Members: 2,477
Congregations: 17
Ministers: 40
CLC reps: Don Fry, David Hersh, Warren Tyson
Annual delegate session: May 2-3, 2003

OFFICERS
David H. Hersh, president (k3lkn@aol.com),
815 Hilltown Pike, Line Lexington PA 18932,
215-822-3870; Earl E. Shutt, vice-president;
Wanda Schirmer, secretary; Douglas Moyer,
treasurer; Philip Bergstresser, James
Musselman, Charles Sprunger

PUBLICATION
The Messenger (Bimonthly), Lynne Rush, editor
(arushjob@vrinter.net), 324 Tohickon Ave,
Quakertown PA 18951, 215-538-5311

COMMISSIONS
Education and Publication. Will Schirmer,
chair (willsch@netreach.net), 1409
Gwynedale Way, Lansdale PA 19446-5378,
215-393-0590; Sheryl Duerksen; Judy High,
Kathy Schettig

**Inter-Conference Pastoral Training
Program Board.** Warren L. Tyson, confer-
ence director (see address above); Steven A.
Musselman, Wayne J. Speigle
Ministerial. Paul H. Wikerd, chair
(pwikerd@enter.net), 253 State Rd,
Hamburg PA 19526, 610-562-3936; David
W. Bartow, secretary; Rose Graber, David H.
Hersh, Charles E. Sprunger, Warren L. Tyson
Missions. John Arn, chair
(twinoaks7@juno.com), 102 Highland Ave,
Lansdale PA 19446, 215-855-4584; Joseph
Haines, vice-chair; Judy McVaugh, secretary;
Don Fry; Don Jantzi, Bob Laubach, Reggie
Wentz
Peace and Social Concerns. Joyce Shutt, co-
chair (jms555@blazenet.net), 878 Mt.
Carmel Rd, Orrtanna PA 17353, 717-642-
5440; Bob Walden, co-chair
(rwaldenpa@entermail.net); Becky Felton
(Franconia Conf), Russ Darling, Carolyn
Boyd (Franconia Conf), C. Leo Hartshorn,
Ryan Kolb (Franconia Conf), Russ Mast, Carl
Yusavitz
Program. Ray Hacker, chair
(r.a.hacker@worldnet.att.net), 5323 Lake
Dr, East Petersburg PA 17520, 717-569-
3460; Edith Landis
Youth Ministry Team. YPU Leadership Team,
junior high worker (to be appointed); young
adult worker (to be appointed)

OTHER CONFERENCE AGENCY AND REPS
MRN Ministry Resources. See section 3 for
separate listing.

CONFERENCES AND CONGREGATIONS

2

Congregations

Bethel Menn Ch of Lancaster (3100) (EDC) 98
2100 Manor Ridge Dr, Lancaster PA 17603-4216
717-392-8184, bethelmc@aol.com
　Emanuel Martin, Interim Pastor

Church of the Good Samaritans (3200) (EDC) . .80
964 Holland Rd, Holland PA 18966
215-355-1442
　Stephen Carl Strunk, Pastor

Comunidad de Amor (3212) (EDC, KB, IMH) 70
PO Box 46332, Philadelphia PA 19160
215-368-5839, fax 215-324-6011
4617 N 5th St
　Luis E. Naranjo, Pastor

Cornerstone Community Menn Ch (3543) (EDC) 68
Rt 2 Box 67, Mifflintown PA 17059
717-436-8585, fax 717-436-9346
Wagner Rd & Old Rt 22
　Albert Gray, Pastor

Deep Run West Menn Ch (3225) (EDC) 250
1008 Deep Run Rd, Perkasie PA 18944
215-766-8157, fax 215-766-8259
　Daniel J. Graber, Interim Pastor
　Rodger K. Schmell, Youth Pastor

Emmanuel Menn Ch (3285) (EDC) 143
1200 W Swartzville Rd, PO Box 341, Reinholds PA
17569-0341
717-336-6130, fax 717-336-3968,
steveemmanuel@dejazzd.com
　Steven Alan Musselman, Pastor
　Brian L. Emery, Associate Pastor

Fairfield Menn Ch (3300) (EDC) 30
201 W Main St, PO Box 258, Fairfield PA 17320-0258
717-642-8936, fax 717-642-8936, fmc606@blazenet.net,
http://www.fairfieldmennonite.org
　Brenda Walter, Director of Ministries

First Menn Ch (3338) (EDC) 101
1213 W Chew St, Allentown PA 18102-3707
610-435-3162, FirstMennonite@hotmail.com
　Joseph J. Kotva Jr, Pastor

Germantown Menn Ch (22079) (EDC, KB, OD) . .96
21 W Washington Ln, Philadelphia PA 19144-2601
215-843-5599, GermantownMennonite@juno.com,
http://www.gtownmenno.org
　Richard J. Lichty, Pastor

**Grace Bible Fell of Huntingdon Valley (3379) (EDC,
KB) 3**
1407 Huntingdon Pike, Huntingdon Valley PA 19006
215-947-1693
　Ray Charles Linberger, Pastor

Grace Menn Ch (3415) (EDC) 318
630 York Ave, Lansdale PA 19446-3329
215-855-7718, fax 215-855-4579,
gstenson@gracemennonite.org
　Samuel Claudio Sr, Hispanic Pastor

**Menn Congregation of Boston (16246) (ACC,
EDC) 49**
155 Powder House Blvd, Somerville MA 02144
617-868-7784, biedrzycki@mindspring.com
　Clarendon Hill Presbyterian Church

New Eden Fell (3260) (EDC) 101
609 Main St, PO Box 308, Schwenksville PA 19473-0308
610-287-7281, fax 610-287-6561, knowgod3@juno.com,
http://www.newedenfellowship.org
　Donald William Fry, Pastor
　Russell M. Detweiler, Pastor of Visitation

Roaring Spring Menn Ch (3665) (EDC) 20
114 Link Ln, Duncansville PA 16635-4530
814-224-4629, fax 814-224-4629
235 Main St
　Elsie Gonsman, Interim Pastor

Upper Milford Menn Ch (3800) (EDC) 147
6450 King's Highway South, PO Box 36, Zionsville PA
18092
610-965-4880, ummchurch@aol.com,
http://www.forministry.com/18092ummc
6450 King's Highway South, Zionsville, PA
　Rose Elaine (Waltner) Graber, Pastor

West Swamp Menn Ch (3825) (EDC) 331
2501 Allentown Rd, Quakertown PA 18951
215-536-7468, fax 215-536-2783, wswamp@enter.net,
http://westswamp.pa.us.mennonite.net
　Wayne Speigle, Pastor

Zion Menn Ch (3880) (EDC) 542
149 Cherry Ln, PO Box 64495, Souderton PA 18964
215-723-3592, fax 215-723-0573, pastorjoe@enter.net,
http://www.zionmennonite.org
　Joseph M. Haines, Pastor
　Scott Springer Benner, Associate Pastor-Youth

Franconia Mennonite Conference

OFFICE
info@fmc-online.org; www.fmc-online.org
215-723-5513, fax 215-723-1211
771 Rte 113, Souderton PA 18964

STAFF
Philip C. Bergey, conference executive
(philb@fmc-online.org)
James M. Lapp, conference pastor
(jamesl@fmc-online.org)
Gay Brunt Miller, director of administration
(gbmiller@fmc-online.org)
Conrad Martin, director of finance
(conradm@fmc-online.org)
Richard A. Moyer, treasurer
(richm@fmc-online.org)
Walter Sawatzky, director of collaborative ministries, chair of Mission Leadership Team,
conference minister
(walters@fmc-online.org)
Donella Clemens, conference minister
(donellac@fmc-online.org)
Marlene Frankenfield, conference youth minister (marlenef@fmc-online.org)
Noah Kolb, conference minister
(noahk@fmc-online.org)
Charlotte Rosenberger, conference minister
(charlotter@fmc-online.org)
Noel Santiago, conference minister
(noels@fmc-online.org)
Ertell Whigham, conference minister
(ertellw@fmc-online.org)

GENERAL INFORMATION
Year founded: 1725
Members: 6,926
Congregations: 44
Ministers: 100
CLC reps: Phil Bergey, Marlene Frankenfield,
Merrill Moyer

Annual Conferences: spring conference assembly, date to be determined; fall conference
assembly, November 7-8, 2003

CONFERENCE BOARD
Merrill Moyer, chair/moderator,
(mernan@fast.net), 334 Fairview Ave,
Souderton PA 18964, 215-721-4517; Charles
Ness, vice-chair/assistant moderator; Sharon
Fransen, Rita Hoover, Diane Kropf, John Landes,
John Nyce, Adamino Ortiz, Bob Schloneger,
Eileen Viau, Roy Yoder. Staff: Philip C. Bergey,
James M. Lapp, Conrad Martin, Gay Brunt
Miller, Walter Sawatzky

PUBLICATION
Intersections (Bimonthly), Craig Pelkey-
Landes, editor (CraigL@MRN.org), 771 Route
113, Souderton PA 18964

CONFERENCE BOARD COMMITTEES
Conference Board Executive Committee:
Merrill Moyer, chair, (mernan@fast.net),
334 Fairview Ave, Souderton PA 18964, 215-
721-4517
Conference Board Finance Committee:
John Landes, chair (landesj@univest.net),
1050 Deer Run Rd, Ottsville PA 18942, 215-
721-2425
Conference Board Ministerial Committee:
Bob Schlonenger, chair (bobenid@netcarri-
er.com), 822 Orchard Rd, Sellersville PA
18960, 215-257-3431

OTHER CONFERENCE AGENCY AND REPS
MRN Ministry Resources. See section 3 for
separate listing.

CONFERENCES AND CONGREGATIONS

2

Congregations

Alpha Menn Ch (23051) (FRC) **27**
901 East Blvd, Alpha NJ 08865-4233
908-454-8345, alphamenno@juno.com
Corner of North & East Boulevards
James D. Townsend, Pastor

Ambler Menn Ch (11353) (FRC, AAMA) **98**
90 E Mount Pleasant Ave, Ambler PA 19002
215-643-4876, fax 215-643-4876,
amblermennonite@erols.com

Bally Menn Ch (11361) (FRC) **168**
PO Box 194, Bally PA 19503
610-845-7780, ballypj@juno.com,
http://www.forministry.com/19503bmc
Rt 100
James Ralph, Pastor

Bethany Menn Ch (11387) (FRC) **30**
Route 100A, #169, PO Box 145, Bridgewater Corners VT
05035
802-672-3488, bethanym@sover.net
Gwendolyn M. Groff, Pastor

Blooming Glen Menn Ch (11403) (FRC) **701**
713 Blooming Glen Rd, PO Box 238, Blooming Glen PA
18911
215-257-3431, fax 215-257-3150, bgmc@netcarrier.com,
http://www.bgmc.net
Enid Elaine Schloneger, Lead Pastor
Robert Schloneger, Lead Pastor
David A. Stevens, Pastor
Benjamin S. Stutzman, Pastor

Boyertown Menn Ch (11411) (FRC) **125**
275 Mill St Rd, Boyertown PA 19512
610-369-1974, bmc19512@yahoo.com,
http://www.virtue.nu/bmc
Nelson J. Shenk, Pastor

Covenant Community Fell (29306) (FRC) **177**
1080 Sumneytown Pike, Lansdale PA 19446
215-721-6490, fax 215-721-6429,
covenant@cc-fellowship.org, http://www.cc-fellowship.org
Elmer S. Frederick, Pastor
Jay Moyer, Co-Pastor
R. Keith Nyce, Co-Pastor

Deep Run Menn Ch East (11437) (FRC) **338**
350 Kellers Church Rd, Perkasie PA 18944-4242
215-766-8380, fax 215-766-2908, dre@depruneast.org,
http://deepruneast.org
Corner of Deep Run & Keller's Church in Bedminster
Township
Timothy D. Weaver, Pastor

Doylestown Menn Ch (11445) (FRC) **196**
590 N Broad St, Doylestown PA 18901
215-345-6377, fax 215-345-9513,
doylestownmc@juno.com
Corner of Broad St & Sandy Ridge Road
Randy E. Heacock, Pastor

Finland Menn Ch (11486) (FRC) **124**
1685 Upper Ridge Rd, Pennsburg PA 18073
215-257-5365, fax 215-257-2266,
finlandmennonitechurch@netcarrier.com,
http://www.finlandmennonitechurch.org
Richard Lewman, Pastor

Franconia Menn Ch (11502) (FRC) **739**
613 Harleysville Pike, PO Box 26, Franconia PA 18924
215-723-3220, fax 215-723-2265,
info@franconiamennonite.org,
http://www.hows.net/18924FMC
John M. Ehst, Pastor
Jeffrey B. Leaman, Youth Pastor
Steven E. Landis, Minister of Pastoral Care
Eric Musser, Minister of Evangelism & Young Adults

Frederick Menn Ch (11528) (FRC) **68**
PO Box 309, Frederick PA 19435
610-754-7238, frederickmen@juno.com
526 Colonial Rd
R. Scott Landes, Pastor

Garden Chapel (11544) (FRC) **34**
PO Box 376, Dover NJ 07802
973-361-8877
89 Washington Ave, Victory Gardens
Jesse U. Adams, Pastor

Hersteins Menn Ch (11569) (FRC) **86**
364 Neiffer Rd, Schwenksville PA 19473
610-495-2065, pbkolb@hotmail.com

Lakeview Menn Ch (11577) (FRC) **64**
RR 1 Box 55, Susquehanna PA 18847
570-756-2793, detwiler@epix.net
R. Blaine Detwiler, Pastor

Line Lexington Menn Ch (11593) (FRC) **264**
80 Hilltown Pike, PO Box 217, Line Lexington PA 18932
215-822-0446, fax 215-822-1546,
makratz@netcarrier.com, http://www.llmc.org
Lowell H. Delp, Pastor
John King, Associate Pastor

Menn Bible Fell (11619) (FRC) **49**
PO Box 301, Morris PA 16938
570-353-2019, pbmorris@epix.net,
http://www.forministry.com/16938mmbf
Rt 287 Main St
Paul K. Benner, Pastor

Methacton Menn Ch (11601) (FRC) **54**
3081 Mill Rd, Norristown PA 19403
610-222-3973, fax 610-584-4080, danrose70s@aol.com
Fairview Village
Dan Graber, Pastor

MillCreek Community Ch (29348) (FRC) **85**
35 Millstone Ct, Langhorne PA 19047
215-891-9544, fax 215-891-8344,
millcreekchurch@aol.com, http://millcreek-church.org
Regan Savage, Pastor

New Beginnings Community Ch (11429) (FRC, AAMA) **49**
Floyd St and Colonial Ave, Bristol PA 19007
215-785-2233, fax 215-785-2233,
Jonfeliciamoore@aol.com
  Jon E. Moore, Pastor

New Life Menn Ch (10013) (FRC) **26**
PO Box 164, Athens PA 18810
570-888-8281
Front Street, East Athens
  Philip James Maenza, Pastor

Norristown New Life Menn Ch (10125) (FRC, AAMA, IMH) **113**
3 E Marshall St, Norristown PA 19401
610-279-5433, fax 610-272-7802, nnl3@juno.com,
http://www.forministry.com/19401nnlmc
  Luke Beidler, Associate Pastor
  Carmen Roman, Associate Pastor
  Ertell M. Whigham Jr, Associate Pastor

Perkasie Menn Ch (11627) (FRC) **113**
320 W Chestnut St, Perkasie PA 18944
215-257-3117, fax 215-258-5950, info@perkmenno.com,
http://www.perkmenno.com
Corner of 4th & Chestnut
  Barbara Shisler, Pastor
  Beth Ranck Yoder, Pastor

Perkiomenville Menn Ch (11635) (FRC) **159**
PO Box 59, Perkiomenville PA 18074
215-234-4011, fax 215-234-9644, perkmc@juno.com,
http://www.forministry.com/18074pmc
Deep Creek Rd
  Charles A. Ness, Pastor

Plains Menn Ch (11643) (FRC) **237**
50 W Orvilla Rd, Hatfield PA 19440-3643
215-362-7640, fax 215-362-4951, plainsmc@erols.com,
http://www.plains.pa.us.mennonite.net
W Main St & Orvilla Rd, Lansdale
  Mary Elizabeth Benner, Pastor
  Michael L. Derstine, Pastor

Providence Menn Ch (11668) (FRC) **41**
109 S Mennonite Rd, Collegeville PA 19426
215-799-0497
  Earl N. Anders Jr, Pastor

River of God Fell (11452) (FRC) **158**
813 Reynolds St, Easton PA 18042
610-252-5351, riverofgod@enter.net
  Charles E. Brunstetter, Pastor

Rockhill Menn Ch (11692) (FRC) **148**
3100 Meetinghouse Rd, Telford PA 18969
215-723-7780, rockhillmc@juno.com
  Robert L. Petersheim, Interim Pastor

Rocky Ridge Menn Ch (11684) (FRC) **162**
114 Rocky Ridge Rd, Quakertown PA 18951
215-536-1269, fax 215-723-3549, larrymoyer@juno.com,
http://www.forministry.com/18951rrmc
  Larry G. Moyer, Pastor
  Robert D. Cooper, Assistant Pastor

Salem Menn Ch (11700) (FRC) **85**
41 E Cherry Rd, Quakertown PA 18951
215-536-1223, fax 215-536-1233, salem@netcarrier.com
  Bruce Eglinton-Woods, Pastor

Salford Menn Ch (11718) (FRC) **500**
480 Groff's Mill Rd, Harleysville PA 19438
215-256-0778, fax 215-256-6562, mail@salfordmc.org,
http://www.salfordmc.org
  James C. Longacre, Pastor
  Miriam F. Book, Associate Pastor
  Diane Kropf, Youth Pastor

Shalom Christian Fell (10018) (FRC) **29**
PO Box 2, Pennsburg PA 18073
215-234-8286, richfern@easy-pages.com
104 Main St, East Greenville, PA 18041
  Duane Hershberger, Pastor
  Richard A. Moyer, Pastor

Souderton Menn Ch (11734) (FRC) **681**
105 W Chestnut St, Souderton PA 18964
215-723-3088, fax 215-723-5651,
soudmen@worldlynx.net,
http://www.soudertonmennonite.org
Corner of Chestnut St & Wile Ave
  Gerald A. Clemmer, Co-Pastor
  David Greiser, Co-Pastor

Spring Mount Menn Ch (11742) (FRC) **54**
20 Perkiomen Ave, PO Box 438, Spring Mount PA 19478-0438
610-287-5280, fax 215-721-7967, mking@netreach.net,
http://www.forministry.com/19478Smmc
  Michael A. King, Pastor

Spruce Lake Fell (26203) (FRC) **25**
RR 1 Box 605, Canadensis PA 18325-9749
570-595-7505, fax 570-595-0328, retreat@enter.net
Spruce Lake Retreat
  Marty Sauder, Pastor

Steel City Menn Ch (11759) (FRC) **114**
2137 Mixsell Ave, Bethlehem PA 18015
610-865-4899, fax 610-758-8156,
SCMCHURCH@AOL.COM,
http://www.steelcitymennonitechurch.org
  David K. Kochsmeier, Pastor

Swamp Menn Ch (11767) (FRC) **220**
2125 Rosedale Rd, Quakertown PA 18951
215-536-7928, fax 215-536-7983, swamppb@fast.net
  William A. Brunk, Pastor

Taftsville Chapel Menn Fell (11775) (FRC) 67
7505 Happy Valley Rd, PO Box 44, Taftsville VT 05073
802-457-5838, fax 802-457-5838, jrccgood@valley.net
  Randy Good, Pastor

Towamencin Menn Ch (11783) (FRC) 170
PO Box 225, Kulpsville PA 19443
215-368-2450, fax 215-368-9710, tmencinmc@juno.com,
http://towamencinmennonite.org
1980 Sumneytown Pike
  Steven C. Nyce, Pastor

Vietnamese Gospel Menn Ch (11128)
(FRC, VIET) 53
771 Rt 113, PO Box 64738, Souderton PA 18964
215-513-4117, tcpham1@netzero.com
Souderton Center, 771 Rt 113
  Thanh Cong Pham, Pastor

Vincent Menn Ch (11809) (FRC) 114
39 Seven Stars Rd, Spring City PA 19475
610-948-6130, fax 610-948-6130 *51,
vincentmennonite@juno.com
  H. Wesley Boyer, Pastor

Wellspring Ch of Skippack (11726) (FRC) 63
1183 Cressman Rd, PO Box 317, Skippack PA 19474
215-393-9836, fax 610-489-1535,
wellspringchurch@juno.com
1183 Cressman Rd Creamery
  Michael A. Meneses, Pastor

West Philadelphia Menn Fell (27276) (FRC,
KB) 68
4740 Baltimore Ave, Philadelphia PA 19143
215-729-2050, fax 215-729-2845, wpmf@mennonite.net,
http://welcome.to/wpmf
418th St & Baltimore Ave
  J. Fred Kauffman, Pastor

Whitehall Menn Ch (10114) (FRC) 50
4138 Wilson St, Whitehall PA 18052
610-262-1270, fax 610-262-7380, wmcfun@yahoo.com

Franklin Mennonite Conference

OFFICE
fmcmb@cvn.net
717-375-4544; fax 717-375-2136
4856 Molly Pitcher Hwy S, Chambersburg PA
17201

STAFF
Larry Lehman, administrative secretary
Darrell Baer, conference minister
Janet Martin, office secretary

GENERAL INFORMATION
Members: 1,180
Congregations: 14
Ministers: 47
CLC reps: Darrell Baer, Ralph Lehman
Annual Conference: October 5, 2003

CONFERENCE BOARD
J. Allen Lehman, moderator (jallen@pa.net),
346 Warm Spring Rd, Chambersburg PA 17201,
717-264-1319; Lloyd Gingrich, assistant moderator; Jerry Roth, secretary; Dale Clugston, treasurer; Joseph Martin, Roger Martin, Cleon Nyce

PUBLICATION
The Burning Bush (Monthly), Peter Zucconi,
editor (same address as above)

COMMISSIONS
Leadership. Ray Geigley, chairperson
(rdgeigley@yellowbananas.com), 3459
Church St, Chambersburg PA 17201, 717-
264-9490; Joanna Lehman, Karen Martin,
Roger Martin, Cleon Nyce, Samuel
Sollenberger

OTHER CONFERENCE AGENCY AND REPS
Franklin Mission Board. Roger Eshleman,
president (eshleman1@earthlink.com), 506
Clayton Ave, Waynesboro PA 17268, 717-
762-7654; Allen Lehman, vice-president;
Richard Lehman, secretary; Glenn Cordell,
treasurer; Dale Horst, fifth member
Mennonite Women. Chris Hampton, president
(timh98@juno.com), 9506 Highlander Cr,
Walkersville MD 21793, 301-845-7106;
Beverly Martin, vice-president; Carole Smith,
secretary
Conference Youth Leaders. Joel and Sue
Sollenberger, (joelsollen@hotmail.com), PO
Box 332, 188 Nelson St, Marion PA 17235,
717-375-4225

Congregations

Bethel Community Ch (18994) (FRK) 42
PO Box 91, Warfordsburg PA 17267
301-678-6526
Bethel Church Rd
  Gary Quackenbos, Pastor
  Lauren B. Horst, Associate Pastor
  Dale E. Lehman, Assistant Pastor

Cedar Street Menn Ch (19000) (FRK) 119
430 Cedar St, Chambersburg PA 17201
717-263-9270, fax 717-263-7440, rdlehman@innernet.net
  Ralph D. Lehman, Interim Pastor
  Dale Eugene Clugston, Ordained Deacon

Chambersburg Menn Ch (19018) (FRK) 137
1800 Philadelphia Ave, Chambersburg PA 17201
717-264-5520, fax 717-375-2136
  Jerry A. Roth, Pastor
  Preston M. Frey, Associate Pastor
  Jere A. Horst, Associate Pastor
  David Henry Martin, Ordained Deacon

Community Menn Ch (14738) (FRK) 17
13505 Olde Mystic Cir, Hagerstown MD 21742
301-733-2147
21108A National Pike, Boonsboro
  Lewis M. Coss, Pastor Emeritus

Faith Community Menn Ch (11309) (FRK) 0
30 W Frederick St, PO Box 143, Walkersville MD 21793-
0143
301-845-7106, fax 301-845-0800, timh98@juno.com
  Timothy S. Hampton, Pastor

Marion Menn Ch (19034) (FRK) 187
4365 Molly Pitcher Hwy, Chambersburg PA 17201
717-375-4309, fax 717-375-2950, marionmc@pa.net,
http://www.marionmennonite.org
    Cleon Nyce, Pastor
    Gerald D. Lehman, Ordained Deacon

Mercersburg Menn Ch (19109) (FRK) 124
PO Box 356, Mercersburg PA 17236
717-328-9282, pastoral2@juno.com
10060 Buchanan Trail W
    Allen R. Eshleman, Pastor
    David Possinger, Associate Pastor
    Irvin E. Cordell, Licensed Deacon
    Lloyd W. Gingrich, Minister of Visitation
    John A. Horst, Ordained Deacon

Mount Zion Menn Ch (14746) (FRK) 61
20544 Benevola Church Rd, Boonsboro MD 21713
717-263-7203, tallowhill@juno.com
    Larry Lehman, Pastor

North Side Menn Ch (16345) (FRK) 58
716 N Locust St, Hagerstown MD 21740
717-597-3294
    Gary L. Zook, Pastor

Pleasant View Menn Ch (19042) (FRK) 117
346 Warm Spring Rd, Chambersburg PA 17201
717-264-1319, jallen@pa.net
    J. Allen Lehman, Pastor
    Dean M. Lehman, Ordained Deacon

Pond Bank Menn Ch (19059) (FRK) 60
6555 Duffield Rd, Chambersburg PA 17201
717-352-2135, mdebersole@pa.net
    Marlin E. Ebersole, Pastor

Rock Hill Menn Ch (19067) (FRK) 18
1255 Candice Ln, Chambersburg PA 17201
717-264-1125, tssol@pa.net
Rock Hill Rd
    Samuel Sollenberger, Pastor
    Glenn D. Showalter, Licensed Deacon

Salem Ridge Menn Ch (19075) (FRK) 140
441 Pensinger Rd, Greencastle PA 17225
717-597-8426, fax 717-593-4644, salemrmc@innernet.net
    G. Joseph Martin, Pastor

Shady Pine Menn Ch (19083) (FRK) 100
14620 Shady Pine Rd, Willow Hill PA 17271
717-349-7160, shadypine@juno.net
    Marlin A. Neil, Pastor
    Glenn Wise, Ordained Deacon

Gulf States Mennonite Conference

OFFICE
gsmc@pngusa.net
662-726-2542 (voice and fax)
311 Jensen St, Macon MS 39341

STAFF
W. Harvey Yoder, moderator
(gsmc@pngusa.net)
Karen S. Yoder, secretary (gsmc@pngusa.net)
George Reno, pastor's advocate

GENERAL INFORMATION
Year founded: 1979
Members: 668
Congregations: 14
Ministers: 16
CLC reps.: Dave Weaver, Harvey Yoder, Karen
Yoder
Annual delegate session: (first Saturday in
November) November 1, 2003
Annual spring inspirational meeting: (first
weekend in May) May 3-4, 2003
Conference historian: Robert O. Zehr

EXECUTIVE COMMITTEE
W. Harvey Yoder, moderator
(gsmc@pngusa.net), 311 Jensen St, Macon MS
39341, 662-726-2542 (voice and fax); Duane
Maust, moderator-elect; Karen S. Yoder, secretary; Mark Roth, treasurer; Lester Hackman Jr,
member-at-large; Dennis and Joanna Miller,
youth commission; Howie Schiedel, PLFC; Edith
Michalovic, Mennonite Women; Christian
Vindel, Hispanic rep; Alice Phillips, African-
American rep; Carol Lee Roth, Native American
rep; Jay Troyer, missions commission; David
Weaver Jr, leadership commission

PUBLICATION
The Fellowship (Quarterly), Linda Williams,
editor (fellowshipgsmc@aol.com), 64320 Lake
Superior Rd, Amite LA 70422, 504-748-4481

COMMISSIONS
Finance and Stewardship. Mark Roth, chair
(croth@choctaw.org), 10390 Rd 852,
Philadelphia MS 39350, 601-656-9302;
Mervin Mast, Dale Weaver
Leadership. David Weaver Jr, chairperson
(dave@starvisionsat.com), 21170 D'Herde
Rd, Gulfport MS 39503, 228-832-0661;
Duane Maust, Glenn Myers, Harvey Yoder,
Robert Zehr
Missions. Jay Troyer, chairperson
(jayt81@excite.com), 1713 Concord Rd,
Macon MS 39341, 662-726-9093; Karl
Bernhard, Marlene Barnhard, Elaine Maust,
Twila Troyer
Peace and Justice Representative. Lester
Hackman Jr, 139 Mimosa Ave, Luling LA
70070, 504-785-8696
Youth. Dennis and Joanna Miller, co-chairs
(dlmandjbm@aol.com), 360 Mt. Vernon
Ave, Jackson MS 39209, 601-355-2962;
Debbie Holliman, Jimmie Wayne

OTHER CONFERENCE AGENCY AND REPS
Gulf States Choice Books. 7705 Smith Rd,
Theodore AL 36582-3831, 334-653-0560;
Naaman Beiler, director; Dot Miller, Leo
Yoder, Robert Zehr
Mennonite Women. Edith Michalovic, presi-
dent (stephenmichalovic@msn.com), 507
Pleasant Valley Dr, Philadelphia MS 39350,
601-656-7551; Mary Bucher, RosaLee
Kanagy, Alice Phillips, Sandy Reno, Carol Lee
Roth
Pine Lake Fellowship Camp. Jeff and Cheryl
Landis, co-directors, 10371 Pine Lake Rd,
Meridian MS 39307, 601-483-CAMP

CONFERENCES AND CONGREGATIONS

2

Congregations

Choctaw Christian Ch (15891) (GS, UNMC) 3
⅝ Mary Bucher, 80 Hill Rd, Macon MS 39341
662-726-5295
Louisville, MS

Cornerstone Community Ch (16212) (GS) 64
PO Box 728, Macon MS 39341-0728
662-726-2512, fax 662-726-2512
Hwy 14 W, Macon, MS
    Lee Hershberger, Interim Pastor

Des Allemands Menn Ch (17897) (GS) 135
PO Box 818, Des Allemands LA 70030
985-758-7550, mennoda@juno.com
17447 Old Spanish Trail
    David Willis Roth, Pastor

First Menn Ch (10777) (GS, CM) 20
810 Camp St, El Dorado AR 71730
870-864-0606, fax 870-863-8661
    Mervin Mast, Pastor

Grace Menn Christian Fell (11144) (GS) 5
PO Box 508, Quitman MS 39355
601-776-6407

Gulfhaven Menn Ch (17947) (GS) 146
21497 Mennonite Rd, Gulfport MS 39503
228-832-6130, fax 228-328-0045, glfhaven@juno.com
    Paul G. Conrad, Lead Pastor
    David W. Weaver Jr, Assistant Pastor

Iglesia Amor Viviente (28258) (GS, IMH, AV) . . .75
116 Pasedena Ave, Metairie LA 70001
504-219-0771, Amorviviente@msn.com
    Carlos (Karl) Enrique Bernhard, Pastor

Jubilee Menn Ch (24547) (GS) 49
812 28th Ave, Meridian MS 39301
601-693-8073, fax 601-693-3665, duelchna@aol.com
    Duane E. Maust, Co-Pastor
    Elaine Maust, Co-Pastor

Lighthouse Fell Ch (25403) (GS) 12
PO Box 1392, Buras LA 70041
985-657-0929
37332 Hwy 11
    George Charles Reno, Retiring Pastor

Nanih Waiya Indian Menn Ch (16352) (GS, UNMC) 42
11150 Rd 781, Philadelphia MS 39350
601-656-9302
Preston MS
    Mark Ray Roth, Senior Pastor
    W. Harvey Yoder, Assistant Pastor
    Ethan Joseph Good, Retiring Pastor

Native Christian Fell (11140) (GS, UNMC) 5
6210 Jack Springs Rd, Atmore AL 36502
251-368-0280
Houma, LA
    Steve W. Cheramie Risingsun, Pastor

Open Door Menn Ch (22046) (GS, AAMA) 24
403 Mt Vernon Ave, Jackson MS 39209
601-355-7523, rhodayoder@yahoo.com
555 Magnolia Road, Jackson, MS
    Robert O. Zehr, Interim Pastor

Pearl River Menn Ch (21790) (GS, UNMC) 43
315 Northwood Dr, Philadelphia MS 39350
601-656-3514, gemyers@nsimailbox.com
State Hwy 16 W
    D. Glenn Myers, Pastor

Poarch Community Ch (16535) (GS, UNMC) 45
6210 Jack Springs Rd, Atmore AL 36504-0385
334-446-3241, fax 334-368-2841
    Steve W. Cheramie Risingsun, Pastor

Illinois Mennonite Conference

OFFICE

ilconinfo@earthlinnk.net or
ilconcoor@earthlink.net
309-925-2111; fax 309-346-5904
(specify Illinois Mennonite Conf)
104 E South St, PO Box 3, Tremont IL 61568

STAFF

Susan Sommer, coordinator
(ilconcoor@earthlink.net)
Wayne Hochstetler, conference minister
(ilconmin@mindspring.com), 1324 E
Vernon Ave, Normal IL 61761, 309-862-
9268
Allan Howe, mission and service director
(ahhowe@aol.com), 723 Seward St,
Evanston IL 60202-2912, 847-475-5041

GENERAL INFORMATION

Year founded: 1872
Members: 6,278
Congregations: 43
Ministers: 95
CLC Reps: Wayne Hochstetler, Susan Sommer,
Zenobia Sowell-Bianchi
Annual conference: April 11-12, 2003
Conference historian: Edwin J. Stalter

PUBLICATION

Missionary Guide, Gerlof Homan, editor
(homan3@juno.com); 113 Eastview Dr, Normal
IL 61761, 309-452-5811

EXECUTIVE COMMITTEE

Virgil Vogt, president (vvvogt@ameritech.net),
726 Monroe, Evanston IL 60204-6017, 847-
869-4599; Roger Kennell, president-elect; Suan
Sommer, secretary; Gene Nafzier, treasurer;
Alice Kennell, Zenobia Sowell-Bianchi

COMMISSIONS

Christian Nurture. Rachel Zehr, chair (rach-
zl@juno.com), 711 S Cottage Ave Apt 102,
Normal IL 61761, 309-452-1850; Michael
Danner, Dave Johnson, Carolyn LeFevre,
Lavonne McGuire, Keith Springer
Committee on Faith, Life, and Practice.
Christina Litwiller, chair
(chrislit@hotmail.com), 711 S Cottage Ave
#110, Normal, IL 61761, 309-452-8961;
Pamela Dominguez, Alice Kennell, Joel
Nafziger, Marvin Wright
Finance and Stewardship. Donald Litwiller,
chair (litwide@dpc.net), 2049 S 4th St,
Morton IL 61550-9311, 309-263-7071;
Eldon Eigsti, Richard Martin, Gene Nafziger,
Christine Sommer
Historical. Edwin J. Stalter, chair,
(staltere@frontiernet.net), PO Box 576,
Flanagan IL 61740-0576, 815-796-2918;
Elaine Gerber, Kenneth Ulrich, Ruth Ulrich,
staff: Gerlof Homan, Susan Sommer
Leadership. Cindy Breeze, chair
(cbreeze4@aol.com), 902 W Springfield
Ave, Urbana IL 61801, 217-687-4132; José
Elizalde, Leota Mann, Doug Roth, Calvin
Zehr; staff: Wayne Hochstetler
Mission, Evangelism and Service. Rich Foss,
chair (richfoss@theramp.net), 19183 Plow
Creek #2, Tiskilwa IL 61368, 815-646-6600;
Lori Graber, Allan Howe, Mike Kristoff,
Duane Sears, Kay Sears, Marilyn Toelke,
Marge Weaver, Chris Wright
Nominating. Virgil Vogt, chair
(vvvogt@ameritech.net), 726 Monroe,
Evanston IL 60204-6017, 847-869-4599;
Marilyn Eigsti, Kathy Roth, Larry Wilson,
Elmer Wyse
Peace and Social Concerns. Peter H. Dyck,
chair (peterhenrydyck@juno.com), PO Box
354, Thomasboro IL 61878-0354, 217-643-
2789; Cecil Graber, James Halteman, Mike
Smith

CONFERENCES AND CONGREGATIONS

2

OTHER CONFERENCE AGENCY AND REPS

Illinois Mennonite Camp Association Inc.
MennoHaven Camp and Retreat Center,
David Horst, executive director
(dhorst@mennohaven.com),
9301 1575 East St, Tiskilwa IL 61368-9710,
815-646-4344, fax 815-646-4301

Mennonite Women. Marge Weaver, president
(weave@trianglenet.net), 309-449-6078

CONFERENCE RELATED MINISTRIES

Chicago Area Mennonites. See separate listing in section 3.

Chicago Mennonite Learning Center. See schools in section 3.

Mennonite Housing Aid. See Mennonite Health Services in section 3.

Chicago Opportunity for Peace in Action (COPA). 4733 S Lamon Ave, Chicago IL 60638-2034, 773-735-5336

Committee for Inter-Mennonite Activities (Illinois). Edwin J. Stalter, IMC, PO Box 576, Flanagan IL 61740, 815-796-2918

Conference Advisory Board for Goshen College. Gene Nafziger, Rachel Zehr; CAM appointee: David Araujo

Mennonite Financial Federal Credit Union (Result of a merger which included Illinois Mennonite Federal Credit Union). See separate listing in section 3.

Lombard Mennonite Peace Center. See separate listing in section 3.

MCC Great Lakes. See separate listing in section 3.

Mennonites Illinois Leadership Education. José Elizalde, LeRoy Kennel, Laverne Nafziger

Metropolitan Outreach Ministries (Umbrella organization for Chicago-area cell groups). 5510 W 25th St, Cicero IL 60650; Juan Laureano, 773-652-6991

Assembly Delegates. B. Elaine Bryant, Jose Elizalde, Sara Fenton, Wayne Hochstetler, Carolyn LeFevre, Karl McKinney, Randall Schertz, Tim Schrag, Susan Sommer, Wayne Sutter, Patty Yordy, alternate: Cindy Breeze

Congregations

Arthur Menn Ch (11817) (IL) **272**
710 E Park St, Arthur IL 61911
217-543-2781, gmartin1545@aol.com.,
http://www.arthur.il.us.mennonite.net
    Gary E. Martin, Interim Pastor

Berhane Wongel Ethiopian Ch (11025) (IL, CAM) **180**
PO Box 308, West Chicago IL 60185
630-293-7331, fax 630-293-7331, yigzaw1@hotmail.com
1004 Greenwood & Maple St, Evanston
    Guenetu Yigzaw, Contact Person

Bethel Menn Community Ch (11825) (IL, CAM, AAMA) **40**
PO Box 5593, Chicago IL 60680
312-922-5333, fax 312-421-2551, gibor@megsinet.net
1434 S Laflin
    Tony Bianchi, Pastor

Bethesda Menn Ch (17814) (IL, AAMA) **62**
2823 Dayton St, St Louis MO 63106
314-535-5336
    Rick Maclin, Pastor
    Jesse Dunigans, Associate Pastor
    Janace Maclin, Associate Pastor

Cazenovia Menn Ch (11841) (IL) **82**
1634 CR 1600 E, c/o Dennis Kennell, Roanoke IL 61561
309-923-6621, kennells@mtco.com
Lowpoint, IL
    Dennis Kennell, Pastor

Centro Cristiano Vida Abundante (28928) (IL, CAM, IMH) **800**
1321 S Austin Blvd, Cicero IL 60804
708-863-6305, fax 708-863-5954, ccVida@aol.com,
http://www.ccVida.abundante@worldnet.att.net
    Andres Gallardo, Pastor
    Gamaliel Aguado, Associate Pastor
    Lilia Gallardo, Associate Pastor

Christ Community Menn Ch (29397) (CDC, IL, CAM) **30**

888 S Roselle Rd, Schaumburg IL 60193-3965
847-895-3654, fax 847-895-3654,
john_bushi@yahoo.com, http://www.ccmc-mennonite.org
    Pauline Kennel, Pastor
    John Bushi, Minister of Evangelism
    Leroy Eldon Kennel, Minister of the Word
    Janice Kennel Ropp, Minister of Counseling

Community Menn Ch (28332) (CDC, IL, CAM, AAMA) 75
16200 Kedzie Ave, Markham IL 60426
708-333-1358, fax 708-333-1684,
chuckneufeld@compuserve.com,
http://community.mennonite.com
    Chuck T. Neufeld, Pastor
    Bonnie Beth Neufeld, Co-Pastor
    Horace McMillon, Associate Pastor

East Bend Menn Ch (11874) (IL) 303
702 CR 3300 N, PO Box 520, Fisher IL 61843
888-269-5963, fax 217-897-6386,
eastbend@earthlink.net,
http://www.ebmennonitechurch.org
    Michael Richard Dean, Pastor
    Jeffrey D. Ressler, Associate Pastor

East Peoria Menn Ch (11940) (IL) 100
1397 CR 700 N, Eureka IL 61530
309-467-3109, fax 309-467-6984, mpyord@mtco.com,
http://www.eastpeoria.il.us.mennonite.net
125 N Norwood, E Peoria, IL
    Maurice J. Yordy, Pastor

Englewood Menn Ch (11882) (IL, CAM, AAMA) .35
PO Box 21569, Chicago IL 60621
773-483-2987, elainebryant@prodigy.net
832 W 68th St
    B. Elaine Bryant, Pastor

Evanston Menn Ch (11890) (CDC, IL, CAM) 27
736 Dobson St, Evanston IL 60202
847-864-3954, fax 847-492-1458, mcb9476@aol.com
    Mitchell C. Brown, Pastor

First Menn Ch of Champaign-Urbana (11924) (CDC, IL) 126
902 W Springfield Ave, Urbana IL 61801
217-367-5353, fax 217-367-2716, ljwilson@net66.com,
http://www.prairienet.org/mennonite
    Larry J. Wilson, Pastor
    Cynthia Massanari Breeze, Associate Pastor

First Menn Ch of Morton (11908) (IL) 266
250 S Baltimore Ave, Morton IL 61550
309-266-7591, fax 309-266-6344, fmmorton@mtco.com
    Doane Brubaker, Pastor
    Chris Wright, Youth Pastor

First Norwood Menn Ch (11916) (IL) 42
6605 W Jones Rd, Peoria IL 61604
309-673-3026
    Harold J. Baer, Pastor

Freeport Menn Ch (11932) (IL) 128
3416 E Brick School Rd, Freeport IL 61032
815-449-2498, fax 815-449-9072, fimc@aeronic.net
    Marvin W. Thill, Interim Pastor

Hopedale Menn Ch (11957) (IL) 308
5192 Hopedale Rd, Hopedale IL 61747
309-449-6600, fax 309-449-5529, hmc@mtco.com
    Kurt Walker, Associate Pastor

Iglesia Cristiana Peniel (11097) (IL) 64
PO Box 573, Summit Argo IL 60501
773-582-6785
    Juan Laureano, Pastor

Iglesia Menonita Getsemani (10638) (IL, IMH, CAM) 23
Juan Jesus Garza Ruiz, Conf Cr Men de Tamaulipas,
Cartagena #111, Frace Casa Blanca, H Matamoros,
Tamaulipas
219-397-9936
1715 Indianapolis Blvd, Whiting IN
    David Araujo, Pastor
    Sonia N. Araujo, Co-Pastor

Joy Fell Menn Ch (27391) (CDC, IL, AAMA) 30
2918 W Montana St, Peoria IL 61605
309-674-0529
    Phillip Maclin, Pastor

Lawndale Menn Ch (11973) (IL, IMH, CAM) 80
2520 S Lawndale Ave, Chicago IL 60623
773-277-6665
    Angel M. Canon, Pastor

Living Love Ministries (11096) (CDC, IL, AV) ...75
PO Box 5473, Peoria IL 61601
309-676-2772
707 NE Perry Ave
    Maria Hatfield, Pastor
    Walter Smeltzer, Associate Pastor

Living Water Community Ch (11151) (IL, CAM, AAMA) 67
1545 W Pratt #101, Chicago IL 60626
773-764-5872, fax 773-262-2371,
livingwatercc@juno.com,
http://livingwatercommunitychurch.org
1545 W Morse Ave, 3rd Floor (United Church of Rogers Park)
    Sally Schreiner, Senior Pastor
    Joe Maniglia, Youth Pastor

Lombard Menn Ch (11981) (IL) 160
528 E Madison St, Lombard IL 60148
630-627-5310, fax 630-627-9893,
LombardMenno@aol.com,
http://lombard.il.us.mennonite.net
    Todd K. Friesen, Lead Pastor
    John M. Stoltzfus, Associate Pastor

Madison Menn Ch (10078) (CDC, IL) 111
PO Box 44522, Madison WI 53744-4522
608-276-7680, mmc@madison-mennonite.org,
http://www.madison-mennonite.org
1501 Gilbert Rd
    Tonya Ramer Wenger, Pastor

Maple Avenue Menn Ch (23697) (CDC, IL, CAM) 39
346 Maple Ave, Waukesha WI 53186
262-547-6937, bfons@webtv.net
    Clarice Kratz, Co-Pastor
    Lawrence M. Kratz, Co-Pastor

CONFERENCES AND CONGREGATIONS

2

Maple Lawn Fell (10049) (IL) 0
700 N Main St, Eureka IL 61530
309-467-2337, fax 309-467-2594,
Doug@Maple-Lawn.com
   Richard Douglas Hicks, Pastor

Menominee River Fell (10135) (IL) 30
PO Box 542, Menominee MI 49858
715-735-0189

Menn Ch of Dillon (11866) (IL) 51
6349 Springfield Rd, Delavan IL 61734
309-244-7153
20549 Peach St
   Robert D. Nafziger, Pastor

Menn Ch of Normal (11833) (CDC, IL) 284
805 S Cottage Ave, Normal IL 61761
309-452-6622, fax 309-452-0478,
normal.mennonite@verizon.net,
http://www.normalmennonite.com
   Tim E. Schrag, Pastor
   Jane Thorley Roeschley, Associate Pastor
   Steve A. Ropp, Youth Pastor

Metamora Menn Ch (12013) (IL) 203
1393 Mennonite Rd, Metamora IL 61548
309-367-4892, fax 309-367-4121, metmenno@mtco.com,
http://www.metmenno.org
   Michael Danner, Lead Pastor

North Suburban Menn Ch (27557) (CDC, IL, CAM) 24
1500 W Hawley St, Mundelein IL 60060-1508
847-566-8386, fax 847-475-1006
   David Kerner, Pastor

Oak Park Menn Ch (24653) (CDC, IL, CAM) 58
PO Box 3091, Oak Park IL 60303
773-343-4251, PWaite6116@aol.com
425 Central Park Ave
   Phil Waite, Pastor

Plow Creek Menn Ch (22335) (CDC, IL) 31
19183 Plow Creek Unit #2, Tiskilwa IL 61368
815-646-6600, fax 815-646-6600, lereha@ilstu.edu,
http://www.plowcreek.org
1925 E 880 N
   Richard Gordon Foss, Lay Minister
   Lynn Reha, Pastoral Elder
   Louise Stahnke, Pastoral Elder

Prairieview Menn Ch (12138) (CDC, IL) 221
13013 N 400 Rd E, PO Box 369, Flanagan IL 61740
815-796-4298

Reba Place Ch (22343) (IL, CAM, AAMA) 135
PO Box 6017, Evanston IL 60204
847-475-1670, fax 847-328-8431,
richudgens@yahoo.com,
http://www.rebaplacechurch.Il.US.Mennonite.net
Custer & Madison
   Ric Hudgens, Pastor

Rehoboth Menn Ch (12062) (IL, CAM, AAMA) 25
c/o Rose Covington, 14220 E 3000 South Rd, St Anne IL 60964
815-944-5961, fax 815-944-5961
15429 E 3000 S Road
   Rose Covington, Elder

Roanoke Menn Ch (12070) (IL) 400
1195 CR 1600 E, Eureka IL 61530
309-467-3460, rmc@mtco.com, http://www.rmc4u.org
1200 N & 1600 E, corner of Woodford Co
   Rick Troyer, Co-Pastor
   Elmer J. Wyse, Co-Pastor

Science Ridge Menn Ch (12104) (IL) 142
1702 E 37th St, Sterling IL 61081
815-626-0538, fax 815-626-0594, sridge@cin.net,
http://www.rusthollar.com
   Mervin Miller, Pastor

Sonido de Alabanza (23432) (IL, IMH, CAM) 700
5510 W 25th St, Cicero IL 60804-3318
708-780-1170, fax 708-780-1176,
sonidodealabanza@earthlink.net
5510 W Rd 25th St
   Juan Ferreras, Pastor
   Esdras Ferreras, Associate Pastor
   Maritza Ferreras, Associate Pastor
   Alejandra Mendoza, Associate Pastor

St Louis Menn Fell (24182) (CDC, IL) 64
1443 Ross Ave, St Louis MO 63146-4563
314-878-2832, jubaer@dgpurdy.com, http://www.slmf.org

Trinity Menn Ch (23549) (IL) 189
1901 S 4th St, Morton IL 61550
309-263-8808, fax 309-263-0133,
trinitymorton@juno.com, http://www.trinity.org
   Michael D. Hutchings, Pastor

Trinity New Life Menn Ch (26732) (IL) 160
PO Box 36, Henry IL 61537
815-646-4678, tnlf@mtco.com
   Thomas L. Schrock, Pastor

Willow Springs Menn Ch (12146) (IL) 66
PO Box 386, Tiskilwa IL 61368
815-646-4287, fax 815-646-4301, wsmenno@juno.com,
http://www.willowsprings.il.us.mennonite.net
16621 Kentville Rd
   Calvin Dean Zehr, Pastor
   John Gray, Associate Pastor

Indiana-Michigan Mennonite Conference

OFFICE
imoffice@im.mennonite.net,
www.immennonite.net
574-534-4006; 800-288-8486;
fax 574-533-5676
212 S Main St., Goshen IN 46526

STAFF
Sherm Kauffman, executive conference minister
(sherm@im.mennonite.net)
Nancy Kauffmann, conference regional minister
(nancy@im.mennonite.net)
Tim Lichti, conference regional minister
(tim@im.mennonite.net)
Richard W. Yoder, interim conference regional
minister (richard@im.mennonite.net)
Bob Yoder, conference minister of youth and
young adults (bob@im.mennonite.net)
Elizabeth Stauffer, *Gospel Evangel* editor
(elizabeth@im.mennonite.net)
Heidi King, administrative coordinator
(heidi@im.mennonite.net)
Charlotte Long, secretary/bookkeeper
(charlotte@im.mennonite.net)
Bj Leichty, secretarial assistant
(bj@im.mennonite.net)

GENERAL INFORMATION
Year founded: 1854
Members: 10,836
Congregations: 92
Ministers: 309
CLC reps: Sherm Kauffman, Mary Ellen Meyer,
David Sutter
Annual Conference: June 19-21, 2003
Conference historian: Leonard Gross

EXECUTIVE COMMITTEE
Randy Detweiler, moderator (pastor-
randy@juno.com), 4763 N 700 E, Kokomo IN
46901, 765-628-2865; David Sutter, moderator-
elect; Jonathan Brown, Karl Cender, Terry
Diener, Brent Eash, James Gerber, Marjorie
Rush Hovde, Mary Ellen Meyer, Homer Nissley,
Mary Swartley, Scot Wilson

PUBLICATION
Gospel Evangel (Monthly), Elizabeth Stauffer,
editor (gospelevangel@im.mennonite.net)
(same address as above)

COMMISSIONS
Church Life. Duane Beck, chair
(duaneb@maplenet.net), 925 Oxford,
Elkhart IN 46516, 574-293-5160; Ruben
Chupp, Bill Miller, Dan Miller, Grace
Whitehead
Conference Program Planning. Mary
Mininger, chair (mininger@blueriver.net),
2589 N CR 100 W, Paoli IN 47454, 812-723-
2459; Barb Gerber, Ken Livengood, staff:
Sherm Kauffman
Gospel Evangel **Advisory.** Stuart Showalter,
chair (stuarts@goshen.edu), 1401 Elmhurst
Ct, Goshen IN 46526, 574-535-7008; Ryan
Ahlgrim, Pat McFarlane, staff: Heidi King
Justice, Peace, and Service. Rich Meyer,
chair (cptcsd@npcc.net), 13416 CR 44,
Millersburg, IN 46543, 574-642-3963;
Eldon Christophel, Al Mortenson, Bob
Whitehead, Rachel Yoder
Mission. Tim Stair, chair
(tim@collegemennonite.org),
202 Constitution Ave, Goshen IN 46526,
574-534-4145; Michele Bollman, Cora
Brown, Carol Bucher Bixler, Art McPhee
Nurture. Esther Lanting, chair
(elanting@maplenet.net), 410 S Washington
St, Wakarusa IN 46573, 574-862-1910;
Randall Miller, Kathy Meyer Reimer, Barb
Stahly, Ruth Ann Wittrig
Stewardship and Finance. Lavonn Hostetler,
chair (lavonnrh@goshen.edu), 25179 SR
119, Goshen IN 46526, 574-862-1012; Karl
Cender, Stanley Kropf, Amy Schrock, Doug
Smoker

CONFERENCES AND CONGREGATIONS

2

OTHER CONFERENCE AGENCY AND REPS

Mennonite Women. Thelma Martin, president, 28090 CR 44, Nappanee IN 46550, 574-862-2930; Oleta Bollman, Debbie Lantz, Carolyn Lichti, Mary Sue Miller, Katie Troyer, Karen Unternahrer

Congregations

Ann Arbor Menn Ch (13508) (CDC, IM) **7**
1455 Kelly Green Dr, Ann Arbor MI 48103-2614
734-996-9815
Arrowwood Community Center, 2566 Arrowwood
  Chibuzor Vincent Ozor, Pastor

Assembly Menn Ch (22582) (CDC, IM) **127**
1201 S 11th St, Goshen IN 46526
574-534-4190, assemblymenn@juno.com,
http://assembly.in.us.mennonite.net
Corner of 11th & New York
  Lois Johns Kaufmann, Co-Pastor
  Karl Schirch Shelly, Co-Pastor
  Mary Lehman Yoder, Co-Pastor

Bean Blossom Menn Ch (12179) (IM) **53**
¼977 Woodland Lake Rd, Morgantown IN 46160
812-988-2189
5046 N SR 135
  Gary L. Link, Pastor

Belmont Menn Ch (12187) (IM) **166**
925 Oxford St, Elkhart IN 46516
574-293-5160, fax 574-293-2061, belmont@maplenet.net
  Duane E. Beck, Pastor
  Nina Bartelt Lanctot, Associate Pastor

Benton Menn Ch (12195) (IM) **93**
15350 CR 44, Goshen IN 46528
574-642-3245, fax 574-642-0144, bmc@maplenet.net,
http://benton.in.us.mennonite.net
  Douglas D.H. Kaufman, Pastor
  Brenda Hostetler Meyer, Pastor

Berea Menn Ch (12203) (IM) **250**
RR 3 Box 317, Loogootee IN 47553
812-636-4181
  Eddie Graber, Pastor

Berkey Avenue Menn Fell (24323) (IM) **174**
2509 Berkey Ave, Goshen IN 46526
574-534-2398, fax 574-534-4748, berkeyave@juno.com,
http://berkeyavenue.in.us.mennonite.net
  Anita Yoder Kehr, Pastor
  Daniel P. Schrock, Pastor

Bethel Menn Ch (12237) (IM) **46**
935 Alpine St., Greenville MI 48838-2503
517-838-2588, joe_pendleton@hotmail.com
  Joe Pendleton, Pastor

Bonneyville Menn Ch (12245) (IM) **124**
15273 SR 120, Bristol IN 46507
574-848-7148, bonvil@npcc.net
NW Corner of SR 120 & CR 131
  Kenneth Livengood, Pastor

Burr Oak Menn Ch (12278) (IM) **64**
11506 W 200 S, Rensselaer IN 47978
219-394-2339, bomc@netnitco.net
Corner of CRs 200 S & 1150 W
  Philip D. Leichty, Pastor
  James R. Armstrong, Overseer

**Carroll Community Worship Center (12153)
(IM)** **46**
4506 Carroll Rd, Fort Wayne IN 46818
260-637-2309, fax 260-637-5998, dove9@juno.com,
http://www.carrollcommunity.org
  Verlin Haarer, Pastor

Cedar Grove Menn Ch (12302) (IM) **14**
1671 River Rd, Manistique MI 49854
906-341-3435, cgmenn@up.net
1275 N Kandall Rd
  James L. Troyer, Pastor

Christian Fell Center (28951) (IM) **44**
PO Box 416, Sturgis MI 49091
269-651-9425
  Glenn Middleton, Pastor

Church Without Walls (10244) (IM, AAMA) **80**
731 Wagner Ave, Elkhart IN 46516
574-293-0776, fax 574-293-0776
  Jonathan Brown, Pastor
  Cora L. Brown, Co-Pastor
  Joe Gary, Other

Clinton Brick Menn Ch (12336) (IM) **121**
PO Box 713, Goshen IN 46527-0713
574-642-3805, rkennel@npcc.net 62499 SR 13
  Ronald L. Kennel, Pastor

Clinton Frame Menn Ch (12328) (IM) **591**
63846 CR 35, Goshen IN 46528
574-642-3165, fax 574-642-3786, cfmc@maplenet.net,
http://clintonframe.in.us.mennonite.net
  Robert L. Shreiner, Pastor
  Terry Diener, Assistant Pastor/Minister of Pastoral Care
    & Counseling
  Terry Diener, Associate Pastor/Youth Ministry Overseer
  Mary Ann Shreiner, Minister of Senior Adults & Special
    Needs Persons
  Aldine Thomas, Minister of Visitation

Coldsprings Menn Ch (12344) (IM) 59
1381 E Phelps, Kalkaska MI 49646
231-587-0806
   Brent Bontrager, Pastor

College Menn Ch (12518) (IM) 1075
1900 S Main St, Goshen IN 46526
574-535-7262, fax 574-535-7165,
cmc@collegemennonite.org
   Lee Dengler, Pastor
   Susan Dengler, Pastor
   Firman Gingerich, Pastor
   Wilfred Kanagy, Pastor
   Klaudia Smucker, Pastor
   Tim Stair, Pastor
   Rosemary Widmer, Pastor
   Kristen Hoober, Youth Pastor

Communion Fell (26997) (IM) 113
116 S 3rd St, Goshen IN 46526
574-533-0315, fax 574-533-0316,
cf@communionfellowship.org, http://npcc.net/~cfgoshen
   Charles Buller, Pastor
   Tina Stoltzfus Horst, Associate Pastor

Community Christian Fell (10243)
(IM, AAMA) 250
17330 Chandler Park Dr, Detroit MI 48224
313-882-2850, fax 313-882-4550
   Samuel A. Wilson, Pastor

East Goshen Menn Ch (12393) (IM) 219
17861 SR 4, Goshen IN 46528
574-533-7161, egmc@eastgoshenmc.org,
http://eastgoshen.in.us.mennonite.net
   Merle Hostetler, Pastor
   Steve E. Slagel, Pastor

Emma Menn Ch (12419) (IM) 278
1900 S 600 W, Topeka IN 46571
260-593-2036, fax 260-593-2564,
emmamc@maplenet.net, http://emma.in.us.mennonite.net
   Gene A. Hartman, Pastor
   Galen Mast, Youth Pastor

Fairhaven Menn Ch (12435) (IM) 56
5401 Winter St, Fort Wayne IN 46806
260-456-6997
   Jimmie Ruffin, Pastor

Faith Menn Ch (10127) (CDC, IM) 35
1201 S 11th St, Goshen IN 46526
574-534-1173, gustazook@aol.com
   Teresa Dutchersmith, Pastor
   Gwen Ann Gustafson-Zook, Pastor

Fellowship of Hope Menn Ch (22210) (IM) 48
1618 S 6th St, Elkhart IN 46516
574-294-1416, fohchurch@msn.com,
http://ofhopechurch.in.us.mennonite.net
   Robert Weidman, Pastor
   Joshua Yoder, Pastor

First Menn Ch (12476) (IM) 75
1213 Saint Marys Ave, Fort Wayne IN 46808
260-422-6702, mennofw@juno.com
   Kathy Colliver, Pastor

First Menn Ch (12450) (IM) 176
4601 Knollton Rd, Indianapolis IN 46228
317-251-1980, fax 317-253-4632, indymenno@juno.com
Corner of 46th & Knollton
   Ryan Jeffrey Ahlgrim, Pastor
   Laura Van Voorhis, Associate Pastor

First Menn Ch (12468) (IM) 389
203 E Lawrence St, PO Box 508, Middlebury IN 46540
574-825-5135, fax 574-825-2569,
fmcoffice@firstmennonite.net,
http://www.firstmennonite.net
   Linford Martin, Pastor
   Myron Bontreger, Associate Pastor and
      Minister of Youth
   Pamela Yoder, Pastoral Care Coordinator

Forks Menn Ch (12492) (IM) 151
11435 W 025 S, Middlebury IN 46540
574-825-9333, ForksMennonite@juno.com
   Wes P. Yoder, Pastor

Germfask Menn Ch (12500) (IM) 34
Rt 1 Box 215, Germfask MI 49836
   J. D. Livermore Jr, Pastor

Good News Community Chapel (12286) (IM) . . .9
PO Box 791, Pinckney MI 48169
734-878-3992
104 E Putnam St
   Jan Esch, Contact Person

Gospel Lighthouse (12526) (IM) 25
Box 257, New Paris IN 46553
574-831-4432
   Eli S. Schmucker, Pastor

Grace Chapel (12534) (IM, AAMA) 68
2202 Janes Ave, Saginaw MI 48601
989-755-3212
   James H. Nelson, Pastor

Grand Marais Menn Ch (12542) (IM) 8
PO Box 457, Grand Marais MI 49839
Randolph & Campbell
   Stephen Post, Pastor

Harlan Menn Fell (23333) (IM) 21
PO Box 493, Ages-Brookside KY 40801
606-573-4844, erstol@kih.net
302 E Clover St, Harlan
   Richard G. Stoltzfus, Contact Person

Harmony Christian Fell (28035) (IM) 10
PO Box 1465, Antioch TN 37013
615-331-4127
   Ken Bowman, Contact Person

CONFERENCES AND CONGREGATIONS

2

Hilltop Menn Fell (12856) (IM) **14**
810 Petoskey St, Petoskey MI 49770
fax, hilltopfellowship@yahoo.com
   James Gerber, Interim Pastor

Holdeman Menn Ch (12567) (IM) **207**
65723 CR 1, Wakarusa IN 46573
574-862-4751, holdemanchurch@juno.com
   David Scott Heusinkveld, Pastor
   Vernard E. Guengerich, Associate Pastor

Hopewell Menn Ch (12575) (IM) **188**
PO Box 316, Kouts IN 46347
219-766-2184
North edge of town on SR 49
   Bill Beck, Co-Pastor
   Chris Birky, Co-Pastor

House of Power (10961) (IM) **5**
28103 CR 20 W, Elkhart IN 46517
574-522-7211
   Robert Crockett, Pastor

Howard-Miami Menn Ch (12583) (IM) **254**
3976 E 1400 S, Kokomo IN 46901
765-395-7509, fax 765-395-8192, howard-
miami@juno.com, http://www.netusa1.net/~cdmiller
   Randy Detweiler, Pastor
   T. Lee Miller, Co-Pastor

Hudson Lake Menn Ch (12591) (IM) **37**
PO Box 903, New Carlisle IN 46552
574-654-8388
7503 N Walker Rd
   Esther Lanting, Pastor

Iglesia Menonita del Buen Pastor (12377)
(IM, IMH) **43**
523 S 6th St, Goshen IN 46526
574-537-8403
   Seferina Garcia DeLeon, Pastor
   Ciro Serrano, Pastor
   Rolando Sosa, Pastor
   Jorge Vielman, Pastor

Kern Road Menn Ch (12617) (IM) **226**
18211 Kern Rd, South Bend IN 46614
574-291-0924, fax 574-291-9437, KRMC1@juno.com,
http://krmc.in.us.mennonite.net
   Andre Gingerich Stoner, Pastor
   David L. Sutter, Pastor
   Janice Yordy Sutter, Pastor

Lafayette Menn Fell (26021) (CDC, IM) **8**
PO Box 355, Lafayette IN 47902-0355
765-743-4876, hovde@dcwi.com,
http://livingfaith.in.us.mennonite.net
102 N Chauncy (First United Methodist), West Lafayette
   David Hovde, Contact Person

Lake Bethel Menn Ch (12625) (IM) **10**
250 Spring Beach Dr, Rome City IN 46784
260-351-3506
   Lewis B. Miller, Pastor

Liberty Menn Ch (12641) (IM) **22**
PO Box 328, Concord MI 49237
517-524-7489, dtmcclin@modempool.com
   David McClintic, Pastor

Locust Grove Menn Ch (12666) (IM) **193**
29525 Findley Rd, Burr Oak MI 49030
269-489-5041, fax 240-220-8027, office@lgrove.org,
http://www.lgrove.org
   John M. Troyer, Pastor

Maple Grove Menn Ch (12690) (IM) **12**
RR 1 Box 136, Gulliver MI 49840
906-283-3117
   Philip Hoffman, Pastor

Maple River Menn Ch (12682) (IM) **49**
PO Box 526, Brutus MI 49716
231-529-6720, bjgerber@freeway.net
3834 Euclid Ave
   James Gerber, Pastor

Maranatha Menn Chapel (24737) (IM) **87**
9636 W Hepton Rd, Nappanee IN 46550
574-773-2740, fax 574-773-9174, nmmc@bnin.net
   Charlie Mullet, Contact Person

Marion Menn Ch (12708) (IM) **112**
PO Box 68, Shipshewana IN 46565
260-562-2910, marmenchurch@netscape.net
5460 N 450 W
   Brian Arbuckle, Pastor

Menn Ch of Warsaw (10007) (IM) **29**
1250 Husky Trail, Warsaw IN 46582
574-269-4449
   Alan E. Leinbach, Pastor

Menn Fell of Bloomington (11426) (IM) **7**
719 W 7th St, Bloomington IN 47404
812-336-6219, eroth@indiana.edu
Meets in homes
   Erin Roth, Contact Person

Michigan Avenue Menn Ch (12716) (IM) **103**
PO Box 507, Pigeon MI 48755
989-453-2451, mamc@avci.net
7004 E Michigan Ave
   Scot Wilson, Pastor

Midland Menn Ch (12724) (IM) **35**
2510 E Stewart Rd, Midland MI 48640
989-839-9451, fax 898-832-3303, donsdetect@aol.com
Corner of Stewart & Patterson
   Don Duford, Interim Pastor

Morning Star Ch (29652) (CDC, IM) **24**
2000 S Hoyt Ave, Muncie IN 47302
765-287-0021
   Gladys Maina, Pastor
   Simon Mungai, Associate Pastor

MSU Menn Fell (12757) (CDC, IM) **40**
PO Box 6068, East Lansing MI 48826
517-482-9961, msumennofell@juno.com,
http://msu.mi.us.mennonite.net
Alumni Memorial Chapel, MSU Campus
   June Mears-Driedger, Pastor

Naubinway Menn Ch (12807) (IM) **10**
PO Box 127, Naubinway MI 49762
906-477-6553, fax 906-477-6553, tomiller@portup.com
Main St
   Timothy O. Miller, Pastor

Ninth Street Menn Ch (12815) (IM, AAMA) **40**
1118 N 9th St, Saginaw MI 48601
989-752-7366, fax 989-755-4123, ninth.street@juno.com
   William L. Scott Jr, Pastor

North Goshen Menn Ch (21998) (IM) **201**
PO Box 505, Goshen IN 46527-0505
574-533-4255, northgoshenmennonite@juno.com
510 N 8th St
   Arthur E. Smoker Jr, Pastor
   Jerry Wittrig, Co-Pastor

North Leo Menn Ch (12773) (IM) **148**
15419 SR 1 N, PO Box 213, Leo IN 46765
260-627-2149, fax 260-627-2149, northleo@juno.com,
http://www.hows.net/46765NLMC
   Douglas J. Zehr, Pastor
   Miriam R. Zehr, Family Life Minister

North Main Street Menn Ch (12781) (IM) **238**
504 N Main St, Nappanee IN 46550
574-773-4558, fax 574-773-5438, nmainmen@bnin.net
   Ruben Chupp, Pastor

Olive Menn Ch (21758) (IM) **141**
61081 CR 3, Elkhart IN 46517
574-293-2320, omc_office@juno.com
   Daniel Z. Miller, Interim Pastor
   Sampson Woelk, Associate Pastor

Paoli Menn Fell (22624) (CDC, IM) **59**
2589 N CR 100 W, Paoli IN 47454
812-723-2414, fax 812-723-3515, mininger@blueriver.net
   Mary Mininger, Co-Pastor
   Philip A. Mininger, Co-Pastor

Parkview Menn Ch (12849) (IM) **68**
1382 E CR 100 N, Kokomo IN 46901
765-459-5714, parkviewchurch@juno.com
   Jacob W. Elias, Intentional Interim
   Lillian Elias, Intentional Interim

**Peace Community Menn Ch (12385) (IM,
AAMA)** **61**
15800 Curtis St, Detroit MI 48235
313-273-7999, fax 313-345-2285
   Evelyn E. Childs, Pastor

Pine Grove Menn Ch (12559) (IM) **45**
1195 N Wattles Rd, Battle Creek MI 49014-7813
616-964-9214, fax 616-964-8718
   Thomas Schwartz, Pastor

Plato Menn Ch (12864) (IM) **50**
2030 S 050 W, LaGrange IN 46761
260-463-2530
US Rt 20 & 5005 E
   Richard E. Martin, Pastor

Pleasant View Menn Ch (12872) (IM) **232**
58529 CR 23, Goshen IN 46528
574-533-2872, fax 574-533-2283, pvmc@maplenet.net,
http://www.mypv.org
   Ronald Diener, Pastor
   Wes Culver, Associate Pastor
   Michael Wayne Peak, Associate Pastor
   Norman Maust, Ordained Deacon

Prairie Street Menn Ch (12880) (IM) **203**
1316 Prairie St, Elkhart IN 46516-3908
574-293-0377, psmc1316@aol.com
   Andrew Kreider, Pastor

Providence Menn Ch (12898) (IM) **225**
R 2, Box 444, Montgomery IN 47558
812-486-3679
   Bert Lengacher, Contact Person

Restoration Menn (10245) (IM, AAMA) **5**
1908 N Fremont, South Bend IN 46628
574-232-4880
   Gregory Gibson, Contact Person

Rexton Menn Ch (12906) (IM, CAM) **38**
N 7970 Church St, Naubinway MI 49762
906-595-7361, fax 906-595-7361, rexton49@hotmail.com
N Rd 7970 Church St (Rexton)
   Timothy O. Miller, Pastor

Ridgeview Menn Ch (12740) (IM) **10**
1344 Lenard Oak Ch Rd, Morgantown KY 42261
270-526-3962
   Harold Johnson, Contact Person

Roselawn Menn Ch (12914) (IM) **38**
54365 Independence St, Elkhart IN 46514
574-264-0035, evoncas@juno.com
54364 Independence St
   Conrad Hochstetler, Contact Person

**Shalom Community Ch (23242) (CDC, IM,
COB)** **45**
PO Box 8080, Ann Arbor MI 48107-8080
734-761-7366, fax 734-761-7366,
shalomcommunitychurch@yahoo.com,
http://www.shalomcommunitychurch.mi.us.mennonite.net
2670 Sequoia Pkwy Rd
   Paul Versluis, Pastor

Shalom Menn Ch (10196) (IM) **56**
6100 E 32nd St, Indianapolis IN 46226
317-549-0577, shalom@usisp.com,
http://www.shalom.complete.org
   Dagne Assefa, Pastor

**CONFERENCES AND
CONGREGATIONS**

2

Shore Menn Ch (12963) (IM) 331
7235 W US Hwy 20, Shipshewana IN 46565
260-768-4240, fax 260-768-4255, shore@locl.net,
http://www.shore.in.us.mennonite.net
  Brent Eash, Pastor
  Carl Horner, Pastor

Soo Hill Community Ch (12971) (IM) 15
PO Box 553, Escanaba MI 49829-0553
906-786-4862
  Chris Holmes, Contact Person

Southside Fell (12930) (CDC, IM) 95
140 W Mishawaka Rd, Elkhart IN 46517
574-293-2825, ssfellow@juno.com
AMBS Chapel, 3003 Benham Ave
  Rhoda M. Schrag, Pastor

Stutsmanville Chapel (12989) (IM) 106
2988 State Rd, Harbor Springs MI 49740
231-526-2335, stuts@freeway.net
  Edward Warner, Pastor

Sunnyside Menn Ch (12997) (IM) 141
23786 Sunnyside Ave, Elkhart IN 46516
574-875-7790, fax 574-875-6336,
sunnysidemc@juno.com,
www.sunnysidemennonitechurch.in.us.mennonite.net
  Terry Zehr, Pastor

Talcum Menn Ch (13003) (IM) 37
9365 Vest-Talcum Rd, Talcum KY 41722
606-251-3303
  Orlo J. Fisher, Pastor

Valparaiso Menn Ch (13037) (IM) 51
1305 Silhavy Rd, Valparaiso IN 46383
219-464-8187, fax 219-464-8187 (call first),
valpomenn@hotmail.com
  Mario Bustos, Pastor

Walnut Hill Menn Ch (13045) (IM) 121
909 N Sixth St, Goshen IN 46528
574-533-8023
  Jane Stoltzfus Buller, Pastor
  Stephen B. Thomas, Pastor

Wasepi Menn Chapel (13052) (IM) 50
PO Box 246, Centreville MI 49032
269-467-4024
  Randy Miller, Contact Person

Waterford Menn Ch (13060) (IM) 391
65975 SR 15, Goshen IN 46526
574-533-5642, fax 574-533-0879,
wmc@waterfordchurch.org,
http://www.waterfordchurch.org
  Joseph S. Miller, Pastor
  Loanne Harms, Minister to Youth
  John C. King, Minister to Older Adults
  Charlene Stoltzfus, Minister to Children

Wawasee Lakeside Chapel (13078) (IM) 192
PO Box 544, Syracuse IN 46567
574-856-2533
  Harlan Steffen, Pastor

Wayside Menn Ch (13086) (IM) 26
66 W 6 Mile, Sault Ste Marie MI 49783
906-635-0459
  Ronald Duane Swartz, Pastor

Wildwood Menn Ch (13110) (IM) 42
Rt 1 Box 145, Engadine MI 49827
906-586-6421
6 miles north of Engadine on M117, 4.5 miles west on
Sandtown Rd
  John L. Troyer, Pastor

Yellow Creek Menn Ch (13128) (IM) 521
64901 CR 11, Goshen IN 46526
574-862-2595, fax 574-862-2178,
info@yellowcreekmc.org, http://www.yellowcreekmc.org
NW Corner of CR 11 & CR 38
  Wes J. Bontreger, Pastor
  Harold J. Yoder, Pastor
  Ben Rheinheimer, Youth Pastor

Lancaster Mennonite Conference

OFFICE

lmccenter@lanmenconf.org,
www.lanmenconf.org
717-293-5246 and 800-216-7249;
fax 717-431-1987
2160 Lincoln Highway East #5,
Lancaster PA 17602

STAFF

Debra Bearden, receptionist
(debra@lanmenconf.org)
Joanne H. Dietzel, administrative coordinator
(joanne@lanmenconf.org)
Janet N. Gehman, editor, Lancaster Conference
NEWS (janet@lanmenconf.org)
Carl A. Hess, financial administrator
(carl@lanmenconf.org)
Gloria Shenk Kniss, data manager
(gloria@lanmenconf.org)
C. Kenneth Martin, conference treasurer
(kenc@epix.net)
James R. Martin, congregational resource staff
(james@lanmenconf.org)
Lindsey A. Robinson, conference minister
(lindsey@lanmenconf.org)
Christina L. Showalter, co-director, leadership
development (christina@lanmenconf.org)
Nathan D. Showalter, co-director, leadership
development (nate@lanmenconf.org)
Alonna Gautsche Sprunger, congregational
resources director
(alonna@lanmenconf.org)
Lorrie Stoltzfus, administrative assistant
(lorrie@lanmenconf.org)
Mary K. Trees, administrative assistant
(mary@lanmenconf.org)
Curtis B. Weaver, congregational resource staff
(curt@lanmenconf.org)
L. Keith Weaver, conference moderator
(keith@lanmenconf.org)

GENERAL INFORMATION

Year founded: 1775
Members: 18,529
Congregations: 203
Active ministers: 351
Total credentialed: 695 (includes ministers plus
deacons, deaconesses, missionary/church
workers and staff at church agencies)
Total active credentialed: 491
CLC reps: Joanne H. Dietzel, Carl E. Horning,
L. Keith Weaver
Districts: Bishops/Overseers/Supervisors;
Bishop Oversight: Nelson L. Bowman;
Bowmansville-Reading: Irvin L. Martin;
Elizabethtown: Enos D. Martin; Ephrata:
L. Keith Weaver; Groffdale: Lloyd E. Hoover;
Harrisburg: Paul W. Nisly; Hess-Landis
Valley: Nelson W. Martin; Juniata: Glen M.
Sell, interim; Lancaster: Harold E. Reed;
Landisville: Dale Stoltzfus; Lebanon: Carl E.
Horning; Manheim: Donald O. Nauman;
Manor: Nathan D. Showalter, interim;
Martindale: Nelson L. Bowman; Mellinger:
Paul M. Zehr; Millwood: Elvin J. Ressler;
New Danville: Ernest M. Hess; New England:
Henry L. Buckwalter; New York City: Monroe
J. Yoder; North Penn: Stephen A. Haupert;
Pequea Valley: Richard L. Buckwalter;
Philadelphia: Freeman J. Miller; Spanish:
Samuel M. Lopez, Jose A. Santiago;
Washington-Baltimore: Melvin B. Delp;
Weaverland-Northeastern PA: C. Kenneth
Martin; Williamsport-Milton area: Linford W.
Good; Willow St-Strasburg: J. Vernon Myers;
York-Adams: Carlton D. Stambaugh
Annual conference (Celebration of Church Life):
March 22 and 23, 2003
Leadership assembly: March 21, 2003
Conference historian: Lancaster Mennonite
Historical Society

BISHOP BOARD EXECUTIVE COMMITTEE

L. Keith Weaver, moderator
(keith@lanmenconf.org), 115 Swamp
Church Rd, Reinholds PA 17569, 717-336-
5253; Carl E. Horning, assistant moderator;

CONFERENCES AND CONGREGATIONS

2

Lloyd E. Hoover, secretary; C. Kenneth
Martin, treasurer; Nelson L. Bowman, member-at-large; Donald O. Nauman, member-
at-large; Jose A. Santiago, member-at-large;
staff: Lindsey Robinson and Joanne H.
Dietzel

PUBLICATIONS
Lancaster Conference *NEWS* (Monthly), Janet
Gehman, editor (janet@lanmenconf.org)
Lancaster Conference Directory (Annually)
Gloria S. Kniss, editor (gloria@lanmenconf.org)
(both same address as above)

COMMISSIONS
Finance. C. Kenneth Martin, chair
   (kenc@epix.net), 238 Reading Rd, East Earl
   PA 17519, 717-445-5736; Millard P. Garrett,
   vice-chair; Aaron L. Groff, Jr, secretary
Leadership Council. Carl E. Horning, chair
   (chorning@redrose.net), 595 Wedgewood
   Dr, Lebanon PA 17042, 717-949-3314
Association of Retired Ministers. Adam
   Esbenshade, chair, 626 S Kinzer Ave, New
   Holland PA 17557, 717-354-9509
**Committee for Abuse Recovery and
   Prevention.** Mary Boll, chair, 319 E
   Meadow Valley Rd, Lititz PA 17543,
   717-627-1611
Women in Leadership Subcommittee. Carol
   J. Oberholtzer, chair
   (doberhol@ptdprolog.net), 115 Rothsville
   Station Rd, Lititz PA 17543, 717-626-9361

OTHER CONFERENCE AGENCY AND REPS
Congregational Resource Center. Alonna
   Gautsche Sprunger, director
   (alonna@lanmenconf.org),
   2160 Lincoln Highway East #5, Lancaster PA
   17602, 717-293-5246
Eastern Mennonite Missions. See separate
   listing in section 3.
Friendship Community. Interim executive
   director, 1149 E Oregon Rd, Lititz PA 17543,
   717-656-2466

Lancaster Mennonite School. J. Richard
   Thomas, principal (thomasjr@lmhs.com),
   2176 Lincoln Hwy E, Lancaster PA 17602,
   717-299-0436
Lancaster Mennonite Historical Society.
   Brinton L. Rutherford, director
   (lmhs@lmhs.org), 2215 Millstream Rd,
   Lancaster PA 17602, 717-393-9745
Landis Homes Retirement Community.
   Edward Longenecker, president
   (info@landishomes.org), 1001 E Oregon
   Rd, Lititz PA 17543, 717-569-3271
Mennonite Women. Elaine W. Good, president
   (rolee-leonelaine@supernet.net), 304 Buch
   Mill Rd, Lititz PA 17543, 717-626-9287
Sharing Programs. 2160 Lincoln Highway E,
   PO Box 10367, Lancaster PA 17605-0367,
   717-293-7100
Philhaven. LaVern Yutzy, CEO
   (ljy@philhaven.com), 283 S Butler Rd, PO
   Box 550, Mount Gretna PA 17064, 717-273-
   8871

LANCASTER AREA COUNCIL OF MENNONITE SCHOOLS (LACMS)
See schools listing in section 3 for Conestoga
Christian, Ephrata Mennonite, Gehmans
Mennonite, Hinkletown Mennonite, Juniata
Mennonite, Kraybill Mennonite, Lancaster
Mennonite School, Linville Hill Mennonite, Lititz
Area Mennonite, Locust Grove Mennonite,
Manheim Christian Day, New Covenant Christian,
New Danville Mennonite, West Fallowfield
Christian.

   *Lancaster Conference congregations not
participating in Mennonite Church USA are indicated with an asterisk (*) after the congregational name.

Congregations

Abundant Life Chinese Menn Ch* (10102) (LAN, KB) **50**
738 Moore St, Philadelphia PA 19148-1718
215-271-5018, fax 215-463-0909, alcmc@juno.com
1731 S Broad St
  Truong Tu, Pastor

ACTS Covenant Fell (28969) (LAN, UNMC) **140**
142-144 E King St, Lancaster PA 17602
717-299-5119, fax 717-299-7131, actscf@juno.com
420 S Christian St
  J. Eric Dombach, Associate Pastor

Agape Fell* (15016) (LAN) **124**
485 E 3rd St, Williamsport PA 17701
570-326-5924, fax 570-326-5924, agape@chilitech.net,
http://www.churchagape.com
  Michael Deal, Pastor
  James Mellinger, Youth Pastor

Alsace Christian Fell (13490) (LAN) **21**
47 Alsace Ave, Temple PA 19560
610-775-9970, smandhm@aol.com
In village of Alsace Manor
  Sherman M. Stoltzfus, Pastor
  Daniel D. Good, Associate Pastor

Arca de Salvacion (22459) (LAN, KB, IMH) **38**
2147-9 N Howard St, Philadelphia PA 19122
215-423-7642
  Juan C. Carmona, Pastor

Beaver Run Menn Ch (10236) (LAN) **37**
RR 2 Box 147, Watsontown PA 17777
717-396-8928, wgiersch@yahoo.com
Beaver Run Rd, Limestoneville
  William E. Giersch, Pastor

Believers Menn Garifuna Ministries (27599) (LAN, AAMA, NYC) **24**
36 Malcolm X Blvd, PO Box 210-463, Brooklyn NY 11221-3008
718-716-6579, believersgarifuna@hotmail.com
  Andrew Nunez, Pastor

Bethlehem Community Fell (29124) (LAN) **40**
1417 Marvine St, Bethlehem PA 18017-6637
610-861-4409, fax 610-868-7907,
wkwendland@netcarrier.com
  Wolfgang Wendland, Pastor

Blainsport Menn Ch (13607) (LAN) **152**
7 Audubon Circle, Stevens PA 17578
717-336-8263, jnfahnestock@dejazzd.com,
http://www.forministry.com/17569bmc
85 S Blainsport Rd, Rheinholds
  James R. Fahnestock, Pastor
  Kevin S. Smoker, Associate Pastor
  Eric P. Marshall, Youth Pastor
  Edwin Ray Martin, Deacon

Blossom Hill Menn Ch (14795) (LAN) **61**
333 Delp Rd, Lancaster PA 17601
717-396-0683, jhp125@juno.com
  Jane Hoober Peifer, Pastor

Bossler Menn Ch (13615) (LAN) **98**
2021 Bossler Rd, Elizabethtown PA 17022-9417
717-367-5215, fgarb@juno.com
Corner of Bossler Rd & Garber Rd
  Fred M. Garber, Pastor
  Kenneth E. Schildt, Licensed Deacon
  Shawlee Wehibe, Licensed Deacon

Boston Bethel Missionary Ch (11433) (LAN) . . .**30**
c/o David Cius, PO Box 255532, Dorchester MA 02125
781-396-6009
1201 Hyde Pk
  David Cius, Pastor

Bowmansville Menn Ch (13623) (LAN) **290**
PO Box 363, Bowmansville PA 17507
717-445-7458, krwitmer@juno.com
129 Pleasant Valley Rd
  Kenneth R. Witmer, Pastor
  Larry H. Weber, Associate Pastor
  Chester E. Yoder, Associate Pastor
  Kelly G. Martin, Youth Pastor
  Harold B. Eberly, Licensed Deacon

Buenas Nuevas (10732) (LAN, IMH) **29**
4319 N 2nd Rd #3, Arlington VA 22203
703-645-8074, buenasnuevas@juno.com
  Eduardo P. Morales, Pastor

Buffalo Menn Ch* (13631) (LAN) **150**
4445 Hoffa Mill Rd, Lewisburg PA 17837
570-966-1458, bhayes@sunlink.net
Hoffa Mill Rd
  Benjamin R. Hayes, Pastor
  C. David Peachey, Associate Pastor
  Alvin Longenecker, Deacon

Byerland Menn Ch (13656) (LAN) **101**
931 Byerland Church Rd, Willow Street PA 17584
717-872-6922, fax 717-872-6922, jygarber@juno.com
SE Corner of Byerland Church Rd & Mt Hope School Rd
  Joe C. Garber, Pastor

Calvary Menn Fell (14670) (LAN) **37**
PO Box 25, Morris Run PA 16939-0025
570-638-2274, rkmartin@ptdprolog.net
Front St
  Robert K. Martin, Pastor
  Ralph N. Bender, Associate Pastor

Cambridge Menn Ch* (13680) (LAN) **56**
c/o Victor R. Weaver, 681 Meadow Dr, Honey Brook PA 19344
610-273-2555
Main St, Cambridge
  Edward R. Beachy, Pastor
  Victor R. Weaver, Associate Pastor
  Isaac R. Petersheim, Ordained Deacon

Canton Menn Ch* (25098) (LAN) 105
PO Box 43, Canton PA 17724
570-673-3418, dgraybil@sosbbs.com
Corner of Union & Center
  Douglas C. Graybill, Pastor

Capital Christian Fell (13805) (LAN) 86
8806 Eastbourne Ln, Laurel MD 20708
301-725-5692, pastor@capitalchristian.org,
http://www.capitalchristian.org
11301 Springfield Rd
  J. David Eshleman, Pastor
  Wilmer Z. Good, Associate Pastor
  Jon Chester Miller-Eshelman, Associate Pastor

Carpenter Community Ch (13698) (LAN) 155
378 Glenbrook Rd, PO Box 37, Talmage PA 17580
717-656-9731, fax 717-859-4269, glennhoo@juno.com
  Glenn A. Hoover, Pastor
  David H. Burkholder, Associate Pastor
  Daryl L. Hoover, Youth Pastor
  James S. Horning, Ordained Deacon

Cedar Hill Community Ch (13706) (LAN) 35
624 Groff Ave, Elizabethtown PA 17022
717-361-8990, lawtonwd@aol.com
5636 Bossler Rd
  Wayne D. Lawton, Pastor

Cedar Lane Chapel (11580) (LAN) 4
PO Box 202, Terre Hill PA 17581
717-445-6697
208 College Ave, Terre Hill PA
  Marlin E. Martin, Pastor

**Centro Evangelistico Cristiano (26724) (LAN,
IMH)** 28
1601 W 4th St, Wilmington DE 19805
302-654-3587
  Rojas Rosemberg, Pastor

Chestnut Hill Menn Ch (13714) (LAN) 112
4050 Marietta Ave, Columbia PA 17512
717-684-5513, dhersh48@aol.com
  Carl E. Hershey, Pastor
  J. Donald Brubaker, Ordained Deacon
  J. Leon Eshleman, Ordained Deacon

Chinese Christian Ch of Malden (10743) (LAN) .55
50 Eastern Ave, Malden MA 02148
781-397-1092, fax 781-322-9977
  Paul Cheung, Pastor

Christ the King Community Ch* (27730) (LAN) 139
2449 Marietta Ave, Lancaster PA 17601
717-656-9571, fax 717-397-6978, evansforjc@juno.com
  Daniele Evans, Lay Leader
  Michael Evans, Lay Leader

Christian Community Fell (25304) (LAN) 23
Meeting House Rd, PO Box 503, Manchester PA 17345
717-632-8641, card@superpa.net
  Carlton D. Stambaugh, Bishop

Christian Life Menn Fell (10122) (LAN, KB) 37
2045 N Carlisle St, Philadelphia PA 19121
215-765-2911
6841 Ardleigh St, Mt Airy
  James Dennis, Pastor
  Ephener Green, Lay Leader
  Raymond L. Jackson, Lay Leader

Churchtown Menn Ch* (13748) (LAN) 69
1732 Weaverland Rd, East Earl PA 17519
717-445-4107
Corner of Glick Rd & Rt 23
  Clair Bennett Good, Pastor
  Kenneth A. Mull, Associate Pastor
  Philip M. Groff, Youth Pastor
  Philip R. Hollinger, Ordained Deacon

Coatesville Menn Ch (13755) (LAN) 28
625 Walnut St, Coatesville PA 19320
717-442-8394, lgroff1460@earthlink.net
  Leonard L. Groff, Pastor
  Mark C. Hickson, Associate Pastor

Columbia Menn Ch* (13771) (LAN) 38
c/o Gregory L. Hershberger, 524 S 16th St, Columbia PA
17512
717-684-5935, ghershberg@aol.com
291 S 4th St
  Gregory L. Hershberger, Pastor

Community Menn Fell (13540) (LAN) 190
PO Box 506, Milton PA 17847
570-742-7315, fax 570-742-7396,
cmfmilton@hotmail.com
RR 3, Box 804
  David Martino, Pastor

**Cornerstone CELLebration Ch and Ministries
(10650) (LAN)** 65
577 Westwood Dr, Downingtown PA 19335
610-363-2662, fax 610-524-7480, cornerstonecel@bee.net
Sheraton Great Valley Hotel at Rt 30 & 202, 707 Lancaster
Pk
  John L. Derstine, Pastor

Cornerstone Christian Fell (27193) (LAN) 64
PO Box 126, Mountain Top PA 18707-0126
570-678-3010
  Thomas H. Miller, Pastor

Covenant Menn Ch (10055) (LAN) 11
1079 Gypsy Hill Rd, Lancaster PA 17602
717-397-4525, njbrubaker@juno.com
Meets in homes

Cristo es la Respuesta (10342) (LAN, IMH) 44
134 Guilford Street, Lebanon PA 17042
717-270-9512
505 Hamilton St, Harrisburg, PA 17102
    Emilio Montanez, Pastor

Crossroads Christian Community (10631) (LAN) 10
PO Box 424, Marlton NJ 08053
856-988-9419, atgoodnews@aol.com
9 Jefferson Ave
    Andrew T Gordon, Pastor

Crossroads Menn (15172) (LAN, AAMA) 141
420 S Christian St, Lancaster PA 17602
717-392-3713, fax 717-392-7368, scsmc2@aol.com,
http://www.homestead.com/churchcrossroads
401 Church St
    Vincent Whitman, Pastor
    Alice W. Whitman, Licensed Deaconess
    E. Ray Witmer, Licensed Deacon
    Meredyth Ann Witmer, Licensed Deaconess

Dawsonville Menn Ch (13847) (LAN) 42
16500 Whites Ferry Rd, PO Box 487, Poolesville MD 20837
301-874-8448, pastor@dawsonvillechurch.org,
http://www.dawsonvillechurch.org
    Ellis Wayne Roberson, Pastor

Delaware County Fell (11562) (LAN) 0
c/o Dave Cosden, 1552 Virginia Ave, Folcraft PA 19032
610-237-8937, teachtruth@juno.com
Woodlyn PA
    David T Cosden, Pastor

Delaware Menn Ch* (13854) (LAN) 34
RR 1 Box 32, Thompsontown PA 17094
717-463-3941, geehoss@juno.com
On Rt 333, East Salem PA
    Glenn D. Hosler, Pastor

Derry Menn Ch (13862) (LAN) 35
c/o Mark B. Boll, 823 Pine Hill Rd, Lititz PA 17543
717-626-8685
RD 8, Box 13, Danville
    Mark B. Boll, Pastor
    Leroy H. Erb, Associate Pastor

Diamond Street Menn Ch (13870) (LAN, AAMA, KB) 65
1632 W Diamond St, Philadelphia PA 19121
215-769-2682, revitalization@juno.com
    Otis M. Banks, Pastor

Diller Menn Ch (13888) (LAN) 49
c/o Larry Strouse, 117 Long Rd, Newville PA 17241
717-423-6213, fax 717-423-0039, tjsheeler@excite.com,
http://diller.pa.us.mennonite.net
345 Creek Rd
    Larry Strouse, Interim Pastor
    Timothy J. Sheeler, Ordained Deacon

Downing Hills Christian Fell (13896) (LAN) 34
107 Garris Rd, Downingtown PA 19335
610-873-1169, nwbrunk@cs.com
    Nathan W. Brunk, Pastor
    Brooke L. Gehman, Associate Pastor

East Chestnut Street Menn Ch (13912) (LAN) .193
434 E Chestnut St, Lancaster PA 17602
717-392-7910, fax 717-392-3601, ecsmc@juno.com
432 E Chestnut St, Lancaster PA
    Ronald W. Adams, Pastor

East Hanover Menn Ch (13938) (LAN) 16
1089 S Meadow Ln, Palmyra PA 17078
717-469-1559
Rt 743, Laudermilch Rd
    Timothy T. Stauffer, Pastor
    Dwight G. Charles, Ordained Deacon

East Petersburg Menn Ch (13946) (LAN) 340
6279 Main St, East Petersburg PA 17520
717-569-9931, epmc1@juno.com
    Karl E. Steffy, Pastor
    K. Eugene Forrey, Associate Pastor
    Daniel W. Neff, Ordained Deacon
    Jay Todd, Ordained Deacon

El Buen Pastor (14167) (LAN, IMH) 67
645 Harrison St, Lancaster PA 17602
717-396-0346
    Juan Gonzalez, Pastor

Elizabethtown Menn Ch (13953) (LAN) 199
300 S Spruce St, PO Box 265, Elizabethtown PA 17022
717-367-7089, etnmenno@earthlink.net,
http://elizabethtown.pa.us.mennonite.net
S Spruce & E Bainbridge
    Conrad L. Kanagy, Pastor
    John M. Myers, Associate Pastor
    Robert E. Fellenbaum, Ordained Deacon

Emmanuel Worship Center (10016) (LAN, NYC, AAMA) 66
c/o M. Abate Woldeabe, 2407 E Tremont Ave, Bronx NY 10461
718-822-8031, fax 718-822-2649,
ewc-ny@worldnet.att.net
    Mulugeta Abate Woldeabe, Pastor
    Mesfin Mamo, Associate Pastor

Ephrata Menn Ch (13961) (LAN) 304
510 Stevens Rd, Ephrata PA 17522
717-733-6688, fax 717-738-2769, epmech@juno.com
    Ray K. Yoder, Interim Pastor
    Jeffery L. High, Leadership Team
    L. Kenneth Hollinger, Ordained Deacon
    Clifford L. Martin, Leadership Team

Erb Menn Ch (13979) (LAN) 149
567 W Lexington Rd, Lititz PA 17543
717-665-7018, pastorwes@paonline.com
    Wesley D. Siegrist, Pastor
    Michael S. Zimmerman, Associate Pastor
    David F. High Jr, Licensed Deacon

Erisman Menn Ch (13987) (LAN) 236
8 S Erisman Rd, Manheim PA 17545
717-653-4791, erismanmc@juno.com
Corner of 772 (Manheim Rd) & S Erisman Rd
   John O. Yoder, Pastor
   Andrew G. Miller Jr, Associate Pastor
   Alma E. Wenger, Licensed Deaconess
   Nelson H. Wenger, Licensed Deacon
   Dale E. Witmer, Licensed Deacon
   Jeanne M. Witmer, Licensed Deaconess

**Ethiopian Evangelical Ch of Baltimore (11108)
(LAN)** 40
1005 Ingleside Ave, Baltimore MD 21228
410-744-3098
7419 Lesada Dr, #24, Baltimore MD
   Ermias Tasefesse, Lay Leader

**Ethiopian Evangelical Ch of Philadelphia (10194)
(LAN, KB)** 30
PO Box 2078, Upper Darby PA 19082-0578
610-789-2784, merid2001@hotmail.com
69th & Chestnut Streets
   Merid Seifu, Lay Leader

Evangelical Garifuna (29660) (LAN, NYC, IMH) .95
c/o Celso C. Jaime, 344 Brooke Ave, Bronx NY 10462
718-792-5455, jaime4ever@aol.com
   Celso C. Jaime, Pastor

Faro Ardiente (22111) (LAN, IMH) 18
728 Wood St, Vineland NJ 08360
609-696-1399
   Carlos M. Maldonado, Pastor

First Deaf Menn Ch (14019) (LAN) 43
2270 Old Philadelphia Pike, Lancaster PA 17602
717-392-6752, fax 717-392-7810, fdmc2270@aol.com
Rte 340 E
   Jeffrey W. Hoffer, Pastor

First Menn Ch of Columbia (14027) (LAN) 15
9580 Old Rt 108, Ellicott City MD 21042
410-465-1233
   J. Daniel Miller, Pastor

Fountain of Life Ch (25320) (LAN) 53
290 Newberry Rd, Middletown PA 17057
717-944-4455, fax 717-994-5952, folministries@juno.com
   Peter L. Logan, Pastor
   Roy Lee Kenneth Shonk, Associate Pastor

Frazer Menn Ch (14050) (LAN) 125
57 Maple Linden Ln, Frazer PA 19355
610-644-3397, fax 610-644-2970, jasonholm9@aol.com
North side of Rd 30, 1 mile east of Rt 30 & Rt 352
Intersection or 3 miles west of Paoli
   Jason Kuniholm, Pastor
   Vernon Zehr Jr, Associate Pastor

Freedom in Christ Fell (11563) (LAN) 25
1119 Chestnut St, Lebanon PA 17042
717-270-1904, millers@paonline.com
12 N Ninth St
   Daniel G. Miller, Pastor

**Friendship Menn Chapel* (15008) (LAN,
AAMA)** 35
235 N Broad St, Carney's Point NJ 08069
856-299-7900, JamesNMel@aol.com
   James L. Wenger Jr, Pastor
   Dan L. Lapp, Associate Pastor
   Paul S. Landis, Visitation Pastor

Gehman Menn Ch (14100) (LAN) 98
PO Box 842, Adamstown PA 19501
717-484-4439, fax 717-484-4473, irvinm3@juno.com
Witmer Road
   Irvin L. Martin, Pastor
   Glen D. Martin, Associate Pastor
   David W. Mohler, Deacon

Gingrichs Menn Ch (14118) (LAN) 264
100 Forney Rd, Lebanon PA 17042-9344
717-274-1521, fax 717-274-8611, jgl@mbcomp.com,
http://www.gingrichsmennonite.com
   John G. Landis, Pastor

Goods Menn Ch (14142) (LAN) 98
2563 Bainbridge Rd, Bainbridge PA 17502
717-367-1938, fax 717-367-8091,
jnbechtold@dejazzd.com
4374 Bossler Rd
   J. Nelson Bechtold, Pastor
   Clair R. Nissley, Ordained Deacon
   Gerald E. Risser, Ordained Deacon

Goodville Menn Ch (14159) (LAN) 92
1556 Main St, PO Box 104, Goodville PA 17528-0104
717-445-6037, fax 717-445-8435,
rscmhess@hydrosoft.net
   Nelson R. Martin, Pastor
   Harold S. Reed, Associate Pastor
   Bruce L. Sauder, Associate Pastor

Grace Community Fell (14084) (LAN) 70
1483 N Colebrook Rd, Manheim PA 17545
717-665-7222, PDB@paonline.com

Great Shepherd Christian Fell (13557) (LAN) .128
975 Benders Church Rd, Pen Argyl PA 18072
610-863-9114, fax 610-863-9114, benders@epix.net
   Jack Rice, Pastor

Green Terrace Menn Ch (14183) (LAN) 41
116 N Galen Hall Rd, Wernersville PA 19565
610-927-4668, pastorleon@pro-usa.net
   Leon L. Stauffer, Pastor
   Nelson B. Zeiset, Associate Pastor
   P. Eugene Stauffer, Licensed Deacon

Groffdale Menn Ch (14191) (LAN) **252**
168 N Groffdale Rd, Leola PA 17540
717-656-6388, fax 717-656-7807, leamanjb@juno.com
James R. Leaman, Interim Pastor
Craig G. Sensenig, Assistant Pastor

Guilford Road Menn Ch (14209) (LAN) **32**
c/o Robert C. Rowe, 8614 Pine Tree Dr, Jessup MD 20794-9530
301-725-0540, fax 410-796-5867, sauder@ineva.com
10140 Guilford Rd
Robert C. Rowe, Pastor
Steven A. Sauder, Associate Pastor
Donald M. Sauder, Licensed Deacon

Habecker Menn Ch (14217) (LAN) **91**
451 Habecker Church Road, Lancaster PA 17603
717-872-5910, giveitall@juno.com
Randall J. Martin, Pastor

Halifax Community Fell (27060) (LAN) **44**
852 Camp Hebron Rd, PO Box 598, Halifax PA 17032
717-896-2637, rlhm@pa.net
Richard Huber Mininger, Pastor

Hammer Creek Menn Ch* (14233) (LAN) **261**
590 Hammer Creek Rd, Lititz PA 17543
717-354-4347
Wilmer S. Musser, Pastor
Samuel S. Burkholder, Associate Pastor
Fred G. Heller, Associate Pastor
Ricky L. Newswanger, Youth Pastor
Mervin M. Gingrich, Ordained Deacon

Hampden Menn Ch (15354) (LAN) **44**
1334 N 14th St, PO Box 14414, Reading PA 19604-1936
610-582-8915, his.servants7@juno.com
Corner of Hampden Blvd & Windsor St
Lee Roy Ritz, Pastor
Kenneth B. Eberly, Associate Pastor

Hernley Menn Ch (14290) (LAN) **128**
746 Lebanon Rd, Manheim PA 17545
717-656-7305, fax 717-656-6481, gmchurst@yahoo.com
1 mile north of Manheim on Rt 72
George M. Hurst, Pastor
Jay M. Peters, Associate Pastor

Herr Street Menn Ch (14266) (LAN, AAMA) . . .**25**
c/o Harold H. Lefever, 16 S Mountain Rd, Harrisburg PA 17112
717-545-1858
1026 Herr St
Harold H. Lefever, Pastor
Louis H. Martin, Licensed Deacon

Hershey Menn Ch* (14282) (LAN) **110**
401 Hershey Church Rd, Kinzers PA 17535
717-768-3150, imchener@hotmail.com
Ramoktoshi Imchen, Pastor
Elmer M. Martin, Ordained Deacon

Hess Menn Ch (14308) (LAN) **108**
1060 E Newport Rd, Lititz PA 17543
717-626-0774, erh.nh.pa@juno.com
Elvin R. Huyard, Pastor
Kyle D. Buckwalter, Associate Pastor
Donald L. Brubaker, Ordained Deacon

Hinkletown Menn Ch* (14316) (LAN) **400**
2031 Division Hwy, Ephrata PA 17522
717-354-9990, sauderspot@juno.com
Rt 322 E
Glenn E. Sauder, Pastor
Jerold R. Martin, Associate Pastor
Michael W. Wenger, Youth Pastor
Albert B. Kunkle, Ordained Deacon

Iglesia Christiana Valle de Jesus (25338) (LAN, NYC, IMH) **25**
c/o Mercedes Gonzalez, 278 Troutman St, Apt 1L, Brooklyn NY 11237
718-418-7824
141 Manhattan Ave
Mercedes Gonzalez, Lay Leader

Iglesia el Verbo (11571) (LAN) **73**
c/o Isaias de la Cruz, PO Box 473, Robbins NC 27325
910-948-3022
Isaias De La Cruz, Lay Leader

Iglesia Manantial de Vida (29116) (LAN, IMH) **55**
1033 N 27th St, Camden NJ 08105
609-365-9236
Hugo E. Garcia, Pastor

Iglesia Menonita Bethel Ch (11435) (LAN) . . .**114**
PO Box 3874, Sanford NC 27330
919-718-1776, fax 919-774-1497
622 Bragg St
Carlos L. Villalobos Mora, Pastor

Iglesia Menonita Hispana Vida Nueva (11572) (LAN, IMH) **40**
c/o Vincente Minino, 10868 Oak Green Ct, Burke VA 22015
703-249-8449, fax 703-249-8449, vicarm1@juno.com
3900 King St, Alexandria
Vincente Minino, Pastor

Iglesia Menonita Puerta de Sion (22897) (LAN, IMH) **35**
c/o Nelson Colon, 328 S Broad St, Trenton NJ 08611
Nelson Colon, Lay Leader

Iglesia Menonita Roca de Salvacion (11301) (LAN, IMH) **21**
637 S Prince St, Lancaster PA 17602
717 299-6789, joses@emm.org
Jose A. Santiago, Pastor

Iglesia Unida de Avivamiento (22350) (LAN, NYC, IMH) **40**
169 Knickerbocker Ave, Brooklyn NY 11237
718-919-1588, unitedrevival@aol.com
Nicolas Angustia, Pastor

CONFERENCES AND CONGREGATIONS

2

Indiantown Menn Ch* (14365) (LAN) 146
255 Indiantown Rd, Ephrata PA 17522
717-733-3150, slm875@dejazzd.com
  Stephen L. Martin, Pastor
  Jay S. Weaver, Associate Pastor
  Paul E. Snader, Ordained Deacon

Indonesian Fell (11568) (LAN) 25
1731 S Broad St, Philadelphia PA 19148
215-467-6001, alcmc@juno.com
  Leonard Burkholder, Associate Pastor
  Liem Piet In, Lay Leader

**International Christian Community Ch (11123)
(LAN, OD, NYC)** 160
c/o Victor S. Amador/ Carolina Amador, 616 Jamaica Ave,
Brooklyn NY 11208
718-235-7249, fax 718-235-2737,
victoramador2001@aol.com
  Victor S. Amador, Pastor

James Street Menn Ch (15396) (LAN) 251
323 W James St, Lancaster PA 17603-2911
717-397-6707, fax 717-397-0829,
info@mennonitechurch.org,
  Marlin E. Thomas, Interim Pastor
  L. Larry Wenger, Ordained Deacon

Kapatiran Christian Ch (11102) (LAN, KB) 40
Beechwood Rd Corner Lawndale Ave, Havertown PA
19083
610-353-1002, Ling011957@yahoo.com
Corner of Beechwood & Lawndale, off Haverford Ave
  Aquilina M. Leduna, Contact Person

Kauffman Menn Ch (14373) (LAN) 57
1355 Lancaster Rd, Manheim PA 17545
717-665-3570, sfstauffer@dejazzd.com
Rt. 72, 2 miles S of Manheim
  Steven B. Stauffer, Pastor
  Jay W. Nissley, Associate Pastor
  Leroy P. Beitzel, Licensed Deacon

Kennett Square Menn Ch* (14381) (LAN) 34
486 N Mill Rd, PO Box 401, Kennett Square PA 19348
610-444-0547, ejressler@kennett.net
  Harold J. Ranck, Lay Leader

**King of Glory Tabernacle (14043) (LAN, AAMA,
NYC)** 80
c/o Michael Banks, 1114 Shernan Ave, Bronx NY 10456
718-299-1211, kgtbronx@aol.com
2019 Grand Ave
  Michael Banks, Pastor

Kinzer Menn Ch (14399) (LAN) 53
45 N Rd Kinzer Rd, Kinzers PA 17535
717-687-8870, paul.clark@fandm.edu
  Paul L. Clark, Pastor
  Dwight L. Groff, Associate Pastor
  Jeffrey G. Pauls, Associate Pastor
  Benjamin L. Clark, Ordained Deacon

Kossuth Community Chapel (25395) (LAN) 13
96 Olive St, Bolivar NY 14715
585-928-2380
7150 Kossuth Rd
  John E. Boll, Pastor
  Marlin M. Miller, Associate Pastor
  John C. Hess, Ordained Deacon

Krall Menn Ch (14407) (LAN) 70
2510 S 5th Ave, Lebanon PA 17042
717-535-9941, georgelois@jc-net.com
2512 S 5th Ave
  George L. Zimmerman, Pastor
  Robert S. Martin, Associate Pastor

Lancaster Anabaptist Fell (11302) (LAN) 0
c/o Paul M. Zehr, 209 Henrietta Ave, Lancaster PA 17602
717-299-6104, zehrpm@emu.edu
Lancaster Theological Seminary, 555 W James St

Landis Valley Menn Ch (14431) (LAN) 90
2420 Kissel Hill Rd, Lancaster PA 17601
717-560-3999, tomhorst@peoplepc.com
  Thomas A. Horst, Pastor
  Gary E. Martin, Associate Pastor

Landisville Menn Ch (14423) (LAN) 320
3320 Bowman Rd, Landisville PA 17538
717-898-0071, sthomas405@aol.com
  J. Samuel Thomas, Pastor
  James M. Gingrich, Licensed Deacon

Lao Menn Fell/Slate Hill (11560) (LAN) 0
1352 Slate Hill Rd, Camp Hill PA 17011
717-737-8016
Meeting at Slate Hill Mennonite Church
  Aaron S. Onelangsy, Pastor

Laurel Street Menn Ch (14449) (LAN) 66
301 Laurel St, Lancaster PA 17603-5429
717-393-5840, rlwitmer@dejazzd.com
  Randall L. Witmer, Pastor

Lauver Menn Ch* (14456) (LAN) 50
HC 63 Box 43, Richfield PA 17086
717-463-9091, fax 717-463-0064, johnwg@nmax.net
On Rt 35
  John W. Gehman, Pastor

Lebanon Christian Fell (24562) (LAN) 30
118 N 14th St, Lebanon PA 17046-4503
717-270-9918, donymartin@juno.com
  J. Donald Martin Jr, Pastor
  Clair H. Weaver, Associate Pastor

Lichty Menn Ch* (14464) (LAN) **174**
c/o Clair R. Long, 5334 Southview Dr, New Holland PA
17557
717-445-6290, fax 717-354-5919
1690 Union Grove Rd, East Earl
   Clair R. Long, Pastor
   James C. Bowman, Associate Pastor
   Aaron Z. Horst, Ordained Deacon
   Eugene H. Sauder, Ordained Deacon

Life Menn Fell* (11294) (LAN) **62**
250 Meadow Ln, Conestoga PA 17516
717-871-3002, fax 717-871-0547,
mschlabach@life-ministries.com
   Mark Schlabach, Pastor
   Nevin Forry, Associate Pastor

Lititz Menn Ch (14480) (LAN) **236**
165 E Front St, Lititz PA 17543-1503
717-626-8237, fax 717-626-1538, lmchurch@dejazzd.com,
http://www.forministry.com/17543lmc
NW Corner Front & Water
   Dennis Wayne Ernest, Pastor
   Rodney A. Martin, Youth Pastor

Living Stones Fell* (10155) (LAN) **136**
2292 Robert Fulton Hwy, Peach Bottom PA 17563
717-786-3890, fax 717-786-3890, rldaed@juno.com
   Raymond L. Deiter, Pastor
   Larry E. Burkhart, Associate Pastor
   James R. Nimon, Associate Pastor
   Roger Stillman, Associate Pastor
   James Arnold Aukamp, Evangelist

Living Water Christian Fell (11567) (LAN) **73**
c/o Gary L. Krabill, PO Box 113, Mifflin PA 17058-0113
717-436-2132
   Gary L. Krabill, Pastor

**Locust Lane Menn Chapel* (14498) (LAN,
AAMA)** **60**
2415 Locust Ln, Harrisburg PA 17109
717-232-6252, locustlanemenn@paonline.com,
http://locustlanemennonite.org
   Lindsey A. Robinson, Pastor

Lost Creek Menn Ch* (14506) (LAN) **127**
RR 2 Box 1405, Mifflintown PA 17059
717-463-2258
   Kenneth Litwiller, Pastor

Love Truth Chinese Menn Ch (27995) (LAN, KB) 50
600 W Chew Ave, Philadelphia PA 19120
215-224-7622, fax 215-924-2248, lemuelso@netscape.net,
http://members.tripod.com/~ltcmc
   Lemuel So, Pastor

Luz de Salvacion (26716) (LAN, IMH) **23**
1401 Lehman St, Lebanon PA 17042
717-272-1232
   Luis Hernandez, Lay Leader

Luz Verdadera (15107) (LAN, IMH) **43**
c/o Jose Gonzalez, 1003 Franklin St, Reading PA 19602
610-374-1071

Lyndon Menn Ch (14514) (LAN) **54**
234 Brenneman Rd, Lancaster PA 17603
717-464-4283, svanpelt1@juno.com
1930 Lyndon Ave
   Steven C. Vanpelt, Pastor
   Dwain D. Livengood, Associate Pastor
   Daniel R. Geib, Licensed Deacon

Manheim Menn Ch* (14530) (LAN) **65**
2474 Wisegarver Rd, Manheim PA 17545
717-665-6411, jlstrite@yahoo.com,
http://www.geocities.com/manheimmenno/index.html
201 W High St
   Kenneth A. Bucher, Pastor
   D. David Martin, Associate Pastor
   James L. Strite, Ordained Deacon

Maranatha Family Christian Fell (10119) (LAN) .70
450 Jacobsburg Rd, Nazareth PA 18064
610-614-0371, mfcf@juno.com
   James R. Snyder, Pastor
   Leonard J. Sabatine, Ordained Deacon

**Marietta Community Chapel (24224)
(LAN)** **115**
1125 River Rd, Marietta PA 17547
717-426-4584, fax 717-426-4584,
mariettachapel@juno.com,
http://www.MariettaChapel.org
   Reuben W. Horst, Pastor

Martindale Menn Ch* (14548) (LAN) **373**
958 Rettew Mill Rd, Ephrata PA 17522
717-733-0291
Hurst Rd
   Robert L. Trupe, Pastor
   David E. Sensenig, Associate Pastor
   J. Martin Hostetter, Ordained Deacon

Masonville Menn Ch (14562) (LAN) **99**
2625 Safe Harbor Rd, Washington Boro PA 17582
717-872-5924, wilann62@juno.com
   J. Wilmer Eby, Pastor

Meadville Menn Ch (14571) (LAN) **47**
920 Quarry Rd, Gap PA 17527-9040
717-768-8334, j6meck@dejazzd.com
5726 Meadville Rd, Gap, PA 17527
   John D. Meck, Pastor
   Lew K. Martin, Youth Pastor

Mechanic Grove Menn Ch* (14589) (LAN) **85**
c/o Jay L. Ranck, 1950 Lancaster Pk, Peach Bottom PA
17563
717-786-4730
Church Rd, Quarryville
   Jay L. Ranck, Pastor
   William E. Hershey, Associate Pastor
   Wayne E. Kreider, Associate Pastor
   Isaac E. Hostetter, Ordained Deacon

**CONFERENCES AND
CONGREGATIONS**

2

Meckville Menn Ch (14597) (LAN) 87
Box 1020 Meckville Rd, Bethel PA 19507
717-273-8797
  J. Donald Martin Sr, Pastor
  J. Daniel Martin, Ordained Deacon

Mellinger Menn Ch (14605) (LAN) 398
1916 Lincoln Hwy E, Lancaster PA 17602
717-397-9360, fax 717-397-9195, mmc@proclaim.net,
http://proclaim.net/~mellinger
  Leon H. Oberholtzer, Pastor
  Barry Lee Stoner, Associate Pastor
  Linford L. Good, Licensed Deacon
  Ray K. Leaman, Licensed Deacon

**Menn Evangelical Tabernacle (26849) (LAN, NYC,
IMH)** 30
c/o Nestalis De Leon, 130 3rd Ave Apt 18G, Brooklyn NY
11207
718-522-5029
623 Wilson Ave
  Nestalis Robles De Leon, Pastor

Metzler Menn Ch (14613) (LAN) 295
120 S 10th St, Akron PA 17501
717-859-2660, richardbuch@juno.com
515 W Metzler Rd, Ephrata
  Richard E. Buch, Pastor
  Roy B. Martin, Associate Pastor
  David Eugene Zoll, Associate Pastor
  Lee Roy M. Martin, Ordained Deacon

Millersville Menn Ch (14639) (LAN) 94
PO Box 283, Millersville PA 17551
717-872-2695, fax 717-872-2493, dellamark@prodigy.net
437 Manor Ave
  Delbert L. Kautz, Pastor
  John Henry Harnish Jr, Ordained Deacon

Millport Menn Ch (14621) (LAN) 145
820 Log Cabin Rd, Leola PA 17540
717-627-0335, millport@email.com,
http://www.forministry.com/17540mmc
  E. Eugene Beyer, Pastor
  Delmar R. Weaver, Associate Pastor
  John A. Bender, Ordained Deacon

Millwood Menn Ch* (14654) (LAN) 62
c/o Menno Fisher, Jr, 2523 Old Philadelphia Pike, Bird-in-
Hand PA 17505-9797
717-442-8500, fax 717-442-4247
441 Amish Rd Gap, PA 17527
  Calvin D. Beiler, Pastor
  Menno Fisher Jr, Associate Pastor
  Eugene M. Lapp, Licensed Deacon

Mount Airy Menn Ch (14753) (LAN) 27
7101 Watersville Rd, Mount Airy MD 21771
301-829-2312
  Irvin S. Martin Jr, Co-Pastor
  Ezra Maust, Co-Pastor

Mount Joy Menn Ch (14688) (LAN) 370
10 Donegal Springs Rd, Mount Joy PA 17552-2906
717-653-5660, fax 717-653-9399, mjmenno@mjmc.org,
http://www.mjmc.org
  Joseph N. Sherer, Pastor
  Randall Shull, Associate Pastor

Mountain View Fell (29975) (LAN) 27
1717 Pleasant Stream Rd, Trout Run PA 17771-9525
570-995-9171
202 Old Barn Rd, Bodines
  M. Craig Zimmerman, Pastor
  J. Herbert Eby, Associate Pastor

Mountville Menn Ch* (14696) (LAN) 191
205 Froelich Ave, Mountville PA 17554
717-285-3610, rayreitz@onemain.com
Corner of Fridy & Froelich
  Raymond E. Reitz, Pastor
  J. Brent Hess, Associate Pastor of Youth

Mt Pleasant Menn Ch (14712) (LAN) 47
PO Box 127, Paradise PA 17562
717-687-6679, bobzook@lgms.pvt.k12.pa.us
Corner of White Oak & Mt Pleasant Rds
  Robert G. Zook, Pastor

Mt Vernon Menn Ch* (14720) (LAN) 187
1 Lighthouse Dr, Kirkwood PA 17536
717-529-6071, fax 717-529-6871,
mtvernonmennonite@juno.com
  Gary L. Roberts, Pastor
  Kendall Ray Keeler, Associate Pastor

Nanticoke Christian Fell (25809) (LAN) 40
112 S Prospect St, Nanticoke PA 18634
570-735-1700, davidp@epix.net,
http://www.forministry.com/18634ncf
  David A. Pegarella, Pastor

New Danville Menn Ch (14837) (LAN) 215
103 Marticville Rd, Lancaster PA 17603
717-872-8111, newdanville@juno.com, http://ndmc.org
  Curtiss Lee Kanagy, Pastor
  Donald W. Hess, Licensed Deacon
  Marshall Hess, Licensed Deacon

New Holland Menn Ch (14811) (LAN) 163
18 Western Ave, New Holland PA 17557
717-354-0602, fax 717-355-2787, nhmc2@juno.com
  A. Richard Weaver, Pastor

**New Holland Spanish Menn (14704)
(LAN, IMH)** 35
PO Box 15, New Holland PA 17557
717-354-9192, fax 717 355-2644
24 N Roberts Ave
  Mario Araya, Lay Leader

New Hope Community Ch (11561) (LAN) 0
333 S 13th St, Harrisburg PA 17104
717-260-0444, fax 717-232-0150,
nhccharrisburg@juno.com
The Agape Fellowship Hall - 13th & Derry St
  Jason R. Rissler, Pastor

New Life Christian Fell (29157) (LAN) 48
212A Hibiscus St, Honolulu HI 96818
808-672-8646
Community Center in urban Honolulu
 Charles W. Callahan, Pastor
 Filemon B. Godoy, Associate Pastor
 Ronald Godoy, Associate Pastor
 Paul Tadashi Horiuchi, Associate Pastor
 Peter K. Louis II, Associate Pastor

New Life Fell (27052) (LAN) 107
420 E Fulton St, Ephrata PA 17522
717-738-0963, nlfephrata@juno.com
 Kevin E. Horning, Pastor

New Mercies Menn Ch (10293) (LAN, KB, AAMA)53
PO Box 43174, Philadelphia PA 19129-3306
215-438-0293, cmercies@aol.com
Meets at Falls Presbyterian Church, 3462 Midvale Ave
 Charles Bulford, Pastor
 Nadine G. Smith Bulford, Associate Pastor

New Providence Menn Ch (14829) (LAN) 85
121 Main St, New Providence PA 17560
717-786-4233, bobharnish@prodigy.net
 Robert A. Harnish, Pastor
 J. Kenneth Hershey, Associate Pastor

New Revival Menn Ch (11570) (LAN) 25
1241 Church St, Reading PA 19601
610-372-1812, rafucho74@hotmail.com
Meets at Shiloh Menn, 421 Bingaman Rd
 Rafael Perez, Pastor

New Song Congregation (11581) (LAN) 40
235 N Broad St, Carney's Point NJ 08069
856-299-7900
Meets at Friendship Mennonite Chapel
 Ricky Alvira, Lay Leader

Newlinville Menn Ch (14845) (LAN) 27
145 Doe Run Rd, Coatesville PA 19320
610-593-6464
 Harold R. Engel, Pastor
 James M. Westmoreland Jr, Associate Pastor

Norma Menn Ch (14860) (LAN) 40
173 Almond Rd, PO Box 313, Norma NJ 08347
856-692-7441, fax 856-692-7441, nmpastor@juno.com,
http://www.forministry.com/08318nm
 Timothy E. Darling, Pastor

North Bronx Menn Ch (29561) (LAN, NYC) 22
c/o Ruth Yoder Wenger, 3262 Rochambeau Ave, Bronx NY
10467-3006
718-881-2824, wengermail@aol.com
302 E 206th St
 Ruth Yoder Wenger, Pastor

Nueva Vida en Cristo (11436) (LAN) 40
762 Centre St, Trenton NJ 08611
609-396-1901
 Eugenio Matos, Pastor

Old Road Menn Ch (14928) (LAN) 141
5795 Old Philadelphia Pike, Gap PA 17527
717 442-8630, oldroadoffice@wjtl.net
PA Rt 340
 Matthew R. Buckwalter, Pastor
 Robert H. Benner, Associate Pastor
 Daniel Lamar Mast, Licensed Deacon

**Oxford Circle Menn Ch (14951) (LAN, KB,
AAMA)** 40
PO Box 28340, Philadelphia PA 19149
215-991-5805, ocmenc@juno.com
Howell & Langdon Sts
 Leonard M. Dow, Pastor
 Vandy L. Parks, Associate Pastor
 Lynn S. Parks, Associate Pastor
 Ronald J. Sider, Associate Pastor

Palo Alto Menn Ch (14969) (LAN) 74
508 E Bacon St, Pottsville PA 17901
570-622-8743, fax 570 628-3787, jerry01@dfnow.com
20 Union St, Corner Cadbury St
 Gerald B. Richter Sr, Pastor
 Ernest W. Martin, Associate Pastor
 Roy W. Musser, Ordained Deacon

Parkesburg Menn Ch (14985) (LAN) 68
PO Box 306, Parkesburg PA 19365
610-857-3761, dlgehman@chesco.com
44 E Second Ave
 David L. Gehman, Pastor

Peabody Street Menn Ch (14993) (LAN, DC) . . .24
245 Peabody St, NW, Washington DC 20011
202-829-0876, fax 202-829-6770,
112322.477@compuserve.com
Brightwood
 George R. Richards, Pastor
 Willie J. Jones, Associate Pastor

Peace Chapel (25353) (LAN) 8
PO Box 1539, Harrisburg PA 17105-1539
206-3rd St, New Cumberland

**Philadelphia Cambodian Menn Ch (10075) (LAN,
KB)** 180
711-715 Snyder Ave, Philadelphia PA 19148
610 463-4677, cindy_lay@netzero.net
 Sarin Lay, Pastor

Pilgrims Menn Ch (24513) (LAN) 55
PO Box 217, Akron PA 17501
717-859-3147, berika@infi.net,
http://www.home.ptd.net/~tburnett
MCC Welcoming Place, 21 S 12th St
 Barry R. Kreider, Pastor

Praise Center (24844) (LAN) 56
84 Hill St, Jersey Shore PA 17740
570-398-3455, DavidKanski@aol.com
270 Henry Street, South Avis
 David K. Kanski, Pastor

CONFERENCES AND
CONGREGATIONS

2

Red Run Menn Ch (15115) (LAN) **88**
987 Martin Church Rd, Denver PA 17517
717-484-4899, kshorning@enter.net
   Paul G. Weaver, Pastor
   Kenneth L. Horning Sr, Interim Pastor
   Randy Fox, Deacon
   Paul H. Gehman, Deacon

Redeeming Grace Fell (24588) (LAN, NYC) **36**
539 Greeley Ave, Staten Island NY 10306-5853
718-979-5952, fax 718-351-1769, Est1man@aol.com
   Stanley Ray Sutter, Pastor

Risser Menn Ch (15123) (LAN) **77**
329 Trail Rd S, Elizabethtown PA 17022
717-367-8587, g-heistand@juno.com
2215 Elizabethtown Rd
   Gerald M. Heistand, Pastor

River Corner Menn Ch (15131) (LAN) **73**
PO Box 9, Conestoga PA 17516
717-872-4085
552 River Corner Rd, Conestoga

Roedersville Menn Ch (15149) (LAN) **42**
c/o Daryl Martin, 16 Cherry St, Pine Grove PA 17963
570-345-2552, dmartin@phfa.org
Roedersville Rd, Roedersville
   Daryl G. Martin, Pastor

Rohrerstown Menn Ch (15156) (LAN) **66**
601 Rohrerstown Rd, Lancaster PA 17603
717-394-0203, davidweaver@juno.com
   David L. Weaver, Pastor
   Nelson H. Hershey, Ordained Deacon

Rossmere Menn Ch (15164) (LAN) **102**
741 Janet Ave, Lancaster PA 17601
717-397-7854, lesmarian@juno.com
   Lester K. Denlinger, Pastor

Salam Menn Fell (11099) (LAN, KB) **20**
8131 Washington Ln, Wyncote PA 19095
215-884-4839, gkuttab@juno.com
   George M. Kuttab, Pastor

Schubert Menn Ch (15180) (LAN) **44**
c/o Thomas A. Hess, 9310 Old 22, Bethel PA 19507-9421
717-933-8434, phess@ptd.net
Kline Rd, Schubert
   Thomas A. Hess, Pastor
   John Charles Zimmerman II, Associate Pastor
   Marlin M. Zimmerman, Ordained Deacon

**Seventh Avenue Menn Ch (15198) (LAN, NYC,
AAMA)** **32**
2522 Adam Clayton Powell Jr Blvd, New York NY 10039
212-368-1103, fax 718-653-5084,
myrybronx@earthlink.net
   Monroe J. Yoder, Pastor

Shiloh Menn Ch* (10765) (LAN) **22**
1225 Fern Ave, Reading PA 19607
610-796-1528, jarhosa@juno.com
421 Bingaman St
   John S. Brubacker, Co-Pastor
   James Sauder, Co-Pastor

Slate Hill Menn Ch (15206) (LAN) **182**
1352 Slate Hill Rd, Camp Hill PA 17011-8013
717-737-8150, fax 717-737-8016, slatehill@paonline.com,
http://slatehill.pa.us.mennonite.net
   W. Lynn Shertzer, Pastor
   Lena H. Brown, Associate Pastor
   Roy H. Stetler IV, Associate Pastor

**South Seventh Street Menn Ch (15222) (LAN,
AAMA)** **53**
415 S 7th St, Reading PA 19602
610-375-6700, smartinhoover@aol.com
   Daniel P. Althouse, Pastor
   Saralee M. Hoover, Associate Pastor
   Thomas R. Hoover, Associate Pastor
   Stephen J. Good, Licensed Deacon

Stauffer Menn Ch (15230) (LAN) **32**
4295 Colebrook Rd, Hershey PA 17033
717-367-3634
   Robert J. Spayde, Pastor
   J. Frank Zeager, Associate Pastor
   Carl H. Snavely, Ordained Deacon

Steelton Menn Ch (15248) (LAN, AAMA) **40**
501 N 3rd St, Steelton PA 17113
717-787-2160
Corner of 3rd & Jefferson
   Victor H. Romain Jr, Pastor

Stony Brook Menn Ch (15255) (LAN) **110**
c/o Jeffrey A. Grosh, 52 Main St, Yorkanna PA 17402-8202
717-755-8756, jcgrosh@aol.com
15 Locust Grove Rd, York
   Jeffrey A. Grosh, Pastor

Strasburg Menn Ch* (15271) (LAN) **192**
1514 Village Rd, Strasburg PA 17579
717-687-8471, stras_men_ch@juno.com
   John Dwight Meck, Pastor
   John F. Mishler, Associate Pastor
   John W. Good, Ordained Deacon

Stumptown Menn Ch (15297) (LAN) **309**
2813 Stumptown Rd, Bird in Hand PA 17505
717-859-2940, dondors@juno.com
   Donald M. Sensenig, Pastor
   John M. Leaman, Associate Pastor
   M. Luke Nolt, Associate Pastor
   Andrew S. Diener Jr, Licensed Deacon
   Ivan B. Leaman, Licensed Deacon

Sunnyside Menn Ch (15305) (LAN) **114**
337 Circle Ave, PO Box 10041, Lancaster PA 17605-0041
717-293-0001, ikurtz@supernet.com
   Ira A. Kurtz, Pastor
   J. Brian Miller, Associate Pastor
   Alma M. Shultz, Licensed Deaconess

Susquehanna Menn Ch* (15313) (LAN) 40
c/o Wesley Groff, RR 1 Box 131G, Mt Pleasant Mills PA 17853
570-539-2575
Peiffer Rd, Port Trevorton
  J. Wesley Groff, Pastor
  Albert W. Heimbach, Pastor

Tinsae Kristos Evangelical Ch (11566) (LAN) . . .20
c/o Berhanu Kebede, 382 Dohner Dr, Lancaster PA 17602
EMM, 53 W Brandt Blvd
  Berhanu Kebede, Lay Leader

University Christian Fell* (10188) (LAN) 22
707 Millwood Rd, Willow Street PA 17584
717-464-3361, dmetzler@marauder.millersv.edu
George St, Millersville
  Duane L. Metzler, Pastor

Vietnamese Christian Fell (29215) (LAN, VIET) .30
720 N King St, Honolulu HI 96817
808-842-1089, fax 808-842-1089, pjhonuluu@juno.com
  Paul Quoccuong Luu, Pastor

Vietnamese Menn Ch (27045) (LAN, KB) 160
6237 Woodland Ave, Philadelphia PA 19142-2005
610-352-8689, msquang@go.com
  Quang Xuan Tran, Pastor

Village Chapel Menn Ch (22491) (LAN) 74
335 Wissler Rd, New Holland PA 17557
717-354-6075, jsjshorst@juno.com
  Jeffrey S. Horst, Pastor
  Chester L. Martin, Associate Pastor
  David L. Musselman, Associate Pastor
  Lester W. Gehman Jr, Youth Pastor

Way Through Christ (10073) (LAN, AAMA) 140
809 Glen Terrace, Chester PA 19013
610-872-5539
2nd & Thurlow
  Alvin Motley, Pastor
  Reginald C. Graham, Ordained Deacon

Weaverland Menn Ch* (15420) (LAN) 575
210 Weaverland Valley Rd, PO Box 328, East Earl PA 17519
717-445-6348, fax 717-354-9716, bpecmartin@juno.com
  Don R. Weaver, Pastor
  Leon R. Hurst, Associate Pastor
  Earl S. Weaver, Associate Pastor
  J. Nevin Hurst, Youth Pastor
  Brian E. Martin, Ordained Deacon
  C. Kenneth Martin, Bishop
  J. Nevin Martin, Ordained Deacon

Welsh Mountain Menn Ch (22061) (LAN) 29
686 Meetinghouse Rd, New Holland PA 17557
717-354-2533, fax 717-354-2533, tchrmrk@aol.com
571 Springville Rd
  J. Robert Kauffman, Pastor
  Paul M. Leaman, Deacon

West End Menn Fell (11174) (LAN) 19
20 N Charlotte St, Lancaster PA 17603
717-299-3228, fax 717-299-3228, josefberthold@aol.com
  Josef V. Berthold, Pastor

West Franklin Menn Ch (15404) (LAN) 11
RR1 Box 248A2, Monroeton PA 18832-9622
570-364-5397
Corner Rt 414 & 514, West Franklin
  Richard B. Martin, Pastor

Wheelerville Menn Ch (15453) (LAN) 19
RR 3 Box 332, Canton PA 17724
570-673-4307
On Rt 154, Wheelerville
  Michael C. Gaiotti, Pastor

Wilkens Avenue Menn Ch (15081) (LAN) 60
c/o Chauncey L. Martin, 1400 Gloster Ave, Baltimore MD 21230-1114
410-566-4769
1616 Wilkens Ave
  Michael S. King, Pastor
  Chauncey L. Martin, Associate Pastor

Willow Street Menn Ch (15461) (LAN) 248
399 Penn Grant Rd, PO Box 220, Willow Street PA 17584-0220
717-464-2422, fax 717-464-5332, willowstmenno@juno.com
Corner of Penn Grant Rd & Hans Herr Dr
  James B. Meador, Pastor
  Gerald B. Garber, Associate Pastor

Witmer Heights Menn Ch (11120) (LAN) 109
2270 Old Philadelphia Pike, Lancaster PA 17602
717-392-6698, fax 717-392-7810, whmc2270@aol.com, http://www.witmerheights.pa.us.mennonite.net
Rt 340 East
  L. Roy Bender, Pastor

New York Mennonite Conference

OFFICE
dotconf@northnet.org,
www.bfn.org/~nymennon
315-376-3734, fax 315-376-3071
PO Box C, 5546 Alger Rd, Martinsburg NY
13404

STAFF
Milton J. Zehr, conference minister
(dotconf@northnet.org)
Dorothy L. Zehr, administrative assistant
(dotconf@northnet.org)

GENERAL INFORMATION
Year founded: 1973
Members: 1,383
Congregations: 17
Ministers: 21
CLC reps: LeRoy Mast and Milton Zehr
Districts: Northern, Emanuel Gingerich
(margeman@northnet.org); Southern, Don
Siegrist (asiegrist@yahoo.com); Western,
Nestali Torres (nestali_torres@msn.com)
Semiannual delegate sessions: fall meeting, Sept.
20-21, 2003; spring meeting, April 2003

COORDINATING COUNCIL
LeRoy Mast, moderator
(revbikeman@juno.com), PO Box 91,
Hammondsport NY 14840, 607-569-3283; Terry
Zehr, assisting moderator; Connie Finney, secre-
tary; John Buckwalter, treasurer; E. Donald
Siegrist; Evan Zehr

PUBLICATION
Life in New York Mennonite Conference (3 per
year), Dorothy L. Zehr, editor (same address as
above)

COMMISSIONS
Leadership. Don Siegrist, chair
(siegrist@yahoo.com), 3465 State Route
417, Jasper NY 14855, 607-792-3710
Finance. John Buckwalter, treasurer
(buckwajd@alfredtech.edu), 5744 East
Valley Rd, Alfred Station NY 14803
Congregational Resourcing. Evan Zehr, chair
(eazehr@northnet.org), 5574 Highland Ave,
Lowville NY 13367, 315-376-3082; Peace
and Justice: Sue Klassen
(sueklassen@isp01.net); Prayer Ministry:
Ginny Gunnison (ginjoe@exotrope.net);
Women's Concerns: Sherry Mast
(lsmast2@juno.com); Worship/Music:
Marvin Zehr (marzedos@yahoo.com);
Christian Education/Stewardship Education:
Evan Zehr (eazehr@northnet.org).

OTHER CONFERENCE AGENCY AND REPS
Celebration Planning. Terry Zehr, chair
(zehrtj@northnet.org), 7377 State Route 12,
Lowville NY 13367, 315-376-5514
NYS Mennonite Medical Sharing Plan.
Victor and Jewel Miller,
(vic-jewel@juno.com), 5210 Salt Rd,
Clarence, NY 14031, 716-759-6330
Executive Board. Harold Miller
(hnmiller@juno.com), 280 Park Ave,
Corning NY 14830, 607-937-5252
MCC East Coast. Judy Buckwalter, 125 Stevens
St, Wellsville NY 14895, 607-356-3379
Eastern Mennonite Missions. Glenn
Brubaker (g-jbrubaker@juno.com), 1580
CR 22, Whitesville NY 14897, 607-356-3379
Goshen College. LeRoy Mast
(revbikeman@juno.com), PO Box 91,
Hammondsport NY 14840, 607-569-3283
Eastern Mennonite University. Harold Miller
(hnmiller@juno.com), 280 Park Ave,
Corning NY 14830, 607-937-5252

Congregations

Alden Menn Ch (10496) (NY) **134**
923 Two Rod Rd, Alden NY 14004
716-937-6977, fax 716-685-0048, AMCpastor@juno.com
   Philip Martin, Pastor
   Dale Meyers, Youth Pastor

Bethsaida Evangelical Ch (11118) (NY) **31**
c/o Tadelech Matewos Baka, 57-C Manor Pkwy, Rochester
NY 14620
585-461-9719, tmatewos@hotmail.com
Trinity Covenant Church, 1235 S Rd Clinton, Rochester
   Tadelech Matewos Baka, Contact Person

**Clarence Center-Akron Menn Ch (16980)
(NY)** **122**
11500 Clarence Center Rd, Akron NY 14001
716-542-9927, fax 716-542-1567, CCAM9927@aol.com
   Keith Zehr, Pastor

**Community Menn Fell of Corning (23614)
(NY)** **85**
290 Park Ave, Corning NY 14830
607-937-5252, hnmiller@juno.com,
http://www.pennynet.org/religion/cmf.htm
   Harold N. Miller, Pastor

First Menn Ch of New Bremen (21964) (NY) . .**267**
PO Box 417, Lowville NY 13367
315-376-6379, fax 315-376-9385, nbmenno@northnet.org
New Bremen
   Gordon Scoville, Interim Pastor

Grace Fell (11170) (NY) **0**
182 Ark Ln, Schoharie NY 12157
518-295-7891, fax 518-295-7556, wfarrell@midtel.net
   William Farrell, Pastor

Harris Hill Menn Ch (10504) (NY) **19**
5225 Harris Hill Rd, Williamsville NY 14221
716-688-6867, tim@buffalo.com,
http://www.forministry.com/14221hhmc
   Timothy J. Schultz, Pastor

Independence Gospel Fell Menn (14357) (NY) .**34**
c/o William Dickerson, 36 Williams Ave, Wellsville NY
14895
716-485-6923, igfchurch@hotmail.com,
http://freenet.buffalo.edu/~nymennon/independ.htm
Independence Rd in Andover
   William D. Dickerson, Administrative Elder
   O. Robert Mitchell, Outreach/Missions Elder
   Robert Volk, Pastoral Elder

Jesus Ch (10138) (NY) **27**
c/o Tim Wright, Creek Hill Apts #10, 1704 Empire Blvd,
Webster NY 14580
585-670-9987, channels@frontiernet.net
Rt Rd 417
   Timothy Lee Wright, Pastor

Lowville Menn Ch (10892) (NY, CM) **260**
PO Box 167, Lowville NY 13367
315-376-3082, eazehr@northnet.org
7705 Ridgeroad
   Evan Zehr, Pastor

Pine Grove Menn Ch (11072) (NY, CM) **53**
8343 Van Amber Rd, Castorland NY 13620
315-376-2593, nrzehr@hotmail.com
Van Amber Rd, Naumburg
   Nathan Zehr, Pastor

Pleasant Valley Menn Ch (15057) (NY) **41**
7601 S Valley Rd, Hammondsport NY 14840
607-569-3651, revbikeman@juno.com
   LeRoy J. Mast, Pastor

Rochester Area Menn Fell (21956) (NY) **26**
10 Avonmore Way, Penfield NY 14526
585-473-0220, fax 585-377-0152, RAMF@earthlink.net,
http://homepage.mac.com/mshelly/RAMF
Looking for a permanent location

Watertown Menn Ch (21980) (NY) **60**
19089 State Rte 3, Watertown NY 13601
315-785-9861, zehrtj@northnet.org,
http://freenet.buffalo.edu/~nymennon/watertwn.htm
Right side of State Rt 3 south of Watertown
   Terry J. Zehr, Pastor

West Union Menn Ch (15412) (NY) **75**
1459 CR 84, Rexville NY 14877
607-225-4421, G-JBrubaker@juno.com
   Glenn E. Brubaker, Co-Pastor
   Robert G. Walters Sr, Co-Pastor

Westside Menn Ch (10068) (NY) **35**
c/o Nestali Torres, pastor, 184 Barton, Buffalo NY 14213
716-883-7035, Nestali_Torres@msn.com
   Nestali Torres, Pastor

Yorks Corners Menn Ch (15487) (NY) **114**
3350 County Rt 29, Wellsville NY 14895
585-593-3287, fax 585-593-1178, Genemile@aol.com
   Eugene N. Miller, Pastor

CONFERENCES AND CONGREGATIONS

2

North Central Mennonite Conference

OFFICE
egschrock@juno.com
715-943-2317
Elwood Schrock, secretary, 166 N State Rd 40, Exeland WI 54835-2176

GENERAL INFORMATION
Year founded: 1920
Members: 513
Congregations: 13
Ministers: 15
CLC reps.: *Fred Kanagy, *John I. Kauffman
Annual Conference: June 6-8, 2003, Strawberry Lake/Detroit Lakes
Historian: Lila Kanagy

EXECUTIVE COMMITTEE
*Fred Kanagy, moderator, (kanagyf@midrivers.com), 753 Road 523, Bloomfield MT 59315, 406-583-7782; *Galen Kauffman, moderator-elect; *Elwood Schrock, secretary, *Mary Ellen Kauffman, treasurer

PUBLICATION
North Central Conference Bulletin, Elwood and Lorene Schrock, editor (same address as above)

COMMISSIONS
Congregational Ministries Commission. *David Hochstetler, chair, (davanna@cheqnet.net), W1216 County Hwy B, Stone Lake WI 54876, 715-865-5403; Darrell Nefzger, secretary; James Davidson
Ministerial Leadership Commission. *Glen Birky, chair (dgbari@tekstar.com), 35272 State Hwy 34, Detroit Lakes MN 56501-8000, 218-847-4988; David Geib, secretary; Ottis Yoder
Mission and Service Commission. *Walter Clinton, chair (clintonwjmc@aol.com), 1406 16th St S, Fargo ND 58013, 701-298-0783; Neville Peterson, secretary; David Book
Stewardship Commission. *Archie Stiyer, chair, 30122 County Hwy 34, Callaway MN 56521, 218-375-3955; Arlen Gerig, James Johnson

OTHER CONFERENCE AGENCY AND REPS
MCC Representative. David Birky (dgbari@tekstar.com), 35268 State Hwy 34, Detroit Lakes MN 56501-8000, 218-847-9351
Mennonite Women. Dorothy Kingsley, president, 15847 25th St SE, Amenia ND 58004, 701-967-8978
Peace Representative. Ottis and Violet Yoder, 32553 County Hwy 34, Ogema MN 56569, 218-983-3477
Youth Ministers. Les and Gayle Hochstetler (lesgayle@hotmail.com), 31837 County Hwy 34, Ogema MN 56569, 218-983-3127

*Member of NC Conference Executive Board

Congregations

Bethlehem Menn Ch (4145) (NC) 74
183 CR 516, Bloomfield MT 59315
406-583-7583, dpnefzgr@midrivers.com
    Darrell Nefzger, Pastor

Casselton Menn Ch (15511) (NC) 19
251 Langer Ave N, PO Box 840, Casselton ND 58012
701-967-8978

Coalridge Menn Ch (15529) (NC) 31
112 Longfellow Rd, Dagmar MT 59219
406-483-5307
108 Longfellow Rd
    David Geib, Pastor

Exeland Menn Ch (15537) (NC) 16
166 N SR 40, Exeland WI 54835-2176
715-943-2317
N9598 Old Murry Rd
    Elwood G. Schrock, Pastor

Lake Region Menn Ch (15578) (NC) 8
16692 Co Hwy 29, Frazee MN 56544-8820
218-847-3914, mmbook@i29.net
Hwy 34 E, Detroit Lakes
  David Book, Pastor

Lakeview Menn Ch (15586) (NC) 47
HC 1 Box 13, Wolford ND 58385
701-583-2836
  Ron Graber, Lay Leader

Morson Community Bible Fell (15495) (NC, UNMC) 27
RR 1, Sleeman ON P0W 1M0
807-488-5927
  Wally Detweiler, Pastor
  William P. Longenecker, Pastor

Point of Pines Menn Ch (15610) (NC) 17
3607 CR 24, International Falls MN 56649
218-283-2498

Prairie Peace Fell (15545) (NC, COB) 82
404 1st Ave SW, PO Box 236, Surrey ND 58785-0236
701-852-4957, fax 701-852-4872,
galenkauffman@hotmail.com,
http://www.boydenia.com/np/np
209 Pleasant Ave South
  Galen E. Kauffman, Pastor

Red Top Menn Ch (15628) (NC) 53
753 CR 523, Bloomfield MT 59315
406-583-7782, kanagyf@midrivers.com
502 CR 523
  Fred Kanagy, Pastor

Sand Lake Menn Chapel (24620) (NC) 15
W1216 County Hwy B, Stone Lake WI 54876
715-865-5403, davanna@cheqnet.net
  David Hochstetler, Pastor

South Lawrence Menn Ch (15636) (NC) 70
N3795 State Highway 73, Glen Flora WI 54526
fax 715-668-5519, alvines@centurytel.net
  Alvin E. Stoll, Pastor

Strawberry Lake Menn Ch (15644) (NC) 54
RR 1 Box 88, Ogema MN 56569
218-983-3490
  Delmar Yoder, Pastor
  Ottis Yoder, Bishop

CONFERENCES AND CONGREGATIONS

2

Ohio Conference of the Mennonite Church

OFFICE
ohmc@zoominternet.net,
www.ohio.mennonite.net
330-857-5421, fax 330-857-5485
13363 Jericho Rd, PO Box 210, Kidron OH
44636

STAFF
Tom Kauffman, conference minister
(tekauffman@sev.org), PO Box 140065,
Toledo OH 43614, 419-385-6865,
fax 419-385-6865
J. Andrew Stoner, Region I pastor
(rpandy@juno.com), 11026 Old Oak Trail,
Ft Wayne IN 46845, 877-321-3289 pin 7093
Wayne and Mary Nitzsche, Region II co-pastors
(menwan@juno.com), 917 Patrick Pl,
Wooster OH 44691, 330-264-2470,
fax 330-264-2470
Eldon King, Region III interim pastor
(eldor@sssnet.com), 551 Tionesta Dr,
Dalton OH 44618, 330-828-1004
Stan Helmuth, financial coordinator
(cboh1@zoominternet.net)
Judy King, administrative assistant
(ohmc@zoominternet.net)
Ann Leaman, conference editor
(ohioevan@aol.com), 854 Sunland St NE,
Louisville OH 44641, 330-453-3793,
fax 330-453-3793
Jan Sohar, Choice Books director
(cboh@zoominternet.net), 330-857-7721
Daryl Arner, Steve Meyer, Jim Stanco, service
representatives

GENERAL INFORMATION
Year founded: 1834
Members: 11,103
Congregations: 77
Ministers: 174

CLC reps: Tom Kauffman, Ann Nofziger, Allen
Rutter
Annual Conference: March 21-22, 2003
Conference historian: Celia Lehman

EXECUTIVE COMMITTEE
Allen Rutter, moderator (alrutter@bright.net),
21-377 CR H50, Stryker OH 43557, 419-
682-5096; Jeff Combs, assistant moderator;
Maxine Bartholomew, secretary; Dan
Greaser, fifth member
Conference Council Members-at-Large: Jim
Bartholomew, Matt Hamsher, Tim Lehman,
Ann Nofziger, Tim Short, Sid Smith, Vikki
Pruitte-Sorrells, Phyllis Yoder, Bob Yoder

PUBLICATION
Ohio Evangel (10 times per year), Ann Leaman,
conf editor, (ohioevan@aol.com), 5854
Sunland St NE, Louisville OH 44641, 330-453-
3793, fax 330-453-3793

COMMISSIONS
Evangelism. Eldon King, co-chair
(eldor@sssnet.com), 551 Tionesta Dr,
Dalton OH 44618, 330-828-1004; Robert
Wengerd, co-chair (bobwengerd@aol.com),
7852 Glenwood Ave, Boardman OH 44512,
330-758-2597; Trish André, Todd Martin,
Mattie Marie Mast; staff: Andy Stoner
Finance. Darrel Schweitzer, chair
(darrels@tbscc.com), 23525 Britton Run
Rd, Spartansburg PA 16434, 814-694-2061;
Paul Bontrager, Sue Schmucker Coblentz, Art
Neuenschwander, Rod Nofziger; staff: Stan
Helmuth and Tom Kauffman
Leadership. Terry Shue, chair,
(tshue@valkyrie.net), 4000 Steinwood Dr,
Dalton OH 44618, 330-857-8866; Mel
Hathaway, Mona Sauder, Jacqui Rozier, Alvin
Yoder; staff: Tom Kauffman
Nurture. John Miller, chair
(johnmiller@nls.net), 15297 Arnold Rd,
Dalton OH 44618, 330-828-8593; Dorothy
Hathaway, Eileen Lehman, Ken Miller, Jim
Roynon; staff: Wayne Nitzsche

Peace-Justice-Service. Robin Miller, chair (robindeanmiller@hotmail.com), 3533 Hildana Rd, Shaker Heights OH 44120, 216-561-8142; Lincoln Nafziger, Mary Naumoff, Bill Shumaker, Jane Yousey; staff: Mary Nitzsche

Stewardship. Jacob Nafziger, chair (jacobnaf@fulton-net.com) 21360 B CR H, Archbold OH 43502, 419-445-2287; Lorene Amstutz, Leon Mast, Ward Mumaw, Darrell Smucker

OTHER CONFERENCE AGENCY AND REPS

Choice Books Management. Paul Helmuth, chair (pjhcpapfs@aol.com), 1731 Edmar St, Louisville OH 44641, 330-875-1273; Gordon Amstutz, George Bixler, Marjorie King, Carol Schrock

Historical. Celia Lehman, chair (cbl@bright.net), 13170 Arnold Rd, Dalton OH 44618, 330-857-7302; Glen Nafziger, Mae Brown

Salary and Benefits. Jeff Combs, chair (jeffcombs@mics.net), 1555 S Limestone St, Springfield OH 45505, 937-322-9130; Darrel Schweitzer, Delmar Hostetler, Sid Smith

Spiritual Formation Resource. Wayne Nitzsche, chair (menwan@juno.com), 917 Patrick Place, Wooster OH 44691, 330-264-2470; John Miller, Beulah Steiner, Wendy Miller

Theological Resource. Jayne Byler, chair (summitmenno@juno.com), 338 Haven, Barberton OH 44203, 330-753-9737; Richard Bartholomew, Paul Conrad, Ron Guengerich, Jim Mullett

Gifts Discernment. Ross Miller, chair (ross@hmhd.com) 844 Basel St, Sugarcreek OH 44681, 330-852-2575; Randy Nafziger, Howard Schmitt, Vickie Yoder

Central Christian High School. Fred Miller, principal (fredmiller@centralchristian.k12.oh.us), PO Box 9, Kidron OH 44636, 330-857-7311

Mennonite Women. Nancy Roynon, president (njroynon@fulton-net.com), V-986 CR 20, Archbold OH 43502, 419-446-2967; Patricia Burdette, Jean Emery, Jennifer Hartzler, Nancy Hostetler, Phyllis Kornhaus, Ellen Nussbaum, Myrna Ramseyer

CONFERENCE RELATED MINISTRIES

Adriel School. Marty Lehman, executive director, Box 188, West Liberty OH 43357, 937-465-0010

Camp Luz. Deb Horst, camp director (camp.luz@juno.com), 168 Kidron Rd, Orrville OH 44667, 330-683-1246

Choice Books of Ohio. Jan Sohar, executive director (cboh@zoominternet.net), PO Box 210, Kidron OH 44636, 330-857-5471; Daryl Arner, Steve Meyer, Jim Stanco, service representatives

Eastern Mennonite University Constituent Conference. John Miller, OMC representative

Goshen College Conference Advisory Board. Joann Short and Denton Yoder, OMC representatives

Great Lakes Discipleship Center. Dee Custar, OMC representative

MCC Great Lakes. René Mejía, OMC representative

Mennonite and Brethren Marriage Encounter. Carl Newcomer, 5437 RD 32 S, West Liberty OH 43357, 937-465-3366

OrrVilla Retirement Community. George Bixler, executive director, 425 Orrvilla Dr, Orrville OH 44667, 330-683-4455

Shalom Ministries. Lenette Moshier, director, 207 Vine St, Archbold OH 43502, 419-445-1552

CONFERENCE REGIONS

Region I – J. Andrew Stoner, Region I pastor
Agora, Bethel (West Liberty), Central, Cincinnati, Columbus, Cornerstone, Emmanuel, Huber, Iglesia Menonita del Buen Pastor, Inlet, Jubilee, Kalida, Lima, Lockport, North Clinton, Oak Grove (West Liberty), Pike, Pine Grove, Primera Iglesia

(Defiance), Primera Iglesia (Fremont), Salem (Elida), Salem (Michigan), Sharon, Southside, South Union, Springdale Chapel, Tedrow, Toledo, West Clinton, Zion

Region II – Wayne and Mary Nitzsche, Region II pastors

Aurora, Beaverdam, Beech, Berean, Bethel (Wadsworth), Crown Hill, Dayspring, First (Canton), Friendship, Gilead, Hartville, Lee Heights, Leetonia, Maple Grove, Martins, Midway, New Mercies, North Lima, Oak Grove (Smithville), Orrville, Peace, Pleasant View, Smithville, Stoner Heights, Summit, Sunnyside, Valley View, University Euclid

Region III – Eldon King (interim) and Wayne Nitzsche, Region III pastors

Berlin, Community Christian Fellowship, Dover, Fairpoint, Fellowship Chapel, Hillside, Kidron, Lafayette Fellowship, Longenecker, Martins Creek, Millersburg, Moorhead, Owl Creek, Salem (Wooster), Sonnenberg, St. Johns, Walnut Creek, Wayside Chapel, Wooster

Congregations

Agora Christian Fell (11103) (CDC, OH) 0
400 W Broad St, Columbus OH 43215
614-280-1212, fax 614-280-0312, agoracf@aol.com
  Rebecca J. Bartholomew, Co-Pastor
  Richard Bartholomew Jr, Co-Pastor

Aurora Menn Ch (15677) (OH) 87
59 E Mennonite Rd, Aurora OH 44202
330-562-8011, fax 330-562-3186, auroramenn@juno.com,
http://members.aol.com/wasc/amc.htm
  Jesse Engle, Co-Pastor
  Naomi Engle, Co-Pastor

Beaverdam Menn Ch (22004) (OH) 134
17721 Rt 89, Corry PA 16407
814-665-5465, PNClemens@TBSCC.com,
http://www.forministry.com/16407bmc
  Philip K. Clemens, Pastor

Beech Menn Ch (15701) (OH) 278
10037 Easton St, Louisville OH 44641
330-875-1133, fax 330-875-1587,
beechmennochurch@cs.com,
http://members.aol.com/BrnchOut
  Ronald L. Blough, Pastor

Berean Fell Ch (15719) (OH, AAMA) 33
1321 Lansdowne Blvd, Youngstown OH 44505
330-747-0471, pastorjt7@aol.com
  Jefferson Thomas Jr, Pastor

Berlin Menn Ch (15727) (OH) 221
4718 US Rt 62 E, PO Box 217, Berlin OH 44610
330-893-2320, fax 330-893-9602, Berlinmc@juno.com
  Ernest Hershberger, Pastor
  Bruce Allen Hamsher, Associate Pastor

Bethel Menn Ch (15768) (OH) 70
2684 Seville Rd, Rittman OH 44270
330-336-4559, tim19nov@hotmail.com
  Tim Short, Pastor

Bethel Menn Ch (15750) (OH) 175
PO Box 549, West Liberty OH 43357-0549
937-465-4587, ayoder@logan.net
416 Washington St Rd
  Alvin Yoder, Pastor

Central Menn Ch (15842) (OH) 525
PO Box 191, Archbold OH 43502
419-445-3856, fax 419-455-5607,
central@powersupply.net
21703 SR 2
  Cliff Brubaker, Interim Pastor
  Jeffrey Wayne Smith, Associate Pastor

Cincinnati Menn Fell (23325) (CDC, OH) 66
3046 Minot Ave, Cincinnati OH 45209
513-871-0035, cmfoffice@juno.com
4229 Brownway Ave
  Pauline Ann Nofziger, Pastor

Columbus Menn Ch (16378) (CDC, OH) 197
35 Oakland Park Ave, Columbus OH 43214
614-784-8957, fax 614-784-9002,
cmc@columbusmennonite.org,
http://www.columbusmennonite.org
  Joyce M. Wyse, Interim Pastor

Community Christian Fell (16485) (OH) 0
444 Wayne Ln, Thurman OH 45685
614-388-9041

Cornerstone Menn Fell (28225) (OH) 68
11672 Lafayette Rd, Plain City OH 43064
614-873-8903
  Walter A. Campbell Jr, Pastor

Crown Hill Menn Ch (15883) (OH) 124
9693 Benner Rd, Rittman OH 44270
330-927-1716, crownhill@bright.net
Corner of Benner Rd & SR 585
  Gordon Miller, Pastor

Dayspring Christian Fell (27334) (OH) 84
733 W Maple St, North Canton OH 44720
330-499-9708, jpbart@juno.com
6200 Frank Ave Rd NW, Canton
    James E. Bartholomew, Pastor
    Kenton Tod Miller, Associate Pastor

Dover Christian Fell (10709) (CDC, OH) 35
206 W 3rd St, Dover OH 44622-2904
330-364-8590, fax 330-364-8590, jpollock@bright.net
    Al Mast, Interim Pastor

Emmanuel Menn Ch (10037) (OH) 10
PO Box 18, Monclova OH 43542
419-445-5094, rshort7@fulton-net.com
8353 Monclova Rd
    Reid Short, Pastor

Fairpoint Menn Ch (15925) (OH) 54
PO Box 47, Fairpoint OH 43927
740-695-0303
    Darrel McVay, Pastor

Fellowship Chapel (11308) (OH) 85
PO Box 67, Vinton OH 45686
740-388-9041
    Paul Ring, Pastor

First Menn Ch (15982) (OH) 59
1935 3rd St SE, Canton OH 44707
330-453-1044, danhooley@netzero.net
    Daniel Hooley, Pastor
    Darin Nissley, Youth Pastor

Friendship Menn Ch (16006) (OH) 91
21881 Libby Rd, Bedford Heights OH 44146
216-662-6788, friendmc@corecomm.net,
http://www.geocities.com/friendshipmc
    David E. Orr, Pastor

Gilead Menn Ch (16014) (OH) 51
PO Box 6, 6790 CR 121, Chesterville OH 43317
330-264-1390, nsteiner@neobright.net
    Nolan Steiner, Pastor

Hartville Menn Ch (16048) (OH) 557
1470 Smith Kramer St NE, PO Box 727, Hartville OH 44632
330-877-2050, fax 330-877-8557,
e-mail@hartvillemennonite.org,
http://www.hartvillemennonite.org
    David L. Hall, Pastor
    Henry Shrock Jr, Associate Pastor
    Chadwick Miller, Youth Pastor

Hillside Chapel (16071) (OH) 31
1751 SR 788, Jackson OH 45640
740-384-3055, sjmullett@yahoo.com,
http://www.hillsidechapel.com
1609 SR 788

Huber Menn Ch (16097) (OH) 73
1885 S Dayton Lakeview Rd, New Carlisle OH 45344
937-849-6720, fax 937-849-6720, fishlaj@juno.com
    Oswaldo Rivera, Spanish Pastor

Iglesia Menonita del Buen Pastor (16022) (OH, IMH) 53
22489 CR F, Archbold OH 43502
419-445-3100, fax 419-445-1268,
goodshepherd@bright.net
    David Tijerina, Pastor
    Ismael Huerta, Associate Pastor

Inlet Menn Ch (16105) (OH) 55
13009-16-3, Wauseon OH 43567
419-452-6425, fax 419-782-0599, yfcjones@hotmail.com
    Rick Jones, Pastor

Jubilee Menn Ch (11111) (CDC, OH) 45
PO Box 428, Bellefontaine OH 43311
937-592-8101, jubilee@2access.net,
http://www.jubileemennonite.com
Friendly Senior Center
    Tim Lehman, Pastor

Kalida Family Outreach Center (16311) (OH) . . .0
PO Box 236, Kalida OH 45853
419-532-2525, fax 419-532-3737, kfoc@bright.net,
http://www.kfoc.org
404 W Northland Dr
    James Swihart, Pastor
    Kenneth Benner, Associate Pastor
    Derrick Wallace, Assistant Pastor

Kidron Menn Ch (16113) (OH) 807
PO Box 232, Kidron OH 44636
330-857-3461, fax 330-857-0593, kmc@valkyrie.net
3987 Kidron Rd
    Terry W. Shue, Pastor
    Herman F. Myers, Associate Pastor
    Jeremy Shue, Youth Pastor
    Laura Shue, Youth Pastor

Lafayette Christian Fell (28191) (OH) 28
108 E Main St, West Lafayette OH 43845
740-545-5234, kevinrainwater@hotmail.com
    Kevin Rainwater, Congregational Chair

Lee Heights Community Ch (16139) (OH, AAMA) 411
4612 Lee Rd, Cleveland OH 44128
216-581-2448, fax 216-581-9283, leeheights@juno.com,
http://community.cleveland.com/cc/leeheightscommunit
    Robin Dean Miller, Pastor

Leetonia Menn Ch (16147) (OH) 120
764 Columbia St, PO Box 226, Leetonia OH 44431
330-427-6827, fax 330-427-2750,
bc958@wmconnect.com
    Robert D. Yoder, Pastor

Lima Menn Ch (16402) (CDC, OH) 80
1318 N Main St, Lima OH 45801
419-222-2120, limamc@bright.net

CONFERENCES AND CONGREGATIONS

2

Lockport Menn Ch (16154) (OH) **440**
9269 CR 21 N, Stryker OH 43557
419-682-1831, lockport@bright.net,
http://www.bright.net/~lockport/index.htm
  Allen G. Rutter, Pastor
  Mark Miller, Associate Pastor
  Wendy Miller, Associate Pastor

Longenecker Menn Ch (16162) (OH) **190**
PO Box 112, Winesburg OH 44690
330-359-5155, revc@sssnet.com,
http://www.longeneckermennonite.org
8451 Holmes CR 186
  Glenn Dale Coblentz, Pastor
  Dennis Hostetler, Youth Pastor

Maple Grove Menn Ch (16170) (OH) **33**
RR 5 Box 439, New Castle PA 16105
330-549-3389, fax 330-549-3389, rbarth1@aol.com
  Maxine Bartholomew, Co-Pastor
  Richard Bartholomew, Co-Pastor

Martins Creek Menn Ch (16196) (OH) **258**
6111 CR 203, Millersburg OH 44654
330-674-1242, fax 330-674-0733, carl@mcmc.org,
http://www.mcmc.org
  Carl Wiebe, Pastor
  Jay Conn, Associate Pastor
  Matt Flinner, Associate Pastor

Martins Menn Ch (16204) (OH) **185**
14027 Church Rd, Orrville OH 44667
330-683-1226, martinsc@sssnet.com,
http://www.martinsmennonite.com
  Randy B. Murray, Pastor

Midway Menn Ch (16261) (OH) **182**
13376 Columbiana-Canfield Rd, Columbiana OH 44408
330-482-3135, fax 330-482-9688,
midwaymenno@juno.com
  Larry D. Rohrer, Pastor

Millersburg Menn Ch (16279) (OH) **157**
288 E Jackson St, PO Box 16, Millersburg OH 44654
330-674-7700, fax 330-674-7700,
tlmmbgmenno@juno.com
  Thomas L. Michaels, Pastor

Moorhead Menn Ch (16295) (OH) **79**
7040 Township Rd 319, Millersburg OH 44654
330-674-2121, bhof53@hotmail.com
10415 CR 329, Shreve
  Rob Burdette, Interim Pastor

New Mercies Community Ch (10899) (OH) **48**
12767 Butternut Rd, Burton OH 44021
440-834-8386, fax 440-834-8386, jdsutt@ncweb.com
  James Sutton, Pastor

North Clinton Menn Ch (16329) (OH) **381**
831 W Linfoot St, Wauseon OH 43567
419-337-4776, fax 419-337-4779,
gary.blosser@northclinton.org,
http://www.northclinton.org
  Gary S. Blosser, Lead Pastor
  Brad Faler, Associate Pastor
  Michael Ray Zehr, Associate Pastor

North Lima Menn Ch (16337) (OH) **108**
90 Mennonite Dr, North Lima OH 44452
330-549-2333, fax 330-549-2333, bobwengerd@aol.com
  Robert D. Wengerd, Pastor

Oak Grove Menn Ch (16428) (CDC, OH) **410**
7843 Smucker Rd, Smithville OH 44677
330-669-2697, fax 330-669-2617, ogsmthvll@aol.com,
http://www.oakgrovemc.org
  Norma B. Duerksen, Pastor
  Joel A. Short, Associate Pastor

Oak Grove Menn Ch (16410) (OH) **168**
1525 Mennonite Church Rd, West Liberty OH 43357
937-465-4749, fax 937-465-4749, oakgrove@juno.com,
http://oakgrove.oh.us.mennonite.net
  Larry Augsburger, Pastor

Orrville Menn Ch (16444) (OH) **252**
1305 W Market St, Orrville OH 44667
330-682-5801, fax 330-682-5841, orrmenno@aol.com,
http://orrville.oh.us.mennonite.net
  Glen A. Horner, Interim Pastor
  Thelma Horner, Interim Pastor

Owl Creek Menn Ch (16451) (OH) **21**
13249 SR 104, Lucasville OH 45648
740-259-5712, rjbapst@zoomnet.net
1442 Germany Rd
  Rodney Bapst, Pastor

Peace Menn Ch (25825) (OH) **42**
9300 W Ridge Rd, Elyria OH 44035
440-322-7344, pmcpastor@aol.com
  Allan Patterson, Pastor

Pike Menn Ch (16469) (OH) **106**
3995 McBride Rd, Elida OH 45807
419-339-3961, fax 419-339-0699, pikemc@bright.net
  James J. Miller, Interim Pastor

Pine Grove Menn Ch (16477) (OH) **72**
4524 CR 2050, Stryker OH 43557
419-682-2981, revbob98@yahoo.com
  Bob Yates, Pastor

Pleasant View Menn Ch (16527) (OH) **94**
14795 Wooster St NW, North Lawrence OH 44666
330-833-0473, johnmiller@nls.net,
http://www.pvmom.com
  John M. Miller, Pastor
  Rebecca Martin, Youth Pastor
  Todd Martin, Youth Pastor

Primera Iglesia Menonita (15974) (OH, IMH) **23**
PO Box 393, Defiance OH 43512
419-782-6761, reneme@defnet.com
1123 Ayersville Ave
  René Mejia, Pastor

Primera Iglesia Menonita (24695) (OH, IMH) . . .**19**
PO Box 178, Helena OH 43435
419-332-2811
  Tony Ortiz Jr, Lay Leader

Salem Menn Ch (16634) (OH, AV) **95**
4275 W State Rd, Elida OH 45807
419-339-1505, salemmc@bright.net
  Melvin R. Hathaway, Pastor

Salem Menn Ch (16618) (OH) **111**
13751 S Tripp Rd, Waldron MI 49288
517-567-8954, dandeecus@cs.com,
http://www.frontiernet.net/~salemc
  Wilmer J. Hartman, Interim Pastor
  Deanna Custar, Preaching Minister
  Robert Stuckey, Preaching Minister
  Ned Wyse, Preaching Minister

Salem Menn Ch (16626) (OH) **43**
7012 Back Orrville Rd, Wooster OH 44691
330-828-0040, rvtadeo1934@valkyrie.net
  Ramsey Wallace, Interim Pastor

Sharon Menn Ch (16659) (OH) **250**
7675 Amity Pike, Plain City OH 43064
614-873-8290, fax 614-873-5925, sharonmc8@juno.com
Plain City
  Howard S. Schmitt, Pastor

Smithville Menn Ch (16667) (OH) **210**
PO Box 455, Smithville OH 44677
330-669-3601, fax 330-669-2490, SMC@valkyrie.net,
http://www.smithvillemennonite.org
6097 Akron Rd
  Burt Preston Parks, Pastor

Sonnenberg Menn Ch (18846) (OH) **281**
PO Box 226, Kidron OH 44636
330-857-8222, fax 330-857-8222, mmmast@juno.com
14367 Hackett Rd
  Michael M. Mast, Pastor
  Mattie Marie Mast, Interim Associate Pastor

South Union Menn Ch (16683) (OH) **84**
PO Box 579, 56 SR 508, West Liberty OH 43357
937-465-6085, southumc@bright.net
56 SR 508
  Keith L. Landis, Pastor

Southside Christian Fell (24034) (OH) **27**
1603 S Limestone St, Springfield OH 45505
937-323-9348, fax 937-323-8126, jeffcombs@mics.net,
http://www.hows.net/45505SCF
  Jeff Combs, Co-Pastor
  Joyce Combs, Co-Pastor

Springdale Chapel (16717) (OH) **45**
3001 Springdale Rd, Cincinnati OH 45251
513-851-1822, ohelton@fuse.net
  Ova Helton Jr, Pastor

St Johns Menn Chapel (16725) (OH) **20**
5756 TR 430 SW, Logan OH 43138
740-385-8971, mwjbender@yahoo.com
19681 SR 664
  Wilbur J. Bender, Pastor

Stoner Heights Menn Ch (16733) (OH) **40**
4975 Stoner Ave Rd, Louisville OH 44641-9171
330-875-1074, wmorton@neo.rr.com
  Walter L. Morton, Pastor

Summit Menn Ch (16741) (OH) **35**
939 Norton Ave, Barberton OH 44203
330-753-2019, fax 330-753-2019,
summitmenno@juno.com
  Jayne M. Byler, Pastor

Sunnyside Menn Ch (16758) (OH) **37**
12981 Foust Rd, Conneaut Lake PA 16316
814-382-6060, smc@mdvl.net

Tedrow Menn Ch (16766) (OH) **145**
252 Windisch St, Wauseon OH 43567
419-445-3486, fax 419-445-3486,
parson@Fulton-net.com,
http://www.tedrowmennonite.org
252 Windisch St in Tedrow
  Randall K. Nafziger, Pastor

Toledo Menn Ch (15685) (OH, AAMA) **112**
5501 Nebraska Ave, Toledo OH 43615
419-536-1251, fax 419-536-1253,
toledomennonite@accesstoledo.com,
http://www.toledo.mennonite.org
  Daniel Slabaugh, Interim Pastor

University Euclid Christ New Testament (16774) (OH, AAMA) **26**
c/o 24580 Ridgeline Dr, Bedford Heights OH 44146-4831
216-581-8579, fax 440-439-9485
1869 E 85th or 8500 Chester Ave, Cleveland
  Warner Jackson, Pastor

Valley View Menn Ch (16782) (OH) **118**
PO Box 216, Spartansburg PA 16434-0216
814-664-7892, ree0817@aol.com
24313 State Hwys 89 & 77
  Robert E. Esh, Pastor

Walnut Creek Menn Ch (16808) (OH) **469**
PO Box 182, Walnut Creek OH 44687
330-852-2560, fax 330-852-4731, rossamiller@juno.com,
http://www.hmhd.com/wcmchurch
2619 County Rd 144
  Ross A. Miller, Pastor
  Matthew W. Hamsher, Associate Pastor

CONFERENCES AND
CONGREGATIONS

2

Wayside Chapel (16816) (OH) 44
16975 SR 93, Pedro OH 45659
740-643-2731, shauna@bright.net
17027 SR 93
    John Kelly, Pastor

West Clinton Menn Ch (16824) (OH) 310
18029 CR C, Wauseon OH 43567
419-445-1195, fax 419-445-1196, wclinton@bright.net,
http://www.bright.net/~wclinton
    James Roynon, Pastor

Wooster Menn Ch (16840) (OH) 154
1563 Beall Ave, Wooster OH 44691
330-262-3631, fax 330-262-0422, woostermc@sssnet.com
    Ralph Reinford, Pastor
    Ryan Clements, Youth Pastor

Zion Menn Ch (16873) (OH) 472
300 Short Buehrer Rd, Archbold OH 43502
419-445-3796, fax 419-445-8214, zionmc@bright.net
    Ronald D. Guengerich, Pastor
    Anne Stuckey, Associate Pastor
    Jeffrey Dale Wintermote, Youth Pastor

Pacific Northwest Mennonite Conference

See addresses under staff; www.pnmc.org

STAFF

Larry Hauder, conference minister (lhauder@earthlink.net), 2102 N 20th St, Boise ID 83702, 208-336-5646

Duncan Smith, conference minister (duncansmithpnmc@cs.com), 19532 NE Glisan, Portland OR 97230, 971-570-4216

Victor Vargas, Hispanic conference minister (wictormv@cs.com), PO Box 185, Woodburn OR 97071

Charlene Schrag, youth coordinator (pmcyouth@teleport.com), 25411 S Holman, Estacada OR 97023, 503-630-7216

William Higgins, director (peacemennonite@juno.com), Northwest Mennonite Theological Education, 19626 NE Glisan St, Portland OR 97013, 503-667-2762

GENERAL INFORMATION

Year founded: 1994
Members: 2,833
Congregations: 33
Ministers: 60
CLC reps: Larry Hauder, Jim Wenger
Annual Conference: mid-June
Conference Historian: Ray Kauffman

EXECUTIVE COMMITTEE

Marion Schrock, moderator (marionschrock@hotmail.com), 1175 Belaire Drive NW, Salem OR 97304, 503-399-0946; Jim Wenger, assistant moderator; Harold Nussbaum, secretary; Don Bacher, treasurer; Janet Buschert, Rob Hanson, Anne Hege, Larry Hildebrand, Cecil Miller, Carl Newswanger, Chak Ng, Simon Rendon

PUBLICATION

Evangel (Quarterly), Betti Erb, editor (jberb@attbi.com), 15017 Linden Ave N, Seattle WA 98133, 206-368-2684

COMMISSIONS

Congregational Nurture. Anne Hege, chair (hecorp@ida.net), 2830 W 2000 S, Aberdeen ID 83210, 208-397-4398

Evangelism and Missions. Chak Ng, board rep. (seattlelapper@yahoo.com), 5536 18th Ave South, Seattle WA 98108, 206-767-7148

Pastoral Leadership. Cecil Miller, chair (cjmiller@atnet.net), 11433 Road E SE, Othello WA 99344, 509-346-2485

Peace and Justice. Rob Hanson, chair (robeeruu@aol.com), 316 Locust St, Boise ID 83712, 208-383-0349

OTHER CONFERENCE AGENCY AND REPS

Hispanic Concilio. Samuel Moran, president (samran77@hotmail.com), PO Box 68008, Oak Grove OR 97268, 503-657-1302

Mennonite Women. Yvonne Leppert, contact person, 226 North St, Filer ID 83328, 208-326-3288

Mennonite Men. John Zook, president, 246 NE 130 Pl, Portland OR 97230, 503-252-4864

Congregations

Albany Menn Ch (17434) (PNW) **140**
3405 Kizer Ave NE, Albany OR 97321
541-926-1443, fax 541-926-0522, amc@proaxis.com
Matthew Charles Friesen, Pastor

Calvary Menn Ch (5180) (PNW, IMH) **237**
6711 S Lone Elder Rd, Aurora OR 97002
503-266-2202, fax 503-263-3126,
calvarymc@integrity.com
Kevin John Schumacher, Pastor
Ramiro Hernandez, Hispanic Ministries Pastor

CONFERENCES AND CONGREGATIONS

2

Comunidad Cristiana de Vida Nueva (11533) (PNW) 0
Box 679, Woodburn OR 97071
503-982-5731
    Gilberto Estrada, Pastor

Corvallis Menn Fell (10141) (PNW) 50
101 NW 23rd St, Corvallis OR 97330
541-754-5388, fax 541-754-9106,
gerryatodi@hotmail.com,
http://homestead.juno.com/corvallismenno

Eugene Menn Ch (17517) (PNW) 57
3590 W 18th Ave, Eugene OR 97402
541-343-9548, eugmenno@efn.org
    Gayle Sheller, Pastor

Evergreen Menn Ch (10145) (PNW) 52
PO Box 100, Bellevue WA 98009-0100
253-529-1073, smatthews@mennonite.net,
http://evergreen.wa.us.mennonite.net
9825 NE 24th St

Filer Menn Ch (17525) (PNW) 75
109 Fifth St, PO Box 157, Filer ID 83328-0157
208-326-5150
    George Earl Leppert, Pastor

First Menn Ch (5335) (PNW) 231
381 Washington & 4th, PO Box 246, Aberdeen ID 83210
208-397-4239, mepluseight@juno.com
    Monty Dell Ledford, Pastor

First Menn Ch (10278) (PNW) 34
903 SW Cedarwood Ave, McMinnville OR 97128
503-472-0217
    Daniel William Rehwalt, Interim Pastor

First Menn Ch (17533) (PNW) 100
1211 6th St N, Nampa ID 83687
208-466-9174, fax 208-463-4344
    Craig Daniel Morton, Interim Pastor

Hyde Park Menn Fell (23663) (PNW) 60
1520 N 12th St, Boise ID 83702
208-336-9872, hydepark2@mindsprng.com,
http://www.netnow.micron.net/~hpmf
    Linda E. Nafziger-Meiser, Pastor

Iglesia Menonita Pentecostes (23556) (PNW, IMH) 150
PO Box 185, Woodburn OR 97071
503-390-1944, fax 503-390-0392, vvictormv@cs.com
198 E Lincoln St
    Victor M. Vargas, Pastor
    Marjorie Mendez, Youth Pastor

Jerusalem Iglesia (28315) (PNW) 0
763 NE 18th, Salem OR 97301
503-363-8687

Lebanon Menn Ch (17574) (PNW) 246
PO Box 575, Lebanon OR 97355
541-258-5789, fax 541-451-5958,
martintroyer@hotmail.com

2100 S Second St
    J. Brent Kauffman, Pastor
    Martin Bradley Troyer, Associate Pastor

Logsden Neighborhood Ch (17582) (PNW) 35
6631 Logsden Rd, Logsden OR 97357
541-444-2820
    Randy Eisele, Pastor

Menno Menn Ch (5550) (PNW) 155
1378 N Damon Rd, Ritzville WA 99169-8717
509-659-0926, fax 509-659-0926, menno@ritzcom.net,
http://www.menno.wa.us.mennonite.net
    Terry Ray Rediger, Pastor

Ministerios Restauracion (11073) (PNW, IMH) . . .0
PO Box 68008, Oak Grove OR 97268
503-657-1302
    Samuel Moran, Pastor

Mountain View Menn Ch (10082) (PNW) 91
795 Mennonite Church Rd, Kalispell MT 59901
406-755-8772, jhollinger@montane.com
    Jeryl Hollinger, Pastor

Pacific Covenant Menn Ch (10142) (PNW) 45
2180 NE Territorial Rd, PO Box 609, Canby OR 97013
503-266-8646, jzyoder@web-ster.com
    Jon Yoder, Pastor

Peace Menn Ch (24380) (PNW) 24
19626 NE Glisan St, Portland OR 97230
503-667-2762, peacemennonite@juno.com
    William S. Higgins, Pastor

Plainview Menn Ch (17590) (PNW) 0
241 1st Ave W, Albany OR 97321-2223
541-926-1946, fax 541-926-1161,
pastorgary@plainview.org,
http://www.plainview.plainview.org
34414 Plainview Dr
    Rob L. Angerman, Pastor
    Roger Hutley, Associate Pastor
    Gary Myers, Associate Pastor
    Scott Anthony Henderson, Youth Pastor

Portland Menn Ch (17608) (PNW) 205
1312 SE 35th Ave, Portland OR 97214
503-234-0559, fax 503-235-5548, pmcpastr@teleport.com
    Rodney Alan Stafford, Pastor
    Charlene Schrag, Youth Pastor

Prince of Peace Menn Ch (10051) (PNW) 18
PO Box 241312, Anchorage AK 99524-1312
907-346-2909, johndavidthacker@hotmail.com
10980 Hillside Dr
    John David Thacker, Pastor

Prince of Peace Menn Ch (17509) (PNW) 73
7234 NE Arnold Ave, Corvallis OR 97330
541-745-5840, PrinceofPeace@exchangenet.net
    Larry Bardell, Interim Pastor
    Bev Cook Rupp, Minister of Pastoral Care

River of Life Fell (10270) (PNW) 85
PO Box 873, Sweet Home OR 97386
541-367-6855, fax 541-367-2795, riveroflife@proaxis.com
1658 Long St
   Gary Dean Hooley, Pastor

Salem Menn Ch (17616) (PNW) 127
1045 Candlewood Dr NE, Salem OR 97303
503-390-2715, menno@open.org,
http://www.open.org/~menno
   Carl K. Newswanger, Pastor

Seattle Menn Ch (28381) (PNW) 120
3120 NE 125th St, Seattle WA 98125-4515
206-361-4630, fax 206-361-6076,
wdnisly@mennonite.net,
http://seattle.wa.us.mennonite.net
   Weldon D. Nisly, Pastor
   Adam Yoder, Youth Pastor

Shalom Ch (5723) (PNW) 17
PO Box 5519, Spokane WA 99205
509-747-1887, janyo@juno.com
35 W Main St
   Gary Lee Jewell, Pastor

Spring Valley Menn Ch (5730) (PNW) 69
4912 Spring Valley Rd, Newport WA 99156
509-447-3588, fax 509-447-3753,
svmennonite@juno.com
   Frank Woelk, Pastor

Warden Menn Ch (5810) (PNW) 58
720 S Pine, PO Box 766, Warden WA 98857
509-349-2444, dmmorrow@mennonite.net,
http://warden.wa.us.mennonite.net
   David Marvin Morrow, Pastor

Western Menn Ch (17632) (PNW) 76
9045 Wallace Rd NW, Salem OR 97304
503-363-2595, fax 503-370-9455, dstutz@wmchurch.org,
http://www.wmchurch.org
   David J. Stutzman, Pastor

Zion Menn Ch (17640) (PNW) 203
6124 S Whiskey Hill Rd, Hubbard OR 97032
503-651-2274, zionmc@teleport.com
   Craig Daniel Morton, Interim Pastor

CONFERENCES AND CONGREGATIONS

2

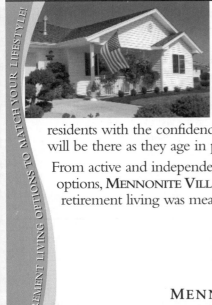

Pacific Southwest Mennonite Conference

OFFICE

admin@pacificsouthwest.org,
www.pacificsouthwest.org
626-720-8100, fax 626-720-8101
Box CAL, 1539 East Howard St, Pasadena CA 91104

STAFF

Brian Bauman, conference minister—Northern California (brian@pacificsouthwest.org)
Gloria Newton, administrator (admin@pacificsouthwest.org)
Vivian Schwartz, bookkeeper (veschwartz@msn.com)
Al Whaley, conference minister—Arizona (al@pacificsouthwest.org)
Jeff Wright, conference minister—Southern California (wrightstuff@pacificsouthwest.org)

GENERAL INFORMATION

Year founded: 1994
Delegate sessions: first weekend in Feb. and third weekend in June
Regions: Arizona, Northern California, Southern California
Members: 3,296
Congregations: 42
Ministers: 95
CLC Representatives: Leah Ann Alcazar, Stan Shantz, Jeff Wright

PUBLICATION

Panorama: (3-4 times/year, available on (www.pacificsouthwest.org), Doreen Martens, editor (panorama@pacificsouthwest.org)

EXECUTIVE COMMITTEE

Officers (executive@pacificsouthwest.org)
Ruth Suter, moderator (ruth@pacificsouthwest.org), PO Box 88, Brisbane CA 94005, 415-468-9676; Stan Shantz, assistant moderator; Ty Buxman, secretary; Myrna Schwartz, treasurer
Board Members—Class of 2002: Doris Greer, Nehemiah James, Art Montoya, Ken Seitz
Board Members—Class of 2003: Joyce Ingold, Jeremy Oswald, Harjono Margono

COMMISSIONS

Gift Discernment. Steve Penner, chair (sngpenner@telis.org)
Mission Team. Jeff Wright, chair (wrightstuff@pacificsouthwest.org)
Pastoral Leadership. Ken Seitz, chair (kenseitz@hotmail.com)
Retreat Ministries. Jeremy Oswald, (joswald@avantehealth.com)

OTHER CONFERENCE AGENCY AND REPS

Center for Anabaptist Leadership (CAL). See separate listing in section 3.
Mennonite Men. Arlen Godshall, president (arlengodshall@aol.com)
Mennonite Women. Nita Kimel, president (netachiro@hotmail.com)

Congregations

Abundant Life Miracle Christian Center (11318) (PSW, AAMA, CAL) 70
2926 W Florence Ave, Los Angeles CA 90043
323-778-4063, clevychic@yahoo.com
Clement Nwani, Co-Pastor
Evelyn Nwani, Co-Pastor

All Souls Christian Center (11583) (PSW, CAL, AAMA) 175
5125 S Crenshaw Blvd, Los Angeles CA 90043
323-291-2235
Charles Opong, Pastor

Bethel Community Ch (5075) (PSW, CAL) 102
9845 Orr and Day Rd, Santa Fe Springs CA 90670
562-860-3464
John Melendrez, Pastor

Calvary Christian Fell (18242) (PSW, CAL, AAMA) 150
2400 W 85th St, Inglewood CA 90043
323-752-8552, aisaacs837@aol.com
  Alvin Isaacs, Pastor
  Richard Reese, Associate Pastor

Casa de Oracion Menonita (24604) (PSW, CAL, IMH) 15
San Diego, CA
  Eusebio Acosta, Pastor

Cupertino Menn Ch (5697) (PSW) 15
10084 Adriana Ave, Cupertino CA 95014
408-253-3638, fax 408-255-2392
  Adam Chu-Tsun Liu, Pastor

Emmanuel Menn Ch (18325) (PSW) 36
PO Box 1679, Surprise AZ 85378-1679
623-583-9902
16002 N Verde St
  D. C. Seville, Pastor

Faith and Love Christian Center (11584) (PSW, AAMA, CAL) 20
5400 S 11th Ave, Los Angeles CA 90043
323-292-8503, fax 323-294-6600, FaithnLoveCC@aol.com
  Doris J. Greer, Senior Pastor
  Tonya Jackson, Youth Pastor

Faith Menn Ch (18259) (PSW, CAL) 20
11821 Old River School Rd, Downey CA 90241
fax 562-927-1219, jbixler@co.la.ca.us

Family Menn Ch (11109) (PSW, CAL, AAMA) . .152
PO Box 621087, Los Angeles CA 90062
323-750-1744, fax 213-758-2844,
familymennonite@aol.com
6520 S Normandie Ave
  Claude Flowers, Pastor

First Menn Ch (5409) (PSW) 116
2343 Park St, Paso Robles CA 93446
805-238-0437, fax 805-238-2445, 1stmc@iolwest.com,
http://members.xoom/1stmennonite.com

First Menn Ch (5321) (PSW) 279
1208 L St, PO Box 111, Reedley CA 93654
559-638-2917, fax 559-637-8826,
menno1st@mobynet.com
  Kenneth L. Seitz Jr, Pastor
  Juan V. Montes, Associate Pastor
  Stephen J. Penner, Associate Pastor

First Menn Ch (5330) (PSW, CAL) 61
PO Box 338, Upland CA 91785-0338
909-982-1669, fax 909-982-1669,
kathleenkrecklow@aol.com,
http://www.forministry.com/91786fmc
379 N Campus Ave
  Nemi Chigoji James, Associate Pastor
  Mark Konkel-White, Minister of Worship and Music
  Jeff Wright, Preaching Minister

First Menn Ch of Phoenix (5312) (PSW) 36
1612 W Northern Ave, Phoenix AZ 85021
602-944-0875, fax 602-944-1732, menn1ofphx@aol.com
  Alan Howard Whaley, Pastor

First Menn Ch of San Francisco (23226) (PSW) 61
PO Box 410656, San Francisco CA 94141
415-695-2812, FMCSF@aol.com, http://www.menno.org
601 Dolores St
  Sheri Hostetler, Pastor

Gereja Kristen Injili Indonesia Zion (10311) (PSW, CAL) 74
14732 Dunnet Ave, La Mirada CA 90638
714-521-5742, fax 714-968-9432, janasria@aol.com
2000 W Valencia, Fullerton
  Frederik Jan Kouttjie, Pastor

Great Commission Deliverance Ch (11172) (PSW, CAL, AAMA) 30
812 E La Brea Dr #11, Inglewood CA 90301
310-671-5672, aebere@earthlink.net
  George Ahanonu, Pastor

Hmong Community Ch (10247) (PSW, HMONG) .46
5015 E Olive Ave, Fresno CA 93727
559-486-0227
  Cong Ya Her, Lay Minister

Hollywood Christian Center (11586) (PSW, CAL) .0
PO Box 2542, Los Angeles CA 90028
310-674-4559
3818 W Imperial Hwy, Inglewood CA
  Shermanita Camp, Pastor

House of the Lord Fell (24885) (PSW, CAL) 50
328 S Azusa Ave, La Puente CA 91744
626-912-1983, fax 626-913-2128, holfmc1@juno.com
17403 E Villa Park St
  Justo Moreno, Senior Pastor
  Irene Mendoza, Associate Pastor
  Fernando Kuan, Youth Pastor

Iglesia Evangelica Bethel (25429) (PSW, CAL, IMH) 154
PO Box 1201, Sun Valley CA 91353
818-508-6467, fax 818-508-9217
6226 Colfax, North Hollywood
  Eliseo Franco, Pastor
  Daniel Gonzalez, Associate Pastor

Iglesia Monte Sinai (24232) (PSW, CAL, IMH) . .30
3119 Liberty Blvd, South Gate CA 90280
323-569-2029
2019 S Ellendale Los Angeles
  Salvador Arana, Pastor

Jemaat Kristen Indonesia Anugrah (10289) (PSW, CAL) 100
1632 Locust St, Pasadena CA 91106
626-564-9869, fax 626-564-9869,
vhandojo@calbaptist.edu
187-197 W Sierra Madre Blvd
  Virgo Handojo, Pastor

CONFERENCES AND CONGREGATIONS

2

Jemaat Kristen Indonesia Hosana (10282) (PSW, CAL) **64**
12027 E End Ave, Chino CA 91710
909-902-9278, fax 909-613-5803,
sutantoadi@worldnet.att.net
1120 W 13th St, Upland
Rudy Gunawan, Associate Pastor

Jemaat Kristen Indonesia Imanuel (10309) (PSW, CAL) **60**
11821 Old River School Rd, Downey CA 90241
626-333-2033, fax 562-928-8033, stevejachin@juno.com
Stephen M. Jachin, Pastor

Jemaat Kristen Indonesia Maranatha (10259) (PSW, CAL) **80**
18419 Sherman Way, Reseda CA 91335
818-757-3580, fax 818-342-6777, haryono@juno.com,
http://www.jkimaranatha.faithweb.com
Petrus Haryono, Pastor

Koinonia Menn Ch (23044) (PSW) **82**
2505 N Dobson Rd, Chandler AZ 85224
602-963-2416, azmennos@juno.com
Rich Sisco, Pastor

Labor for Christ Ministry (11269) (PSW, CAL, AAMA) **65**
1243 W 46 St, Los Angeles CA 90037
323-292-8139
Albert Asante, Pastor

Los Angeles Faith Chapel (11088) (PSW, IMH, CAL, AAMA) **155**
3818 W Imperial Hwy, Inglewood CA 90303
310-677-0270, fax 310-677-3586, faithchap@aol.com
Chuwang Rwang Pam, Pastor
Cornelius Johnson, Associate Pastor

Menn Community Ch (28373) (PSW) **105**
5015 E Olive Ave, Fresno CA 93727
559-251-5703, fax 559-251-5778,
mennocom@worldnet.att.net,
http://www.geocities.com/mennocom
Jane Dick, Co-Pastor
Mervin Dick, Co-Pastor

Miracle of Faith Menn Ch (24612) (PSW, CAL, AAMA) **60**
7860 S Western Ave, Los Angeles CA 90047
323-466-4117, fax 323-758-2844, ddbdor@aol.com
Egbert Pascacio, Pastor

Mountain View Menn Ch (18309) (PSW, CAL) . .**51**
1120 W 13th St, Upland CA 91786
909-982-6238, fax 909-982-0073, rricher@juno.com
Roger Richer, Pastor

Pasadena Menn Ch (28142) (PSW, CAL) **80**
1041 N Altadena Dr, Pasadena CA 91107
626-398-8224, fax 626-398-7626, pasamenno@aol.com,
http://physics.usc.edu/~tbuxman/pmc
James E. Brenneman, Pastor
Elbert Walker Newton, Associate Pastor
Kristin Klompeen Zabriskie, Associate Pastor

Peace House Fell (10027) (PSW, CAL, BIC) **30**
225 W Monterrey Dr, Claremont CA 91711
909-338-8666, fax 626-815-3809, daugsburger@msn.com,
http://www.forministry.com/91711pfhco
Members' homes

Prince of Peace Anabaptist Fell (18267) (PSW, CAL, AAMA) **10**
1654 Hi Point St, Los Angeles CA 90035
323-939-6478, wilshay@aol.com
William J. Irvin, Pastor

Royal Dominion Family Chapel (11319) (PSW, CAL, AAMA) **50**
PO Box 431434, Los Angeles CA 90043
323-759-6608, fax 323-759-6858,
royaldominion@excite.com,
http://www.royaldominion.org
6505 S Normandie Ave
Windell Moody, Pastor
Olwfemi A. Fatunmbi, Founding Pastor
Olatunde Olanrewaju, Evangelist

San Diego Menn Ch (10001) (PSW, CAL) **22**
4361 35th St, San Diego CA 92104
619-281-3240, ann.moyer@sharp.com
3219 Adams Ave
Ann Bender Moyer, Pastor

San Francisco Chinese Menn Ch (5692) (PSW) . .**36**
4021 California St, San Francisco CA 94118
415-221-7115, fax 415-221-7115, sf_cmc@yahoo.com

Shalom Menn Fell (22418) (PSW) **61**
6044 E 30th St, Tucson AZ 85711
520-748-7082, shalommennonite@mac.com,
http://homepage.mac.com/shalommennonite/1
Leanne Yoder, Co-Pastor
Gary Daught, Minister of Teaching and Preaching

Sunnyslope Menn Ch (18317) (PSW) **99**
9835 N 7th St, Phoenix AZ 85020
602-997-7171, fax 602-331-0652,
sunnyslopemc@juno.com
Steven Joe Good, Pastor

Trinity Chinese Menn Ch (5183) (PSW, CAL) . . .**42**
60 Grant, Irvine CA 92620
949-653-2785, fax 949-653-2785, jtancpa@aol.com
7000 Beach Blvd, Buena Park
Nelson Kuang-Daw Kao, Pastor

Trinity Menn Ch (18333) (PSW) **352**
4334 W Vista Ave, Glendale AZ 85301
623-931-9241, fax 623-931-2932, trinitymc@juno.com,
http://www.geocities.com/trinitymennonite
Stan Shantz, Pastor
Stephen Intagliata, Associate Pastor
Kathy Keener Shantz, Associate Pastor

Rocky Mountain Mennonite Conference

OFFICE
rmmc@rmmc.org, www.rmmc.org
303-795-0090, fax 303-795-0090
6610 S Williams Circle W, Centennial CO 80121

STAFF
Ed and Kathrine Rempel, conference ministers
(edfrem@aol.com)
Rae Shellenberger, secretary and *ECHO* editor
(rsshell1@juno.com)

GENERAL INFORMATION
Year founded: 1962
Members: 1,465
Congregations: 20
Ministers: 36
CLC reps: Lauren Martin and Kathrine Rempel
Annual Conference: May 2-4, 2003

EXECUTIVE COMMITTEE
Leon Stutzman, moderator
(stutzman@juno.com), 6394 W Burgundy Dr,
Littleton CO 80123, 303-797-3551; Lauren
Martin, past moderator; Rae Shellenberger, secretary; Jim Zook, treasurer

PUBLICATION
ECHO (Bimonthly), Rae Shellenberger, editor
(rsshell1@juno.com), 5462 Bestwood Dr,
Larkspur CO 80118

COMMISSIONS
Leadership. Merv Birky, chair
(mervbirky@bethelmennonite.org), 1219
Yuma, Colorado Springs CO 80909, 719-636-2716
Finance. Carroll Miller, chair
(cmiller107@juno.com), 5601 18th St #28,
Greeley CO 80634, 970-330-1119
Mission. Roy Walls, chair
(pastor@peacemennonite.com),
13601 E Alameda Ave, Aurora CO 80012,
303-340-1555
Youth. Ron and Char Roth, co-chairs
(rcroth@juno.com), 402 11th St, Greeley
CO 80631, 970-353-7224
Nurture Commission.
Peace and Justice Commission.

OTHER CONFERENCE AGENCY AND REPS
Mennonite Women. Kim Martin, president
(lkmsplace@juno.com), 2401 Blake Ave,
Glenwood Springs CO 81601, 970-945-8851

Congregations

Albuquerque Menn Ch (11311) (RM) 34
2210 Silver SE, Albuquerque NM 87106
505-254-1824, amc@flash.net, http://www.rmmc.org/amc
Anita F. Amstutz, Pastor

Beth-El Menn Ch (20792) (RM) 176
1219 Yuma St, Colorado Springs CO 80909
719-636-2716, fax 719-636-0005,
bethel@bethelmennonite.org,
http://www.bethelmennonite.org
Mervin R. Birky, Pastor

Carlsbad Menn Ch (20818) (RM) 43
1204 W Mckay St, Carlsbad NM 88220
505-887-5104, cmchurch@cavemen.net
Amzie Yoder, Pastor

East Holbrook Menn Ch (20834) (RM) 66
PO Box 68, Cheraw CO 81030
719-853-6377, mlwelty@rural-com.com
32723 Rd 33
Merritt Welty, Pastor

Emmanuel Menn Ch (20842) (RM) 84
502 Harriett Ave, La Junta CO 81050
719-384-9673, pastor@emclj.org, http://www.emclj.org
Steven Gary Schmidt, Pastor

First Menn Ch of Colorado Springs (20867) (RM) 47
11 N 22nd St, Colorado Springs CO 80904-3431
719-635-5593, fax 719-635-5593
Donald L. Thomassen, Pastor

First Menn Ch of Denver (20859) (RM, MUM) .270
430 W 9th Ave, Denver CO 80204
303-892-1038, fax 303-892-6106, fmcdenver@aol.com,
http://www.fmcdenver.org
  Vernon K. Rempel, Pastor

Fort Collins Menn Fell (24687) (RM, WDC) 42
300 E Oak St, Fort Collins CO 80524
970-416-1687, revjborg@juno.com,
http://www.fortnet.org/fcmf
  Jeffrey A. Borg, Pastor

**Glennon Heights Menn Ch (20883) (RM,
MUM)** 99
11480 W Virginia Ave, Lakewood CO 80226
303-985-3606, fax 303-985-3930, ghmenno@att.net,
http://glennonheights.co.us.mennonite.net
  Dean A. Linsenmeyer, Pastor

Glenwood Menn Ch (20891) (RM) 30
2306 Blake Ave, Glenwood Springs CO 81601
970-945-5245, fax 970-945-5245,
glenwoodmenno@juno.com
  Lauren R. Martin, Pastor

Greeley Menn Ch (20917) (RM) 108
402 11th Street, Greeley CO 80631
970-353-7224, rcroth@juno.com
  Charlene Roth, Pastor
  Ron Roth, Pastor

**Hmong Menn Ch (11119) (RM, WDC, HMONG,
MUM)** 45
c/o Shoua Moua, 9980 W 59th Pl #1, Arvada CO 80004-
5015
303-463-0257
  Shoua Moua, Pastor

Light of Life Menn Ch (10656) (RM, UNMC) 40
PO Box 6763, Farmington NM 87499
505-327-7056
  George Wero, Pastor

Menn Ch of La Jara (20925) (RM, OD) 7
PO Box 306, La Jara CO 81140
719-843-5118, alicep@amigo.net
5th & Walnut

**Mountain Community Menn Ch (25247) (RM,
WDC)** 97
PO Box 502, Palmer Lake CO 80133
719-481-3155, mcmc1@juno.com,
http://www.rmmc.org/mcmc
643 Hwy 105
  Don Rheinheimer, Co-Pastor
  Jan Lynette Rheinheimer, Co-Pastor

**Peace Menn Community Ch (28605) (RM, WDC,
MUM)** 41
13601 E Alameda Ave, Aurora CO 80012
303-340-1555, fax 303-340-1141,
pastor@peacemennonite.com
  Wilbur Roy Walls Jr, Pastor

Perryton Menn Ch (20958) (RM) 47
2821 S Ash St, Perryton TX 79070
806-435-3817, ptnmenno@hotmail.com

Pueblo Menn Ch (21774) (RM) 40
634 Goodnight Ave, Pueblo CO 81005
719-738-3611
  David Foncannon, Pastor

Rocky Ford Menn Ch (20966) (RM) 76
PO Box 66, Rocky Ford CO 81067
719-254-3283
20480 County Rd EE 25
  Don Penner, Pastor

Walsenburg Menn Ch (20982) (RM) 9
PO Box 88, Walsenburg CO 81089
719-738-1496
6th & Leon

South Central Mennonite Conference

OFFICE
scc@mennoscc.org
316-283-7080, fax 316-283-0620
2517 N Main, PO Box 448, North Newton KS 67117

STAFF
Robert Nolt, conference minister
(rnolt@mennoscc.org)
Ritch Hochstetler, youth minister
(ritch@mennowdc.org)
Phyllis Regier, treasurer
(pregier@mennowdc.org)

GENERAL INFORMATION
Year founded: 1876
Members: 4,283
Congregations: 49
Ministers: 57
CLC reps: Felipe Hinojosa, Robert Nolt, Margie Wiens
Districts: Arkansas-Missouri, Kansas-Oklahoma, Mid-Texas, South Texas (UCIM)
Annual Conference: August 1-2, 2003, joint with Western District Conference
Conference historian: Bernice Hostetler

EXECUTIVE COMMITTEE
Heber Ramer, moderator
(hramer@wiredks.com), 502 W 15th St, Harper KS 67058, 316-896-2792; John C. Murray, moderator-elect; Duane Beachey, Anna Ruth Beck, Grace Brunner, Leona Diener, Israel Hernandez, Spike Hostetler, Kathy Goering Reid, Ken Steckly, Bob Simonsick, Loren Swartzendruber, Victor Vargas

PUBLICATION
Messenger (Bimonthly), Lois Loflin, editor
(loflin@mennowdc.org), Box 448, North Newton KS 67117

COMMISSIONS
Finance and Stewardship. Ken King, chair
(kjdking@mindspring.com), 6003 E Eales Rd, Hutchinson KS 67501 620-663-1470; Dan Miller, Gloria Hostetler, Dave Weaver
Missions. Margie Wiens, chair
(weinsm@southwind.net), 417 N Streeter, Hesston KS 67062, 316-327-4473; Mervin Hershberger, Sam Nance
Peace and Service. Marion Bontrager, chair
(marionb@hesston.edu), Box 3000, Hesston KS 67062, 316-327-8291; Richard Davis, Leona Diener
Youth Ministry. Torrey Ball, chair
(tball@ourtown.usa), 808 S Poplar, South Hutchinson KS 67505, 316-663-4244; Pam Gerber
Program Planning. Heber Ramer, chair
(hramer@wiredks.com), 502 W 15th, Harper KS 67058, 620-896-2792; Joan Boyer, John Murray, Rigoberto Negron

OTHER CONFERENCE AGENCY AND REPS
Mennonite Women. Anna Ruth Beck, president (howann@southwind.net), 205 S Weaver, Hesston KS 67062, 620-327-4530; Marilyn Hartman, Mary Alice Hertzler, Mary Shue
Integration Transition. Alice Price, facilitator (alicep@amigo.net), 609 Walnut Ave, Box 306, La Jara CO 81140, 719-843-5118; Gloria Hostetler, Dennis LeFevre, Robert Nolt, John Otto

CONFERENCES AND CONGREGATIONS

2

Congregations

Argentine Menn Ch (17798) (SC) 21
3701 Metropolitan Ave, Kansas City KS 66106-2796
913-831-3621; argentinemenn@aol.com
Mervin Hershberger, Pastor

Austin Menn Ch (28761) (SC, WDC) 64
5801 Westminster Dr, Austin TX 78723-2640
512-926-3121, fax 512-926-3121, kathy@thn.org,
http://www.mennochurch.org
Kathryn Goering Reid, Pastor
Steven Breck Reid, Associate Pastor

Berea Menn Community Ch (17806) (SC) 21
Rt 1, Box 30A, Birch Tree MO 65438-9606
573-292-3553, brewer@coocket.net
Hwy Rd FF
Douglas W. Brewer, Pastor

Calico Rock Menn Fell (17855) (SC) 37
HC 79 Box 181, Calico Rock AR 72519
870-297-8091, crmf+@centurytel.net
Fellowship Rd
Robert Simonsick, Pastor

Calvary Menn Ch (17863) (SC, IMH) 120
PO Box 207, Mathis TX 78368
361-547-3727
719 W San Patricio Ave
Armando J. Calderon, Pastor

Casa de Oracion (26971) (SC, IMH) 42
PO Box 3114, Alamo TX 78516
956-787-8346
Elizabeth Hernandez, Pastor

**Centro Cristiano Menonita Jerusalem (27601)
(SC)** 0
Calle 13 lote 19 entre calle 15 y, Dante Delgado Col
Venustiano Carranza, Cd Boca del Rio, Veracruz
abelardold@hotmail.com
Abelardo Diaz, Pastor

**Comunidad de Esperanza (6240) (SC, WDC,
IMH)** 25
1721 N Garrett Ave, Dallas TX 75206
214-428-7131, damain_rodriguez@msn.com
Damian Rodriguez, Pastor

Crystal Springs Menn Ch (17889) (SC) 20
c/o Joe Zimmerman, 424 NW 90 Rd, Harper KS 67058
620-896-2962

Evening Shade Menn Ch (17913) (SC) 32
RR 2 Box 243, Warsaw MO 65355
816-438-6084
Elwin D. Yoder, Pastor

Faith Menn Ch (27425) (SC, WDC) 32
404 LaVista, Dodge City KS 67054
620-846-2663, faithmenno@juno.com
Doug Harris, Pastor

Faith Menn Ch (24356) (SC) 50
1403 S Main St, South Hutchinson KS 67505
316-662-2502, faithmennonite@juno.com,
http://faithmennonitechurch.ks.us.mennonite.net
Jim M. Unruh, Pastor

Greensburg Menn Ch (17939) (SC) 85
310 W Pennsylvania Ave, Greensburg KS 67054
620-723-2620, gburgmennchurch@juno.com
Jeffrey D. Blackburn, Pastor

Hesston Inter-Menn Fell (17970) (SC, WDC) . . .245
505 S Ridge Rd, PO Box 786, Hesston KS 67062
620-327-2101, fax 620-327-4918,
scott.miller@prairieinet.net, http://www.himf.org
Scott David Miller, Pastor
Arlon Fishburn, Minister of Helps
J. D. Hershberger, Minister of Worship

Hesston Menn Ch (17962) (SC) 614
PO Box 3000, Hesston KS 67062
620-327-4885, fax 620-327-8300,
hesstonmc@prairieinet.net,
http://hesston.ks.us.mennonite.net
309 S Main
John C. Murray, Pastor
Cheryl Hershberger, Associate Pastor

Hope Fell (10012) (SC, WDC) 20
1700 Morrow Ave, Waco TX 76707
254-754-5942, hopecmty@flash.net
1721 Sanger Ave
Joe Gatlin, Co-Pastor
Nancy Gatlin, Co-Pastor
Norma Torres, Associate Pastor

Houston Menn Ch (23184) (SC, WDC) 45
1231 Wirt Rd, Houston TX 77055
713-464-4865, pastor@houstonmennonite.org,
http://www.houstonmennonite.org

**Iglesia Cristiana Menonita de Dallas (11273) (SC,
WDC, IMH)** 12
427 N Marlborough Ave, Dallas TX 75208
214-946-2910
Serapio Antonio Caceros, Pastor

Iglesia Ebenezer (27600) (SC) 0
Rayon Y Zaragosa, Calle Benito Quijano #500, Col Nuevo
Amanecer, Cd Reynosa, Tamaulipas
martinezvelazquez@yahoo.com.mx
Alfonso Martinez, Pastor

Iglesia Evangelica Galilea (27604) (SC) 0
calle 16 de septiembre #56, esquina Zona Centro CP
88500, Reynosa, Tamaulipas
Julio Cesar Flores Lopez, Pastor

**Iglesia Evangelica Menonita Gethsemani (27602)
(SC)** 0
calle Lomas de Bolado #86, Col Loma Alta, H Matamoros
Tamaulipas
011-868-835-7708
Odilon Zaleta Sanchez, Pastor

Iglesia Menonita Buenas Nuevas (28001) (SC, IMH) 32
c/o 2408 Fern Ave, San Juan TX 78589
956-782-8057, fax 956-782-8057,
conrado_hinojosa@hotmail.com
    Raul Longoria & El Dora
    Conrado Hinojosa, Pastor

Iglesia Menonita del Cordero (17830) (SC, IMH) 89
1033 N Minnesota Ave, Brownsville TX 78521
956-831-4404, fax 956-831-4404, rigonegron@juno.com
    Rigoberto Negron, Pastor

Iglesia Menonita Luz del Evangelio (6512) (SC, WDC, IMH) 30
1524 Dowdy Ferry Rd, Dallas TX 75217-9227
214-324-9409
    Juan Fernando Limones, Pastor

Iglesia Menonita Rey de Gloria (27111) (SC, IMH) 40
823 N Minnesota Ave, Brownsville TX 78521
956-831-7193, fax 956-831-7193, lupeaguilar@juno.com
6711 Tallowood Circle
    Guadalupe Aguilar, Pastor

Iglesia Menonita Rios de Agua Viva (10681) (SC) 0
calle Div del Norte #156, Col Guillermo Guajardo, H
Matamoros, Tamaulipas
011-52-88-14-07-51
    Racquel Lozano Palomino, Pastor

Manhattan Menn Ch (24174) (SC, WDC, USMBC) 75
1000 Fremont St, Manhattan KS 66502-5425
785-539-4079, menno@oz-online.net,
http://www.manhattan.ks.us.mennonite.net
    Barbara Krehbiel Gehring, Co-Pastor
    Richard L. Gehring, Co-Pastor

Menn Ch of the Servant (23317) (SC, WDC) 30
1650 Fairview Ave, Wichita KS 67203
316-267-4625, carolarose@juno.com
    Carol Ann Rose, Pastor

Mount Pisgah Menn Ch (18002) (SC) 58
892 Hwy B, PO Box 108, Leonard MO 63451-0108
660-762-4400, mtpisgah4@juno.com
    Darrell E. Zook, Pastor

New Life Christian Center (29546) (SC, IMH) . . .86
925 Zillock Rd, San Benito TX 78586
956-399-3794
    Eduardo Hinojosa, Pastor

Nueva Jerusalem (27605) (SC) 0
Calle 11 entre Rayon y Zaragoza, #606, Matamoros,
Tamaulipas CP 87300
011-868-813-9297
    Hector Salinas, Pastor

Pea Ridge Menn Ch (18044) (SC) 47
3284 CR 230, Palmyra MO 63461
573-439-5827, darzook@juno.com
    Darrell E. Zook, Pastor

Peace Menn Ch (17921) (SC, WDC) 82
11001 Midway Rd, PO Box 59926, Dallas TX 75229
214-902-8141, fax 214-902-8141, pmc@airmail.net,
http://www.web2.airmail.net/pmc
    Richard Douglas Davis, Pastor
    Tammerie Brotzman Spires, Associate Pastor

Peace Menn Ch (23853) (SC, WDC) 72
1204 Oread Ave, Lawrence KS 66044
785-841-8614, peacemennonite@msn.com
    Vicki Lynn Penner, Pastor

Pleasant Valley Menn Ch (18051) (SC) 270
1020 E 14th St, Harper KS 67058
620-896-2004, rvogt@cyberlodge.com
    Royce W. Vogt, Pastor

Pleasant View Menn Ch (18069) (SC) 210
RR 1 Box 152B, Hydro OK 73048
405-663-2703, josephwood@juno.com
    Joseph A. Wood, Pastor

Prince of Peace Menn Ch (18077) (SC, IMH) . . .54
1802 Horne Rd, Corpus Christi TX 78415
361-853-8554
    Felipe Almodovar, Pastor

Protection Menn Ch (18085) (SC) 122
PO Box 185, Protection KS 67127
316-622-4342

Rogers Menn/Ch of the Brethren (29745) (SC, COB) 21
PO Box 548, Pea Ridge AR 72757
417-341-1005, fax 417-435-2031, gengle@leru.net
1618 Hwy 12 E, Rogers
    Larry E. Graber, Minister
    George W. Engle, Elder
    Eli Miller, Elder

San Antonio Menn Ch (25239) (SC, WDC) 39
1443 S Saint Marys St, San Antonio TX 78210
210-533-0642, fax 210-341-8358,
gloria.beachey@prodigy.net,
http://www.sanantonio.tx.us.mennonite.net
    Duane Beachey, Lead Pastor
    Gloria Beachey, Pastor

Shalom Menn Ch (10130) (SC, WDC) 164
800 E 1st St, Newton KS 67114
316-283-7395, shalom@southwind.net,
http://home.southwind.net/~shalom
    Eric Massanari, Pastor

South Hutchinson Menn Ch (18101) (SC) 448
808 S Poplar St, South Hutchinson KS 67505
620-663-4244, fax 620-663-4449,
shmcoffice@shmc-online.net, http://www.shmc-online.net
    Howard L. Wagler, Lead Pastor
    Jonathan A. Smith, Associate Pastor
    Torrey D. Ball, Youth Pastor

CONFERENCES AND CONGREGATIONS

2

Southern Hills Menn Ch (6740) (SC, WDC) 91
511 SE 37th St, Topeka KS 66605
785-266-9403, fax 785-266-4512,
southernhillsmc@networksplus.net
    Cynthia Neufeld Smith, Co-Pastor
    Roger Neufeld Smith, Co-Pastor

Spring Valley Menn Ch (18127) (SC) 32
1089 29th Ave, Canton KS 67428
620-628-4818, fax 620-628-4964
2896 Frontier Rd
    Loyal Martin, Interim Pastor

Sycamore Grove Menn Ch (18135) (SC) 170
PO Box 320, Garden City MO 64747
816-862-6477, kendars@casstel.net
27221 S Sycamore Rd
    Kenneth Steckly, Pastor
    Mike Bates, Assistant Pastor

Tabernaculo de Fe (28316) (SC, IMH) 27
PO Box 1034, Mathis TX 78368
361-547-0299

United Menn Ch (18168) (SC, USMBC) 8
PO Box 1278, Premont TX 78375
361-348-2872
SW 6th at Bernice
    Lewis E. McDorman, Pastor
    Forest Whitcher, Assistant Pastor

Whitestone Menn Ch (18184) (SC, WDC) 328
629 Crescent Dr, Hesston KS 67062
620-327-4123, wmc@southwind.net,
http://whitestone.ks.us.mennonite.net
    Leonard C. Wiebe, Interim Pastor

Yoder Menn Ch (18192) (SC) 173
3605 E Longview Rd, Haven KS 67543
620-663-2657, yoderchurch@ourtownusa.net
    Dennis Stutzman, Pastor

Southeast Mennonite Conference

OFFICE

smc5245@juno.com
941-342-9959, fax 941-342-0318
1004 Ponder Ave, Sarasota FL 34232-6633

STAFF

Amie Kain, administrative assistant
(smc5245@juno.com)
Ken Nauman, conference minister
(kenmirna@sunline.net)
Nan Kanagy, youth minister
(nanbvmenno@comcast.net)

GENERAL INFORMATION

Year founded: 1967
Members: 2,451
Congregations: 29
Ministers: 65
CLC reps: Marlin Birkey, Ken Nauman
Districts: Georgia-South Carolina, North Central
Florida, Tampa Bay, Southwest Florida,
Sarasota, South Florida
Annual conference: October 3-5, 2003

CONFERENCE COUNCIL

Marlin Birkey, moderator and Sarasota district
minister (mbirkey1@comcast.net), 2895
Ashton Road, Sarasota FL 34231-6289, 941-
924-3993; Lesly Bertrand, Haitian advocate;
Ambrosio Encarnacion, Hispanic advocate; Dale
Ivy, assistant moderator; Nan Kanagy, youth
advocate; Jonathan Larson, GA/SC district minister; Madeline Maldonado, secretary of faith and
life; Ken Nauman, conference minister and
Southwest FL district minister; Byron Pellecer,
South FL district minister; Tom Renno, congregational outreach secretary; Becky Sommers,
Mennonite Women president; Roy Williams,
Tampa Bay district minister and stewardship
and business secretary

PUBLICATION

Proclamation (Bimonthly), Amie Kain, interim
editor (smc5245@juno.com), 1004 Ponder
Ave, Sarasota FL 34232-6633, 941-342-9959

COMMISSIONS

Congregational Leadership. Ken Nauman,
chair (kenmirna@sunline.net), 922 W
Hickory St, Arcadia FL 34266-3361, 863-
993-9353; Marlin Birkey, Dale Ivy, Jonathan
Larson, Byron Pellecer, Roy Williams
Congregational Outreach Secretary. Tom
Renno (tjrenno@aol.com), 2156 E Leewynn
Dr, Sarasota FL 34240-8791, 941-412-9316
Faith and Life Secretary. Madeline
Maldonado (arkofsalvation7@aol.com),
3225 4th St W, Lehigh Acres FL 33971-1909,
941-368-3551
Financial Planning. Marlin Birkey, chair
(mbirkey1@comcast.net), 2895 Ashton Rd,
Sarasota FL 34231-6289, 941-924-3993;
Ken Nauman, Roy Williams; staff: Amie Kain
Nominating. Lewis Overholt, Roy Williams, Lil
Worley, Loren Zehr
Personnel. Marlin Birkey, chair
(mbirkey1@comcast.net), 2895 Ashton
Road, Sarasota FL 34231-6289, 941-924-
3993; Ken Nauman, Roy Williams
Stewardship and Business Secretary. Roy
Williams (rrrsjw@aol.com), 3506 Machado
St N, Tampa FL 33605-1362, 813-247-2798

OTHER CONFERENCE AGENCY AND REPS

Charis Center Board. Naomi Schlabach, chair,
5885 Ibis St, Sarasota FL 34241-9282, 941-
923-1387; Janet Hamilton, Jan Henry-
Rinehart, Yvonne Keim, Barbara Kiracofe,
Rick Marsden, Danny Miller, Dale Stoll
Haitain Advocate. Lesly Bertrand
(leslyb2002@Yahoo.com), 11650 NW 10th
Ave, Miami FL 33168-6250
Hispanic Advocate. Ambrosio Encarnacion
(felino8@aol.com), 2591 Apache St,
Sarasota FL 34231-5009, 941-926-0843

CONFERENCES AND CONGREGATIONS

2

MCC East Coast Board Rep. Lloyd Miller (lp_miller-sara@juno.com), 3343 Tallywood Ct, Sarasota FL 34237-3224, 941-952-5062

Mennonite Disaster Service. Jesse Yoder, chair (jesseyoder@juno.com), 4464 Beacon Dr, Sarasota FL 34232, 941-371-5245; Omer Herschberger, C. Nelson Hostetter, Scott Kauffman, C. J. Mayer, Ervin Miller, Jim Miller, Esther Mills, Andrew Nisley, Merle Sommers, Paul Yoder, Paul W. Yoder, Philip Yoder

Mennonite Women. Rebecca Sommers, chair (sommersmr7@juno.com), 3904 Bellwood Dr, Sarasota FL 34232-3308, 941-341-0153; Sally Eisner, Colleen Fisher, Sharon Lehman, Elizabeth Perez, Osa Russell

Sunnyside Properties Board. Allen Mast, chair (mastcpa@email.com), 1001 N Washington Blvd, Ste 107, Sarasota FL 34236, 941-953-5036; Glen Denlinger, Wade Harris, Hertha Isaac, H Greg Lee, Danny Miller, Sharon Peachy, Clarence Plank, Naomi Schlabach; staff: David Ray Miller

Urban Minister for South Florida. Chuck Goertz (hmstdmenno@juno.com), 30695 SW 162nd Ave., Homestead FL 33033-4122, 305-248-1659

Urban Minister for Tampa. Roy Williams (rrrsjw@aol.com), 3506 Machado St N, Tampa FL 33605-1362, 813-247-2798

Youth Council. Nan Kanagy, chair (nanbvmenno@comcast.net), 4041 Bahia Vista St, Sarasota FL 34232-2421, 941-377-4041; Michelle Kennell, Charity Miller, Seth Miller

Congregations

Americus Menn Fell (10067) (SE) 56
PO Box 1785, Americus GA 31709
229-928-0176
409 E Rd Hill St
 Lewis Overholt, Pastor

Ashton Menn Ch (13524) (SE) 95
2895 Ashton Rd, Sarasota FL 34231
941-924-3993, fax 941-924-3321,
ashton.church@verizon.net
 Marlin Keith Birkey, Pastor
 Dion Hunt, Minister of Youth

Assemblee de la Grace (11299) (SE) 30
PO Box 1010, Immokalee FL 33934
941-369-7158
 Laurent Louis, Pastor
 Marie Gilot, Associate Pastor

Bahia Vista Menn Ch (18903) (SE) 365
4041 Bahia Vista St, Sarasota FL 34232
941-377-4041, fax 941-378-9674,
BVMenno@comcast.net, http://www.bahiavista.org
 Glenn M. Steiner, Pastor
 Nanette M. Kanagy, Minister of Children and Youth
 Glen M. Denlinger, Minister of Adult Christian
  Education & Family Life
 Randall L. Spaulding, Minister of Music and Worship
 Harold F. Shearer, Minister of Visitation
 Irene Shearer, Minister of Visitation

Bay Shore Menn Ch (15693) (SE) 525
3809 Chapel Dr SE, Sarasota FL 34234
941-355-4168, fax 941-351-1969,
duane@theshepherd.com,
http://www.theshepherd.com/bayshore
 Duane Allen Yoder, Pastor
 Rocky Miller, Associate Pastor
 Albert E. Miller Jr, Associate Pastor
 David M. Barkema, Youth Pastor
 Lee E. Miller, Minister of Administration
 Hazel Shirk, Minister of Special Care

Berea Menn Ch (13565) (SE) 50
PO Box 17564, Atlanta GA 30316-0564
404-244-0289, BereaMennonite@juno.com,
http://www.bereamennonitechurch.com
1088 Bouldercrest Dr SE
 Jonathan Larson, Pastor
 Andy Johnston, Assistant Pastor
 Dorothy Harding, Minister of Urban Evangelism

Cape Christian Fell (28175) (SE) 275
PO Box 150777, Cape Coral FL 33915
239-772-5683, fax 239-458-4463,
CapeChristian@juno.com, http://www.cape-christian.org
2110 Chiquita Blvd S., Cape Coral, FL 33991
 Dennis D. Gingerich, Senior Pastor
 Jerry Sprague, Associate Pastor
 David Messenger, Worship Pastor
 Brett Furlong, Pastor of Youth Ministries
 Rick Brock, Pastor of Family Ministries
 Loren Zehr, Minister of Nurture
 Tony Hostetler, Pastor of Visitation

College Hill Menn Ch (13797) (SE, AAMA) 105
3506 Machado St Rd,, Tampa FL 33605
813-247-2798, fax 813-248-4339, rrrsjw@aol.com
   Roy W. Williams, Pastor
   Irene Moore, Minister of Visitation
   Carl A. Walcott, Minister of Visitation

Covenant Menn Fell (12196) (SE) 15
3205 Southgate Circle, Sarasota FL 34239
Goshen College Building

Ebenezer Christian Ch (25049) (SE, IMH) 75
PO Box 1954, Apopka FL 32704
407-886-0020, fax 407-886-9778
9 N Park Ave

Eglise du Nouveau Testament (28449) (SE) 20
281 NW 79th St, Miami FL 33150
305-687-3949
   Simon Daux, Pastor

Emmanuel Menn Ch (25080) (SE) 36
1320 W University Ave # A, Gainesville FL 32603
352-377-6577, gnvmenno@bellsouth.net
   Eve B. MacMaster, Pastor

Evangelical Garifuna Ch (12051) (SE) 18
4148 NW 45 Terrace, Lauderdale Lakes FL 33319
954-739-8449
   Mario Dominguez, Pastor

Good Shepherd Evangelical (10972) (SE) 21
PO Box 381282, Miami FL 33238
305-891-1651
   Martin Menard, Pastor

Homestead Menn Ch (14332) (SE) 64
30695 SW 162nd Ave, Homestead FL 33033
305-248-1659, fax 305-247-3758,
HmstdMenno@juno.com,
http://homestead.fl.us.mennonite.net
   Charles G. Goertz, Pastor
   José R. Hernández Jr, Associate Pastor

Iglesia Amor Viviente/Ft Lauderdale (11161) (SE, AV) 30
8040 NW 96 Terra Apt 106, Tamarac FL 33321
954-718-7401
   Gabriel F. Licona Callejas, Pastor

Iglesia Menonita Arca de Salvacion (27904) (SE, IMH) 100
PO Box 50058, Fort Myers FL 33994-0058
239-332-7556, fax 239-332-7556,
arkofsalvation7@aol.com
3645 Michigan Ave
   David Maldonado, Pastor
   Madeline Maldonado, Associate Pastor

Iglesia Menonita Encuentro de Renovacion (10284) (SE, IMH) 70
c/o Byron C. Pellecer, 741 NW 45th Ave #42, Miami-Dade
FL 33126-2490
305-529-9244, fax 305-648-3951, bpellece@bellsouth.net
Airport Regency Hotel
   Byron Pellecer, Pastor

Iglesia Seguidores de Cristo (25072) (SE, IMH) .45
PO Box 50292, Sarasota FL 34278
941-377-8198
1001 Ponder Ave
   Juan Jose Rivera, Pastor

Laurel Worship Center (10281) (SE) 50
312 E Laurel Rd, PO Box 235, Laurel FL 34272
941-484-1343, fax 941-484-7071, LaurelWC@juno.com,
http://www.LaurelWorship.org
1900 E Laurel Rd

Luz y Verdad (10212) (SE) 18
13411 Misti Loop, Lakeland FL 33809
863-853-3878
   Artemio De Jesus, Pastor

New Beginning Community Ch (19531) (SE, AAMA) 20
2701 13th St S, St Petersburg FL 33705
727-398-4211, fax 727-823-0346
   Celestin Hill Biandudi, Pastor

Newtown Gospel Chapel (18762) (SE, AAMA) . .30
1815 Gillespie Ave, Sarasota FL 34234
941-951-6967
   Walter Lewis Crawford, Pastor

North Tampa Christian Fell (14886) (SE) 25
206 W 131st Ave, Tampa FL 33612-3446
813-933-1288
   Isaias Robles, Pastor

Oak Terrace Menn Ch (12823) (SE) 19
16970 NW 22nd St, Blountstown FL 32424
850-674-5731, fax 850-674-2385, twodivys@gtcom.net
   Clifford Dale Ivy, Pastor

Peace Christian Fell (10241) (SE) 94
3010 Sumter Blvd, North Port FL 34287
941-423-8746, PCFofNP@juno.com
   Brian Siegrist, Pastor
   Robert Huffman Jr, Minister of Youth

Pine Creek Chapel (22376) (SE) 45
1267 SW Pine Chapel Dr, Arcadia FL 34266
863-993-3910, KenMirNa@sunline.net
Pine Chapel Dr & SR 72
   David L. Kniss, Interim Pastor

Tabernacle of Bethlehem (10253) (SE) 110
PO Box 380386, Miami-Dade FL 33238-0386
305-769-0280
900 W Dr
   Dieudonne Brutus, Pastor

Unity Pentecostal Ch of God (11153) (SE) 45
801 NW 111th St, Miami FL 33168
305-754-2900
   Ducois Forestal, Pastor

CONFERENCES AND CONGREGATIONS

2

Virginia Mennonite Conference

OFFICE

info@vmconf.org, www.vmconf.org
540-434-9727 and 800-707-5535,
fax 540-434-7627
901 Parkwood Dr, Harrisonburg VA 22802

STAFF

Owen E. Burkholder, conference minister
Kimberlee S. Greenawalt, youth minister
Evelyn W. Kratz, financial and office manager
Jill K. Landis, staff assistant
Lavonne Lehman, administrative assistant
Rachel Smith, communications associate
Kenneth J. Weaver, administrative associate

GENERAL INFORMATION

Year founded: 1835
Members: 8,631
Congregations: 65
Ministers: 237
CLC reps: Owen Burkholder, Joe Longacher,
  Jan Showalter
Districts bishops and overseers: Central,
  Glendon L. Blosser, Paul L. Kratz; Eastern
  Carolina, Raymond Martin; Harrisonburg,
  Truman Brunk; Norfolk, Raymond Martin;
  Northern, H. Michael Shenk, II; Samuel O.
  Weaver; Ohio, Frank Nice; Potomac, Evelyn
  Nice, Frank Nice; Southern, John Kiblinger,
  Richard Showalter; Tennessee-Carolina-
  Kentucky, Edward Godshall; Warwick, Leslie
  W. Francisco III; Raymond Martin
Annual conference: June 12-14, 2003,
  Harrisonburg VA

EXECUTIVE COMMITTEE

Joseph W. Longacher Jr, moderator
(corjlong@erols.com), 1502 Chauncey Ln,
Richmond VA 23233, 804-740-1544; Mark R.
Wenger, assistant moderator; Joseph E.
Bontrager, secretary; Ronald E. Piper, treasurer

PUBLICATION

Connections (Monthly), Gloria Lehman, editor;
Rachel Smith, assistant editor (same address as
above)

COMMISSIONS

Consititution and Bylaws. Gordon Zook,
  chair, 156 Robinhood Ln, Newport News VA
  23602, 757-866-4247
Faith and Life. Elroy J. Miller, chair
  (millere@emu.edu), 1401 College Ave,
  Harrisonburg VA 22802, 540-432-9382;
  H. Michael Shenk II, vice-chair; Paul Kratz,
  secretary
Finance. Ronald E. Piper, chair
  (piperr@emu.edu), 1535 Park Rd,
  Harrisonburg VA 22802, 540-434-5057
Gift Discernment. Samuel O. Weaver, chair
  (weaverso@emu.edu), 1550 College Ave,
  Harrisonburg VA 22802, 540-434-2985
Health and Mutual Care. Howard Miller,
  chair (howard@lindale.org), 4368 Zion
  Church Rd, Broadway VA 22815, 540-896-
  4014; Mary Reitz, secretary
Historical. James Rush, chair, 780 Parkwood
  Dr, Harrisonburg VA 22802
Nurture. Sanford Snider, chair
  (snidergs@juno.com), 7140 Turner Rd,
  Richmond VA 23231, 804-705-2646; Gloria
  Lehman, secretary
Peace. James Hershberger, chair
  (hershberg@aol.com), 5647 Wengers Mill
  Rd, Linville VA 22834, 540-833-8033
Young Adult. Rachel Smith, chair
  (rsmith2627@juno.com), 1542 N College
  Ave Apt 1, Harrisonburg VA 22802, 540-442-
  8659

OTHER CONFERENCE AGENCY AND REPS

Eastern Mennonite High School. J. David
  Yoder, principal (jdavidy757@aol.com),
  801 Parkwood Dr, Harrisonburg VA 22802,
  540-432-4500

Family Life Resource Center. James R. Glanzer, executive director (services@flrc.org), 273 Newman Ave, Harrisonburg VA 22802, 540-434-8450

Highland Retreat. Paul Beiler, administrator (highlandrt@juno.com) 14783 Upper Highland Dr, Bergton VA 22811-9712, 540-852-3226

Mennonite Congregational Resource Center. Kathy Weaver Wenger, director (wengerkw@emu.edu); Claire Osinkosky, staff, 1200 Park Rd, Harrisonburg VA 22802, 540-432-4219

Pleasant View Inc. Nancy Hopkins-Garriss, executive director (nhg_pv@intelos.net), PO Box 486, Broadway VA 22815, 540-896-8255

Virginia Mennonite Auto Aid Plan and Property Aid Plan. Brent W. Eberly, executive director (beberly@vmap.org), 901 Parkwood Dr, Harrisonburg VA 22802, 540-434-9727

Virginia Mennonite Board of Missions. See separate listing in section 3.

Virginia Mennonite Retirement Community. Ronald E. Yoder, executive director (roney@vmrc.org), 1501 Virginia Ave, Harrisonburg VA 22802, 540-564-3400

Williamsburg Christian Retreat Center. Herb Lantz, executive director (wcrc@visi.net), 9275 Barnes Road, Toano VA 23168, 757-566-2256

Congregations

Asheville Menn Ch (24281) (VA) **77**
49 Bull Mountain Rd, Asheville NC 28805
828-298-4487, avlmenno@juno.com
　Patrick J. McFarren, Pastor

Beldor Menn Ch (18341) (VA) **44**
5647 Wengers Mill Rd, Linville VA 22834
540-833-8033, hershbergl@aol.com
Beldor Rd, Elkton
　James L. Hershberger, Pastor

Big Spring Menn Ch (18374) (VA) **44**
2545 Mims Rd, Luray VA 22835
540-867-0409, clarkka@emu.edu
　Kevin A. Clark, Pastor

Broad Street Menn Ch (18382) (VA, AAMA) . . .**17**
PO Box 46, Harrisonburg VA 22803
540-434-1972, huberhe@emu.edu
481 Broad St

Calvary Community Ch (27409) (VA, AAMA) **2072**
2311 Tower Pl, Hampton VA 23666
757-825-1133, fax 757-825-0567,
pastor@calvarycommunity.org,
http://www.calvarycommunity.org
　Leslie W. Francisco III, Pastor
　Karla Francisco, Associate Pastor
　Natalie A. Francisco, Associate Pastor
　Steven H. Francisco, Associate Pastor
　Nan Williams, Associate Pastor
　Robert Williams, Associate Pastor

Charlottesville Menn Ch (18408) (VA) **49**
102 Linda Ct, Charlottesville VA 22901
434-296-5289, fax 434-296-5289,
pastorcmc@earthlink.net, http://www.avenue.org/cmc
701 Monticello Ave
　Maren Tyedmers Hange, Co-Pastor
　Roy Hange, Co-Pastor

Chestnut Ridge Menn Ch (18416) (VA) **113**
14366 Church Rd, Orrville OH 44667
330-682-3175
　Robert Yutzy, Pastor

Christian Conquest Fell (10010) (VA, DC, AAMA) **33**
PO Box 60923, Washington DC 20039-0923
202-397-8148, fax 202-291-1759,
powell.dorthy@hq.navy.mil
1205 K St, NE
　Paul Gaskins, Pastor
　Louis N. Jones, Associate Pastor

Christiansburg Menn Fell (25296) (VA) **47**
40 Farmview Rd, Christiansburg VA 24073
540-382-8787, fax 540-382-8787, glenn.horst@juno.com
　Glenn R. Horst, Pastor

Community Menn Ch (22178) (VA) **225**
70 S High St, Harrisonburg VA 22801
540-433-2148, fax 540-434-4430, cmchurch@ntelos.net,
http://home.ntelos.net/~cmchurch
　Ray N. Hurst, Co-Pastor
　Margaret O'Brien, Co-Pastor

Concord Menn Ch (18424) (VA) **27**
2720 Tsawasi Rd, Knoxville TN 37931
423-966-5782, matteson@mfire.com
　F. Matthew Matteson, Pastor

Crest Hill Community Ch (18432) (VA) 6
PO Box 64, Wardensville WV 26851-0064
304-874-4247, mclyndak@citlink.net
1 mile north of Wardensville on Rt 259
    Milford E. Lyndaker, Pastor
    Carolyn Z. Lyndaker, Associate Pastor

Crossroads Menn Ch (18465) (VA) 28
PO Box 396, Broadway VA 22815
540-896-3877, crossroadschurch@rica.net
7024 Crossroads Ln, Timberville
    William F. Greene, Pastor

Durham Menn Ch (18481) (VA, AAMA) 38
603 Lynn Rd, Durham NC 27703
919-598-7533, pgodshall@verizon.net,
http://www.rtpnet.org/~dmc
    Paul Godshall, Pastor
    Kevin Nice, Youth Pastor

Family of Hope (29900) (VA) 13
1135 Hamlet Dr, Harrisonburg VA 22802
540-432-0531, fax 540-433-3805, harvyoder@aol.com
House church - no one location
    Harvey Yoder, Pastor

Fellowship of Christ (23473) (VA, AAMA) 124
1001 Tarboro St, Rocky Mount NC 27801
919-977-1901, focrockymt@hotmail.com
    Ronnie Bernard Pride Jr, Pastor

First Menn Ch of Richmond (18523) (VA) 82
2350 Staples Mill Rd, Richmond VA 23230
804-359-1340, muzet@juno.com
    Barry W. Loop, Pastor

Gospel Hill Menn Ch (18549) (VA) 93
1037 Smith Ave, Harrisonburg VA 22802-2324
540-433-6584, horstkr@vmbm.org
Hopkins Gap Rd
    Kenneth R. Horst, Pastor
    Roy F. Good, Associate Pastor

Grace Menn Fell (11158) (VA) 101
5379 Klines Mill Rd, Linville VA 22834
540-442-6235, rearly@shentel.net
Lacey Spring
    Richard K. Early, Pastor
    Diana Breeden, Associate Pastor
    Marlon W. Breeden, Associate Pastor
    Mark Landis, Associate Pastor

Greenmonte Menn Ch (18556) (VA) 109
1661 Cold Springs Rd, Stuarts Draft VA 24477
540-337-3599, greenmonte@juno.com
    Paul T. Yoder, Pastor

Greensboro Menn Fell (29744) (VA) 17
4899 Chaucer Dr, Greensboro NC 27407
336-299-1369, dbrenn1934@aol.com
815 Walker Ave

Harrisonburg Menn Ch (18564) (VA) 630
1552 S High St, Harrisonburg VA 22801
540-434-4463, fax 540-433-7389, bjantzi@aol.com,
http://members.aol.com/mailhmc/hmc.htm
    Beryl M. Jantzi, Lead Pastor
    Truman H. Brunk Jr, Associate Pastor
    Kathryn J. Hochstedler, Associate Pastor
    Harry Jarrett, Associate Pastor
    Mark Haven Keller, Associate Pastor

Hebron Menn Ch (18572) (VA) 76
12467 Millertown Rd, Fulks Run VA 22830
540-896-1149
    Donald Bare, Pastor

Hickory Menn Ch (18580) (VA) 46
1405 Second St Dr SW, PO Box 3369, Hickory NC 28603
828-328-4761, jimannroth@yahoo.com

Huntington Menn Ch (18614) (VA) 134
785 Harpersville Rd, Newport News VA 23601
757-595-6889, fax 757-595-6484, hmcnnva@juno.com,
http://www.huntingtonmennonite.org
    G. Edwin Bontrager, Pastor
    Glenda Mosemann, Director of Children's Ministries
    Gerald W. Showalter, Minister of Pastoral Care
    Jim Thornton, Minister of Preaching/Teaching

**Iglesia del Evangelio Completo Alpha y Omega
(23465) (VA, IMH)** 121
5327 16th St NW, Washington DC 20011
202-726-8161, alfacruz@msn.com
421 East-West Hwy, Hyattsville, MD 20782
    Justiniano Cruz, Pastor
    Jose Franscisco Borjas, Associate Pastor
    Gerardo Herrera, Associate Pastor

Immanuel Menn Ch (10144) (VA, AAMA) 90
446 E Rock St, Harrisonburg VA 22802
540-432-0711, basil@rica.net
400 Kelly St
    Basil Marin, Pastor
    Richard Anthony Pannell, Associate Pastor

Knoxville Menn Ch (18622) (VA) 38
4401 Sullivan Rd, Knoxville TN 37921-1343
865-588-8420, c4748F@aol.com
    John Forsyth, Congregational Leader

Lambert Menn Ch (18630) (VA) 26
RR 3 Bx 70, Belington WV 26250
304-823-2178, fax 304-823-2178
Lambert Rd, Wymer
    Boyd Wyatt Jr, Pastor
    Richard White, Associate Pastor

Landstown Community Ch (24349) (VA) 85
3220 Monet Dr, Virginia Beach VA 23456
757-468-6509, fax 757-468-6509,
unityinjesus@netzero.net
    Merlin L. Miller, Pastor

Lindale Menn Ch (18655) (VA) 338
PO Box 1082, Harrisonburg VA 22803
540-833-5171, fax 540-833-2212, admin@lindale.org,
http://www.lindale.org
6255 Jesse Bennett Way in Linville
   Wayne G. North, Interim Pastor
   Howard Miller, Associate Pastor
   Raymond W. Shank, Associate Pastor

Lynside Menn Ch (18671) (VA) 73
PO Box 124, Lyndhurst VA 22952
540-949-7474, marchand@ntelos.net
648 Mt Rd Torrey Rd
   James C. Marchand, Pastor

Mathias Menn Ch (18689) (VA) 58
20721 Lower Highland Dr, Bergton VA 22811
304-897-5930
Rt 259, Mathias
   Dean E. Williams, Pastor

Mount Clinton Menn Ch (18721) (VA) 160
6954 Mt Clinton Pike, Harrisonburg VA 22802
540-867-5885, mcmchurch@juno.com,
http://mountclinton.va.us.mennonite.net
   Lee Martin, Pastor

Mount Pleasant Menn Ch (18747) (VA) 283
2041 Mount Pleasant Rd, Chesapeake VA 23322
757-482-2215, fax 757-482-6485, mtplmen@exis.net
   J. Harold Bergey, Pastor

Mount Vernon Menn Ch (18754) (VA) 77
13188 Port Republic Rd, Grottoes VA 24441-9342
540-249-4684, huyard@planetcomm.net
   Alvin M. Huyard, Co-Pastor
   Rose Huyard, Co-Pastor

Mountain View Menn Ch (18713) (VA) 87
5252 W NC 10 Hwy, Hickory NC 28602
704-462-1707, edwardgo@aol.com

Mountain View Menn Ch (18705) (VA) 124
PO Box 208, Lyndhurst VA 22952
540-337-1062, rskiser@hotmail.com,
http://home.rica.net/earlshome
55 Love Rd
   Earl B. Monroe, Pastor

New Beginnings Ch (27517) (VA) 78
PO Box 126, Bridgewater VA 22812
540-828-1188, fax 540-828-7138,
vcanbeginagain@yahoo.com
Turner Ashby High School
   Tim Green, Pastor
   Edwin M. Heatwole, Pastor

Northern Virginia Menn Ch (23457) (VA, DC) . .62
3729 Old Lee Highway, Fairfax VA 22030
703-359-0990, fax 703-359-0990, nvmc1@juno.com,
http://www.nvmc.net

Park View Menn Ch (18788) (VA) 378
1600 College Ave, Harrisonburg VA 22802
540-434-1604, fax 540-801-0023, office@pvmchurch.org,
http://www.pvmchurch.org
   Philip L. Kniss, Pastor
   Barbara Moyer Lehman, Associate Pastor

Pleasant Grove Menn Ch (18796) (VA) 9
HC 69 Box 228, Fort Seybert WV 26806
304-249-5224

Powhatan Menn Ch (18804) (VA) 134
PO Box 220, Powhatan VA 23139
804-598-0240
   Timothy D. Kennell, Pastor

Providence Menn Ch (16550) (VA) 72
13101 Warwick Blvd, Newport News VA 23602
757-249-2702, providence@mennonite.net,
http://www.providence.va.us.mennonite.net
   R. Todd Bowman, Pastor

Raleigh Menn Ch (28266) (VA) 66
PO Box 25545, Raleigh NC 27611-5545
919-833-1182, JBender770@aol.com,
http://www.rtpnet.org/~rmc
1116 N Blount St
   John Paul Bender, Co-Pastor
   Marilyn Handrich Bender, Co-Pastor
   Mauricio Chenlo, Peace Director and Youth Pastor

Ridgeway Menn Ch (18812) (VA) 185
546 E Franklin St, Harrisonburg VA 22801
540-434-3476, ridgewaymennonitechurch@yahoo.com,
http://www.geocities.com/ridgewaymennonite
   Lee E. Ebersole, Pastor
   Richard L. Headings, Pastor

Riverside Menn Ch (18820) (VA) 28
PO Box 176, Harman WV 26270
304-227-3647, rolowenger@juno.com
   Robert G. Wenger, Pastor

Shalom Menn Congregation (29009) (VA) 36
EMU, Box 93, Harrisonburg VA 22802
540-433-5227, shalommc@shentel.net
Strite Auditorium, EMU
   Earl S. Zimmerman, Co-Pastor

Springdale Menn Ch (18853) (VA) 200
170 Hall School Rd, Waynesboro VA 22980
540-949-8945, fax 540-943-3553, sprngdle@intelos.net
   Kathryn W. Wenger, Co-Pastor
   Mark R. Wenger, Co-Pastor

Staunton Menn Ch (18861) (VA) 42
2405 3rd St, Staunton VA 24401
540-886-5869
   James S. Delp, Pastor

Stephens City Menn Ch (18879) (VA) 55
c/o Musser, 5540 Valley Pike, Stephens City VA 22655
540-869-5037, scmc@visuallink.com,
http://www.visuallink.net/scmc
   James W. Musser, Pastor

CONFERENCES AND
CONGREGATIONS

2

Stuarts Draft Menn Ch (18887) (VA) 62
PO Box 763, Stuarts Draft VA 24477
540-337-3792, fax 540-337-3792, sdmchurch@juno.com
Howardsville Turnpike (Rt Rd 610)

Trissels Menn Ch (18895) (VA) 121
PO Box 549, Broadway VA 22815
540-896-7289, Trisselsmc@juno.com
11246 Hisers Ln
  Philip C. Kanagy, Pastor

Valley View Menn Ch (18911) (VA) 77
1345 Hillcrest Dr, Harrisonburg VA 22802
540-434-0578, shenkp@emu.edu
21806 Criders Rd, Criders
  H. Michael Shenk II, Pastor
  H. Michael Shenk III, Pastor

Vietnamese Christian Fell (10104) (VA, DC, VIET) 73
3871 Scibilia Rd, Fairfax VA 22033
703-802-0139, fax 703-802-0139, lpham@forministry.com,
http://www25.brinkster.com/hted
3022 Woodlawn Ave, Falls Church
  Can Ngoc Le, Pastor
  Xuan (Lisa) Huong Pham, Pastor

Warwick River Menn Ch (18929) (VA) 201
250 Lucas Creek Rd, Newport News VA 23602-6251
757-874-0794, fax 757-877-6510, wrmc1@juno.com,
http://warwickriver.va.us.mennonite.net
  Stephen H. Gibbs, Pastor
  Elizabeth Anne Gibbs, Assoicate Pastor of Youth and
  Worship

Washington Community Fell (24778) (VA, DC, AAMA) 33
907 Maryland Ave, NE, Washington DC 20002
202-543-1926, fax 202-543-0287, office@wcfchurch.org,
http://www.wcfchurch.org
  Del Glick, Interim Pastor
  Faith Evans, Associate Pastor for Youth

Waynesboro Menn Ch (24760) (VA) 140
1801 Monroe St, Waynesboro VA 22980
540-949-0446, wmchurch@intelos.net
Hopeman Parkway at Monroe St
  Stanlee D. Kauffman, Senior Pastor
  Kyle D. Stutzman, Minister of Youth and Christian
  Education
  John Joseph Arbaugh II, Minister of Missions
  Sharon Wenger, Minister of Music

Weavers Menn Ch (18937) (VA) 294
2501 Rawley Pike, Harrisonburg VA 22801
540-434-7758, weaversmc@juno.com,
http://weavers.va.us.mennonite.net
Hwy 33 W
  Edith N. Shenk, Pastor
  Joseph C. Shenk, Pastor

West Liberty Menn Ch (18457) (VA) 18
91 Highway 191, West Liberty KY 41472
606-743-9390, wgmeh@mrtc.com
52 Fyffe Ct
  Willis Hunsberger, Pastor

Williamsburg Menn Ch (23135) (VA) 75
7800 Croaker Rd, Williamsburg VA 23188
757-566-3026, wmbgmenno@widomakerl.com

Woodland Menn Ch (18960) (VA) 28
5236 Alum Springs Rd, Edinburg VA 22824
540-856-2873

Word of Life Menn Ch (18770) (VA, AAMA) 9
6501 Pierce St, Norfolk VA 23513
757-895-8822
  William Vaughn, Jr., Pastor

Zion Hill Menn Ch (18986) (VA) 106
PO Box 23, Singers Glen VA 22850
540-833-4207, lowellhaarer@juno.com
6311 Mayberry Rd
  Lowell W. Haarer, Pastor

Zion Menn Ch (18978) (VA) 244
3260 Zion Church Rd, Broadway VA 22815
540-896-7577, fax 540-896-7577,
zionmennonitechurch@juno.com
  Clyde G. Kratz, Pastor

Western District Conference

OFFICE
wdc@mennowdc.org, www.mennowdc.org
316 283-6300, fax 316-283-0620
2517 Main, PO Box 306, North Newton KS
67117

STAFF
Marvin Zehr, conference minister
(marvz@mennowdc.org)
Beginning Jan. 2003: Dorothy Nickel Friesen,
conference minister
Marco Guete, associate conference minister
(marcoguete@sbcglobal.net)
Steve Goering, area conference minister for CO
(swgoering@aol.com)
Robert Nolt, area conference minister for OK
(rnolt@mennoscc.org)
Ritch Hochstetler, youth minister
(ritch@mennowdc.org)
Marlene Bogard, minister of Christian nurture
(crlib@mennowdc.org) and resource
library director
Kathy Goering, conference administrator
(kathyg@mennowdc.org)
Phyllis Regier, treasurer
(pregier@mennowdc.org)
Nancy Shear, administrative secretary
(wdc@mennowdc.org)
Deron and Krista Nisly, camp directors
(campmno@mennowdc.org), Camp
Mennoscah, Box 65, Murdock KS 67111,
316-297-3290
Lois Barrett, Great Plains Seminary Education
Program director (lbarrett@ambs.edu)

GENERAL INFORMATION
Year founded: 1891
Members: 11,571
Congregations: 71
Ministers: 177
CLC reps: Marvin Zehr, Vern Preheim, Debbie
Schmidt

Next annual delegate session: August 1-2, 2003,
joint with South Central Conference

EXECUTIVE COMMITTEE
Vern Preheim, moderator
(vpreheim@mail.mcc.org), 127 S Main, Newton
KS 67114, 316-283-4018; Roger Neufeld Smith
(southernhillsmc@networksplus.net), moderator elect, 1331 SW Jewell, Topeka KS 66604,
785-232-5781; Kay Schmidt, secretary; Joyce
Franz, education; Chuck Beth, evangelism;
Leonard Wiebe, home mission; Jim Stucky, ministerial; Mark Wiens, peace/social concerns;
Allen Jantz, retreat; E. Fred Goering, steward-
ship/budget

PUBLICATION
Western District News (Bimonthly), Lois Loflin,
editor (loflin@mennowdc.org), Box 306, North
Newton KS 67117

OTHER CONFERENCE AGENCY AND REPS
Western District Women in Mission.
Vernelle Voth, president
(hlv@ourtownusa.net), Box 488, 104 S
Salina, Haven KS 67543, 620-465-03301
Mennonite Men of the Plains. Ken Neufeld,
president (cfn@wwwebservice.net), 614 S
Ash, Hillsboro KS 67063, 620-947-3665
Agri-urban. Alvin Kroeker, president, 638
Buckskin Rd, Inman KS 67546, 620-585-
2234
Integration Transition Committee. Alice
Price, facilitator (alicep@amigo.net), 609
Walnue Ave, Box 306, LaJara CO 81140,
719-843-5118; Marvin Zehr, Kathy Goering
Reid
Oklahoma Convention. Verlin Koehn, presi-
dent (verkoehn@21stcomm.com), 3527
Edgewater, Enid OK 73703, 580-242-2772
Mid-Texas Convention. Esther Martinez, co-
chair (emartine@airmail.net), 3701 Florest
Lawn Rd, Balch Springs TX 75180, 972-285-
1342; Blanca Vargas, co-chair
(blancavargas@prodigy.net), 1710 Lynette
#606, San Antonio TX 78209, 210-533-0642

CONFERENCES AND CONGREGATIONS

2

AMBS – Great Plains Extension. Floyd Bartel, director (floydb@mennowdc.org), 2916 Wildwood Way, North Newton KS 67117, 316-283-7890

DEO (Discipleship, Encounter, Outreach). Ritch Hochstetler, Director (ritch@ mennowdc.org), PO Box 306, North Newton KS 67117, 316-283-6300

Congregations

Alexanderwohl Menn Ch (6005) (WDC) 528
1304 K-15 Hwy, PO Box 8, Goessel KS 67053-0008
620-367-8192, alexmenno@wwwebservice.net,
http://www.prairienet.org/mennolink/congregations
   James L. Dunn, Pastor
   Mark Allen Wiens, Associate Pastor

Arvada Menn Ch (6020) (WDC, MUM) 44
5927 Miller St, Arvada CO 80004
303-424-6261, fax 303-424-0081,
arvadamennonite1@yahoo.com

Austin Menn Ch (28761) (SC, WDC) 64
5801 Westminster Dr, Austin TX 78723-2640
512-926-3121, fax 512-926-3121, kathy@thn.org,
http://www.mennochurch.org
   Kathryn Goering Reid, Pastor
   Steven Breck Reid, Associate Pastor

Beatrice Menn Ch (6030) (WDC) 150
1220 Summit St, Beatrice NE 68310-2432
402-228-3644, bm84101@alltel.net,
http://www.beatrice.ne.us.mennonite.net
   Denton R. Jantzi, Pastor

Bergthal Menn Ch (6045) (WDC) 79
PO Box 236, Pawnee Rock KS 67567-0236
620-982-4886
SW 30 Rd & SW 110 Ave
   Lynn Schlosser, Co-Pastor
   Todd Schlosser, Co-Pastor

Bethel College Menn Ch (6070) (WDC) 672
2600 College Ave, PO Box 364, North Newton KS 67117-0364
316-283-3667, fax 316-283-2079, bcmc@southwind.net,
http://www2.southwind.net/~bcmc
   Heidi Regier Kreider, Pastor
   Norma J. Johnson, Associate Pastor
   Steven J. Yoder, Associate Pastor

Bethel Menn Ch (6085) (WDC, MILC) 25
1001 Savage, PO Box 116, Hammon OK 73650
405-473-2224

Bethel Menn Ch (6090) (WDC) 80
RR 3 Box 84, Hydro OK 73048
405-663-2749
6th & Coffee
   Raymond Unruh, Pastor

Bethel Menn Ch (6095) (WDC) 383
256 8th Ave, PO Box 306, Inman KS 67546
620-585-6964, fax 620-585-6958,
bethelch@southwind.net
   Michael Knowles, Pastor
   Christopher Z. Weaver, Associate Pastor

Boulder Menn Ch (6153) (WDC, MUM, COB) . . .58
1520 Euclid Ave, Boulder CO 80302
303-443-3889, fax 303-444-6523,
bouldermennonite@juno.com,
http://boulder.co.us.mennonite.net
   Steven William Goering, Co-Pastor
   Susan Ortman Goering, Co-Pastor
   Melissa Bennett, Youth Pastor

Buhler Menn Ch (6165) (WDC) 422
220 W Ave B, PO Box 188, Buhler KS 67522
620-543-2733
   Robert Eugene Dalke, Pastor
   Monte C. Wilson, Associate Pastor

Burrton Menn Ch (6170) (WDC) 85
411 N Reno Ave, PO Box 227, Burrton KS 67020-0227
620-463-3415, mgundy@kscable.com
   James Ralph Gundy, Pastor

Calvary Menn Ch (6185) (WDC) 39
831 S New York Ave, Liberal KS 67901
620-624-5530, fax 620-624-5530
   Ervey A. Unruh, Pastor

Central Heights Menn Ch (6196) (WDC) 44
120 Meadow Ln, Hesston KS 67062-9155
620-327-4938, junia@southwind.net
Rt 1, Durham

Comunidad de Esperanza (6240) (SC, WDC, IMH) 25
1721 N Garrett Ave, Dallas TX 75206
214-428-7131, damain_rodriguez@msn.com
   Damian Rodriguez, Pastor

Comunidad de Vida (27410) (WDC) 0
1443 S St Marys, San Antonio TX 78210
210-533-0642, blancavargas@prodigy.net
   Blanca Vargas, Pastor
   Victor Serafin Vargas, Pastor

Deer Creek Menn Ch (6230) (WDC) 69
201 S Lee St, PO Box 66, Deer Creek OK 74636
580-267-3376, pji201@aol.com
Third & Lee
   Paul J. Isaak, Pastor

Eden Menn Ch (6250) (WDC) 193
21905 E 600 Rd, Inola OK 74036
918-543-2739, fax 918-543-3250,
edenmennonite@juno.com
  Dewayne Isaac, Pastor
  Philip Voth, Youth Pastor

Eden Menn Ch (6255) (WDC) 773
109 E Hirschler St, PO Box 406, Moundridge KS 67107
620-345-8320, fax 620-345-8325, edenmc@mtelco.net
401 18th Ave
  Lawrence Lee Lever, Pastor
  James W. Ostlund, Associate Pastor

Faith Menn Ch (27425) (SC, WDC) 32
404 LaVista, Dodge City KS 67054
620-846-2663, faithmenno@juno.com
  Doug Harris, Pastor

Faith Menn Ch (6325) (WDC) 374
627 Northridge Rd, Newton KS 67114
316-283-6370, faith@sbcglobal.net
  Gordon Louis Smith, Pastor
  Alan Lepard, Youth and Young Adult Pastor

First Menn Ch (6341) (WDC) 245
6714 W State Hwy 4, Beatrice NE 68310-6864
402-228-2052, firstmenno@yahoo.com,
http://firstmennonite.ne.us.mennonite.net
3 miles west on Highway 4
  Florence Eileen Schloneger, Co-Pastor
  Weldon Ray Schloneger, Co-Pastor

First Menn Ch (6362) (WDC) 60
700 S 19th St, Clinton OK 73601-5132
580-323-3694, mennoknights@itlnet.net
  David Gerbrandt, Pastor

First Menn Ch (6374) (WDC) 285
427 W 4th St, Halstead KS 67056
316-835-2282
  Cleo H. Koop, Pastor
  Maeanna Regier, Associate Pastor

First Menn Ch (6376) (WDC) 326
102 S Ash St, Hillsboro KS 67063
620-947-5662, fax 620-947-2774, fmc@wwwebservice.net
  Kenneth James Peterson, Pastor
  Todd A. Lehman, Youth Pastor

First Menn Ch (6382) (WDC) 241
52 Rambler Rd, Hutchinson KS 67502
620-662-9385, fax 620-662-9261,
fmchutch@southwind.net,
http://home.southwind.net/~fmchutch
  Debra Ann Schmidt, Pastor
  Laverle Schrag, Associate Pastor

First Menn Ch (6391) (WDC) 212
1161 E Ave A, McPherson KS 67460
620-241-4040, fax 620-241-1468, neilafmc@earthlink.net
1161 E Ave A
  Neil B. Amstutz, Pastor

First Menn Ch (6403) (WDC) 633
PO Box 291, 429 E1st, Newton KS 67114
316-283-0273, fax 316-283-0277,
fstmenno@southwind.net
429 E First St
  Clarence E. Rempel, Pastor
  Rusty Bonham, Pastor of Youth and Caregiving
  Joan Boyer, Minister of Outreach

First Menn Ch (6315) (WDC) 406
315 S Ash, PO Box 127, Pretty Prairie KS 67570
620-459-6344, fax 620-459-6771, lzook@southwind.net
1718 W Pretty Prairie Rd
  Lester L. Zook, Pastor

First Menn Ch (6318) (WDC) 96
RR 1 Box 69, Ransom KS 67572-9709
785-731-2758, buller@gbta.net
Corner of Ogden & Massachusetts
  Eric Buller, Pastor

First Menn Ch of Christian (6330) (WDC) 227
719 S Christian, PO Box 66, Moundridge KS 67107
620-345-8766, fmcc@mtelco.net,
http://firstofchristian.ks.us.mennonite.net
  Gordon K. Allaby, Pastor

Fort Collins Menn Fell (24687) (RM, WDC) 42
300 Oak St, Fort Collins CO 80524-2915
970-416-1687, revjborg@juno.com,
http://www.fortnet.org/fcmf
  Jeffrey A. Borg, Pastor

Goessel Menn Ch (6370) (WDC) 170
109 S Church, PO Box 38, Goessel KS 67053-0038
620-367-2446, goesselchurch@juno.com
  Kevin T. Goertzen, Pastor

Grace Hill Menn Ch (6390) (WDC) 214
10218 SE 12th, Whitewater KS 67154
316-283-2644, fax 316-799-2238, jvoth@cox.net,
http://gracehill.ks.us.mennonite.net
  James Joel Voth, Pastor

Grace Menn Ch (6410) (WDC) 100
902 S Adams St, Enid OK 73701
580-234-2078, fax 580-234-2078 (call first),
gracemen@netzero.net
  Dennis Treat, Interim Pastor
  Don Froese, Contact Person

Greenfield Menn Ch (6425) (WDC) 23
405 N 4th St, PO Box 655, Ft Cobb OK 73038
405-643-5142

Hanston Menn Ch (6430) (WDC) 21
RR 1 Box 45A, Hanston KS 67849
620-623-2965, cvincent@pld.com
  Carl Vincent, Pastor

Herold Menn Ch (6445) (WDC) 129
1313 N College St, Cordell OK 73632-1809
580-832-3435, awjohnson@itlnet.net
RR, Bessie
  Arlee Johnson, Pastor

Hesston Inter-Menn Fell (17970) (SC, WDC) . . .245
505 S Ridge Rd, PO Box 786, Hesston KS 67062
620-327-2101, fax 620-327-4918,
scott.miller@prairieinet.net, http://www.himf.org
    Scott David Miller, Pastor
    Arlon Fishburn, Minister of Helps
    J. D. Hershberger, Minister of Worship

Hmong Menn Ch (11119) (RM, WDC, HMONG, MUM) 45
c/o Shoua Moua, 9980 W 59th Pl #1, Arvada CO 80004-5015
303-463-0257
    Shoua Moua, Pastor

Hoffnungsau Menn Ch (6460) (WDC) 278
43 13th Ave, Inman KS 67546
620-585-6733, hmc@ourtownusa.net
    Willmar Toews Harder, Pastor

Hope Fell (10012) (SC, WDC) 20
1700 Morrow Ave, Waco TX 76707
254-754-5942, hopecmty@flash.net
1721 Sanger Ave
    Joe Gatlin, Co-Pastor
    Nancy Gatlin, Co-Pastor
    Norma Torres, Associate Pastor

Hope Menn Ch (6468) (WDC) 202
868 N Maize Rd, Wichita KS 67212
316-722-0903, fax 316-722-5173,
pastor@hopemennonite.com,
http://www.hopemennonite.com
    Douglas Ray Luginbill, Pastor
    Linda Ewert, Associate Pastor

Hopefield Menn Ch (6470) (WDC) 77
PO Box E, Moundridge KS 67107-0583
620-345-8556

Houston Menn Ch (23184) (SC, WDC) 45
1231 Wirt Rd, Houston TX 77055
713-464-4865, pastor@houstonmennonite.org,
http://www.houstonmennonite.org
    Jose Elizade, Pastor

Iglesia Cristiana Menonita de Dallas (11273) (SC, WDC, IMH) 12
427 N Marlborough Ave, Dallas TX 75208
214-946-2910
    Serapio Antonio Caceros, Pastor

Iglesia Menonita Luz del Evangelio (6512) (SC, WDC, IMH) 30
1524 Dowdy Ferry Rd, Dallas TX 75217-9227
214-324-9409
    Juan Fernando Limones, Pastor

Inman Menn Ch (6505) (WDC) 130
PO Box 236, Inman KS 67546
620-585-6550, jkaiser@southwind.net
304 S Pine
    Jerry Lee Kaiser, Pastor

Joy Menn Ch (6642) (WDC) 12
4708 Outpost Dr, Spencer OK 73084
405-771-4743, mosesmast@aol.com,
http://joy.ok.us.mennonite.net
504 NE 16th St, Oklahoma City
    Moses Mast, Pastor

Kingman Menn Ch (6511) (WDC) 92
PO Box 306, Kingman KS 67068
620-532-5330, darev@websurf.net
1620 S Main St
    Bradley B. Penner, Pastor

Koinonia Menn Ch (6575) (WDC, MILC) 23
c/o Lawrence Hart, RR 1 Box 3040, Clinton OK 73601
580-323-5320

Lorraine Avenue Menn Ch (6525) (WDC) 329
655 S Lorraine St, Wichita KS 67211-3093
316-682-4555, fax 316-682-2644,
lamcsecretary@prodigy.net,
http://lorraineavenue.ks.us.mennonite.net
    Lois Marie Harder, Co-Pastor
    Thomas L. Harder, Co-Pastor
    Larry Nussbaum, Associate Pastor

Manhattan Menn Ch (24174) (SC, WDC, USMBC) 75
1000 Fremont St, Manhattan KS 66502-5425
785-539-4079, menno@oz-online.net,
http://www.manhattan.ks.us.mennonite.net
    Barbara Krehbiel Gehring, Co-Pastor
    Richard L. Gehring, Co-Pastor

Menn Ch of the Servant (23317) (SC, WDC) 30
1650 Fairview Ave, Wichita KS 67203
316-267-4625, carolarose@juno.com
    Carol Ann Rose, Pastor

Menn Indian Ch (6558) (WDC, MILC) 12
c/o Norma Smith, PO Box 378, Seiling OK 73663-0378
580-886-2664

Mountain Community Menn Ch (25247) (RM, WDC) 97
PO Box 502, Palmer Lake CO 80133
719-481-3155, mcmc1@juno.com,
http://www.rmmc.org/mcmc
643 Hwy 105
    Don Rheinheimer, Co-Pastor
    Jan Lynette Rheinheimer, Co-Pastor

New Creation Fell (6596) (WDC) 50
221 Muse St, Newton KS 67114-3827
316-283-1363, fax 315-283-1363, ncfc@southwind.net,
http://www.southwind.net/~ncfc
    Ruth Penner, Pastor
    Wesley Bergen, Associate Pastor

Peace Menn Ch (17921) (SC, WDC) 82
11001 Midway Rd, PO Box 59926, Dallas TX 75229
214-902-8141, fax 214-902-8141, pmc@airmail.net,
http://www.web2.airmail.net/pmc
    Richard Douglas Davis, Pastor
    Tammerie Brotzman Spires, Associate Pastor

Peace Menn Ch (23853) (SC, WDC) 72
1204 Oread Ave, Lawrence KS 66044
785-841-8614, peacemennonite@msn.com
  Vicki Lynn Penner, Pastor

Peace Menn Community Ch (28605) (RM, WDC, MUM) 90
13601 E Alameda Ave, Aurora CO 80012
303-340-1555, fax 303-340-1141,
pastor@peacemennonite.com
  Wilbur Roy Walls Jr, Pastor

Rainbow Menn Ch (18093) (WDC) 207
1444 Southwest Blvd, Kansas City KS 66103
913-236-8820, fax 913-236-6838, rainbow606@juno.com,
http://rainbow.ks.us.mennonite.net
  Robert Kaufman, Pastor

Salina Menn Ch (6691) (WDC) 62
2026 Starlight Dr, Salina KS 67401
785-825-2663, smckspg@jkansas.com,
http://homepage.netspaceonline.com/~kpitts/smc
  Val R. Krehbiel, Pastor

San Antonio Menn Ch (25239) (SC, WDC) 39
1443 S Saint Marys St, San Antonio TX 78210
210-533-0642, fax 210-341-8358,
gloria.beachey@prodigy.net,
http://www.sanantonio.tx.us.mennonite.net
  Duane Beachey, Lead Pastor
  Gloria Beachey, Pastor

Shalom Menn Ch (10130) (SC, WDC) 164
800 E 1st St, Newton KS 67114
316-283-7395, shalom@southwind.net,
http://home.southwind.net/~shalom
  Eric Massanari, Pastor

Southern Hills Menn Ch (6740) (SC, WDC) 91
511 SE 37th St, Topeka KS 66605
785-266-9403, fax 785-266-4512,
southernhillsmc@networksplus.net
  Cynthia Neufeld Smith, Co-Pastor
  Roger Neufeld Smith, Co-Pastor

Tabor Menn Ch (6765) (WDC) 333
891Chisholm Trail, Newton KS 67114-7503
620-367-2318, fax 620-367-2309, tabormc@mtelco.net
  Corey Lee Miller, Pastor
  Karen Andres, Associate Pastor

Trinity Menn Ch (6780) (WDC) 261
211 S Elm St, Hillsboro KS 67063
620-947-3824, fax 620-947-3422,
tkliewer@southwind.net
  Tim Kliewer, Pastor

Turpin Menn Ch (6785) (WDC) 100
RR 2 Box 21, Turpin OK 73950
580-259-6440
  Jeff Wintermore, Pastor

West Zion Menn Ch (6830) (WDC) 225
101 S Washington Ave, PO Box 758, Moundridge KS 67107-0758
620-345-8143, fax 316-345-8143,
westzionmc@wwwebservice.net
  Marcia Ann Yoder-Schrock, Pastor
  John Lamar Yoder-Schrock, Co-Pastor

Whitestone Menn Ch (18184) (SC, WDC) 328
629 Crescent Dr, Hesston KS 67062
620-327-4123, wmc@southwind.net,
http://whitestone.ks.us.mennonite.net
  Leonard C. Wiebe, Interim Pastor

Zion Menn Ch (6865) (WDC) 144
525 N Main St, PO Box 68, Elbing KS 67041
620-799-2071, zion@iwichita.com,
http://www.zion~elbing.org
  Floyd E. Born, Pastor

CONFERENCES AND CONGREGATIONS

2

South American Conference

Congregations

Igreja Evangelica Menonita (11274) (SA) 285
Rua Cristiano Strobel, 1667-81720-140, Curitiba, Parana

Igreja Evangelica Menonita de Witmarsum (11276) (SA) 324
Witmarsum 84130000, Palmeria, Parana
fax, iemwit@uol.com.br

Igreja Menonita de Vila Guaira (11275) (SA) . .132
Rua Amazonas 986, 80610-030, Curitiba, Parana
41-329-2502, fax 41-329-5456, imvg@softall.com.br

Mennoniten Gemeinde Asuncion (11278) (SA) 335
cdc 166-Mennonniten heim 1050, Republica de Colombia, Asunción
21-595-292-665, fax 21-595-292-665, amae@rieder.net.py
Concordia Kirche-Samaniego c/Enciso
  Walter Thielmann, Pastor
  Werner Franz, Associate Pastor

Mennoniten Gemeinde Delta (11283) (SA) . . .157
80002 Ecilda, Paullier
00598-340-9084, fax 00598-349-2340,
updueck@adinet.com.uy
Colonia Delta

Mennoniten Gemeinde Fernheim (11279) (SA) 850
cdc 984, Filadelfia 599, Asunción
megemfer@telesurf.com.py

Mennoniten Gemeinde Gartental (11286) (SA) .93
Colonia Gartental, Tres Bocas 65001, Rio Negro
00598-560-9032, magsein@adinet.com.uy

Mennoniten Gemeinde Montevideo (11284) (SA) 131
CDC 788, Montevideo 11000

Mennoniten Gemeinde Neuland (11281) (SA) 604
cdc 1153, Asunción
011-595-951-210, fax 011-595-951-309

Mennoniten Gemeinde Volendam (11282) (SA) 250
Colonie Volendam 8340, Puerto Mbopicua
002-595-451-20220

Mennoniten Gemeinde zu Friesland (11280) (SA) 314
Kolonie Frieland, cdc 166, Asunción

Segunda Igreja Evangelica Menonita de Witmarsum (11277) (SA) 244
Colonia Witmarsum, 84130-000, Palmeria, Parana
55 42 2541315, siemw@bol.com.br

Organizational Index

3

A

Abbreviations
—see page 10

ACTV Christian Television and Media Ministries
jeff@actvonline.com, www.actvonline.com
610-378-1378, fax 610-378-7892
326 Penn Ave, West Reading PA 19611

STAFF
Jeff Stoltzfus, general manager
 (jeff@actvonline.com)
Jon Carlson, production assistant
 (jon@actvonline.com)
Rebecca Strause, administrative assistant
 (becky@actvonline.com)

INFORMATION
ACTV uses the media as a tool of evangelism, broadening the opportunity of the local church to fulfill the great commission, impacting lives with God's Word, and nurturing believers through innovative Christian programming.

 ACTV works with a wide variety of churches and ministries. ACTV was founded by members of Zion Mennonite Church in 1973.

BOARD
John Rush, chair (jrush@actvonline.com),
326 Penn Ave, West Reading PA 19611 (610-208-0406); Mike Reinert, vice-chair; Bertha Collins, treasurer; Santo Torcivia, secretary; Linda Evers, Esq.; Ken Herr; Jeffrey D. Miller

PUBLICATION
ACTV News (Quarterly)

Africa Inter-Mennonite Mission (AIMM)
aim@aimmintl.org, www.aimmintl.org
574-875-5552, fax 574-875-6567
59466 CR 113, Elkhart IN 46517-3644
AIMM Canada, Box 1268, Steinbach MB R0A 2A0

STAFF
Garry Prieb, executive secretary
 (garry@aimmintl.org)
Leona Schrag, assistant executive secretary
 (leona@aimmintl.org)
Wade Handrich, controller
 (wade@aimmintl.org)

INFORMATION
AIMM's focus centers on the church in Africa. Its objective is to plant an evangelical church where none exists, nurture the established church, and partner with the church in witness and service.

 AIMM is an evangelical partnership including: EMC-US, EMC Canada, EMMC, MB, MC Canada, MC USA. AIMM works with European Mennonites, two Congo Mennonite churches, Mennonite Church of Burkina Faso, and African Independent Churches.

Organized as Congo Inland Mission in 1912, AIMM has expanded ministries to various ethnic and language groups in Botswana, Burkina Faso, Lesotho, Senegal, and South Africa.

BOARD
Peter Rempel, chair (prempel@mennonitechurch.ca), MC Canada Witness, 600 Shaftesbury Blvd, Winnipeg MB R3P 0M4 (204-888-6781); Tim Bergdahl (MB), vice-chair; Len Sawatzky (EMMC), financial consultant; Steve Wiebe Johnson (MC USA), secretary; Len Barkman (EMC-Canada); Earl Cecil (EMC-US); Martini Janz (Women's Auxiliary); Nzash Lumeya (MB); Janet Plenert (MC Canada Witness); Shirley Ries (at-large)

PUBLICATION
AIMM Messenger (annually), Leona Schrag, editor (same address as above); *AIMM To Inform* (quarterly)

African-American Mennonite Association (AAMA)
aama_org@yahoo.com, www.aamaorg.org
757-262-0128, fax 757-825-8771
2311 Tower Place, Hampton VA 23666

STAFF
Steven Brown, consultant
CLC rep: Yvonne Bailey

INFORMATION
The African-American Mennonite Association (AAMA) is a ministry of Mennonite Church USA serving as a voice of advocacy, informing, educating, and empowering African-Americans and integrated congregations within MC USA. The organization holds an assembly every two years.

The African-American Mennonite Association

was founded in 1982 and was preceded by the Minority Ministries Council and the Black Caucus which date back to the early 1970s.

AAMA's membership consists of approximately 62 churches which are included in the appropriate conference listing with the AAMA code.

BOARD
Leslie W. Francisco III, president, 2311 Tower Place, Hampton VA 23666 (757-825-1133); Alvin Isaacs; George E. Providence II; Kenneth L. Thompson; Sheri Williams

PUBLICATION
AAMA/Lark Newsletter (Semiannual)

Allegheny Mennonite Conference
—see section 2: Conferences and Congregations

AMAS
—see Association of Mutual Aid Societies

AMBS
—see Associated Mennonite Biblical Seminary

Anabaptist and Brethren Agency
—see MutualAid eXchange

Anabaptist Center for Health Care Ethics
574-596-8285
1737 Crabtree Lane, Elkhart IN 46514

STAFF
George Stoltzfus (geobs@juno.com)

INFORMATION
The Anabaptist Center for Health Care Ethics was created as a service to pastors, counselors, physicians, and other health care professionals who work with believers confronting difficult ethical decisions relating to health care. The

center provides resources and support to further the discussion of issues within a faith context.

The Anabaptist Center for Health Care Ethics is a consortium of church agencies and individuals who represent them: Mennonite Central Committee (J. Daryl Byler); Mennonite Chaplains' Association (Ray Geigley); Mennonite Health Services (Rick Stiffney); Mennonite Medical Association (George Brenneman and Jep Hostetler); Mennonite Mutual Aid (Karl Sommers); Mennonite Nurses Association (Anne Hershberger).

Anabaptist Deaf Ministries
fdmc2270@aol.com
717-392-6752
2270 Old Philadelphia Pike, Lancaster PA
17602-3417

INFORMATION
Founded 1976. Anabaptist Deaf Ministries' mission is to facilitate, encourage, and support deaf people to receive the good news of Jesus Christ and actively participate (and serve) in an Anabaptist or other Christian church. Relates to MMA Disabilities Resources.

BOARD
Jeff Hoffer, president (jjhoffer@aol.com), 340 N George St, Millersville PA 17551; Peter C. Myers, representative Church of the Brethren; Bonnie Geiser, Ron Gerbrandt, Michele Showalter, Sheila Stopher Yoder.

PUBLICATION
Deaf Ministries NEWS (Semiannual), Sheila Stopher Yoder, editor, MMA PO 483 Goshen IN 46527-0483 (800-348-7468)

Archives
—see Executive Board in section 1

Area Conferences
—see section 2: Conferences and Congregations

Associated Mennonite Biblical Seminary
rreschly@ambs.edu, www.ambs.edu
574-295-3726, fax 574-295-0092
3003 Benham Ave, Elkhart IN 46517

STAFF
J. Nelson Kraybill, president
   (nkraybill@ambs.edu)
Loren L. Johns, dean (ljohns@ambs.edu)
Mark Weidner, vice president
   (mweidner@ambs.edu)
Jeffrey Miller, business administrator
   (jmiller@ambs.edu)
Eileen K. Saner, librarian and director of educational resources (esaner@ambs.edu)

INFORMATION
Associated Mennonite Biblical Seminary (AMBS) is dedicated to helping followers of Jesus Christ grow toward spiritual maturity, theological depth and discernment, wise pastoral practice, and personal commitment to God's reign of peace and righteousness through the enabling power of the Holy Spirit.

AMBS is a binational Mennonite educational institution committed to the Anabaptist heritage and the Christian Church's global mission. AMBS is owned and supported by Mennonite Church Canada and Mennonite Church USA. Degrees offered: master of divinity, master of arts in theological studies, master of arts in mission and evangelism, master of arts in Christian formation, master of arts in peace studies, dual-degree master of arts in peace studies and master of social work, and dual-degree master of divinity and master of social work. Mennonite Biblical Seminary, founded in 1945, and Goshen Biblical Seminary, founded in 1946, began associating in 1958 and incorporated as one seminary in 1994.

AMBS is accredited by the Association of Theological Schools in the United States and Canada (ATS) and the North Central Association of College and Schools (NCA).

ORGANIZATIONAL INDEX

3

BOARD

Rick Stiffney, chair (rick@mhsonline.org), 234 S Main St, Goshen IN 46526 (574-534-9689); Jim Williams, vice-chair; Teresa Moser, secretary; David W. Boshart, Robert Carlson, John A. Esau, Ray Friesen, Sherri Martin, John R. Peters, Robert Peters, George Schmidt, Margaret Richer Smith, Beulah Steiner, Mary Stueben, Karen Martens Zimmerly

Institute of Mennonite Studies—see separate listing in this section.

Pastoral Studies Distance Education. Jewel Gingerich Longenecker, director, (jglongenecker@ambs.edu), 3003 Benham Ave, Elkhart IN 46517 (574-296-6222, fax 574-295-0092); Ruth Liechty, registrar, (rliechty@ambs.edu)

AMBS-Great Plains. AMBS-Great Plains is an extension site of AMBS, serving central Kansas with theological education programs. Lois Barrett, director, (lbarrett@ambs.edu), PO Box 306, 2517 Main, North Newton KS 67117 (316-283-6300). Board: Janette Amstutz, Susan Balzer, Palmer Becker, John A. Esau, Duane Friesen, Kathy Goering, Cheryl Hershberger, Deb Schmidt, Marvin Zehr

PUBLICATIONS

AMBS Window, Mary E. Klassen, editor (same address as above); *Vision: A Journal for Church and Theology*, co-published by AMBS and Canadian Mennonite Bible College/Canadian Mennonite University, editors: Mary H. Schertz, AMBS (same address as above) and Dan Epp-Tiessen, CMBC/CMU

Association of Anabaptist Risk Management

www.aarm-web.com
717-293-7840, fax 717-293-7854
2160 Lincoln Hwy E, Ste 6, Lancaster PA 17602

STAFF

Philip B. Leaman, president, CEO (pleaman@dejazzd.com)

INFORMATION

AARM provides risk management and insurance services to Anabaptist not-for-profit institutions.

BOARD

Henry Rosenberger), chair (hlr@rosenberger.com), 818 Blooming Glen Rd, Blooming Glen PA 18911; Edgar Stoesz, secretary; Paul E. Witter, treasurer

Association of Mennonite Credit Unions

larry@mennonitefinancial.com
800-451-5719 and 717-291-1364
1532 Lititz Pike, PO Box 10455, Lancaster PA 17605-0455

INFORMATION

Founded 1988. Provides a fellowship setting for those who share a common interest in Mennonite Church based credit unions and mutual aid programs; to share experiences as formally organized financial cooperatives; to assist those communities who are interested in developing their own credit unions; and to encourage a Christian perspective in developing a credit union philosophy. For more information about Mennonite credit unions, contact one of the persons listed below.

CONTACTS

Larry Miller, Mennonite Financial Federal Credit Union (larry@mennonitefinancial.com)—see separate listing; John Beiler, Parkview Mennonite Federal Credit Union (jbeiler@pvfcu.org)—see separate listing; Nick Driedger, Mennonite Savings and Credit Union (ndrieger@mscu.com)

Association of Mutual Aid Societies—AMAS

tjyousey@northnet.org
315-376-4737, fax 315-376-8433
7383M Utica Blvd., Lowville NY 13367

STAFF
Holly Yousey, conference coordinator

INFORMATION
Founded 1954. Fosters cooperation among various Anabaptist mutual aid organizations, promotes Christian mutual aid, serves as a clearinghouse for ideas and information, and fosters good management of member organizations.

Membership is open to Anabaptist mutual aid organizations and insurance companies. See separate listing under Mutual Aid and Insurance Agencies for member organizations.

BOARD
Allen Schroeder, chair; Bob Rabenstein, vice-chair; Larry Litwiller, secretary; Larry Jantzi, treasurer; Ron Mathies, Holly Yousey, Joe Christophel, Nelson Scheifele, Bob Sutter

Atlantic Coast Mennonite Conference
—see section 2: Conferences and Congregations

Atlanta 2003
—see Office of Communication Planning, Executive Board, in section 1: Churchwide Agencies

B

Bethel College
webmaster@bethelks.edu, www.bethelks.edu
316-283-2500, fax 316-284-5286
300 E 27th St, North Newton KS 67117

STAFF
E. LaVerne Epp, president (lepp@bethelks.edu)
Dale Schrag, director of church relations
 (drs@bethelks.edu)

INFORMATION
A four-year, co-educational and primarily residential liberal arts college, Bethel grants B.A., B.S., and B.S. in nursing and social work degrees. Bethel offers 27 majors including restorative community justice and global peace and justice studies, and a certificate in youth ministry.

Bethel, affiliated with Mennonite Church USA, Associated Colleges of Central Kansas, Council of Christian Colleges and Universities, and Council of Independent Colleges, emphasizes personal discipleship and commitment to Christian community.

Bethel, the oldest Mennonite college in North America, was founded in 1887, and averages an enrollment of 525 students yearly.

BOARD
Dee Gaeddert, chair (dgaeddert@msn.com), 10475 Hadley Ave N, Grant MN 55110 (651-762-2837); Ray Penner, vice-chair; Delon Martens, secretary; John Penner, treasurer

PUBLICATION
Context (three times yearly), Carla Reimer, editor (same address as above)

Bluffton College
www.bluffton.edu
800-488-3257 and 419-358-3000,
fax 419-358-3323
280 W College Avenue, Ste 1, Bluffton OH 45817-1196

STAFF
Lee F. Snyder, president
 (president@bluffton.edu)
John I. Kampen, vice-president and dean of academic affairs (kampenj@bluffton.edu)

Sue Hardwick, administrative assistant to the president (hardwicks@bluffton.edu)

INFORMATION
Bluffton College is a four-year liberal arts college in northwest Ohio. Founded by the General Conference Mennonite Church in 1899, Bluffton is affiliated with the Mennonite Church USA. It offers 38 majors and grants three degrees— bachelor of arts; master of arts in education; master of arts in organizational management.

Bluffton College is accredited by the Higher Learning Commission and a member of the North Central Association of Colleges and Schools (www.ncahigherlearningcommission.org) (312-263-0456). Program accreditations include social work, dietetics, and music.

BOARD
Morris Stutzman, chair (mstutzman@lhslaw.com), 2171-B Eagle Pass, Wooster OH 44691 (330-264-6115); David Baumgartner, vice-chairperson; Joanne Sauder, secretary; Elaine Moyer, treasurer; Sarah Arn; James Bassett; Charles Bishop; James Blankemeyer; Richard Cripe; David Ewert; James Frank; Joyce Frey; Katherine Grusy; Edith Landis; Jerry Lewis; Floyd Liechty; Ronald Lora; Lawrence Milan; Roberta Mohr; Louise Reeser; James Sommer; Gary Stenson; Mark Weidner; Allen Yoder

PUBLICATION
Bluffton magazine (Quarterly), Laurie Wurth-Pressel, editor (same address as above)

Books Abroad and at Home
(Coordinating Office)
cindyy@mennonitemission.net
574-294-7523, fax 574-294-8669
Box 370, Elkhart IN 46515-0370

AREA OFFICES
Paxton IL: Marilyn Litwiller (mjlitwiller@juno.com), 1415 CR 3500 N, Paxton IL 60957 (217-396-4061)
Tremont IL: Julie G. Largent, 712 Prairie Ln, PO Box 1520, Tremont IL 61568-1520 (309-925-5692)
Goshen/South Bend IN: Joyce Schertz (joycems@aol.com), 705 S Ironwood Dr, South Bend IL 46615 (574-289-6864) Workroom located at The Depot, 1013 Division St, Goshen IN 46526 (574-534-4070)
Lititz PA: Ethel Brendle, 1001 E Oregon Rd, Lititz PA 17543 (717-509-5453) Workroom located at MCC Material Resource Center, 517 Trout Run Rd, Ephrata PA 17522
Scottdale PA: Milford and Winifred Paul, 12 Park Ave, Scottdale PA 15683 (724-887-6145)
Harrisonburg VA: Vivian Beachy (vbeachy@mymailstation.com), 1640 Park Rd Apt B, Harrisonburg VA 22802 (540-434-9405)

INFORMATION
Founded 1961. A program for sharing good used books and printed material in over 80 countries abroad as well as to emerging young churches in North America. Coordinated by staff at Mennonite Mission Network, and carried out by groups and individuals across the church with locally donated books and funds.

Bookstores
—see Mennonite Publishing House in section 1: Churchwide Agencies

Brethren in Christ
—see section 5: Sister Denominations

Builder
—Mennonite Publishing House in section 1: Churchwide Agencies

C

CAL
—see Center for Anabaptist Leadership

Calendar
—see churchwide calendar on the web at www.MennoniteUSA.org

Camps
—see Mennonite Camping Association

Canadian Mennonite
—see Mennonite Church Canada in section 5: Sister Denominations

Cascadia Publishing House
(formerly Pandora Press U.S.)
mking@netreach.net,
www.PandoraPressUS.com
215-723-9125, fax 215-721-7967
126 Klingerman Road, Telford PA 18969

STAFF
Michael A. King, president

INFORMATION
Founded 1997. Releases Anabaptist-related scholarly volumes; also publishes popular books under the DreamSeeker Books imprint and faith-related general audience articles through DreamSeeker Magazine. Relates to Herald Press, Mennonite Church USA, Mennonite Church Canada, and Anbaptist-related colleges and seminaries.

Center for Anabaptist Leadership (CAL)
cal@uscwm.org, www.urban-anabaptist.org
626-720-1800, fax 626-720-8101
Box CAL, 1539 E Howard St, Pasadena CA 91104

STAFF
Jeff Wright, executive director
  (wrightstuff@pacificsouthwest.org)
Gloria Newton, administrator (cal@uscwm.org)

INFORMATION
The Center for Anabaptist Leadership equips church leaders through grassroots training, personal coaching, and strategic consulting, so that congregations become vital centers of God's mission in the city.

CAL's primary focus is serving Mennonite and Church of the Brethren congregations and pastors of the Pacific Southwest. However, relationships with other Anabaptist groups both locally and globally are actively developed and welcomed.

Founded 1987 by Southern California pastors, the Center for Anabaptist Leadership is an urban mission resource to congregations.

BOARD
Valentina Satvedi, chair
(vsatvedi@worldnet.att.net), 2761 W 190th St, Redondo Beach CA 90278 (310-371-0411); Steve Penner, vice-chair; Joyce Welch, treasurer; Myrna Wheeler, secretary; Doris J. Greer, Gilbert Romero, Henny van der Zwaag, Erin Dufault-Hunter, Tig Intagliata, Raúl Serradell, Jim Brenneman, Alvin Isaacs, Juan Martínez

Center for Peace and Nonviolence
andrekrmc@juno.com
574-631-8758 or 574-291-0924
921 Eddy St, South Bend IN 46617

INFORMATION
The Center for Peace and Nonviolence is an ecumenical group of churches in St. Joseph County, Indiana, which "seeks to explore and promote Jesus" nonviolent way of righting wrong and establishing justice. We welcome people of all faith traditions who are committed to the values of justice and nonviolence to join

ORGANIZATIONAL INDEX

3

us in action and conversation." Begun in the mid-1980s through Kern Road Mennonite Church, the Center has sponsored a variety of educational events, prayer vigils at murder sites and gun buy-backs. Presently the Center is giving primary energy to birthing a church-based community organizing project.

BOARD
Andre Gingerich Stoner, chair, (andrekrmc@juno.com), Kern Road Mennonite Church, 18211 Kern Road, South Bend IN 46614, 574-291-0924; Jay Caponigro, Pastor Larry Fourman, Jan Jenkins, Jay Landry, Rev. Michael Patton, Rev. Gilbert Washington, Sr. Marilyn Zugish

Center on Conscience & War (NISBCO)
nisbco@nisbco.org, www.nisbco.org
800-379-2679 and 202-483-2220
1830 Connecticut Avenue, NW, Washington DC 20009

STAFF
J. E. McNeil, executive director
Bill Galvin, counseling coordinator

INFORMATION
CCW works to defend and extend the rights of conscientious objectors. CCW supports, for free, those who question participation in war: U.S. citizens, immigrants—or citizens in other countries.

CCW's advisory council includes MCC, COB, and other Anabaptist traditions. CCW participates in the G. I. Rights Hotline, a national referral and counseling service for military personnel. CCW was formed in 1940 by an association of religious bodies including MCC and various Mennonite and other Anabaptist churches.

BOARD
Jonathan Ogle, chair, Philadelphia Yearly Meeting rep. (jonathanogle@westtown.edu),

Westtown School, Westtown PA 19395 (610-339-1435); Titus Peachey, MCC rep, secretary; Mary Miller, Episcopal Church rep; Ibrahim Ramey; Irving Ruderman, Jewish Peace Fellowship reps; Greg Davidson Lazakovitz, Church of the Brethren rep; Dan Seeger; James Feldman; Michael Hovey, Pax Christie rep

PUBLICATIONS
The Reporter for Conscience' Sake (Quarterly), J. E. McNeil, editor (same address as above)

Central District Conference
—see section 2: Conferences and Congregations

Central Plains Mennonite Conference
—see section 2: Conferences and Congregations

Chicago Area Mennonites
vvogt@ameritech.net
847 869 4599, fax 847 328 8431
726 Monroe St, Evanston IL 60202

EXECUTIVE COMMITTEE
Virgil Vogt, president, vvogt@ameritech.net; Allan Howe, treasurer; Jose Elizalde; Wayne Hochstetler

INFORMATION
Chicago Area Mennonites seeks to develop relationships and build cooperation among all Mennonite congregations and ministries in the Chicago area. At present there are 21 congregations and 8 additional ministries.

China Education Exchange
—see Council of Anabaptist International Ministries

Child Welfare Services
—see Mennonite Health Services

Choice Books

CENTRAL OFFICE
info@choicebooks.org, www.choicebooks.org
540-434-1827, fax 540-434-9894
2387 Grace Chapel Road, Harrisonburg VA
22801

STAFF
John M. Bomberger, chief executive officer
(bombergerj@choicebooks.org)

INFORMATION
Year founded: 1962
Mission statement: "To share the good news of
Jesus Christ in the general marketplace through
inspiring and wholesome reading material."
Choice Books operates through a network of
nine regional distributors working cooperatively
with each other through a Central Office in
Harrisonburg VA. Choice Books distributors
service more than 5,700 book displays nationwide located in a variety of retail stores (i.e.;
supermarkets, drug stores, mass merchandis-
ers, travel centers, hospitals, airports, military
bases). In 2001 Choice Books sold a record
3,783,594 books.

BOARD OF DIRECTORS
Norman Shenk, chair (normans@emm.org),
53 W Brandt Blvd., PO Box 458, Salunga PA
17538-0458 (717-898-2251); Curvin M. Hursh,
vice-chair; Paul Helmuth, secretary-treasurer;
Nathan Miller, Harley Nisly, Rick Zoss, Simon
Schrock, Ronald Schertz, Edgar Stoesz

DISTRIBUTORS/OWNERS
Choice Books of Great Lakes-Rosedale, 9920
Rosedale Milford Center Road, Irwin OH
43029, Alvin Troyer, executive director
(740-857-1368, fax 520-569-8076);
info@glr.choicebooks.org
Choice Books of Gulf States, 6115 Old
Pascagoula Road, Theodore AL 36582,
Naaman Beiler, executive director (251-653-
0560, fax 251-653-0620);
info@gs.choicebooks.org
Choice Books of Kansas, 7217 West Mills
Avenue, Hutchinson KS 67501, Arno Miller,
executive director (620-567-2162, fax 620-
567-2419); info@ks.choicebooks.org
Choice Books of Midwest, PO Box 166,
Metamora IL 61548 (309-367-2152, fax
309-367-9541); info@mw.choicebooks.org
Choice Books of Northern Virginia, PO Box
4080, Manassas VA 20108, Simon Schrock,
executive director (703-530-9993, fax 703-
530-9983); info@nva.choicebooks.org
Choice Books of Ohio, Box 210, 13363 Jericho
Road, Kidron OH 44636, Jan Sohar, executive director (330-857-5471, fax 330-857-
5485); info@oh.choicebooks.org
Choice Books of Pennsylvania, PO Box 458,
Salunga PA 17538, Ray Brubaker, executive
director (717-665-3933, fax 717-665-
3059); info@pa.choicebooks.org
Choice Books of Southwest, 1013 N 13th Street,
Phoenix AZ 85006, Vernon Hochstetler,
executive director (602-258-0977, fax 602-
258-0971); info@sw.choicebooks.org
Choice Books of West Coast, 2708 Heath Road,
Bakersfield CA 93312, Ken Becker, executive
director (661-588-4487, fax 661-588-
5296); info@wc.choicebooks.org

Christian Peacemaker Teams (CPT)
cpt@igc.org, www.cpt.org
773-277-0253, fax 773-277-0291
PO Box 6508, Chicago IL 60680-6508

STAFF
Gene Stoltzfus, director/program coordinator
(cpt@igc.org)
Kryss Chupp, training coordinator
(synapses@igc.org)
Rich Meyer, Middle East support
(cptcsd@npcc.net)
Duane Ediger, Colombia support
(duane.ediger@prodigy.net)

INFORMATION

Founded 1988. Sends teams of trained peace-makers into places of conflict around the world. Works through active spiritually-centered peacemaking, including nonviolent direct action, negotiations, human rights work, and various ministries of presence. Sponsoring denominations include Mennonite Church USA, Mennonite Church Canada, Church of the Brethren, and Friends United Meeting. Congregational support and team make-up is ecumenical.

BOARD

John Stoner, chair (jkstoner@ptd.net), 728 Fulton, Akron PA 17501, 717-859-1958; Muriel Stackley, co-chair; Bob Bartel, treasurer; Orlando Redekopp, secretary; Paul Dodd, Susan Mark Landis, Pat Hostetter Martin, David Jehnsen, Cliff Kindy, Nancy Maeder, Hedy Swadsky

PUBLICATION

Signs of the Times (Quarterly), staff editor (same address as above)

Church Extension Services, Inc.

ces@mennoniteusa.org
316-283-5100, fax 316-283-0454
722 N Main St, PO Box 347, Newton KS 67114

STAFF

Ted W. Stuckey, president
    (teds@mennoniteusa.org)
J. Jarrett Stucky, treasurer
    (jarretts@mennoniteusa.org)
Karen Kaufman, administrative assistant
    (karenk@mennoniteusa.org)

INFORMATION

Church Extension Services (CES) operates as an affiliate of Mennonite Church USA, making low-interest loans to denomination congregations and affiliated organizations for the acquisition, construction, or improvement of worship and other church-related facilities. Funds for making church loans are primarily received through investments by individuals and organizations.

Currently, CES can offer investments to eligible investors in 16 states.

CES was founded by General Conference Mennonite Church and separately incorporated in 1958.

BOARD

R. Lee Delp, chair, 840 Keeler Rd, Lansdale PA 19446; James M. Harder, secretary; Darrell Ediger; Byron Pellecer; Duncan Smith; Jeff Wright; and Allen Yoder, Jr.

Church of the Brethren

—see section 5: Sister Denominations

Churchwide Calendar

—see churchwide calendar on the web at www.MennoniteUSA.org

CLC

—see Constituency Leaders Council, Executive Board, in section 1: Churchwide Agencies

CIM

—see Council of International Anabaptist Ministries

Colleges

—See specific listings for Bethel, Bluffton, Eastern Mennonite, Goshen, and Hesston in this section

Conferences

—see section 2: Conferences and Congregations

Congregational Life

—see Executive Board in section 1: Churchwide Agencies

Congregational Resource Centers

—see section 2 conference listings for Eastern District, Franconia, Lancaster, Virginia, Western District

Conservative Mennonite Conference

—see section 5: Sister Denominations

Constituency Leaders Council

—see Executive Board in section 1: Churchwide Agencies

Conventions

—see Executive Board in section 1: Churchwide Agencies

Council of International Anabaptist Ministries

600 Shaftesbury Blvd, Winnipeg MB R3P 0M4 Canada, 204-888-6781, fax 204-831-5675
Peter H. Rempel, coordinator
(prempel@mennonitechurch.ca)

INFORMATION

The Council of International Anabaptist Ministries (CIM) is an association of North American Mennonite and Brethren in Christ international and service agencies. The executive leadership and program administrators meet annually to exchange information, study issues and plan joint projects.

CIM AGENCIES

Africa Inter-Mennonite Missions, 59466 CR 113, Elkhart IN 46517, 574-875-5552, fax 574-875-6567, aimm@aimmintl.org

Brethren in Christ World Missions, P O Box 390, Grantham PA 17027-0390, 717-697-2634, fax 717-691-6053, bicwm@messiah.edu

China Educational Exchange, 1251 Virginia Ave, Harrisonburg VA 22801, 540-432-6983, fax 540-434-5556, chinaedex@aol.com

Eastern Mennonite Missions, 53 Brandt Blvd, PO Box 458, Salunga PA 17538-0458, 717-898-2251, fax 717-898-8092, info@emm.org

Eastern Mennonite University, 1200 Park Rd, Harrisonburg VA 22802, 540-432-4466, fax 540-432-4444, info@emu.org

Evangelical Mennonite Church, International Missions, 1420 Kerrway Ct, Ft Wayne IN 46805-5402, 219-423-3649, fax 219-420-1905, earl@emctoday.com

Evangelical Mennonite Conference, Board of Missions, Box 1268, Steinbach MB R0A 2A0, 204-326-6401, fax 204-326-1613, emconf@mts.net

Evangelical Mennonite Missions Conference, PO Box 52029, Niakwa Post Office, Winnipeg MB R2M 5P9, 204-253-7929, fax 204-256-7384, emmc@mb.sympatico.ca

Franconia Mennonite Conference, 771 Route 113, Souderton PA 18964, 215-723-5513, fax 215-723-1211, info@fmc-online.org

Global Disciples Network, 319 Manor Ave, Millersville PA 17551-1117, 717-872-7404, fax 717-872-6064, mail@globaldisciples.org

Mennonite Brethren Biblical Seminary, 4824 E Butler Ave, Fresno CA 93727, 559-251-8628, fax 559-251-7212, mbaker@mbseminary.com

Mennonite Brethren Missions/Services International, 4867 E Townsend Ave, Fresno CA 93727-5006, 559-456-4600, fax 559-251-1342, mbmsi@mbmsinternational.org

Mennonite Central Committee, 21 S 12th St, P O Box 500, Akron PA 17501-0500, 717-859-1151, fax 717-859-2171, mailbox@mcc.org

Mennonite Church Canada Witness, 600 Shaftesbury Blvd., Winnipeg MB R3P 0M4, 204-888-6751, fax 204-8331-5675, mail@mennonitechurch.ca

Mennonite Economic Development Associates, International Operations, 302-280 Smith St, Winnipeg MB R3C 1K2, 204-956-6430, fax 204-942-4001, meda@meda.org

Mennonite Medical Association, 193 East Frambes Ave, Columbus OH 43201, 614-299-8922, fax 614-299-8922, mma@mennmed.org

Mennonite Mission Network
Great Lakes Office: 500 S Main St, PO Box 370, Elkhart IN 46515-0370, 574-294-7523, fax 574-294-8869, info@mennonitemission.net
Great Plains Office: 722 Main St, P O Box 347, Newton KS 67114-0347, 316-283-5100, fax 316-283-0454, info@mennonitemission.net

ORGANIZATIONAL INDEX

3

Mission Study Center, c/o AMBS, 3003 Benham Ave, Elkhart IN 46517-1999, 574-295-3726, fax 574-295-0092, wsawatsky@ambs.edu

Pacific Northwest Mennonite Conference, 19532 NE Glison St, Portland OR 97230, 503-492-4216, pnmcmissions@juno.com

Rosedale Mennonite Missions, 9920 Rosedale Milford Center Rd, Irwin OH 43029, 740-857-1366, fax 740-857,1605, info@rmmoffice.org

Virginia Mennonite Board of Missions, 901 Parkwood Dr, Harrisonburg VA 22801, 540-434-9727, fax 540-434-7627, info@vmbm.org

Council on Church and Media

churchandmedia@mennoniteusa.org
574-294-7523, fax 574-293-1892
500 S Main St, PO Box 1245, Elkhart IN 46515-1245

OFFICERS

Steve Shenk, chair (shenks@bluffton.edu), Bluffton College, Bluffton OH 45817, 419-358-3453; Tony Krabill, vice-chair; Rosa Perez, treasurer; Cindy Snider, ex officio; Kathryn Rodgers, office associate

INFORMATION

A forum of Mennonite Church USA, Brethren in Christ, Church of the Brethren, and related churches founded in 1985 to foster media creativity, integrity and quality. CCM is organized to facilitate and enhance communication, professional enrichment, fellowship, and development among its members. Annual convention each spring.

PUBLICATION

Forum (three times per year), same address as above.

CPT

—see Christian Peacemaker Teams

D

Dallas Peace Center

admin@dallaspeacecenter.org,
www.dallaspeacecenter.org
214-823-7793, fax 214-823-8356
4301 Bryan Street, Ste 202, Dallas TX 75204

STAFF

Lon Burnam, director
Phyllis Hodge, office manager
Duane Ediger, communications director

INFORMATION

Founded 1981 by Peace Mennonite Church in Dallas, Texas.

BOARD

Cherry Haymes (cherry0@airmail.net), president, 5514 Lobello Drive, Dallas, TX 75229, 214-696-1900; Ellen Danielson, Rev. Dick Davis, Isabel Docampo, Joy Flora, Demetrius Gilbert, Rev. Holsey Hickman, Rev. Charles Hunter, Hadi Jawad, Rev. Bill Matthews, Armando Pacheco, Tina Patterson, Julie Ryan, Gail Smith Ron Wilhelm, and Sam Nance (ex officio)

PUBLICATION

The Dallas Peace Times (six times a year), Duane Ediger, editor

Damascus Road Anti-Racism Program

—see Mennonite Central Committee U.S.

Dates in the Church Year

—see pages 8 and 9

Denver Ministries

—see Mennonite Urban Ministries of Denver

DEO

—see Mennonite Mission Network in section 1: Churchwide Agencies

Developmental Disabilities Services
—see Mennonite Health Services

DOOR
—see Mennonite Mission Network in section 1: Churchwide Agencies

E

Eastern District Conference
—see section 2: Conferences and Congregations

Eastern Mennonite Missions
info@emm.org, www.emm.org
717-898-2251, fax 717-898-8092
53 W Brandt Blvd, PO Box 458, Salunga PA
17538-0458

STAFF
Richard Showalter, president
(richards@emm.org)

INFORMATION
EMM equips, sends, and supports over 345 workers in global witness and service in the way of Christ. Programs include long-term and short-term (Youth Evangelism Service, Summer Training Action Teams).

Supported primarily by approximately 200 congregations in Lancaster Mennonite Conference. Other churches, conferences, and agencies in North America also participate, including ACC, Franklin Conference, Global Community Network, GNF, and New York Mennonite Conference.

Founded 1894 as Home Mission Advocates, and known from 1895 to 1914 as Mennonite Sunday School Mission. Organized 1914 and incorporated in 1916 as Eastern Mennonite Board of Missions and Charities.

BOARD
Carlton Stambaugh, chair, RD 3 Box 425, Hanover PA 17331 (717-632-8641); Joseph Sherer, vice-chair; Timothy E. Darling, secretary; David Gingrich, Ronald Hershey, Dale Martin, Jay Martin, Lindsey Robinson, Kathy Smucker, Thelma Thomas, Keith Weaver

PUBLICATION
Missionary Messenger (Monthly), Stephanie Knudsen, editor (mm@emm.org)

Eastern Mennonite Seminary
info@emu.edu, www.emu.edu
540-432-4260, fax 540-432-4444
1200 Park Rd, Harrisonburg VA 22802

STAFF
Joseph L. Lapp, president (lappj@emu.edu)
Ervin R. Stutzman, dean (stutzerv@emu.edu)

INFORMATION
EMS offers graduate theological education as preparation for Christian ministries and is accredited by ATS and SACS.

EMS was founded in 1965 as an outgrowth of Eastern Mennonite College and is under the control of the Eastern Mennonite University Board of Trustees and the Mennonite Education Agency.

EMS offers the Master of Divinity degree, the Master of Arts in Church Leadership and Master of Arts in Religion degrees, Clinical Pastoral Education, and Certificates in Ministry and Theological Studies.

Enrollment at EMS for 2001-2002 was 125 full- and part-time students.

FACULTY
George R. Brunk III, Kevin A. Clark, Kenton T. Derstine, James R. Engle, Daniel Garrett, Brenda Martin Hurst, Wendy J. Miller, Mark T. Nation, N. Gerald Shenk, Sara Wenger Shenk, Anil D. Solanki, Ervin R. Stutzman, Linford L. Stutzman, Dorothy Jean Weaver, Heidi Miller Yoder, Lawrence M. Yoder, Lonnie D. Yoder, Nathan E. Yoder, Paul M. Zehr

Eastern Mennonite University

info@emu.edu, www.emu.edu
540-432-4000, fax 540-432-4444
1200 Park Rd, Harrisonburg VA 22802

STAFF
Joe Lapp, president (lappj@emu.edu)
Beryl Brubaker, provost, (brubakeb@emu.edu)
Marie Morris, undergraduate dean,
    (morrisms@emu.edu)

INFORMATION
EMU is a national liberal arts school offering
degrees at the undergraduate, graduate, and
seminary levels. All students participate in a
cross-cultural term. (See separate listing for
Eastern Mennonite Seminary.)

EMU is affiliated with Mennonite Church USA
and accredited by the Southern Association of
Colleges and Schools. It is a member of the
Council for Christian Colleges and Universities.

Founded in 1917 as a Bible academy, EMU
grew in size and reputation over the years,
becoming a university in 1994. Total enrollment
is 1,450 in undergraduate, graduate, and seminary programs.

BOARD
Sheryl Wyse, chair (skwyse@aol.com), 1857 N
College Ave, Harrisonburg VA 22802 (540-434-
1260); Clair Sauder, vice-chair; Nora Hess, sec-
retary-treasurer; Harold Bergey, Curtis Berry,
Susan Godshall, Curt Hartman, Linford King,
Herb Noll, Rosalie Hess Roland, Charlotte
Graber Rosenberger, Dick Thomas, Diane
Umble

PUBLICATIONS
Crossroads (Quarterly), Paul Souder, editor
(same address as above); *Weather Vane*
(Weekly student newspaper), *Shenandoah*
(Annual student yearbook)

Education
—see Mennonite Education Agency in section
1: Churchwide Agencies

Elementary schools
—see Schools

Environment
—see Mennonite Environmental Task Force

Every Church a Peace Church
(formerly New Call to Peacemaking)
jstoner@ecapc.org, www.ecapc.org
717-859-1958, fax 717-859-1958
PO Box 500, Akron PA 17501

STAFF
John Stoner, coordinator (jstoner@ecapc.org)

INFORMATION
ECAPC widens the peace and nonviolent struggle
education of New Call to Peacemaking to invite
all denominations and Christians to embrace the
nonviolent heart of Jesus' life and teachings.
The website and conferences are the key modes
of communication.

The support base is individuals representing
Baptist, Catholic, Lutheran, United Methodist,
United Church of Christ, ecumenical fellowships, peace fellowships, and other denominations in addition to the historic peace churches.

New Call to Peacemaking was formed in
1975, and is being disbanded as Every Church A
Peace Church incorporates and forms new
board in 2002.

BOARD
In the process of being formed.

PUBLICATION
Online ECAPC Newsletter (occasional) John
Stoner, editor. Available at www.ecapc.org.

Executive Board
—see section 1: Churchwide Agencies

A Challenge...

within and beyond the classroom from professors and peers who want our students to excel.

A Change...

of scenery that can take our students from our western Virginia campus to any part of the world.

A Choice...

to own your faith...to get involved and make a difference...to discover your passion...to prepare for life.

F

Faith & Life Press
—see Mennonite Publishing House, Information, in section 1: Churchwide Agencies

Faith & Life Resources
—see Mennonite Publishing House in section 1: Churchwide Agencies

Financial Services
—see MMA in section 1: Churchwide Agencies

Franconia Mennonite Conference
—see section 2: Conferences and Congregations

Franklin Mennonite Conference
—see section 2: Conferences and Congregations

G

Geographic listing of congregations
—see section 7

Global Disciples Network
Mail@globaldisciples.org,
www.GlobalDisciples.org
717-872-7404, fax 717-872-7404
319 Manor Ave, Millersville PA 17551

STAFF
Galen Burkholder, executive director
   (galen@globaldisciples.org)
Tim Pfautz, operations manager
   (mail@globaldisciples.org)

INFORMATION
Global Disciples Network is connecting churches, businesses, and mission groups internationally to see disciples trained, witnesses to unreached peoples mobilized, and leaders equipped so the world will know Jesus.

Alliance building and facilitating places Global Disciples in partnership with about thirty different conferences, synods, or dioceses of churches, mostly Anabaptist related groups, in Africa, Asia, Europe, Latin America and North America. (Member CIM)

Global Disciples Network was founded in 1996. Their board of directors combined with the board of Mennonite Christian Leadership Foundation in 2001, and one board now governs the two organizations.

BOARD
Marlin Thomas, chair, 100 Willow Valley Lakes Dr, Willow Street PA 17584 (717-464-2741); Dale Weaver, vice-chair; George Hurst, treasurer; Eugene Witmer, secretary

PUBLICATION
Connecting (Bimonthly), staff editors (same address as above)

Good Books
custserv@goodbks.com, www.goodbks.com
800-762-7171 and 717-768-7171,
   fax 888-768-3433
PO Box 419, 3513 Old Philadelphia Pike,
Intercourse PA 17534

STAFF
Merle Good, publisher (mgood@goodbks.com)
Phyllis Pellman Good, senior book editor
   (pgood@goodbks.com)

INFORMATION
Founded 1979. Good Books seeks to bring the Mennonite-related milieu to the general public. Specializes in books about parenting and family, fiction, biography, history, peace, cooking, decorative arts, children's books, and educational books about Mennonite and Amish faith and life.

Books for Leaders

Meditations for Meetings: *Thoughtful Meditations for Board Meetings and for Leaders*
collected by Edgar Stoesz

The moment comes to begin a board meeting. Where does a leader turn to find an appropriate comment to open the occasion, to prepare the setting for doing good work?

Each meditation begins with a Scripture, moves on to a personal story, and ends with a brief prayer.

Each is about leadership—the courage it requires, the clarity it demands, the celebration it sometimes offers. **Paperback, $9.95**

Common Sense for Board Members, *by Edgar Stoesz*

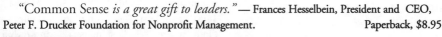

You've just joined a board. You're enthused about the organization's contribution and mission. But you're suddenly uncertain about what's expected of you beside reading reports and attending meetings.

Edgar Stoesz, who served for years as chairman of Habitat for Humanity International, covers many practical matters in brief but thoughtful fashion. Among the more than 40 topics that he deals with are "Whose Rules of Order?", "When Did You Last Vote Nay?", "Delegating: Who Is Responsible?", "Boardroom Bullies," and "Dealing With a Crisis."

"Common Sense is a great gift to leaders." — Frances Hesselbein, President and CEO, Peter F. Drucker Foundation for Nonprofit Management. **Paperback, $8.95**

Doing Good Better: *How to Be an Effective Board Member of a Nonprofit Organization*
by Edgar Stoesz & Chester Raber

NEW, UPDATED EDITION! In these days of tightening budgets, organizations cannot afford weak board members. In this time when many qualified persons have few discretionary hours, they have little time for training. *Doing Good Better* speaks to both needs efficiently and thoroughly. Highly recommended.

"A very fine book on board leadership of nonprofit organizations." — Millard Fuller, President and Founder, Habitat for Humanity, International. **Paperback, $9.95**

Available at local bookstores or directly from the publisher.
Call toll-free 800/762-7171 • P.O. Box 419, Intercourse, PA 17534
Mastercard, Visa, Discover, and American Express accepted.
For shipping and handling, add 10% ($3.00 minimum).
Visit our secure internet store: www.goodbks.com
(check our weekly specials—35% off!).

Good Books™

Goodville Mutual Casualty Company

goodville@goodville.com, www.goodville.com
800-448-4622 and 717-354-4921,
 fax 717-354-5158
625 W Main Street, PO Box 489, New Holland
PA 17557-0489

STAFF
Herman D. Bontrager, president and CEO
   (hermanbontrager@goodville.com)
Philip E. Nolt, vice-president
   (philip.nolt@goodville.com)

INFORMATION
Goodville provides auto, home, farm, business, church, and general liability insurance coverages in Delaware, Indiana, Illinois, Kansas, Maryland, Ohio, Oklahoma, Pennsylvania and Virginia.
   Founded in 1926 the company serves Mennonites, Brethren in Christ, Church of the Brethren, and others who meet company standards. Member of Association of Mutual Aid Societies (AMAS).

BOARD
Carlton L. Miller, chair
(carlton@onemain.com); Kenneth L. Beiler, vice-chair; Herman D. Bontrager, president; John L. Frankenfield, secretary; Allon H. Lefever, treasurer; Glenn E. Rutt; Sanford L. Alderfer; John R. Buckwalter; D. Stanley Jones; Paul M. King; Keith W. Lehman; Donald L. Nice; Glennys H. Shouey; Mim Shirk; Harley K. Smith.

Goshen College

info@goshen.edu, www.goshen.edu
800-348-7422 and 574-535-7000,
fax 574-535-7660
1700 S Main St, Goshen IN 46526

STAFF
Shirley H. Showalter, president
   (president@goshen.edu)

Sheldon W. Burkhalter, director of church relations (sheldonwb@goshen.edu)
Karen Lowe Raftus, director of admissions
   (admissions@goshen.edu)

INFORMATION
Goshen College is a national liberal arts college known for leadership in international education, service-learning, and peace and justice issues in the Anabaptist-Mennonite tradition. GC is recognized for its unique Study-Service Term program and exceptional educational value.
   Degrees: BA, BS, and BS in Nursing, certificate programs. Accredited by North Central Association of Colleges and Schools, National Council for Accreditation of Teacher Education, National League for Nursing and Council on Social Work Education, Member of Coalition for Christian Colleges and Universities, International 50 and Council of Independent Colleges. Founded 1874. Goshen College Sarasota (Fla.) established in 1998.

BOARD
Virgil Miller, chair
(vmiller@saudermanufacturing.com), 22494 County Road B, Archbold OH 43502 (419-445-1100); Paul Bast, Tom Bishop, Ervin Bontrager, Cindy Breeze, John Koshmider, J. Elvin Kraybill, Ivorie Lowe, Lonnie Sears, Terry Shue, Randy Springer, Rebecca Stoltzfus

PUBLICATION
Bulletin (Quarterly alumni magazine), Rachel Lapp, editor (racheljl@goshen.edu)

Great Lakes Discipleship Center
—see Mennonite Mission Network in section 1: Churchwide Agencies

Gulf States Mennonite Conference
—see section 2: Conferences and Congregations

H

Harmonies Workshop

office@harmonies.org, www.harmonies.org
800-201-2680 pin 0101 and 717-656-2749,
 fax 717-656-8265
34 W Eby Rd, Leola PA 17540

STAFF

Glenn Lehman, executive director
   (office@harmonies.org)

INFORMATION

Sponsors the Table Singers, a choir focusing on
20th-century Mennonite music; Foresingers, an
ensemble focusing on early Mennonite music;
and events and materials for the promotion of
church music. Harmonies is a fraternal organization of Lancaster Mennonite Conference.
Harmonies was founded in 1987 and incorporated in 1992 to better serve a growing range of
church music leadership needs.

BOARD

Steven L. Shenk, chair (stevens478@aol.com),
2268 Old Philadelphia Pk, Lancaster PA 17602
(717-295-3105); Earl Rohrer, treasurer; Stanley
Godshall, Dorcas M. Lehman, Glenn M. Lehman,
Rachel Pellman, David Rempel Smucker

PUBLICATION

Notes (Quarterly), Glenn Lehman, editor (same
address as above)

Healthcare Agencies

—see Mennonite Health Services

Herald Press

—see Mennonite Publishing House in section 1:
Churchwide Agencies

Heritage Centers

—see Historical Centers

Hesston College

admissions@hesston.edu; alumni@hesston.edu,
www.hesston.edu
866-437-7866 (toll-free), 620-327-4221 and
620-327-8233, fax 620-327-8300
325 S College, PO Box 3000, Hesston KS
67062-2093

STAFF

Loren E. Swartzendruber, president
   (lorens@hesston.edu)
Marcus Yoder, executive vice-president for academic affairs (marcy@hesston.edu)
Dallas Stutzman, church relations director
   (dallass@hesston.edu)

INFORMATION

Founded: 1909. A two-year college with students
from 30 states and 20 countries including
Canada. Enrollment: 389 full-time and 56 part-
time. Degrees offered: Associate of Arts,
Associate of Science, and Associate of Applied
Arts and Sciences with majors in aviation, Bible,
business, computer information technology,
early childhood education, nursing, and pastoral ministries. Accreditation: Affiliated and
accredited by NCA. Board of control: Mennonite
Education Agency.

BOARD

Arlan Yoder, chair (ayoder@southwind.net),
112 Park Rd, Hesston KS 67062 (620-327-
2794); Pam Boyts Gerber, vice-chair; Deb
Whetzel, secretary; Ginny Birky, Wilbur
Bontrager, Abe Clymer, Dee Custar, Jose
Elizalde, Denton R. Jantzi, Harley Kooker, Phyllis
Nofziger, Norm Yoder, Tim Burkholder

PUBLICATION

Hesston College Today, Phil Richard, editor
(philr@hesston.edu)

Hispanic Mennonite Church

—see Iglesia Hispana Menonita

ORGANIZATIONAL INDEX

3

Historical Committee
—see Executive Board in section 1: Churchwide Agencies

Hospitals
—see Mennonite Health Services

Historical Organizations

CHURCHWIDE

See Archives of Mennonite Church USA under Executive Board in section 1: Churchwide Agencies.

DELAWARE

Delaware Mennonite Historical Assoc.
PO Box 238, Greenwood DE 19950

ILLINOIS

Illinois Amish Interpretive Center
iaic@one-eleven.net, www.amishcenter.com
217-268-3599 or 1-888-45AMISH, fax 217-268-4810
PO Box 413, 111 S Locust St, Arcola IL 61910
Conrad Wetzel, executive director; Wilmer Otto, board chair
   Founded 1995. Interprets the Amish faith and culture through introductory video, museum, bookstore, and guided tours of the Amish community.

Illinois Mennonite Heritage Ctr
gnafzig@mtco.com, www.rootsweb.com/~ilmhgs
309-367-2551 or 309-392-2518, fax 309-392-2518
PO Box 1007, Rte 116 West, Metamora IL 61548
   Founded 1982. Mennonite museum, historical and genealogical library, farm museum, restored grandfather house and barn, amid native trees and prairie grasses.

Illinois Mennonite Historical and Genealogical Society
gnafzig@mtco.com, www.rootsweb.com/~ilmhgs
309-367-2551 or 309-392-2518, fax 309-392-2518
PO Box 1007, Metamora IL 61548-1007
Carolyn Nafziger, president; Gordon Oyer, museum chair; Steven R. Estes, archives chair; Ruth Ulrich, library chair
   Founded 1969. Collects, preserves, interprets, shares artifacts and information relating to faith and life of Mennonites in Illinois. Publications; operates Heritage Center.

INDIANA

Howard-Miami County Heritage Society, Inc.
Jjhorner@aol.com
765-395-3790
PO Box 156, Greentown IN 46936
David Rogers, president; Arlenee Rogers, treasurer
   Founded 1996. Mission is to discover and to tell the stories of the Amish, Mennonite, and other related families who settled in central Indiana in 1848ff.

Menno-Hof
mennohof@tln.net, www.mennohof.org or ww.mennohof.com/
219-768-4117, fax 219-768-4118
510 S Van Buren, SR 5, PO Box 701, Shipshewana IN 46565-0701
Joseph Yoder, director
   Founded 1988. An interpretive center of Mennonite and Amish history and faith. Visitors are invited to consider faith and to discover others of similar faith in their home communities.

Mennonite Historical Library (IN)
mhl@goshen.edu, www.goshen.edu/mhl
574-535-7418 or 574-535-7433,
fax 574-535-7438
1700 S Main St, Goshen IN 46526-9989
John D. Roth, director
   Founded 1906. Holdings of over 55,000 volumes documenting Reformation and Anabaptist history and various Mennonite and related groups throughout the world. Owned by Goshen College with support from AMBS.

Mennonite Historical Society (IN)
bieseckermasts@bluffton.edu
574-535-7433, fax 574-535-7438
1700 Main St, Goshen IN 46526
   Founded 1921. Promotes Anabaptist-Mennonite studies, broadly defined. Hosts local lectures, publishes The Mennonite Quarterly Review, Studies in Anabaptist and Mennonite History, and the C. Henry Smith Series. Also sponsors annual publication and research grants.

Michiana Anabaptist Historians
574-293-2453 or 574-537-4017, fax 574-533-8063
206 Marine Ave, Elkhart IN 46516
John Bender, president, 1997-2000
   Founded 1992. Assists congregational and local historians and others interested in gathering and preserving Mennonite/Anabaptist-related materials. Promotes historical awareness through spring and fall meetings, tours, seminars, and biannual newsletter.

IOWA

Mennonite Historical Society of Iowa and Archives
319-656-3271, fax 319-656-3732
PO Box 576, Kalona IA 52247-0576
Frank Yoder, president
   Founded 1948. Holdings include IA-NE Conference records, local church and community historical records, genealogy and family records.

KANSAS

Kauffman Museum
kauffman@bethelks.edu,
www.bethelks.edu/kauffman.html
316-283-1612, fax 316-283-2107
Bethel College, 27th and Main, North Newton KS
67117-0531
Rachel Pannabecker, director; Chuck Regier, curator of
exhibits
Founded 1941. Interprets Mennonites in relation to
the cultural and natural history of the Great Plains.
Traveling exhibitions.

Mennonite Heritage Museum
mhmuseum@futureks.net,
www.skyways.lib.ks.us/towns/goessel/museum
316-367-8200
200 N Poplar, PO Box 231, Goessel KS 67053
Kristine Schmucker, director/curator
Founded 1974. A tribute to the Alexanderwohl
Mennonite Church congregation immigrants that settled in the Goessel community in 1874.

Pioneer Mennonite Adobe House Museum
316-947-3775, fax 316-947-3506
501 S Ash St, Hillsboro KS 67063
David F. Wiebe, director
Founded 1958. Operates a four-acre Hillsboro
Heritage Park that includes Pioneer Mennonite Adobe
House built in 1876 by Peter Loewen.

MARYLAND

Casselman River Area Historians
301-895-4488
PO Box 591, Grantsville MD 21536-0591
David I. Miller, chairman; Paul H. Yoder, secretary
Founded 1987. Encourages and implements the
preservation of Amish/Mennonite history in the
Casselman River area.

Penn Alps and Spruce Forest Artisan Village
info@pennalps.com, www.pennalps.com
301-895-5985, fax 301-895-5942
125 Casselman Rd, Grantsville MD 21536

OHIO

Amish & Mennonite Heritage Center (OH) (formerly Mennonite Information Center)
behalt@sssnet.com, www.pages.sssnet.com/behalt
330-893-3192, fax 330-893-3529
PO Box 324, 5798 County Rd 77, Berlin OH 44610-
0324
Paul J. Miller, executive director; Verna Schlabach, assistant director
Founded 1982. Presents Anabaptist history through
tours of Behalt, a 265-ft. mural-in-the-round of
Mennonite, Amish and Hutterite story, plus video, bookstore, Ten Thousand Villages crafts, art, and more.

Bluffton College Archives
weaverp@bluffton.edu
419-358-3286, fax 419-358-3384
280 W. College Ave, Bluffton OH 45817-1704
Paul L. Weaver, archivist
Founded 1930. Materials held pertain to Bluffton
College, Central District Conference, Africa Inter-
Mennonite Mission, and Mennonite Mutual Aid societies.

Kidron Community Historical Society
kidron@sssnet.com, www.sssnet.com/kidron
330-857-9111
13153 Emerson Rd, PO Box 234, Kidron OH 44636-
0234
Bruce Detweiler Breckbill, director
Founded 1977. Preserves the history and heritage of
the Kidron-Sonnenberg community. Member of the
Ohio Association of Historical Societies and Museums.

Mennonite Historical Library OH)
hiltya@bluffton.edu
419-358-3365, fax 419-358-3384
280 W College Ave, Bluffton OH 45817-1704
Ann Hilty, librarian
Founded 1930. Holdings of materials dealing with
Mennonites and related groups, emphasizing those of
Swiss-French-South German background.

Stark County Mennonite and Amish Historical Society
330-877-9566, 1136 S Prospect Ave, Hartville OH
44632
Elmer S. Yoder, president
Founded 1979. Focuses on the history and culture of
the Stark County (Ohio) Mennonite and Amish communities. Publishes Heritage, a quarterly paper.
Administered by a five-member board of trustees.

Swiss Community Historical Society
Keith Sommer, Box 5, Bluffton OH 45817

OREGON

Oregon Mennonite Historical and Genealogical Society
503-363-2000, fax 503-873-6406
9045 Wallace Rd NW, Salem OR 97304
Jerry Barkman, president; Margaret Shetler, secretary
and archivist
Founded 1988. Records and preserves the history
and genealogies of Mennonite and related groups in
Oregon. Supervises the Oregon Mennonite Archives
and Library.

Oregon Mennonite Archives and Library
503-363-2000, fax 503-873-6406
9045 Wallace Rd NW, Salem OR 97304
Charity Kropf, librarian; Margaret Shetler, archivist
Founded 1960. Official repository for records of the
former PCC and PDC and the present Pacific Northwest
Mennonite Conference. Also historical and genealogical
publications.

PENNSYLVANIA

Allegheny Mennonite Conference Archives
PO Box 12, Somerset PA 15501-0012
Mark Moyer, chair, 1000 Vista Dr Apt 922, Davidsville, PA 15928 (814 288-4575)
Administered by the Historical Committee of the Allegheny Conference, and preserves the records of the conference.

Eastern Mennonite Associated Libraries and Archives
ebbpinola@juno.com
717-393-9745, fax 717-530-8595
c/o Lancaster Mennonite Historical Society, 2215 Millstream Rd, Lancaster PA 17602
Edsel Burdge Jr, chair; Lloyd Zeager, secretary.
Founded 1959. Consortium of Mennonite Historical Libraries/Archives in PA, MD, and VA. including BIC Archive/Historical Society; Germantown Mennonite Historic Trust; Home Messenger Library; Juniata District Mennonite Historical Society; Lancaster Mennonite Historical Society; Menno Simons Historical Library & Archives; Mennonite Historians of Eastern Pennsylvania; Mennonite Historical Association of the Cumberland Valley; Mifflin County Mennonite Historical Society; Muddy Creek Farm Library; Pequla Bruderschaft Library; Young Center for Anabaptist and Pietist Studies.

Germantown Mennonite Historic Trust
gmht@aol.com
215-843-0943, fax 215-843-6263
6133 Germantown Ave, Philadelphia PA 19144
Randall K. Nyce, executive director
Founded 1952. An inter-Mennonite historical trust which nurtures and enriches contemporary Mennonite identity through the preservation and interpretation of the historic Germantown Mennonite meetinghouse, its adjacent cemetery, grounds, and other historical materials related to North America's first Mennonite settlement. James L. Derstine, chair

Hans Herr House Museum
www.netconexinc.com/hansherr
717-464-4438
1849 Hans Herr Dr, Willow Street PA 17584
Doug Nyce, director; Julia Whitfield, educator
Founded 1974. Oldest house in Lancaster County (1719), built by Christian Herr, an early Mennonite settler. Open to the public.

Juniata Mennonite Historical Society
717-694-3211, fax 717-694-3543
PO Box 81, Richfield PA 17086-0081
J. Lloyd Gingrich, secretary; Noah L. Zimmerman, director
Founded 1977. Preserves and protects records and related materials for study and research.

Lancaster Mennonite Historical Society
lmhs@lmhs.org, www.lmhs.org
717-393-9745, fax 717-393-8751
2215 Millstream Rd, Lancaster PA 17602-1499
Brinton L. Rutherford, director; Lloyd R. Zeager, librarian
Founded 1958. Provides library, archives, research services, publications, book sales (new/used), exhibits, speakers, and educational programs (lectures, field trips, seminars, conferences). Archives for Lancaster and Atlantic Coast area conferences of the Mennonite Church. Publications include Pennsylvania Mennonite Heritage, Mirror, and, occasionally, books.

Mennonite Heritage Center (PA)
info@mhep.org, www.mhep.org
215-256-3020, fax 215-256-3023
PO Box 82, 565 Yoder Rd, Harleysville PA 19438-0082
Sarah Wolfgang Heffner, director
Founded 1974. Presents the 300-year history of Mennonite life in southeastern Pennsylvania. Describes both past and present Mennonite life in eastern Pennsylvania. Operated by the Mennonite Historians of Eastern Pennsylvania. Includes gift shop, historical library, and archives.

Mennonite Historians of Eastern Pennsylvania
info@mhep.org, www.mhep.org
215-256-3020, fax 215-256-3023
565 Yoder Rd, PO Box 82, Harleysville PA 19438-0082
Sarah Wolfgang Heffner, director; Joel D. Alderfer, librarian/curator
Founded 1974. Operates the Mennonite Heritage Center, a museum, historical library and archives, and gift shop. Preserves and perpetuates the Anabaptist-Mennonite heritage of the past three centuries in eastern Pennsylvania. The historical library and archives (founded 1967) carries collections of materials on Mennonite life in Bucks, Montgomery, Lehigh, Northampton, Chester, and Philadelphia counties.

Mennonite Historical Association of the Cumberland Valley
ebbpinola@juno.com
717-375-4544, fax 301-733-2184
4850 Molly Pitcher Hwy S, Chambersburg PA 17201
Roy M. Showalter, curator; Merle Cordell, chair; Edsel Burdge Jr, editor, publishes Conococheague Mennonist.
Founded 1957. Houses a historical library, archives, and small museum. The library collection focuses on Mennonite and other peace churches in Franklin County, PA, and Washington County, MD, as well as genealogy and local history.

Mennonite Information Center (PA)
menninfctr@desupernet.net, mennoniteinfoctr.com
717-299-0954, fax 717-290-1585
2209 Millstream Rd, Lancaster PA 17602-1494
R. Wesley Newswanger, director
     Founded 1959. Interprets the faith of Mennonites,
Amish, and other Anabaptist groups local and worldwide. Offers a lecture-tour of an actual-size reproduc-
tion of the Hebrew tabernacle.

Mifflin County Mennonite Historical Society
717-935-5574
PO Box 5603, Belleville PA 17004-5603
Paul E. Bender, president, Zelda Yoder, librarian
     Founded 1985. Open Wednesday and Saturday or by
appointment. Call 717-935-2598.

Muddy Creek Farm Library
717-484-4849, fax 717-484-1042
376 N Muddy Creek Rd, Denver PA 17517-9125

The People's Place
custserv@thepeoplesplace.com,
www.thepeoplesplace.com
800-762-7171 and 717-768-7171, fax 888-768-3433
and 717-768-3433
3513 Old Philadelphia Pike, PO Box 419, Intercourse PA
17534-0419
Staff: Merle and Phyllis Good, executive directors
(mgood@goodbks.com and pgood@goodbks.com)
     Founded 1976. A nationally-recognized educational
and heritage center about the Mennonites and the
Amish. Includes a dramatic three-screen feature, Who
are the Amish? (30 minutes); 20 Questions: A
Discovery Museum for All Ages (questions are
answered from both an Old Order point of view as well
as a modern point of view); an extensive bookstore, art
gallery, pottery gallery, and fair-trade craft shop.

The People's Place Quilt Museum
custserv@ppquiltmuseum.com,
www.ppquiltmuseum.com
800-828-8218 or 717-768-7101, fax 888-768-3433 and
717-768-3433
3513 Old Philadelphia Pk, PO Box 419, Intercourse PA
17534
Staff: Phyllis Pellman Good, curator
(pgood@goodbks.com)
     Founded 1988. Features a new exhibit each year of
exquisite antique Amish and/or Mennonite quilts (usu-
ally pre-1940) and other decorative arts. Occasionally
includes quilts from other traditions, such as African-
American and antique applique quilts. Museum Shoppe
adjacent.

SOUTH DAKOTA

Freeman Academy Heritage Archives
605 925-4237
748 S Main St, PO Box 1000, Freeman SD 57209
Duane Schrag and LaNae Waltner, archivists; Cleon
Graber, museum curator
     Founded 1955. Includes original diaries, Mennonite
and local writings, genealogy books, and records of the
Northern District Conference.

VIRGINIA

Menno Simons Historical Library/Archives
bowmanlb@emu.edu, www.emu.edu
540-432-4177 or 540-432-4184, fax 540-432-4977
Eastern Mennonite University, 1200 Park Rd,
Harrisonburg VA 22802-2462
Lois B. Bowman, librarian; Harold E. Huber, library
assistant
     Founded 1955. Anabaptist, Mennonite, Amish, and
Shenandoah Valley holdings. Archives for EMU and
Virginia Mennonite Conference. Member of Eastern
Mennonite Associated Libraries and Archives.

Shenandoah Valley Mennonite Historians
shenkp@emu.edu
540 434-0578
H. Michael Shenk, 1345 Hillcrest Dr, Harrisonburg VA
22802
     Founded 1993. Promotes the study, preservation,
and communication of the Mennonite heritage in
Shenandoah Valley of Virginia. Relates to Virginia
Mennonite Conference and Mennonite Church USA
Historical Committee.

Valley Brethren-Mennonite Heritage Center
yoderne@emu.edu, www.valleybmhc.mennonite.net
540-432-4255, fax 540-432-4444
1675-D Virginia Avenue, Harrisonburg VA 22802
Nate Yoder, president
     Founded 1999. The mission is to share and celebrate
the faith story of the Brethren and Mennonite people
of the Shenandoah Valley. Still in planning stage.
Developing under direction of a board representing
both Mennonites and Brethren.

Iglesia Menonita Hispana

STAFF
Juan Montes, executive director
(jvmontes@juno.com), 1208 "L" St, Box 111,
Reedley CA 93654 (559-638-7723, iglesia; 559-637-9787, casa; fax 559-637-8826)

ADMINISTRATIVE BOARD
Juan Montes, executive director (see staff);
Byron Pellecer, moderator, 741 NW 45th Ave,
Apt 42, Miami FL 33126, 305-529-9244,
(bpellece@bellsouth.net); Samuel Lopez, treasurer, (smlopez573@juno.com), PO Box 125,
New Holland PA 17557 (717-354-9192, 717-355-2642); Madeline Maldonado, secretary;
Ricardo Rodriquez, assistant moderator; Nicolas
Angustia, Maggie DeLeon, Damian Rodriguez,
Nancy Rodriguez Lora

WOMEN'S COMMITTEE 2000
Sociedad de Damas Cristianas en Accion
(SDCA)
Madeline Maldonado, coordinator,
(dvemady@aol.com), 3225 4th St W, Lehigh
Acres FL 33971 (941-369-0568, 941-332-7556); Celita Pacheco, secretary; Cecelia
Moreno, treasurer; Maggie DeLeon, representative to Mennonite Women

INFORMATION
Founded in 2000 from the former Mennonite
Association of Hispanic Churches (AMIGA) and
Hispanic Mennonite Convention. Iglesia
Menonita Hispana is the recognized organization of the Hispanic Mennonites. Its purpose is
to strengthen the identity and unity of the
Spanish congregations. IMH interprets the work
and provides opportunities for Hispanics to
relate to each other. IMH holds an assembly
every two years. CLC reps: Juan Montes, Samuel
Lopez

PUBLICATION
ENCUENTRO (Bimonthly), Samuel Lopez, editor
(smlopez573@juno.com), PO Box 125, New
Holland PA 17557 (717-354-9192)

Illinois Mennonite Conference
—see section 2: Conferences and Congregations

Indiana-Michigan Mennonite Conference
—see section 2: Conferences and Congregations

Information Centers
—see Historical Organizations

Institute of Mennonite Studies
ims@ambs.edu, www.ambs.edu/IMS
574-295-3726, fax 574-295-0092
3003 Benham Ave, Elkhart IN 46517-1999

STAFF
Mary Schertz, director (mschertz@ambs.edu)

INFORMATION
Founded in 1958, IMS is the research agency of
AMBS and sponsors consultations and publications for Anabaptist-Mennonite studies in the
areas of history, theology, ethics, mission, and
church, as well as in church ministry areas.

EXECUTIVE COMMITTEE
Loren Johns, chair (ljohns @ambs.edu), AMBS,
3003 Benham Ave, Elkhart IN 46517-1999
(574-295-3726); Arthur Paul Boers; J. Nelson
Kraybill; Ben C. Ollenburger; Walter W. Sawatsky

PUBLICATION
Vision: A Journal for Church and Theology
(with CMBC); Mary Schertz, AMBS editor
(vision@ambs.edu), www.MennoVision.org.
Vision seeks to encourage theological reflection
by church leaders on the identity, mission, and
practices of the church from an Anabaptist-Mennonite perspective.

Insurance
—see listing for Mutual Aid and Insurance Agencies in this section and MMA in section 1: Churchwide Agencies

Inter-Church, Inc.
myronsa@aol.com
540-432-4260, fax 540-432-4444
1549 Hillcrest Dr, Harrisonburg VA 22802

STAFF
Myron Augsburger, president
    (myronsa@aol.com)
Abram Clymer, board chair

INFORMATION
Founded 1960. Sponsors Myron and Esther Augsburger's work in evangelism, art conferences, and international seminars.

International Guest House
igh-dc@juno.com
202-726-5808, fax 202-882-2228
1441 Kennedy St NW, Washington DC 20011

STAFF
Rudy and Ruth Friesen, host/hostess;
Sharon Baker, Irene Martin, Danita Greaser

INFORMATION
The IGH is a nonprofit house maintained by the Allegheny Conference of the Mennonite Church to provide clean, inexpensive lodging for international/national visitors in a homelike atmosphere.

BOARD
Annabelle Kratz, chair, 13495 Brighton Dam Rd, Clarksville MD 21029; Gene Miller, secretary; Ilene Weinbenner, treasurer; Glen Gehman

K

Kansas Mennonite Men's Chorus
620-543-2320
102 Rainbow Ct, Buhler KS 67522
Irvin A. Pauls, historian

INFORMATION
Founded 1969. The chorus of about 375 singers presents four concerts per year.

Kingdom Builders
(formerly Philadelphia Mennonite Council)
ldow@mcc.org
215-991-0590
190 W Phil-Ellena, Philadelphia PA 19119

STAFF
Leonard Dow, treasurer

INFORMATION
Founded 1972. Meets monthly to facilitate fellowship, economic development and education within the Philadelphia Anabaptist Network. Related organizations include Crossroads Community Center, Diamond Street Community Center, Germantown Mennonite Historic Trust, and Philadelphia Mennonite High School.

BOARD
Fred Kauffman, chair (wpmf@mail.com), 4740 Baltimore Ave, Philadelphia PA 19143 (215-729-2050, fax 215-729-2845); Leonard Dow, treasurer

L

Lancaster Mennonite Conference
—see section 2: Conferences and Congregations

ORGANIZATIONAL INDEX

3

Lao Mennonite Ministries

kuayingt@mennonitemission.net;
kteng2@cogeco.ca
905-646-3651, fax 905-646-3651
71 Lakeshore Road, St Catharines, ON L2N 2T3
Canada

STAFF
Kuaying Teng

Leadership Discernment Committee

—see Executive Board in section 1: Churchwide Agencies

Lombard Mennonite Peace Center

admin@lmpeacecenter.org,
www.lmpeacecenter.org
630-627-0507, fax 627-0519
1263 South Highland Ave, Suite 1N, Lombard IL 60148

STAFF
Richard Blackburn, executive director
Bob Williamson, associate director
Marty Farahat, assistant director

INFORMATION
LMPC seeks to "proclaim Christ's good news, the gospel of peace and justice and to be active in the sacred ministry of reconciliation," resourcing churches of all denominations.

Begun in 1983, LMPC has a long history of providing training in biblical foundation for peacemaking, conflict transformation and mediation skills, healthy congregations, and consulting with conflicted churches.

BOARD
Judd Peter, chair (judd peter@earthlink.net), 27 Ashlawn Ave, Oswego IL 60543 (630-554-1217); Cal Zehr, vice-chair; Elton Martin, treasurer; Mary Lou Farmer, finance committee chair; Richard Blackburn, ex-officio; Earl Sutter; Terry Gladstone; Gretchen Horsch

PUBLICATION
LMPC Newsletter (Quarterly)

M

Marriage Encounter
—see Mennonite and Brethren Marriage
Encounter

MAX
—see MutualAid eXchange

MCC
—see Mennonite Central Committee

MEDA
—see Mennonite Economic Development
Associates

Menno House
—see New York City Council of Mennonite
Churches

Menno Travel Service, Inc. d/b/a MTS TRAVEL
mts-pa@mtstravel.com, www.mtstravel.com
717-733-4131 or 800-642-8315,
fax 717-733-1909
Home office: 124 E Main St 4th Fl, Ephrata PA
17522

STAFF
Kermit Yoder, president and CEO
(kermity@mtstravel.com)
Jim Buddendorf, COO (jimb@mtstravel.com)
Vickie Unruh, CFO (vickieu@mtstravel.com)

INFORMATION
The largest nationwide, full-service travel company specializing in religious, mission, and nonprofit travel. MTS Travel also offers custom
group tours, all types of vacations, meetings
management, and corporate travel. The company is the Official Travel Agency for Mennonite
World Conference 2003 in Zimbabwe.
  Branch offices: Newton KS, 800-835-0106;
Bloomfield NJ, 800-526-6278; Claremont CA,
800-854-7979; Colorado Springs CO, 800-542-
5577; Jackson MS, 800-647-5296; Jacksonville
FL, 800-888-8292; Knoxville TN, 800-234-8166
  Founded 1947 as travel department of
Mennonite Central Committee. Incorporated
1955 as a full-service travel agency.

BOARD
Keith Stuckey, chair (keith@mhsonline.org);
Kermit Yoder, president; Vickie Unruh, treasur-
er; Jim Buddendorf, secretary; Jim Smucker,
asst chair; Linda Zuendel, asst secretary;
J. E. Lehman, Michael Hering, Richard
Huneryager, Byron Ediger, Daniel Hess, Paul Kurtz

PUBLICATIONS
Travel News (Quarterly), Gwen Kuebler, editor
(Bloomfield NJ office)

Mennofolk Music Festival
wendy@mennofolk.org, www.mennofolk.org
419-358-4326
139 N Spring St, Bluffton, Ohio 45817

STAFF
Wendy Chappell-Dick (wendy@mennofolk.org)
Andy Chappell-Dick, (andy@mennofolk.org)

INFORMATION
Mennofolk is a yearly gathering of Mennonite
folk musicians and those who love their music,
serving as an outreach through music to the
surrounding communities, and an acknowledg-
ment of the many fine professional and amateur
musicians of various genres among us.
  Mennofolk is supported by the Peace,
Service, and Justice Committee of the Central
District Conference at this time, with the future
goal of becoming an independent organization.
  The website maintains a database of
Mennonite folk musicians across the country as
well as giving information about location and
time of the next Mennofolk festival.

ORGANIZATIONAL INDEX

3

BOARD

Members of the Peace, Service, and Justice Committee of Central District Conference

Mennonite and Brethren Marriage Encounter

love@marriageencounter.org,
www.marriageencounter.org
804-795-2646 U.S.; 519-293-3869 Canada
7140 Turner Rd, Richmond VA 23231

STAFF

Gloria and Sanford Snider, moderators; Ruth Smith, secretary

INFORMATION

Founded 1980. M&BME fosters improved marital love between husband and wife, and with God, based upon Christian ideals of marriage. Engaged encounter is also offered. Affiliated with Mennonite Church USA, Mennonite Church Canada, Brethren in Christ, Church of the Brethren and Mennonite Brethren.

Mennonite Association of Retired Persons

marp-soop@juno.com,
www.marp.mennonite.net
215-721-7730
771 Route 113, Souderton PA 18964

STAFF

Helen L. Lapp, executive director

INFORMATION

MARP links older adults in the Anabaptist fellowship and challenges its membership to ongoing learning and service opportunities. The organization's guiding theme is "Older Adults Living with Spirit."

Founded in 1987 as an outgrowth of Inter-Mennonite Council on Aging, MARP is open to all over 50. Its vision for continuing response to Christ's call finds expression in the cooperative short-term service project, SOOP (Service Opportunities for Older People).

BOARD

Robert Ebersole, chair (eber@bright.net), 708 Jantzi Dr, Archbold OH 43502 (419-445-5781); Eleanor C. Ruth, secretary; Charles B. Longenecker, Ralph Witmer, Ann Bender, Al Albrecht, Ken H. Schmidt, Kay Sears

PUBLICATION

PAGES (Quarterly newsletter sent to members and related church agencies), Helen L. Lapp, editor

Mennonite Brethren

—see section 5: Sister Denominations

Mennonite Camping Association (MCA)

office@mennonitecamping.org;
www.mennonitecamping.org
574-294-7523, fax 574-293-1892
PO Box 1245, Elkhart IN 46515-1245

STAFF

Evon Castro, secretary
    (evonc@mennoniteusa.org)

INFORMATION

Founded 1960. Mennonite Camping Association is a binational organization which serves as a clearinghouse for directing and promoting Christian camping among Anabaptist/Mennonite conferences and congregations in North America through a network of camps and retreat centers located in Canada and the United States. Vision Statement (1998): "Seeking God's face in creation, Receiving God's love in Christ, Radiating God's Spirit in the world." Affiliated camps are listed on page 149.

BOARD

Keith Zehr, president (president@ mennonitecamping.org), 111 Main St, Akron NY 14001 (716 542-9927); Jerry Markus, president-elect; Laurie Weaver, secretary/treasurer; Christine Epp, fourth member; Bob Wiebe, past president; Ken Hawkley, Mennonite Church USA

representative; Elsie Rempel, Mennonite Church Canada representative; Brethren in Christ and Mennonite Brethren representatives, currently vacant

PUBLICATION

MCA Newsletter (Quarterly), Jim Penner, editor (editor@mennonitecamping.org), 63 Appalachian Cres, Kitchener ON N2E 1A3, Canada (519-743-4304, fax 519-743-8480)

Camps and Retreat Centers

*Member of Mennonite Camping Association.

ARIZONA

Arizona Mennonite Children's Camp
632-931-9241
4334 W Vista Ave, Glendale AZ 85301
Laurie King, contact

CALIFORNIA

Camp Keola*
info@campkeola.org, www.campkeola.org
559-439-7880 or 559-893-3505 (June-Oct.),
fax 559-439-4973
PO Box 25925, Fresno CA 93729-5925
George Harper, executive director
    Founded 1964. Located in the Sierra Nevada
Mountains at Huntington Lake. Offers wholesome
retreat programs which draw people closer to Jesus
Christ and to each other. Affiliated with Pacific
Southwest Mennonite Conference.

Hartland Christian Camp
info@hartlandcamp.com, www.hartlandcamp.com
559-337-2349, fax 559-337-2251
57611 Eshom Valley Dr, Badger CA 93603
Bob Nunziazo, executive director
    Founded 1946. A Christian camp desired for evan-
gelism, spiritual growth, fellowship, and physical
refreshment.

Mile High Pines Camp
mhpcamp@aol.com, www.milehighpines.com
909-794-2824, fax 909-794-8884
42739 Hwy 38, Angelus Oaks CA 92305
Gabriel Valencia, director
    Founded 1948. A year-round camp dedicated to
retreat, reflection, and renewal. Sponsored by Pacific
Conference-Brethren in Christ.

COLORADO

Deer Creek Christian Camp
303-838-5647
228 S Pine Dr, Bailey CO 80421
Joe Graham, contact
    Founded 1962. Available year round for camping,
family reunions and church retreats.

Rocky Mountain Mennonite Camp*
info@rmmcamp.org, www.rmmcamp.org
719-687-9506, fax 719-687-2582
709 County Road 62, Divide CO 80814
Corbin Graber, executive director
    Founded 1952. Provides Christ-centered camping
programs for all ages, year-round, as well as facilities
for non-profit guest groups and families. Sponsored by

Rocky Mountain and South Central (Kansas) conferences.

FLORIDA

Lakewood Retreat Center*
info@Lakewoodretreat.org, www.Lakewoodretreat.org
352-796-4097, fax 352-796-7577
25458 Dan Brown Hill Rd, Brooksville FL 34602
Rick Brock, executive director
    Founded 1965. A 114-acre youth and family camp,
conference, and retreat center. Offers a year-round program for congregations throughout the Southeast.

IDAHO

Palisades Mennonite Church Camp
mepluseight@juno.com
208-397-4239
PO Box 246, Aberdeen ID 83210-0246
Monty Ledford, contact
    Founded 1957. Located in the Targhee National
Forest in eastern Idaho. Provides summer Bible camp
and retreats for children, youth, and adults. Operated
by First Mennonite Church in Aberdeen with volunteer
help from other Idaho Mennonites and area churches
of other denominations.

ILLINOIS

Menno Haven Camp and Retreat Center*
camp@mennohaven.com, www.mennohaven.com
815-646-4344 and 800-636-6642, fax 815-646-4301
9301 1575 East St, Tiskilwa IL 61368-9710
David Horst, executive director
    Founded 1958. Provides summer youth camps,
extensive high ropes and initiatives course as well as
year-round facilities and services for family and church
events.

INDIANA

Bible Memory Ministries*
biblemem@maplenet.net, www.bible-memory.org
574-533-5388, fax 574-534-6444
PO Box 823, Goshen IN 46527-0823
Lon Erb, executive director
    Founded 1953. Educates children and youth in the
Word of God through scripture memorization, corre-
spondence lessons, summer camps, winter camps, and
area youth activities.
Bible Memory leases camps for our programs.

Merry Lea Environmental Learning Center*
lukeag@goshen.edu, www.goshen.edu/merrylea
260-799-5869, fax 260-799-5875
PO Box 263, Wolf Lake IN 46796-0263
Luke A. Gascho, director
    Donated to Goshen College in 1980. A 1,150-acre
nature preserve of fields, forests, wetlands, bogs,

ORGANIZATIONAL INDEX

3

lakeshores, and meadows. Managed as a nature sanctuary and serves as the classroom for environmental education programs for kindergarteners through adults.

IOWA

Crooked Creek Christian Camp*
ccccamp@juno.com
319-653-3611, fax 319-653-3611
2830 Coppock Rd, Washington IA 52353-9317
Mary Lou Farmer, administrator
Founded 1981. Multi-purpose year-round facility for retreats, family reunions, and children's camping programs.

KANSAS

Camp Mennoscah*
campmno@mennowdc.org, www.mennowdc.org
620-297-3290
PO Box 65, Murdock KS 67111-0065
Deron and Krista Nisly, co-directors
Founded 1948. Sponsors camping programs for children, senior citizens, developmentally disabled, families, and others. A year-round facility. Owned by Western District Conference.

KENTUCKY

Bethel Mennonite Camp*
grow@bethelcamp.org, www.bethelcamp.org
606-666-4911, fax 606-666-4911
2952 Bethel Church Rd, Clayhole KY 41317
Roger Voth, director
Founded 1957. Mission is to reach kids for Christ through 8 weeks of summer camps.

MICHIGAN

Amigo Centre*
info@amigocentre.org, www.amigocentre.org
269-651-2811, fax 269-659-0084
26455 Banker Rd, Sturgis MI 49091-9355
Dana Sommers, executive director
Founded 1957. Camp and retreat center for church and family groups. Sponsors youth, adult, and family programs. A year-round facility.

Camp Friedenswald*
info@friedenswald.org, www.friedenswald.org
269-476-9744, fax 269-476-9745
15406 Watercress Dr, Cassopolis MI 49031-9532
Todd Kirkton, executive director; David Moser, program director; Micah Thieszen, outdoor learning director
Founded 1950. A year-round facility that sponsors various youth and family camp programs. Rents facilities to other groups.

Little Eden Camp*
LittleEden@juno.com
231-889-4294, fax 231-889-4294
3721 Portage Point Dr, Onekama MI 49675-9751
Wendell Beck, contact
Founded 1944. Provides camping programs for children, families, and seniors during the summer. Hosts church retreats and family gatherings the rest of the year.

Miracle Camp
miraclecamp@juno.com, www.miraclecamp.com
616-624-6161, fax 616-624-1566
25281 80th Ave, Lawton MI 49065
Established 1965 by the Evangelical Mennonite Camping Board. Year-round camping center for groups and families up to 320. Programs include 8 weeks of summer camp for children and youth; four winter youth retreats, senior adult and family camps. Available for guest groups.

Northern Michigan Mennonite Camp
ar265@tcnet.org
616-258-3402, fax 616-258-3491
6361 Myers Rd., Kalkaska MI 49646
Sponsors snow camps in the winter and several retreats in the summer.

The Hermitage Community
thehermitage@juno.com
269-244-8696, fax 269-244-5856
11321 Dutch Settlement, Three Rivers MI 49093
David and Naomi Wenger, co-directors
Founded 1985. The Hermitage mission is to provide a place of welcoming hospitality where individuals and small groups can explore their sense of call and deepen their relationship with God.

MINNESOTA

Wilderness Wind Camp*
wildernesswind@juno.com
218-365-5873 or 316-283-5132 (Oct.-Apr.)
2945 Hwy 169, Ely MN 55731
Kathy Landis, director
Founded 1986. Offers wilderness canoeing and backpacking trips that integrate Christian spirituality, care of the environment, and wilderness ethics and skills. Address (Oct.-Apr.): 511 W 11th St, Newton KS 67114.

MISSISSIPPI

Pine Lake Fellowship Camp*
pinelakecamp@juno.com
601-483-2267
10371 Pine Lake Rd, Meridian MS 39307
Jeff and Cheryl Landis, directors
Founded 1966. Welcomes groups or individuals to plan their own retreat during the week or on weekends year-round. Rustic cabins or lodge facilities available. Owned by Gulf States Mennonite Conference.

MISSOURI

Lakeside Mennonite Camp
660-547-2512
Rt 3 Box 3065, Lincoln MO 65338
Sylvia McMillin, secretary
One week camping program for 4th to 8th graders. Sponsored by the Mennonite churches of Missouri.

NEW YORK

Beaver Camp*
info@beavercamp.org, www.beavercamp.org
315-376-2640, fax 315-376-7011
HC 62 Box 221, Lowville NY 13367
Emanuel Gingerich, administrator
Founded 1969. Year-round children's camp and retreat facility.

Camp Deerpark, Inc*
deerpark@warwick.net
845-754-8669, fax 845-754-8217
200 Brandt Rd, PO Box 394, Westbrookville NY 12785
Ken Bontrager, administrator; Jesus Cruz, board chair
Founded 1969. Mission is to empower youth to serve Christ in the city. Summer children's camps. Year-round retreat facility.

OHIO

Camp Buckeye Retreat Center*
campbuck@tusco.net
330-756-2380
10055 Camp Rd NW, Beach City OH 44608
Eric Raber, administrator
Located in wooded hills of east-central Ohio with over 90 acres of hiking trails. Facilities include a lodge, cabins, and Adirondacks with accommodations for 100 campers in summer. Program focus is for disadvantaged children.

Camp Luz*
camp.luz@juno.com, www.campluz.mennonite.net
330-683-1246
152 Kidron Rd, Orrville OH 44667-9699
Deb Horst, camp director
Founded 1953. Offers summer camps for children and youth, programmed retreats, and rental facilities for Christian groups.

OKLAHOMA

Oklahoma Mennonite Retreat
405-663-2523
Rt 3 Box 11, Hydro OK 73048

OREGON

Drift Creek Camp*
driftcreek@harborside.com, www.driftcreek.org
541-996-3978, fax 541-764-5115
PO Box 1110, Lincoln City OR 97367
Jerry and Amy Markus, administrators
Founded 1960 by Mennonite Camp Association of Oregon, Inc. Provides Christian youth camp and retreat facilities in a temperate rain forest setting of the Siuslaw National Forest.

PENNSYLVANIA

Black Rock Retreat*
main@brr.org, www.brr.org
717-529-3232 and 800-858-9299, fax 717-786-6022
1345 Kirkwood Pike, Quarryville PA 17566-9539
Robert M. Bender, administrator; John E. Riddell, business manager
Founded 1954. Dedicated to spreading the Gospel of Jesus Christ and strengthening his church.

Camp Andrews*
campandrews@yahoo.com, www.campandrews.org
717-284-2624, fax 717-284-2852
1226 Silver Spring Rd, Holtwood PA 17532
Phil Herschberger, administrator
Founded 1983. To introduce urban youth to Jesus in a rustic, affordable, natural setting.

Camp Hebron, Inc.*
hebron@camphebron.org, www.camphebron.org
717-896-3441 and 800-864-7747, fax 717-896-3391
957 Camp Hebron Rd, Halifax PA 17032-9520
Lanny Millette, executive director; Mike Ford, program director; Russ Negley, operations director
Founded 1957. A place where people connect with God, nature, and each other. The vision is to be a Christ-centered sanctuary where people find renewal and growth through recreation, teaching, and fellowship in God's creation.

Camp Men-O-Lan*
info@menolan.org, www.menolan.org
215-679-5144, fax 215-679-0226
1415 Doerr Rd, Quakertown PA 18951-2042
Gerald C. Musselman, administrator; Robert Hartz, program director
Founded 1941. Year-round Christian camping and retreat facilities. and programs for all ages. Cottages, cabins, dormitory, RV, and tent sites. Summer overnight and day camps, trip/adventure camps. Sponsored by Eastern District.

Christian Retreat Center
crctims2@starband.net, www.crctims2.org
717-734-3627, fax 717-734-3339
RR 1 Box 13A, East Waterford PA 17021
Bud Wagner, director
Founded 1979. A year-round camping ministry located 40 miles NW of Harrisburg, Pa. Program includes summer camps for youth, ages 8-18, as well as host of short-term missions groups. Facilities available for 130 people. Owned by Brethren in Christ.

ORGANIZATIONAL INDEX

3

Cove Valley Christian Youth Camp*
covevalley@pa.net
717-328-3055, fax 717-328-2350
5357 Little Cove Rd, Mercersburg PA 17236
Allen R. Eshleman, camp director
   Founded 1967. Children's summer camps, winter retreats, adult, family, and senior retreats. Open for rental groups.

Herrbrook Farm Retreat Cottage
housers@onemain.com,
www.home.supernet.com/~housers
717-872-2848
2256 New Danville Pike, Lancaster PA 17603
Mary Lou and Rod Houser, directors
   Founded 1988. A nineteenth-century farmstead which offers a place of aesthetic quiet surrounded by gardens, a labyrinth, and a rural landscape. Accommodates one to four persons. Spiritual direction available.

Kairos School of Spiritual Formation
kairos@on-the-journey.org, www.on-the-journey.org
717-569-7456, fax 717-653-4976
PO Box 5022, Lancaster PA 17606-5022
Cheryl Lehman, director
   Founded 1992. Meets at a Jesuit retreat center. Explores ways people may have a more intimate relationship with God in their daily routine. Offers space and time to experience the spiritual disciplines. Training for spiritual directors is available.

Kenbrook Bible Camp
info@kenbrook.org, www.kenbrook.com
717-865-4547, fax 717-865-0995
190 Pine Meadow Road, Lebanon PA 17046
Dan Krug, director
   Founded 1949. Year-round retreat facility, 18 rooms handicapped accessible. Summer youth camp ministry with facilities available for groups spring and fall. Emphasizes in-depth relationship with God, self, others, and the created world. Sponsored by Brethren in Christ.

Laurelville Mennonite Church Center*
info@laurelville.org, www.laurelville.org
800-839-1021 and 724-423-2056, fax 724-423-2096
RR 5 Box 145, Mt Pleasant PA 15666
Jerry Troyer, executive director; Robert Kanagy, program director
   Founded 1943. Year-round conference and retreat center. Owned and operated by Laurelville Mennonite Church Center Association, Gloria Horst Rosenberger, president.

Penn Valley Christian Retreat
pvcr@juno.com
717-899-5000 and 717-899-5001, fax 717-899-7295
7980 Ferguson Valley Rd, McVeytown PA 17051
Wayne Schrock, chairman
   Founded 1986. Provides a haven for encouragement, healing, and support in a structured Christian environment.

Penn-York Camp
pennyork@penn.com, www.pennyork.com
814-848-9811, fax 814-848-7471
226 Northern Potter Rd, Ulysses PA 16948
Gene Miller, camp administrator; Brent Peters, camp manager
   Founded 1970. Develops dedicated followers of Jesus Christ by building spirit, mind, and body in a natural setting.

Roxbury Holiness Camp
roxburycamp@onemain.com, www.roxburycamp.com
717-532-2208, fax 717-532-9392
PO Box 28, Roxbury PA 17251
Roy Heisey, administrator
   Founded 1936. Located at the foot of the Allegheny Mountains. Open year-round with various housing and meeting facilities including conference center, guesthouse, motel, dormitories and cabins. Suitable for retreats, camping, reunions. Sponsoring organization: Brethren in Christ Church.

Spruce Lake Retreat*
info@sprucelake.org, www.sprucelake.org
570-595-7505, fax 570-595-0328
RR 1 Box 605, Canadensis PA 18325-9749
Dan Ziegler, executive director
   Founded 1963. Christ-centered retreat center that features outdoor school, wilderness camp and expeditions, family programming and guest group ministries. Situated on 370 acres in the Pocono Mountains. Relates to Franconia Mennonite Camp Association.

Tel Hai Camp and Retreat
telhai@uscom.com, www.telhaicamp.org
610-273-3969, fax 610-273-3558
31 Lasso Dr, Honey Brook PA 19344-9261
Mike Willoughby, director
   Founded 1950. A Christian camp and retreat center with year-round facilities for church groups.

Woodcrest Retreat*
woodcrest@juno.com
717-738-2233, fax 717-738-3128
225 Woodcrest Dr, Ephrata PA 17522-9397
Cliff Martin, administrator; Phil Horning, program director
   Founded 1959. Sharing Christ's love with children, youth, and families in a beautiful camp setting. Sponsored by Woodcrest Retreat Association.

SOUTH CAROLINA

Hartwell Mennonite Center
190 Stalling Ridge Rd, Pickens SC 29671

SOUTH DAKOTA

Swan Lake Christian Camp*
slcc@iw.net, www.slcc.tripod.com
605-326-5690, fax 605-326-5690
45474 288th St, Viborg SD 57070

Jerry and Judi Kroeker, co-directors
    Founded 1955. A year-round facility providing youth camping and retreat facilities. Sponsored by the Swan Lake Christian Camp Association.

VERMONT

Bethany Birches Camp*
bbc@valley.net, www.vtchildrenscamp.com
802-672-5220
2610 Lynds Hill Rd, Plymouth VT 05056
Mike Wenger, executive director; Ann Wenger, program director
    Founded 1965. Provides an affordable Christian summer camp experience for children in Vermont and surrounding states. Programming includes seven weeks of overnight camp in the summer for boys and girls ages 8-18, day camp, winter snow camps, and a winterized cabin for retreats and family gatherings.

VIRGINIA

Highland Retreat*
highlandrt@juno.com
540-852-3226, fax 540-852-9272
14783 Upper Highland Dr, Bergton VA 22811-9712
Paul Beiler, administrator
    Founded 1958. Year-round camp and retreat setting in NW Virginia. Outdoor setting for wholesome recreation and spiritual renewal. Includes a summer youth camping program, retreat center, youth lodge, and campground. Relates primarily to churches of Virginia Conference.

Williamsburg Christian Retreat Center*
wcrc@visi.net, www.wcrc.info
757-566-2256, fax 757-566-4875
9275 Barnes Road, Toano VA 23168
Herb Lantz, executive director; Margaret Trivett,
hosted guest services director
    Founded 1984. Provides Christ-centered retreat facilities, services, and programs to encourage fellowship, growth, and renewal. Features cottages, motel-style rooms, and an RV campground. Ideal for church, family, and personal retreats. Also has a summer camp program for children and youth. Relates to Virginia Mennonite Conference.

WASHINGTON

Camp Camrec*
camrec@rightathome.com, www.camrec.mennonite.net
509-548-7245
18899 Little Chumstick Crk Rd, Leavenworth WA 98826
Roger and Carmen Reimer, managers
    Founded 1963. A Christian camping and retreat center operated by the Mennonite churches of the state of Washington.

WEST VIRGINIA

Harman Mt. Farm Campground
304-227-3647
Hc 70 Box 67a, Harman WV 26270
Robert and Lois Wenger, campground managers
    Founded 1971. Offers camping in quiet, natural mountain beauty with bathhouse, pavilion, and hook-ups.

Mountain Retreat
lmlind@neumedia.net, www.neumedia.net/~lmlind
304-227-4427
PO Box 266, Harman WV 26270
Lester and Mary Beth Lind, co-directors
    Founded 1991. A retreat center offering personal and group retreats focused on nature, prayer, and spirituality. Facilities available for rental.

Mennonite Central Committee
mailbox@mcc.org, www.mcc.org
888-563-4676 and 717-859-1151,
fax 717-859-2171
21 S 12th St, PO Box 500, Akron PA 17501-0500

STAFF
Ronald J. R. Mathies, executive director (rjm@mcc.org)
Bruce McCrae, director of administration and resources (brm@mcc.org)

INFORMATION
Mennonite Central Committee is the relief, service, and development agency of North American Mennonite and Brethren in Christ churches. Members include Beachy Amish, Brethren in Christ, Chortitzer Mennonites, Conservative Mennonite Conference, Evangelical Mennonite Church, Evangelical Mennonite Conference, Lancaster Mennonite Conference, Mennonite Brethren, Mennonite Church USA, Mennonite Church Canada, Old Colony, Old Order Amish, Old Order Mennonite, Sommerfelder Mennonite. MCC was founded in 1920 in response to hunger and human need caused by war and revolution in Russia and the Ukraine.

ORGANIZATIONAL INDEX

3

BOARD (*EXECUTIVE COMMITTEE MEMBERS*)
*Karen Klassen Harder, chair, 118 Sunset Dr, Bluffton OH 45817 (419-358-0698), *Eric Rempel, vice-chair; *Patricia Leaman, secretary; *Vidya Narimalla, treasurer; *Harriet Sider Bicksler, Kay Bontrager-Singer, Martha Burka, *Donella Clemens, Lynn Cober, Rose Covington, *Harold Dick, *Ron Dueck, Marty Freeburne, Clarke Fretz, Kim Vu Friesen, Ann Graber Hershberger, John Hess-Yoder, Hedie Hintz, Gerald Hughes, *Vernon Jantzi, Phil Klassen, Jeanette Hertzler Martin, Ronald J. R. Mathies, David Miller, Erin Morash, *Jeanette Neufeld, Aldred Neufeldt, Eric Olfert, Tim Penner, Daniel Schipani, Joe Showalter, Richard Showalter, Donald Steelberg, Debbie Taylor, *Paul Toews, Lucille Wall, Glenn Wiebe, *John Wiens, Wai Young, Greg Zimmerman

PUBLICATIONS
A Common Place

Mennonite Central Committee U.S.
mailbox@mcc.org, www.mcc.org
717-859-3889, fax 717-859-3875
21 S 12th St, PO Box 500, Akron PA 17501-0500

STAFF
Jose Ortiz, executive director (jortiz@mcc.org)

BOARD (*EXECUTIVE COMMITTEE MEMBERS*)
*Harriet Sider Bicksler, chair, 127 Holly Dr, Mechanicsburg PA 17055 (717-795-9151); Kay Bontrager-Singer, vice-chair; Samuel Resendez, secretary-treasurer; Lois Bartel, Danny Begaye, *William Braun, *Rose Covington, Lawrence Hart, *Ann Graber Hershberger, David Miller, Jon Showalter, Richard Spearman, *Donald Steelberg, Sharon Swartzentruber, Greg Zimmerman

REGIONAL OFFICES AND MATERIAL RESOURCES CENTERS
West Coast MCC and Material Resources Center
    209-638-6911, fax 209-638-6914,
    1010 G St, Reedley CA 93654
MCC Central States and Material Resources Center
    316-283-2720, fax 316-283-8727,
    121 E 30th St, PO Box 235, North Newton KS 67117
MCC Great Lakes
    330-857-7721, fax 330-857-7722,
    13363 Jericho Rd, PO Box 82, Kidron OH 44636
MCC East Coast
    717-859-3889, fax 717-859-3875,
    21 S 12th St, PO Box 500, Akron PA 17501-0500
MCC Material Resources Center
    717-733-2847, fax 717-733-7329,
    517 W Trout Run Rd, Ephrata PA 17522

WASHINGTON OFFICE
202-544-6564, fax 202-544-2820
110 Maryland Ave NE #502, Washington DC 20002
J. Daryl Byler, director (jdb@mcc.org)

UNITED NATIONS OFFICE
unoffice@mcc.org
212-223-4062, fax 212-750-1194
866 United Nations Plaza, Room 575, New York NY 10017

PEACE AND JUSTICE MINISTRIES OFFICE
mailbox@mcc.org, www.mcc.org
717-859-3889, fax 717 859-3875
21 S 12th St, PO Box 500, Akron PA 17501-0500
Iris de Leon-Hartshorn, director
    The Peace and Justice Ministries Office grew out the MCC Peace Section. Departments in the Peace and Justice Ministries Office include the Anti-Racism Program, the Immigration desk, Mennonite Conciliation Services, the Office on Crime and Justice, the Peace Education Office, and Women's Concerns desk.

For more information, contact one of the following:
Central States
719-843-5118, PO Box 306, La Jara CO 81140; Alice Price, regional coordinator
East Coast
540-433-5426, 1134 Sumter Ct, Harrisonburg VA 22801; Nancy Good Sider, regional coordinator
Great Lakes
708-627-5310, 528 E Madison, Lombard IL 60148; Richard Blackburn, regional coordinator
West Coast
209-453-2064, 1717 S Chestnut, Fresno CA 93702; Ron Claassen, regional coordinator

THRIFT SHOPS
www.mcc.org
21 S 12th St PO Box 500, Akron PA 17501-0500, 717-859-1151, fax 717-859-2171
For a listing of over 100 shops, go to www.mcc.org and click on "get involved."

Staff
Barb Schrag, U.S. coordinator:
(bkschrag@mcc.org), PO Box 416, Freeman SD 67029

Information
The Mennonite Central Committee Thrift Shop Network is the result of constituent concern for human need both locally and globally. Thrift Shop volunteers commit themselves to Christian faith in action by volunteering their time and talent for receiving and reselling donated items and sending shop proceeds to benefit the work of MCC. Shops offer a friendly, caring presence in the community and inform the churches and community of the Mennonite Central Committee mission.

TEN THOUSAND VILLAGES
inquiry@villages-mcc.org,
www.tenthousandvillages.org
717-859-8100, fax 717-859-2622
704 Main St, PO Box 500, Akron PA 17501-0500
For a complete store listing, visit www.tenthousandvillages.org.

Staff
Paul E. Myers, director

Information
Ten Thousand Villages provides vital, fair income to third world people by selling their handicrafts and telling their stories in North America. Ten Thousand Villages works with artisans who would otherwise be unemployed or underemployed. This income helps pay for food, education, health care, and housing. Thousands of volunteers in Canada and the United States work with Ten Thousand Villages in their home communities. Ten Thousand Villages is a nonprofit program of Mennonite Central Committee, the relief and development agency of Mennonite and Brethren in Christ churches in North America. Ten Thousand Villages has been working with people around the world since 1946.

Publications
Peace Office Newsletter, Washington Memo, Jottings, Women's Concerns Report and *Conciliation Quarterly* (same address as above)

Mennonite Chaplains Association
loubeellen@aol.com
610-782-0523, fax 610-395-6126
517 N Lafayette St, Allentown PA 18104

STAFF
President: Mary Lou E. Simmons, chaplain
President Elect: Myra Raab, BCC, M.Div.
Past-President: Rev. Janet Peifer, chaplain

INFORMATION
Founded 1962. Organized to provide support, collaboration, resources, collegiality, and continuing education for chaplains affiliated with

Mennonite/Anabaptist-related congregations or organizations, and to stimulate professional growth.

Mennonite Christian Leadership Foundation

mail@globaldisciples.org,
www.globaldisciples.org
717-872-7404, fax 717-872-7404
319 Manor Ave, Millersville PA 17551

STAFF

Galen Burkholder, executive director
 (galen@globaldisciples.org)
Tim Pfautz, operations manager
 (mail@globaldisciples.org)

INFORMATION

Mennonite Christian Leadership Foundation helps provide teachers for local leadership training initiatives of church groups around the world that are a part of the leadership training alliance facilitated by Global Disciples Network.

MCLF, with Global Disciples Network, is focused on developing an alliance of locally operated leadership training programs among 60 conferences of churches related to Mennonite World Conference that have expressed interest.

MCLF was founded in 1969 and for 30 years provided in-service training for church leaders globally. Their board joined with Global Disciples board in 2001. One board now governs both organizations.

Mennonite Church Canada
—see section 5: Sister Denominations

Mennonite Church USA Executive Board
—see section 1: Churchwide Agencies

Mennonite Conciliation Services
—see Mennonite Central Committee U.S.

Mennonite Disaster Service

mds@mdsbinat.org, www.mds.mennonite.net
717-859-2210, fax 717-859-4910
1018 Main St, Akron PA 17501

STAFF

Tom Smucker, executive coordinator
 (tes@mdsbinat.org)
Carla Hunt, assistant coordinator
 (letacjh@mdsbinat.org)
Ted Houser, communication coordinator
 (tes@mdsbinat.org)

INFORMATION

Mennonite Disaster Service (MDS) answers calls for disaster service in all emergencies such as floods, tornadoes, hurricanes, earthquakes, and fires. MDS coordinates volunteers from Anabaptist constituent churches for disaster response.

BOARD

Paul Brubacher, chair, 2900 Best Rd, Morgantown PA 19543 (610-286-5298); Rocky Miller, vice-chair; Brenda Wagner, secretary; Millard Garrett, treasurer; Vernon Miller, Ottis Mast, Wilmer Leichty, Bernard Martin, Paul Unruh, Gordon Friesen, Eldon King, Abe Ens, Dan Miller, Dan Houck, Jason Yoder, Amos Schwartz , Willis Hochstetler, David Hoover, Marvin Toews, Albert Schrock, Vernon Schmucker, Jane Kuepfer, Sanford Swartzendruber, Anne Wiens, Carlos Santiago, William McCoy, Fred Kathler, Betty Kasdorf, Stella Toews

PUBLICATION

Behind the Hammer (Quarterly), Ted Houser, editor (same address as above)

Mennonite Economic Development Associates

www.meda.org,
www.businessasacalling.org,
www.saronafund.com

To contact all offices (Corporate in Winnipeg MB; International Economic Development in Waterloo ON; or North American Services in Lancaster PA): 1-800-665-7026 or meda@meda.org

STAFF
Allan Sauder, president
Ed Epp, Director, international operations
Howard Good, director, North American services

INFORMATION
Founded 1953. Mennonite Economic Development Associates (MEDA) is an organization for Christians who seek to connect their faith and daily work in a needy world. Together we help support MEDA's business-oriented development programs in the developing world, as well as providing assistance to low-income entrepreneurs in North America.

BOARD
Ronald J. Haarer, president, 732 West Deer Valley Rd, Phoenix AZ 85027; executive committee: Verda Beachy, Gloria E. Eby, Kevin Lambright, Daniel J. Miller, Lowell Peachey, John E. Yoder

PUBLICATION
The Marketplace (six times a year), Wally Kroeker, editor

Mennonite Education Agency
—see section 1: Churchwide Agencies

Mennonite Elementary Education Council (MEEC)
—see schools in this section and Mennonite Education Agency in section 1.

Mennonite Environmental Task Force
noels@MennoniteUSA.org
215-723-5513, fax 215-723-1211

c/o Noel Santiago, 771 Rte 113, Souderton PA 18964

STAFF
Noel Santiago, assistant director, Witness and Peace Ministries, MC USA Executive Board Office of Congregational Life

INFORMATION
Founded in 1989 at the joint assembly of the Mennonite Church and General Conference Mennonite Church upon the adoption of resolution by the two bodies. Purpose: to be more caring of the earth in individual and family life, to encourage congregations and conferences to promote discussion and action on ways the Christian faith relates to environmental issues, to encourage Mennonite schools to place special emphasis on environmental curricula, and to promote a deeper understanding of the issues.

BOARD
David Neufeld, co-chair (eraconsulting@yahoo.ca), 224 Wright Ave, Toronto ON M6R 1L3; Canada (416-535-7917); Melvin D. Schmidt, co-chair (melschmidt@msn.com), 4212 Longfellow St, Hyattsville MD 20781-1650 (301-927-0420); Roberta Krehbiel, Jocele Meyer; David Ortman, Steve Cheramie Risingsun

PUBLICATION
An occasional newsletter is published and distributed.

Mennonite Financial Federal Credit Union
info@mennonitefinancial.com, www.mennonitefinancial.com
800-451-5719, fax 717-392-8997
PO Box 10455, Lancaster PA 17605

STAFF
Larry D. Miller, president/CEO (larry@mennonitefinancial.com)

ORGANIZATIONAL INDEX

3

W. Kent Hartzler, vice-president of lending
(kent@mennonitefinancial.com)
Deborah Millslagle, vice-president of operations
(debbie@mennonitefinancial.com)
J. Lorne Peachey, vice-president of marketing
(lorne@mennonitefinancial.com)

INFORMATION

A cooperative that provides full financial services for Mennonites, Amish, and Brethren in Christ in Pennsylvania, Ohio, and Illinois. Employees and family members of Mennonite organizations are also eligible for membership.

Services include loans, credit cards, savings, checking, IRAs, certificates, and other related financial products. Branch office locations: Scottdale PA (800-322-0440); Belleville PA (717-935-0025); Ephrata, PA (717-721-6180); and Kidron OH (800-315-4306)

Founded in 2000 from a merger of Pennsylvania Mennonite FCU (1955), Ohio Mennonite FCU (1985), and Illinois Mennonite FCU (1988).

BOARD

Aaron Martin Jr., chair
(vze29kk9@verizon.net); Marian Buckwalter, Jesus Cruz, Art Neuenschwander, Richard Reimer, Dwight Rohrer, Becky Sprinkle, Dena Stauffer, Michael Zehr

Mennonite Foundation
—see MMA in section 1: Churchwide Agencies

Mennonite Health Assembly
info@mhsonline.org, www.mhsonline.org
800-611-4007 and 574-534-9689,
fax 574-534-3254
234 S Main St, Suite 1, Goshen IN 46526

STAFF

Mim Shirk, director (mim@mhsonline.org)
Wendy Rohn, registrar (wendy@mhsonline.org)

INFORMATION

The annual Mennonite Health Assembly draws practitioners and leaders of Anabaptist health and human services to explore innovative ways to carry out ministry in the context of our faith. Attendees include administrators, board members, chaplains, church leaders, congregational health promoters, counselors, executives, nurses, pastors, physicians, psychologists, social workers, and students. The Assembly is co-sponsored by MHS and MMA.

Mennonite Health Services (MHS)

info@mhsonline.org, www.mhsonline.org
800-611-4007 and 574-534-9689, fax 574-534-3254
234 S Main St, Suite 1, Goshen IN 46526

STAFF

Rick Stiffney, president (rick@mhsonline.org)
Mim Shirk, vice president
  (mim@mhsonline.org)
Keith Stuckey, vice president
  (keith@mhsonline.org)

INFORMATION

MHS sponsors 18 organizations and promotes networking among 60 member ministries, strengthening board and executive leadership, enhancing relationships with churches and co-sponsoring the annual Mennonite Health Assembly (see separate listing).

Members include Mennonite, Mennonite Brethren, and Brethren in Christ health and human service ministries (see separate health care listings below for child welfare services, developmental disability services, hospitals, mental health agencies, and retirement centers). MHS is accountable to the church through denominational appointments to its board.

MHS was founded by MCC in 1947 as Mennonite Mental Health Services. It broadened its scope in 1989 to include other Anabaptist health and human service ministries.

BOARD

Carl B. Harman, chair, 1848 N College Ave, Harrisonburg VA 22801 (540-434-4459); J. Kenneth Brubaker, M.D., vice-chair; Ronald Price, treasurer; Bonnie L. Weaver, secretary; Lenora Stern, assistant secretary; Daniel Grimes, Harold Loewen, Roland Reimer, James Wenger, Beulah Hess Yoder

PUBLICATION

Connections (Bimonthly), Mim Shirk, editor (same address as above)

ORGANIZATIONAL INDEX

3

Health Care Agencies

*Denotes members of Mennonite Health Services.
+Denotes organizations sponsored by MHS.

CHILD WELFARE SERVICES

Adriel School Inc.+
mlehman@adriel.org; www.adriel.org
937-465-0010 and 1-800-262-0065, fax 937-465-8690
PO Box 188, 414 North Detroit St, West Liberty OH 43357
  A multiservice center for children and their families with specialized programs including residential treatment, treatment foster care, day treatment, and outpatient therapy services. Sponsors **Ben-El Child Development Center** and co-sponsors **Shalom**

Ministries (see separate entries below). Board appointed by MHS, Ohio Conference, and three local Mennonite churches. Dwight Spencer, chair

Associated Youth Services
dvanderpool@aysusa.org,
913-831-2820, fax 913-831-0262
1620 S 37th, PO Box 6145, Kansas City KS 66106-6145
Dennis Vanderpool, CEO (dvanderpool@ayusa.org); Debra Caro Terrell, senior vice-president (dterrell@aysusa.org); Susan Maier, board chair 913-573-5292 (smaier@wycokck.org).
  Founded 1972. Serving over 1,000 youth and families annually. AYS exists to advance the social, educational, and emotional health and success of youth and families.

DEVELOPMENTAL DISABILITIES SERVICES

Central California Mennonite Residential Services Inc.*
559-227-2940, fax 559-222-1180
PO Box 5298, Fresno CA 93755
David Hebert, executive director

Christian Residential Opportunities and Social Services Inc.*
grace@innernet.net
717-530-1788, fax 717-530-1788
712 Pinola Rd, Shippensburg PA 17257
Emily Yardley, executive director
Founded 1985. Provides residential and social services to adults with developmental disabilities.

Faith Mission Home Inc.
434-985-2294, fax 434-985-7633
3540 Mission Home Ln, Free Union VA 22940-0114
Reuben Yoder, director
Christian residential care and vocational training for 60 mentally handicapped children and young adults in a beautiful rural environment.

Friendship Community*
office@friendship-comm.org; www.friendship-comm.org
717-656-2466 and 717-299-1795, fax 717-656-0459
1149 E Oregon Rd, Lititz PA 17543-9208
Myron Stoner, interim executive director
A Christian ministry providing residential and social services for people with developmental disabilities and their families in Lancaster County and surrounding counties.

Indian Creek Foundation Inc.*
sbechtel@indiancreekfoundation.org; www.indiancreekfoundation.org
215-256-1500, fax 215-256-3018
573 Yoder Rd, PO Box 225, Harleysville PA 19438-0225
David H. Crosson, executive director
Founded 1975. Provides care for the developmentally disabled through group homes, community living programs, vocational training with work activities center, job placement, and family services for all ages. Includes Indian Creek Homes Inc. and Indian Creek Industries Inc.

Jubilee Association of Maryland Inc.*
twiens@jubileemd.org; www.jubileemd.org
301-949-8628 and 301-949-8626, fax 301-949-4628
10408 Montgomery Ave, Kensington MD 20895
Tim Wiens, executive director
Founded 1978. Provides group home and supported living services to adults in Montgomery County, MD.

Mennonite Disabilities Committee*
mdc@medonline.org; www.mdconline.org
574-533-9720 and 574-534-0452, fax 574-534-9817
1518 College Ave, Goshen IN 46526
Leroy G. Willems, administrator; Gina Leichty, director of operations

Founded 1977. Provides respite care and long-term residential services for individuals with developmental disabilities.

Oregon Mennonite Residential Services Inc.+
omrs@mennonitehome.org
503-474-1213, fax 503-474-1145
117 NE 5th St Ste E, McMinnville OR 97128
Karen Litwiller, executive director (omrs@mennonitehome.com); Bruce Flaming, board chair (bjflaming@msn.com)
Founded 1986. Operates and maintains group homes for adults with developmental disabilities in the Willamette Valley.

Peaceful Living+
jlandis@voicenet.com
610-287-1200, fax 610-287-7121
PO Box 154, Lederach, PA 19450
Joe Landis, executive director

Pleasant View Inc.*
nhg_pv@intelos.net; www.pleasantview-inc.com
540-896-8255, fax 540-896-8454
PO Box 426, Broadway VA 22815-0426
Founded 1971. Serves adults with developmental disabilities. Provides group homes, apartment living, in-home services, intermediate care, specialized home services, day support, and supported employment. A mission of Virginia Mennonite Conference.

Sunshine Inc. of Northwest Ohio+
info@sunshineincnwo.org; www.sunshineincnwo.org
419-865-0251, fax 419-865-9715
7223 Maumee Western Rd, Maumee OH 43537-9656
John L. Martin, executive director; Sherry L. Ashenfelter CPS, executive secretary; Douglas Siebenaler, director of development
Founded 1949. Mission is to enhance the lives of people with developmental disabilities and their families. Provides supportive, loving communities through residential and related services. Board consists of local community leaders.

HOSPITALS

BroMenn Healthcare
www.bromenn.com
309-454-1400
PO Box 2850, Bloomington IL 61702-2850
Roger Hunt, interim CEO (rhunt@bromenn.org)
Acute care hospital, primary care and pediatric physician practices.

Mid-Valley Healthcare*
www.samhealth.org
541-258-2101, fax 541-451-7862
525 N Santiam Hwy, PO Box 739, Lebanon OR 97355
Larry Mullins, president/CEO of Samaritan Health Services; Steve Jasperson, executive vice-president of hospital operations
Founded 1952. Provides integrated health and hospital services primarily for the people of Linn County.

Samaritan Health Services Inc.*
stevej@goodsam.com; www.samhealth.org
541-757-5002 and 541-757-5009, fax 541-757-5100
PO Box 1068, Corvallis OR 97339
Larry Mullins, president/CEO; Steve Jasperson, executive vice-president hospital operations

MENTAL HEALTH AGENCIES

Ben-El Child Development Center
www.adriel.com
937-652-4555 and 800-224-0422, fax 937-652-4945
643 Bodey Circle, Urbana OH 43078
Founded 1989. A mental health center for children that provides the full array of mental health services. Serving Champaign and Logan counties for over 10 years.
Primarily funded by the Mental Health, Alcohol, and Drug Services Board of Logan and Champaign counties. Sponsored by Adriel School.

Brook Lane Health Services+
curtm@brooklane.org; www.brooklane.org
301-733-0330 and 800-342-2992, fax 301-733-4038
13218 Brook Ln Dr, PO Box 1945, Hagerstown MD 21742
R. Lynn Rushing, CEO; Ray Geigley, board chair
Founded 1946. Provides mental health services for children, adolescents, adults, and older adults in an atmosphere reflecting God's love for each person. Sponsored by local church and community board.

Crown Centre for Counseling
330-927-2020, fax 330-927-2020
9693 Benner Rd, Rittman OH 44270
Dave Stauffer and Twila Zimmerly, co-directors
Founded 1984 as an independent entity. Reorganized in 2002 as an outreach of the church.

Family Life Resource Center*
services@flrc.org; www.flrc.org
540-434-8450 and 800-655-2055, fax 540-433-3805
273 Newman Ave, Harrisonburg VA 22801
Jim Glanzer, director (jim@flrc.org)

Kings View Mental Health System+
gneufeld@kingsview.org; www.kingsview.org
559-638-2880, fax 559-638-3845
42675 Rd 44, Reedley CA 93654
Gerald Neufeld, CEO
Founded 1951. Kings View provides community behavorial health for the people of Central and Northern California, including mental health, chemical dependency, and services for developmentally challenged individuals.

Oaklawn+
info@oaklawn.org; www.oaklawn.org
574-533-1234 and 800-282-0809, fax 574-537-2673
330 Lakeview Dr, PO Box 809, Goshen IN 46527-0809
Harold C. Loewen, President/CEO; Carl N. Rutt, M.D., medical director

Founded 1962. Oaklawn offers a comprehensive range of mental health and addictions services for children, adolescents, adults, and older adults.

Penn Foundation Inc.+
jgoshow@pennfoundation.org; www.pennfoundation.org
215-257-6551 and 800-245-7366, fax 215-257-9347
807 Lawn Ave, PO Box 32, Sellersville PA 18960-0032
Vernon H. Kratz, medical director; John Goshow, president and CEO
Founded 1955. Mission is to provide comprehensive behavioral health care to persons in need of hope, healing, and compassion.

Philhaven+
dale@philhaven.com; www.philhaven.com
717-273-8871 and 717-270-2443, fax 717-270-2456
PO Box 550, 283 S Butler Rd, Mt Gretna PA 17064-0550
Founded 1952. Provides broad range of behavioral health services for persons of all ages in south central Pennsylvania. Services include inpatient, residential, day hospital, outpatient, and numerous community based services. Additional programs include Recovery of Hope, Employee Assistance Programs, and Adventure Challenge Experience.

Prairie View Inc.+
info@prairieview.org; www.prairieview.org
316-284-6400 and 800-362-0180, fax 316-284-6491
PO Box 467, 1901 E First St, Newton KS 67114-0467
Founded 1954. Nonprofit behavioral and mental health organization providing services for disorders such as depression, anxiety, substance abuse, and childhood and adolescent emotional disorders.

Shalom Ministries
lmoshier@adriel2.org
419-445-1552, fax 419-445-1401
207 Vine St, Archbold, OH 43502
Lenette Moshier, director (lmoshier@adriel2.org)
Founded 1998. Co-sponsored by Adriel School and Northwest Ohio Mennonite Ministers Fellowship. Serving Ohio (primarily Northwest Ohio) and Southern Michigan. Mission: to provide consultation, counseling, reconciliation, education, guidance, and other services to individuals, churches and other groups.

Shalom Wellness Center (a program of Shalom Ministries)
Darlene Rohrer-Meck, LISW, director (drmeck@adriel2.org)
Individual, couple, children, and family therapy. Pastoral consultations, support groups, wellness education and spiritual direction. Other services offered through Shalom Ministries: VORP (Victim Offender Reconciliation Program) and mediation services.

OTHER HEALTH AND HUMAN SERVICES AGENCIES

Bridge of Hope
bridgepage@aol.com; www.bridgeofhopeinc.org
610-380-1360 and 717-394-7707, fax 610-380-9278
PO Box 1223, 1516 Olive St, Coatesville PA 19320-1223
Edith Yoder, executive director (edithyoder@aol.com)
Bridge of Hope ends and prevents homelessness for single mothers with the help of trained mentoring groups within Christian congregations. Will help start Bridge of Hope in other geographical areas.

Paxton Ministries*
cbook@paxtonmin.org; www.paxtonmin.org
717-236-5508, fax 717-236-3099
2001 Paxton St, Harrisburg PA 17111
Chris Book, executive director (cbook@paxtonmin.org).
Provides long term housing and supportive services to 90 adults who are poor and dealing with mental illness or developmental disabilities.

RETIREMENT CENTERS

AuSable Valley Apartments and Village*
AVA@Northland.lib.mi.us
517-848-5630, fax 517-848-5261
1441 Maple Dr, Fairview MI 48621
Rachel E. Lee, administrator
Founded 1980. Elderly subsidized housing and retirement community.

AuSable Valley Home+
avh@M33Access.com; www.comcaring.org
517-848-2241, fax 517-848-5526
1390 Maple Dr, PO Box 9, Fairview MI 48621
Leta Gerber, administrator; Catherine Schraudt, director of nursing
A Medicare/Medicaid certified skilled nursing facility in rural northern Michigan serving the immediate community and counties. Member of state and national aging associations.

Bethesda Home*
bethesda@mtleco.net; www.bethesdahome.org
620-367-2291, fax 620-367-2294
408 E Main St, Box 37, Goessel KS 67053-0037
Founded 1899. Organized to care for frail elderly and disabled. Offers assisted living, independent living, skilled nursing care, adult day care, and Alzheimer's special care unit.

Beth-Haven Nursing Home and Residential Care*
573-221-6000 and 573-221-3815, fax 573-248-1523
2500 Pleasant St, Hannibal MO 63401-2699

Brementowne Manor Apartments*
btmtinpk@mindspring.com
708-429-4088; fax 708-532-1397

16130 Oak Park Ave, Tinley Park IL 60477
James R. Durnbaugh, site manager
Housing for senior citizens and disabled persons.

Casa del Sol Retirement Community
info@casadelsollj.org; www.casadelsollj.org
719-384-0342, fax 719-384-0342
1002 Casa del Sol Dr, La Junta CO 81050
Linda Welty, manager (linda@casadelsollj.org); Howard E. Stutzman, M.D., board chair (719-384-5261) (hestutz@earthlink.net).
Founded in 1992. 52 apartments, 6 eight-plexes, and two duplexes. Community for independent living for adults over 55 years of age.

Community Home Services*
715-723-1906, fax 715-723-1590
PO Box 158, Franconia PA 18924
Diane Tihansky, administrator
Founded 1995. Promotes emotional, physical, and spiritual well-being by providing services so that persons may remain in their homes. Member organizations include: Dock Woods Community, Frederick Mennonite Community, Peter Becker Community, Rockhill Mennonite Community, Souderton Mennonite Homes, FCMC and EDC Mennonite Conferences, Atlantic Northeast COB Conference.

Dock Woods Community Inc.*
moreinfo@dockwoods.com; www.dockwoods.com
215-368-4438, fax 215-362-2682
275 Dock Drive, Lansdale PA 19446
Edward D. Brubaker, NHA executive director
Founded 1942. Offers a wide range of housing for seniors and families, along with support services and ongoing activities for all residents.

Fairlawn Haven
fairlawn01@adelphia.net
419-445-3075, fax 419-446-2699
407 E Lutz Rd, Archbold OH 43502
Steven A. Ringenberg, executive director; Calvin Britsch, board chair
Founded 1961. Provides a variety of housing facilities for the elderly, recreational facility, stores, and conference room.

Fairmount Homes
fairmont@epix.net
717-354-4111, fax 717-354-6665
219 Cats Back Rd, Ephrata PA 17522-8629
James R. Oswald, president.
Fairmount is a continuing care retirement community providing a wide range of quality services in a continuum of care ranging from cottages to nursing and rehabilitative care. Founded in 1967, Fairmount is a ministry of the Weaverland Conference Mennonite Churches.

Frederick Mennonite Community*
khummel@frederick-mennonite.org;
www.frederick-mennonite.org

610-754-7878, fax 610-754-6475
2849 Big Rd, PO Box 498, Frederick PA 19435-0498
  80 acre campus, 100 independent living, 106-person assisted living, 24-person Alzheimer's facility, and 62 nursing beds.

Friendship Haven*
mofelkey@netusal.net
765-459-9343, fax 765-459-9343
2600 W Jefferson, Kokomo IN 46901
Maureen Felkey, administrator

Friendship Retirement Corporation, d/b/a Glencroft+
www.glencroft.com
623-939-9475 and 623-847-3001, fax 623-842-9588
8611 N 67th Ave, Glendale AZ 85302
F. Jay Shetler, president/ceo; Dale Rinard, board chair
  Founded 1970. A retirement community of 900 residents in all levels of care. Sponsored by MHS with the involvement of local MC, COB, Apostolic Christian, and Friends churches.

Garden Spot Village*
bgerig@gardenspotvillage.org;
www.gardenspotvillage.org
717-355-6000, fax 717-355-6006
433 South Kinzer Ave, New Holland PA 17557
Stephen Lindsey, CEO
(slindsey@gardenspotvillage.org); Philip Burkholder, CFO; Bonnie Gerig, director of marketing
  Approximately 600 residents. Services include cottage and apartment living, assisted living, memory support unit, skilled nursing center. Amenities include pool and fitness area, bank, computer lab.

Glencroft
—see Friendship Retirement Corporation

Greencroft Retirement Communities Inc.+
info@greencroft.org; www.greencroft.org
574-537-4000, fax 574-533-8063
1721 Greencroft Blvd, PO Box 819, Goshen IN 46527-0819
Gene E. Yoder, President/CEO, Toni Johnson, board chair
  Founded 1962. Continuing Care Retirement Community (CCRC) with 1200 residents and several levels of care. Administers Evergreen Place (assisted living), Manor II, Manor III, Manor IV, Juniper Place Court Apartments, Greencroft Health Care, a senior center, and Thelma A. Schrock Homestead adult day services.

Harmony Village Inc.*
hvillage@sky-access.com
330-482-3430, fax 330-482-0359
901 S Main St, Columbiana OH 44408
Cheryl Luli, project administrator: Gloria Wilson, office supervisor, Richard Simpson, maintenance supervisor
  Founded 1983. A government subsidized apartment complex for the very-low income elderly and the physically handicapped who require an especially adapted apartment.

Hickory Homes
—see Schowalter Villa

Kidron Bethel Village
richh@kidronbethel.org; www.kidronbethel.org
316-284-2900, fax 316-284-0173
3001 Ivy Dr, North Newton KS 67117
Richard I. Heim, president
  Founded 1926. A continuing care retirement community with independent living residences, HUD apartments, and skilled nursing beds. Serving 260 seniors in 161 retirement townhomes and apartments. 60 skilled nursing beds. Wellness center, adult day care, transportation, buffet dining, in-home services, recreational activities, walking trails, chaplaincy/chapel, maintenance services.

Landis Homes Retirement Community+
info@landishomes.org; www.landishomes.org
717-569-3271 and 717-581-3935, fax 717-569-5203
1001 East Oregon Rd, Lititz PA 17543-9206
Edward M. Longenecker, president; Virginia Musser, director of admissions
  Founded 1964. Provides quality programs for senior adults in an environment of Christian love. A ministry of the Lancaster Mennonite Conference.

Maple Lawn Homes+
rob@maple-lawn.com; www.maple-lawn.com
309-467-2337 and 309-467-9041, fax 309-467-9097
700 N Main St, Eureka IL 61530
  Founded 1922. Organized to provide long-term care, retirement housing, and support services to the elderly of central Illinois.

Maple Lawn Manor Inc.
mlmanor@hintonet.net
405-663-2455 and 888-663-2114, fax 405-663-2443
PO Box 66, 800 Arapaho, Hydro OK 73048
Betty Palesano, administrator
(bpalesano@hotmail.com); Dale Beerwinkle, board chair
  Founded 1968. Long-term care facility with 22 beds, locked Alzheimer's unit. Serving elderly and handicapped residents of all ages.

Meadows Mennonite Retirement Community*
rbertsche@meadowshome.org
309-747-2702 and 309-747-3658, fax 309-747-2944
24588 Church St, Chenoa IL 61726
  Founded 1923. Organized to serve the long-term care needs and provide retirement housing for the elderly of McLean and Livingston counties. Sponsored by MMRC Association of Churches. Participating denominations: MC and EMC.

Menno Haven Inc.*
mennohaven.org; www.mennohaven.org
717-262-1000, fax 717-261-0860
1427 Philadelphia Ave, Chambersburg PA 17201
Ray L. Miller, president/CEO; Carole Fries, vice-president of marketing

Founded 1964. Accredited CCRC providing care for 1000 seniors on 3 campuses; 387 independent and 272 residential/assisted living apts, 233 skilled nursing beds, and adult day care services.

Mennonite Home Communities*
info@mennonitehome.org; www.mennonitehome.org
717-393-1301 and 717-390-4100, fax 717-393-1389
1520 Harrisburg Pk, Lancaster PA 17601
J. Nelson Kling, president/CEO; John Sauder, vice president health services
Founded 1903. A Continuing Care Retirement Community (CCRC) providing services to seniors in a Christian environment.

Mennonite Housing Aid Inc.
martin101@attbi.com
847-492-1458, fax 847-492-1458
PO Box 6056, Evanston IL 60204-6056
Richard E. Martin, administrator
Founded 1976. Promotes retirement housing, community, and service in the Chicago metropolitan area.

Mennonite Manor*
vernon_king@mennonitemanor.org;
www.mennonitemanor.org
620-663-7175, fax 620-663-4221
600 W Blanchard, South Hutchinson KS 67505-1599
Vernon King, CEO
Founded 1973. Provides health care services in a continuing care retirement community.

Mennonite Memorial Home*
mmh@wcoil.com
419-358-1015, fax 419-358-1919
410 W Elm St, Bluffton OH 45817
Offers the full continuum of care within the community, with duplexes, independent apartments, assisted living, and nursing. Also offers home health, mobile meals, and transportation services.

Mennonite Village+
info@mennonitevillage.org; www.mennonitevillage.org
541-928-7232, fax 541-917-1399
5353 Columbus St SE, Albany OR 97322
Ron Litwiller, executive director; Chet Patterson, chief financial officer
Founded 1947. Continuing care retirement community whose covenant is to be a Christ-centered community providing life-enriching services.

Mennowood Retirement Community
www.mennowood.com
757-249-0355, fax 757-249-7621
13030 Warwick Blvd, Newport News VA 23602
Robby Ackerman, executive director
(robby@mennowood.com)
Includes 24 independent living apartments and 71 assisted living apartments on Sluice Mill Pond.

Messiah Village*
life@messiahvillage.com;www.messiahvillage.com
717-697-4666 and 717-790-8222, fax 717-790-8200
100 Mount Allen Dr, PO Box 2015, Mechanicsburg PA 17055-2015
Emerson L. Lesher, president
Founded 1896. Provides housing, supportive services, and health care to older people in an atmosphere of Christ-like love and concern for the whole person.

Mountain View Nursing Home
540-948-6831, fax 540-948-5402
HC 5 Box 186, Aroda VA 22709
Eldon Hochstetler, administrator
Founded 1962. 40 nursing care beds. Began as a community service ministry staffed by a voluntary service unit.

OrrVilla Retirement Community Inc.*
orrvilla@raex.com
330-683-4455, fax 330-683-7575
333 E Sassafras St, Orrville OH 44667
George Bixler, executive director; Morris Stutzman, president

Pioneer Lodge*
kpcorner@midway.net
620-582-2123 and 620-823-3136, fax 620-582-2461
300 West 3rd St, PO Box 487, Coldwater KS 67029
Founded 1964. Nursing care and residential care levels.

Pleasantview Home*
pvadmin@pvhome.org
319-656-2421, fax 319-656-2439
811 Third St, PO Box 309, Kalona IA 52247-0309
Sandy Gingerich, administrator; Phyllis Litwiller, director of nursing; Philip Marner, board president.
Founded 1958. A continuing care retirement community serving the elderly of Kalona and the surrounding communities.

Rock of Ages Mennonite Home/Valley View Retirement Village
delvinz@onlinemac.com
503-472-6212, fax 503-472-4797
15600 SW Rock of Ages Rd, Mc Minnville OR 97128
Delvin Zook, administrator
Founded 1949. Care center for the elderly, retirement homes, community service providing care to seniors in home.

Rockhill Mennonite Community*
elandis@rmcomm.org; www.rmcomm.org
215-257-2751, fax 215-257-7390
3250 State Rd, Sellersville PA 18960
Ron Sawatsky, chief executive officer
Founded 1935. A continuing care retirement community that provides a wide range of services in an atmosphere of Christian love.

ORGANIZATIONAL INDEX

3

Salem Mennonite Home

smhoffice@gwtc.net
605-925-4994, fax 605-925-4764
106 West 7th St, Freeman SD 57029
Stewart Hofer, administrator

An assisted living center caring for elderly residents in the Freeman, South Dakota, community for over 50 years.

Schowalter Villa and Hickory Homes+

swvilla@schowalter-villa.org; www.schowalter-villa.org
620-327-4261, fax 620-327-4262
200 West Cedar, Hesston KS 67062
James M. Krehbiel, president; Lillian Claassen, vice president of health services

Founded 1961. Mission Statement: Schowalter Villa provides optimal quality of life and quality of care to enrich those we serve in a Christian not-for-profit retirement community.

Sierra View Homes Inc.*

admin@sierraview.org; www.sierraview.org
559-638-9226 and 559-638-9227, fax 559-638-6857
1155 E Springfield Ave, Reedley CA 93654

Founded 1960. A retirement community offering a continuum of housing and health care services on a monthly rental basis.

Souderton Mennonite Homes*

smh@netcarrier.com
215-723-9881, fax 215-723-9876
207 W Summit St, Souderton PA 18964
Margaret Zook, executive director; Willis A Miller, board chair

Founded 1917. Private, not-for-profit continuing care retirement community providing a continuum of housing and services for older adults.

Sunnyside Village/Health Center*

davidray08@aol.com; www.sunnysidevillage.org
941-371-2750 and 941-371-2729, fax 941-377-2571
5201 Bahia Vista St, Sarasota FL 34232
David Ray Miller, executive director

Founded 1968. Retirement community, assisted living facility, and skilled nursing facility. Sponsored by area Mennonite churches.

Swiss Village Retirement Community*

inquiries@swissvillage.org; www.swissvillage.org
260-589-3173, fax 260-589-8369
1350 W Main St, Berne IN 46711
Daryl L. Martin, executive director

Founded 1968. Provides health care and retirement living facilities and services that enhance life with dignity, meaning, and appropriate care within a Christian environment. Sponsored by First Mennonite Church, Berne.

Tel Hai Services Inc.*

www.telhai.org
610-273-9333, fax 610-273-4141
1200 Tel Hai Cir, PO Box 190,
Honey Brook PA 19344-0190
Joseph J. Swartz, president/CEO (jswartz@telhai.org); David Stott, vice-president of operations (dstott@telhai.org); Sue Verdegem, vice-president of finance (sverdegem@telhai.org); Paul King, board chair

Founded 1950. Offers a continuum of high quality care and services for aging individuals as a demonstration of God's love to over 500 residents.

Thurston Woods Village+

theoomo@aol.com
616-651-7841, fax 616-651-2050
307 N Franks Ave, Sturgis MI 49091
Theo Omo, CEO

Founded 1968. Provides responsible housing, health care, and services, valuing every individual in the spirit of Christian love.

Valley View Retirement Community*

valleyview@acsworld.net
717-935-2105, fax 717-935-5109
4702 E Main St, Belleville PA 17004
Randy Sheaffer, administrator (rsheaffer@acsworld.net)

Founded in 1963. 122 skilled nursing beds, 79 assisted living apartments, 118 independent living cottages. Providing a continuum of quality residential and long-term care services in a manner demonstrating Christian love and compassion.

Valley View Retirement Village

– see Rock of Ages

Virginia Mennonite Retirement Community*

roney@vmrc.org; www.vmrc.org
540-564-3400 and 888-564-VMRC, fax 540-564-3700
1501 Virginia Avenue, Harrisonburg VA 22802-2452
Ronald E. Yoder, president/CEO; Carolyn Nesselrodt, executive assistant

Founded 1954. Offers comprehensive, high quality service and care to the aging with Christian love and compassion in assisted living, nursing, independent housing, and wellness facilities.

Wayland Mennonite Home Association

parkview@farmtel.net
319-256-3525 and 319-256-2775, fax 319-256-4022
Parkview Home, 102 N Jackson St, Wayland IA 52654
Tanya Lucas, administrator; Joyce Roth, director of nursing

Founded 1961. Retirement community serving a broad spectrum of needs. Administers Parkview Home, Parkview Apartments, and Parkview Village.

Welsh Mountain Home*

wmhome@dejazzd.com
717-355-9522, fax 717-354-7103
567 Springville Rd, New Holland PA 17557
Harold E. Yoder, administrator; Paul Smoker, board chair

Founded 1924. Offers personal care services and housing primarily for persons in their retirement years. Member of Lancaster Mennonite Conference.

Mennonite Indian Leaders Council (MILC)

—see also United Native Ministries
milc@mennonitemission.net
316-283-5100, fax 316-283-0454; 722 Main St,
Newton KS 67114-0347
or 574-294-7523, fax 574-294-8669; 500 S
Main St, PO Box 370, Elkhart IN 46515-0370

INFORMATION

The Mennonite Indian Leaders Council (MILC)
was formed in 1969 to help Indian churches in
the United States and Hopi Mission School to
decide goals and programs of Indian ministries.
The Mennonite Mission Network is a partner
with MILC and funds their program with budget
monies. (Relates to Mennonite Mission Network.)
CLC rep: Lawrence Hart (ccctr@itlnet.net)

Mennonite Marriage Encounter

—see Mennonite and Brethren Marriage
Encounter

Mennonite Media

—see Mennonite Mission Network in section 1:
Churchwide Agencies

Mennonite Medical Association

mma@mennmed.org, www.mennmed.org
614-299-8922, fax 614-299-8922
193 E Frambes Ave, Columbus OH 43201-1409

STAFF

Jep Hostetler, executive secretary
Joyce Hostetler, administrative assistant

INFORMATION

Mennonite Medical Association (MMA) is a fellowship of physicians, dentists, and
medical/dental students who are members of
congregations of the Mennonite Central
Committee church constituency.

MMA supports the Anabaptist Center for
Healthcare Ethics
(www.mennmed.org/ache.htm), convenes an
annual convention with Mennonite Nurses
Association, connects members to short-term
mission projects, and provides funding for
Student Elective Term abroad. MMA was founded in 1944 by returning missionary physicians
and other concerned Mennonite physicians.

BOARD

Changes biannually. Richard Hostetter, M.D.,
president: 2001-2003, Goshen IN; Donald R.
Martin, M.D., president elect: 2003-2005,
Baltimore, MD; David Wiebe, M.D., secretary
treasurer, Kearny NE

PUBLICATION

Mennonite Health Journal (Quarterly), Molly
Hastings, editor (mollyeditor@aol.com), 457
Charleston Ave, Columbus OH 43214
(614-846-0621),

Mennonite Men

jimg@mennoniteusa.org,
www.mennonitemen.org
316-283-5100, fax 316-283-0454
PO Box 347, 722 Main St, Newton KS 67117-0347

STAFF

Jim Gingerich, coordinator
  (jimg@mennoniteusa.org)

INFORMATION

Mennonite Men aims to provide an Anabaptist
perspective on manhood that speaks to current
issues. It provides resources for men's groups
in local congregations and develops materials
on specific men's issues.

Mennonite Men is a jointly owned partnership of Mennonite Church Canada and
Mennonite Church USA. Mennonite Men began
in the General Conference Mennonite Church in
1950. In 1983, the Tenth Man church building
program began which provides grants to young
congregations acquiring their first church building.

ORGANIZATIONAL INDEX

3

BOARD

Don Schmidt, president (dmschmidt@ wwwebservice.net), 715 Country Club Dr, Newton KS 67114 (316-283-2031); Warren Habegger, vice-president; Lowell Detweiler, secretary; Carl Thieszen, treasurer; Jean-Jacques Goulet, executive committee; Rodney Frey, Robert W Friesen, Arlen Goshall, Mark A. Kniss, David L Lehman, John Zook; CLC rep: Jim Gingerich

Mennonite Mission Network

—see section 1: Churchwide Agencies

Mennonite Mutual Aid

—see section 1: Churchwide Agencies

Mennonite Nurses Association

mna.mennonite.net
937-465-3362
193 E Frambes Ave, Columbus OH 43201-1409

INFORMATION

Mennonite Nurses Association (MNA) is an organization dedicated to the promotion of nursing and the provision of support for the Christian nurse within the Anabaptist tradition.

MNA supports the Anabaptist Center for Healthcare Ethics, convenes an annual convention with Mennonite Medical Association, supports scholarships for nursing students, nursing education in foreign countries, projects of missionary nurses, and other health enhancing projects. Projects are selected from Mennonite mission agencies and other health related agencies.

BOARD

Changes biannually. Barbara Landes, president: 2002-2004 (jblandes@logan.net), RN, BSN, CDE, West Liberty OH

PUBLICATION

MNA produces a semiannual MNA newsletter for its members. *Mennonite Health Journal* (Quarterly), Molly Hastings, editor, (mollyeditor@aol.com),457 Charleston Ave, Columbus OH 43214 (614-846-0621)

Mennonite Press, Inc.

www.mennonitepress.com
800-536-4686 and 316-283-4680, fax 316-283-2068
532 N Oliver Rd, Newton KS 67114

STAFF

Steven Rudiger, managing director
(stevenr@mennonitepress.com)

INFORMATION

Founded 1902. Mennonite Press, Inc. is a for-profit commercial printing company. Mennonite Church USA is the majority stockholder. Other sales concentrations are with self-publishers, educational institutions, advertising agencies, and other religious organizations.

BOARD

Roger Williams, chair (clbacctg@juno.com), 2000 Evangel Way, Nappanee IN 46550 (574-773-3164); Dennis Good, secretary; Steven Rudiger, treasurer; Ted Stuckey

Mennonite Publishing House

—see section 1: Churchwide Agencies

Mennonite Quarterly Review

mqr@goshen.edu, www.goshen.edu/mqr
574-535-7433, 574-535-7418, fax 574-535-7438
1700 S Main St, Goshen College, Goshen IN 46526

INFORMATION

Founded 1927. An interdisciplinary journal devoted to Anabaptist-Mennonite history, thought, life, and affairs. Published jointly by Mennonite Historical Society, Goshen College, and Associated Mennonite Biblical Seminary.

Mennonite Resources Network

—see MRN Ministry Resources

Mennonite Retirement Trust

—see MMA in section 1: Churchwide Agencies

Mennonite Secondary Education Council (MSEC)

—see schools in this section and Mennonite Education Agency in section 1.

Mennonite Urban Corps Pittsburgh

412-362-2268
5615 Stanton Ave, Pittsburgh PA 15206
Heather Kropf and Steve Kriss, directors

Mennonite Urban Ministries of Denver

303-892-6416, fax 303-892-6106
430 W 9th Ave, Denver CO 80204

STAFF

Gail Valetta, director

INFORMATION

Founded 1960, 1997. Mennonite Urban Ministries is a coordinating and support resource for the Denver/Boulder area Mennonite Churches. The agency assists each local congregation with developing, enhancing, and strengthening its outreach and service in its own community.

BOARD

Chairperson: Eldon Mast, 1528 Elmhurst Dr, Longmont CO 80513 (303-684-6733); Ken Tribby, Steve Friesen, Eldon Mast, David Claasen-Wilson, Dana Williams, Sam Thornham, Robin Ottoson, Don Sager, Mike Barber, Rose Weaver, Paul Johnson

Mennonite Voluntary Service

—see Mennonite Mission Network in section 1: Churchwide Agencies

Mennonite Weekly Review

editor@mennoweekly.org,
www.mennoweekly.org
800-424-0178 and 316-283-3670,
fax 316-283-6502
129 W Sixth St, PO Box 568, Newton KS 67114

STAFF

Paul Schrag, editor (editor@mennoweekly.org)
Robert Rhodes, assistant editor
  (rrhodes@mennoweekly.org)
Robert M. Schrag, publisher
  (rschrag@mennoweekly.org)

INFORMATION

MWR, Inc., a church-related nonprofit corporation, owns and publishes *Mennonite Weekly Review,* an inter-Mennonite newspaper providing global coverage of Mennonite news for subscribers across the U.S. Member: Meetinghouse Association and Council on Church and Media. Participating bodies: Mennonite Church USA, Mennonite Brethren U.S. Conference, and others. MWR, Inc. was founded as Herald Publishing Co. in 1920 by Henry P. Krehbiel and other Mennonite church leaders and laypeople.

BOARD

John A. Lapp, president (jalapp@infi.net), 13 Knollwood Dr, Akron PA 17501 (717-859-4412); Raylene Hinz-Penner, vice-president; Pat Swartzendruber, treasurer; Don Ratzlaff, secretary; James Harder, Janeen Bertsche Johnson, Clarence Rempel, Steve Shenk, Paul Toews

PUBLICATION

Mennonite Weekly Review (weekly since 1923), Paul Schrag, editor (same address as above)

Mennonite Women USA

OFFICE

mwusa@mennonitewomenusa.org
316-283-5100, fax 316-283-0454
722 Main St, PO Box 347, Newton KS 67114-0347

ORGANIZATIONAL INDEX

3

STAFF

Rhoda Keener, executive director, 5207 Heisey Rd, Shippensburg PA 17257, phone/fax 717-532-9723, (rhodak@mennonitewomenusa.org)

Cathleen Hockman-Wert, editor, 30213 S Stuwe Rd, Canby OR 97013, 503-263-1210, (timbrel@mennonitewomenusa.org)

Carol Peterson, administrative assistant, Newton KS office, (carolp@mennonitewomenusa.org)

INFORMATION:

Year founded: Mennonite Women USA will begin February 1, 2003, and is the U.S. portion of Mennonite Women (1997-January 31, 2003). Mennonite Women USA's mission is to minister to the women of Mennonite Church USA by resourcing women's groups and individual women as we nurture our life in Christ, study the Bible, utilize our gifts, hear each other, and engage in mission and service. Mennonite Women USA administers an International Women's Fund and relates to women's groups and individual women in 21 conferences of Mennonite Church USA.

BOARD

Elaine W. Good, president (rolee-leonelaine@desupernet.net), 304 Buch Mill Rd, Lititz PA 17543 (717-626-9287); Paula Brunk Kuhns, vice-president; Gail Shetler, secretary; Sue Schmucker Coblentz, treasurer; Yvonne Bailey, Maggie DeLeon, Anne Hege, Susan E. Janzen, Nancy R. Sauder, Rickey Schrag, Barbara R. Voth; CLC reps: Elaine Good and Rhoda Kenner

PUBLICATION

Timbrel (six issues per year), Cathleen Hockman-Wert, editor (address above). Mennonite Women USA also produces an annual Bible study guide and a biannual *Women Together: Ideas for Groups*. Publications are shared with Canadian Women in Mission.

Mennonite World Conference
—see section 4

Mennonite Your Way Tours and Hospitality Directory

myw1525@aol.com, www.mywtours.com
717-653-9288 and 800-296-1991, fax 717-653-0990
PO Box 425 Landisville PA 17538-0425

STAFF

Leon and Nancy Stauffer, founders and co-partners

INFORMATION

The Mennonite Your Way program seeks to help fellowship happen among members of the Mennonite Church USA and across international and denominational boundaries. The Tours program offers escorted tours throughout North America and numerous international locations. The Hospitality Directory lists private homes across the USA and Canada and from other countries around the world willing to host/assist overnight guests who travel through their area.

BOARD

Leon and Nancy Stauffer (co-partners), 647 N Strickler Rd, Manheim PA 17545 (members of Landisville Mennonite Church, Lancaster Mennonite Conference)

PUBLICATION

MYW Tour Notes (three times per year), Leon Stauffer, editor
Mennonite Your Way Hospitality Directory (every two years)

Mennonite.net

info@mennonite.net
888-868-7099 and 574-535-7730, fax 574-535-7017
1700 S Main St, Goshen IN 46526

STAFF
Michael Sherer, director
(msherer@goshen.edu)
Umesh Balasubramaniam, systems administrator
(umeshajb@goshen.edu)

INFORMATION
Founded in 1998, Mennonite.net provides low-cost technology services to the Mennonite church, including database-generated, customizable websites for Mennonite churches, conferences and organizations; web hosting; a searchable online directory; and a growing suite of churchwide services. Mennonite.net also provides web and database-oriented consulting and development services.

Mental Health Agencies
—see Mennonite Health Services and Mental Illness Ministries

MHS
—see Mennonite Health Services

MILC
—see Mennonite Indian Leaders Council

Millersville International House
mih.usa@juno.com
717-872-7085, fax 717-872-7085
321 Manor Ave, Millersville PA 17551

STAFF
Daniel L. Gehman, director

INFORMATION
Founded 1986. A housing facility with the capacity for 25 students located near the Millersville University campus. Provides an environment that engenders sensitivity to various culture and ideological differences and encourages students to investigate the Christian faith.

Services include English tutoring, counseling, Bible studies, and consultation with families who host international students.

BOARD
Administered by Eastern Mennonite Missions

Ministerial Leadership
—see Executive Board in section 1: Churchwide Agencies

Mission Study Center
(formerly Mission Training Center)
waltersawatsky@cs.com
574-295-3726, fax 574-295-0092
c/o AMBS, 3003 Benham Ave, Elkhart IN 46517-1999

STAFF
Walter Sawatsky, director
Karmen Fehr, administrative assistant
(kfehr@ambs.edu)

INFORMATION
The Mission Study Center is a cooperative venture among Associated Mennonite Biblical Seminary, Mennonite Mission Network (MC USA), Christian Witness Council (MC Canada) and the Mennonite Central Committee. Its director is a member of the AMBS faculty and auxiliary staff of the mission/service agencies, consulting with colleagues on identifying and preparing workers, and consultation on missiological issues.

A coordinating committee annually reviews program and budget. Chaired by AMBS Dean Loren Johns, its members are Stanley Green and James Krabill (Mission Network), Jack Suderman and Janet Plenert (Witness Council), Ron Mathies and Ron Flaming (MCC), with Art McPhee and Walter Sawatsky (ex-officio).

PUBLICATION
Mission Focus: Annual Review, Walter Sawatsky, editor (same address as above)

Missional Church Advancement

—see Mennonite Mission Network in section 1: Churchwide Agencies

MMA

—see Mennonite Mutual Aid in section 1

MPH

—see Mennonite Publishing House in section 1: Churchwide Agencies

MRN Ministry Resources

info@mrn.org, www.mrn.org
215-723-5513, fax 215-723-1211
771 Route 113, Souderton PA 18964

STAFF

Philip C. Bergey, executive director
(philb@fmc-online.org)
Tana Pelkey-Landes, director of operations
(tanalandes97@yahoo.com)

Noel Santiago, prayer ministries and church
health consultant (noels@fmc-online.org)

INFORMATION

MRN provides Great Commission resources to empower Jesus-followers in making new disciples. Resources include a team of consultants working in areas of church health, community development, antiracism, organizational change, and more.

Partners include Design for Ministry, Eastern District Conference, Franconia Conference, Mennonite Media, Mennonite World Conference, Pandora Press U.S., and Ted and Lee Theaterworks.

MRN began in 1997 through Franconia Conference. Eastern District Conference joined in 1998, and other partners have joined since that time.

BOARD

Henry L. Rosenberger, chair
(hcrosen@voicenet.com), PO Box 86,

Blooming Glen PA 18911

PUBLICATION
Living Springs (Quarterly), Craig Pelkey-Landes, editor (same address as above). Subscriptions $15.00/yr. Online version: www.MRN.org/LivingSprings/index.htm

MutualAid eXchange
Anabaptist and Brethren Agency (see also Association of Mutual Aid Societies AMAS)
mutualaid@mutualaidexchange.com, www.mutualaidexchange.com
877-971-6300 and 913-338-1100, toll free fax 877-785-0085
8717 W 110th St, Ste 100, Overland Park KS 66210

STAFF
David Wine, president/CEO
Bentley Peters, vice-president of administration
Glenn Welborn, director of external operations
Bob Gast, director of internal operations
Joni Goode, president of finance

INFORMATION
MutualAid eXchange (MAX) is a reciprocal insurance company exclusively for Anabaptists throughout the United States and Canada. MAX provides high quality home, farm, church, and auto coverage.

Member Agency Companies of MAX are: Virginia Mennonite Property Aid Plan, Sharing Services Agency, Mennonite Property Aid Association, Mennonite Aid Union of Kansas, Iowa Mennonite Mutual Aid Association, Mennonite Aid Society, Mennonite Aid Plan, Mennonite Aid Union (Canada), Mennonite Mutual Insurance Association and New York Mennonite Agency, Inc.

Anabaptist and Brethren Agency was founded in 1996 and is the overall agency of MutualAid eXchange (MAX).

MAX was founded in January 2000. A Mid-Atlantic Region branch was opened in February 2002 and MAX Canada Insurance Group was established in April 2002.

BOARD
James Gascho, chair (jgascho@maaim.com), 1013 Division St, PO Box 773, Goshen IN 46527-0773; David Wine, President/CEO; Phil Marner, secretary; Peter Dyck, Brent Eberly, Jay Goering, Larry Litwiller, Homer Myers, Jose Ortiz, Arlan Ortman, Robert Rabenstein, Nelson Scheifele and Allen Schroeder, board members

Mutual Aid and Insurance Agencies
Mutual aid and insurance agencies that are members of Associated Mutual Aid Societies (AMAS) and/or MutualAid eXchange (MAX) are listed below (pages 176-177). See also Association of Mutual Aid Societies and MutualAid eXchange.

ORGANIZATIONAL INDEX

3

Mutual Aid and Insurance Agencies

*AMAS member   +MAX member company

CALIFORNIA

Mennonite Aid Plan of the Pacific Coast*
mennonite@mennoniteinsurance.com;
www.mennoniteinsurance.com
800-447-4493 and 559-638-2327, fax 559-638-3336
1110 J St, PO Box 878, Fresno, CA 93654
Ron Licata, general manager
Coverage offered: home and farm. Serves AZ, CA, OR and WA.

INDIANA

CAM Mutual Aid Association*
cammutualaid@maplenet.net
800-363-5644 and 574-825-5644, fax 574-825-2123
13841 US 20, Middlebury, IN 46540
Wayne Chupp, president
Coverage offered: home, farm, fire and extended coverages. Serves Conservative and Amish Mennonite in 28 states. Call for more information.

Mennonite Aid Association of Indiana and Michigan*+
Sharing Services Agency Inc.
sharing@sharingservices.com;
www.sharingservices.com
800-832-4689 and 574-533-5396, fax 574-533-5275
1013 Division St (The Depot), PO Box 733, Goshen, IN 46527
Jim Gascho, president/CEO
(jgascho@sharingservices.com)
Coverage offered: home, farm, fire, and extended coverages. Serves Anabaptists in IN, MI and KY.

Mennonite Mutual Aid Association*
memberinfo@mma-online.org; www.mma-online.org
800-348-7468 and 574-533-9511, fax 574-533-5264
1110 North Main St, PO Box 483, Goshen, IN 46527
Coverage offered: health, life, mutual funds, annuities, financial services, charitable gift plans, personal trusts. Serves U.S.

IOWA

Iowa Mennonite Mutual Aid Association*+
immaa@kctc.net
800-622-5883 and 319-656-2211, fax 319-656-2215
435 B Ave, PO Box 428, Kalona, IA 52247
Phil Marner, secretary/treasurer
Coverage offered: home, farm, fire and extended coverage. Serves IA.

KANSAS

Mennonite Aid Union of Kansas*+
info@maukansas.com
620-327-2761, fax 620-327-2108
371 North Old Highway 81, PO Box 989, Hesston, KS 67062
Larry Litwiller, general manager
(larry@maukansas.com)
Coverage offered: commercial, home, farm, fire and extended coverages. Serves KS.

Mennonite Property Aid Association*+
mpaa@mtelco.net; www.mpaa-misi.com
800-748-7838 and 620-345-2837, fax 620-345-2836
101 North Christian Ave, PO Box 639, Moundridge, KS 67107
Jay Goering, general manager (mpaajay@yahoo.com)
Coverage offered: home, farm, fire and extended coverage. Serves Central U.S. (call for other states).

The Mutual Aid Association of the Church of the Brethren*
maa@maabrethren.com; www.maabrethren.com
800-255-1243 and 785-598-2212, fax 800-238-7535
3094 Jeep Rd, Abilene, KS 67410-6064
Jean Hendricks, president and general manager
(jean@maabrethren.com)
Coverage offered: home, farm, fire, and extended coverage. Serves Church of the Brethren members in the U.S.

MutualAid eXchange*—see separate listing

MINNESOTA

Mennonite Mutual Insurance Association*+
mmiaajs@rconnect.com
800-210-6168 and 507-427-2343, fax 507-427-2585
206 N 10th St, PO Box 309, Mountain Lake, MN 56159
Allen Schroeder, general manager
Coverage offered: home, farm, fire and extended coverage, auto physical damage—Serves MN and MT.

NEW YORK

New York Mennonite Mutual Aid Plan*+
New York Mennonite Agency, Inc.
thjyousy@northnet.org
315-376-4737, fax 315-376-8433
7383M Utica Blvd, Lowville, NY 13367
Holly Yousey, general manager
Coverage offered: home, farm, fire and extended coverage. Serves NY.

OHIO

Mennonite Aid Plan*+
rnrmap@bright.net
937-465-5808, fax 937-465-5808 (Fax on request)
1582 SR 245 West, West Liberty, OH 43357-9747
Robert Rabenstein, secretary
Coverage offered: home, farm, fire and extended coverage. Serves OH.

Mennonite Mutual Aid Society*
419-358-9840, fax 419-358-9840 (Fax on request)
331 North Main St, Bluffton, OH 45817
Lois King, secretary
Coverage offered: home, farm, fire and extended coverage. Serves OH.

PENNSYLVANIA

Goodville Mutual Casualty Company*—see separate listing

SOUTH DAKOTA

Mennonite Aid Society*+
rarafarm@gwtc.net
605-648-3734
44760 283rd St, Hurley, SD 57036
Ray Neufeld, secretary
Coverage offered: home, farm, fire and extended coverages. Serves SD.

VIRGINIA

Virginia Mennonite Property and Auto Aid Plans*+
Virginia Mennonite Aid, Inc.
info@dmap.org
800-830-0311 and 540-434-9727, fax 540-434-7627
901 Pakrwood Dr, Harrisonburg, VA 22802
Brent Eberly, executive director (beberly@dmap.org)
Coverage offered: home, farm, fire and extended coverage; commercial fire; auto physical damage. Serves FL, GA, KY, MD, NC, OH, SC, TN, VA and WV.

N

National Campaign for a Peace Tax Fund

info@peacetaxfund.org, www.peacetaxfund.org
202-483-3751 and 888-PEACETAX (732-2382), fax 202-986-0667
2121 Decatur Place NW, Washington DC 20008

STAFF

Marian Franz, executive director

INFORMATION

Founded 1972. The National Campaign for a Peace Tax Fund advocates for legislation enabling conscientious objectors to war to pay their full federal taxes into a fund which could not be used for the military. A lobbying organization supported by both secular and faith organizations. Related issues include peace/conscientious objection and religious/civil liberty.

PUBLICATION

Quarterly Update (Quarterly), staff editor (same address as above)

New Call to Peacemaking
—see Every Church a Peace Church

New York City Council of Mennonite Churches

Bronx Mennonite Church office (nyccmc2019bx@yahoo.com), 2019 Grand Ave, Bronx NY 14053, phone/fax 718-294-7280
Brooklyn Mennonite Church office (arpac@aol.com), 1423 E 34th St, Brooklyn NY 11210, phone/fax 718-253-7267

STAFF

Kendra S. Henderson, office secretary
     (Bronx office)
Anna Pacheco, office secretary
     (Brooklyn office)

INFORMATION

Founded 1980. The underlying purpose is to promote a spirit of Christian unity and fellowship among the congregations and members of the council in fulfilling their mission. It comprises 17 congregations of the Lancaster (11) and Atlantic Coast (6) Conferences.

ORGANIZATIONAL INDEX

3

BOARD

Monroe Yoder (Lancaster Bishop), moderator, 268 Van Cortlandt Ave E, Apt 2, Bronx NY 10467 (718-652-2307); Reinaldo Pacheo (Atlantic Coast Overseer), vice-moderator; John Rempel, secretary/treasurer; Nicholas Angustia (Lancaster), assistant bishop; Michael Banks (Lancaster), assistant bishop; Warren Tyson (Atlantic Coast), interim overseer

PROGRAMS AND PROJECTS

Camp Deerpark, PO Box 394, Westbrookville NY 12785, 914-754-88669, Ken Bontrager, director

Heartease Home, 216 E 70th St, New York NY 10021, 212-249-3107 (ministry temporarily closed)

Menno House, 314 E 19th St, New York NY 10003, 212-677-1611, sponsored by Manhattan Mennonite Fellowship

New York Mennonite Conference

—see section 2: Conferences and Congregations

North American Vietnamese Mennonite Fellowship

nhienp@hotmail.com
604-324-1200
7155 Sherbrooke St, Vancouver BC V5X 4E3, Canada

INFORMATION

Founded 1997. NAVMF promotes fellowship and cooperation among its members in the areas of leadership development and church planting. Members include Vietnamese Mennonite churches in North America. It currently has nine member churches.

EXECUTIVE COMMITTEE

Nhien Huu Pham, president (nhienp@hotmail.com), 13477 60 Ave Surrey BC V3X 2M4; Tuyen Thanh Nguyen, vice presi-

dent; Hoa Van Chau, treasurer; Chau Hong Dang, secretary; Can Ngoc Le, mission coordinator

North Central Mennonite Conference

—see section 2: Conferences and Congregations

O

Ohio Mennonite Conference

—see section 2: Conferences and Congregations

On the Line

—see Mennonite Publishing House in section 1: Churchwide Agencies

P

Pacific Northwest Mennonite Conference

—see section 2: Conferences and Congregations

Pacific Southwest Mennonite Conference

—see section 2: Conferences and Congregations

Pandora Press U.S.

—see Cascadia Publishing House

Park View Federal Credit Union

info@pvfcu.org, www.pvfcu.com
888-900-6444 and 540-434-6444,
fax 540-433-0108
1675 Virginia Ave, Harrisonburg VA 22802

STAFF

John Beiler, corporate executive officer (pvfcu@pvfcu.org)

INFORMATION
Founded 1969. A full-service financial cooperative serving the Mennonite Community in
Harrisonburg/Rockingham County, Va. Also students, alumni, residents, and employees of listed Mennonite-affiliated organizations. Services
include mortgage and home equity loans, vehi-
cle and student loans, credit cards, savings,
checking, money market, certificates,
ATM/check cards, online banking and bill pay-
ment, IRAs and Coverdell ESAs. Member-owned;
volunteer board of directors elected by membership.

Philadelphia Mennonite Council
—see Kingdom Builders

Peace Advocacy
—see Executive Board in section 1: Churchwide
Agencies

Peace and Justice Support Network
leoh@mennonitemission.net,
www.peace.mennolink.org
717-399-8353, fax 717-391-6512
202 South Ann St, Lancaster PA 17602

STAFF
Leo Hartshorn, minister of peace and justice
    (leoh@mennonitemission.net)
Susan Mark Landis, peace advocate
    (susanml@mennoniteusa.org)

INFORMATION
Formed in March 2003. PSJN is an inclusive
group open to anyone who wants to support in a
special way MC USA's work of peace and justice.
    Tasks of the network include: creating and
keeping clear the vision of peace and justice in
Mennonite Church USA, promoting the expan-
sion of peace and justice through gatherings for
inspiration, providing counsel to MC USA's agencies and executive board, sharing and publiciz-
ing resources for congregations, and communi-
cating peace and justice work to the wider constituency.

REFERENCE COMMITTEE
Richard Davis, facilitator (pmc@airmail.net),
Peace Mennonite Church, PO Box 59926, Dallas
TX 75229 (214-350-5244); Malinda Berry, Titus
Peachey, Mark Frey, and Yvonne Keeler.

PUBLICATION
Yet-to-be-named quarterly newsletter to be
released Spring 2003, Leo Hartshorn, editor
(same address as above).

Pittsburgh Hospitality House
412-731-3372
211 Thomas Blvd, Pittsburgh PA 15208
Fred Kraybill, contact

Provident Bookstores
—see Mennonite Publishing House in section 1:
Churchwide Agencies

Purpose
—see Mennonite Publishing House in section 1:
Churchwide Agencies

Q

Quickfind
—see pages at end of directory

R

RAD
—see Mennonite Mission Network in section 1:
Churchwide Agencies

Rejoice!
—see Mennonite Publishing House in section 1:
Churchwide Agencies

Retirement Centers
—see Mennonite Health Services

Retreat Centers
—see Mennonite Camping Association

Rocky Mountain Mennonite Conference
—see section 2: Conferences and Congregations

S

Schools
—For elementary and secondary schools, see list below.

For colleges, see specific listings for Bethel, Bluffton, Eastern Mennonite, Goshen, and Hesston earlier in this section.

For seminaries, see specific listings for Associated Mennonite Biblical Seminary and Eastern Mennonite Seminary earlier in this section.

Elementary and Secondary Schools

The sponsoring body is noted with each school. Schools that are members of Mennonite Secondary Education Council (MSEC) are identified with an asterisk (*), of the Mennonite Elementary Education Council (MEEC) with a pound sign (#), and of the Lancaster Area Council of Mennonite Schools with a caret (^).

Other affiliations are indicated by the following abbreviations: Association of Christian Schools International (ACSI), Mid-Atlantic Christian School Association (MACSA), Middle States Association of Colleges and Schools (MSA), National Institute for Learning Disabilities (NILD), Northwest Association of Schools and Colleges (NASC), and Southern Association of Colleges and Schools (SACS).

Belleville Mennonite School *#
bmsinfo@pa.net, www.bellevillemennoniteschool.org
717-935-2184, fax 717-935-5641
4105 Front Mountain Rd, PO Box 847, Belleville PA 17004-0847
Founded: 1945. Sponsor: Patrons Association.
    Ken Hartzler, administrator. 2001-02 enrollment: 87 students, grades 9-12; 210 students, grades P-8. Affiliated with MACSA. Aquilla Kanagy, board chair (717-667-6600)

Bethany Christian Schools *
info@bethanycs.net, www.bethanycs.net
574-534-2567, fax 574-533-0150
2904 S Main St, Goshen IN 46526-5499
Founded: 1954/1996. Sponsor: Indiana-Michigan Mennonite Conference (IM).
    Allan Dueck, principal. 2001-02 enrollment: 208 students, grades 9-12; 99 students, grades 6-8. Accredited by Indiana Department of Education. Eldon Heatwole, board chair (574-875-8059), eldonheatwole@hotmail.com.

Calvary Christian Academy
757-825-1133, fax 757-825-8711
2311 Tower Pl, Hampton VA 23666
Sponsor: Calvary Community Church (V).
    L. W. Francisco III, chief administrator. 2001-02 enrollment: 214 students, grades P-8. Accredited by Accrediting Commission International; affiliated with ACSI. L. W. Francisco III, board chair

Calvary Christian School
calvary@ccfc-s.org, www.ccfc-s.org/School.html
323-752-7594 or 323-752-7406, fax 323-752-1481
2400 W 85th St, Inglewood CA 90305
Founded: 1970. Sponsor: Calvary Christian Fellowship Church (PSMC).
    Linda V. Blades, principal. 2001-02 enrollment: 350 students, grades P-8. Affiliated with ACSI. Alvin L. Isaacs, pastor/board chair (323-752-8552)

Central Christian School *
FredMiller@centralchristian.k12.oh.us, www.centralchristian.k12.oh.us
330-857-7311, fax 330-857-7331
3970 Kidron Rd, PO Box 9, Kidron OH 44636-0009
Founded: 1961. Sponsor: Ohio Mennonite Conference (OH).
    Frederic A. Miller, superintendent; TBA, high school principal; Deborah Friesen, middle school principal; Joyce Taylor, learning center principal. 2001-02 enrollment: 207 students, grades 9-12; 183 students, grades P-8.

Chicago Mennonite Learning Center #
cmlc@infolaunch.com, www.cmlc.infolaunch.com
773-735-9304, fax 773-735-9832
4647 W 47th St, Chicago IL 60632
Founded: 1981. Sponsor: Illinois Menn Conf (IMC)/Central Dist Conf (CDC).
    Ib Thomsen, principal; Sarah Sales, assistant principal. 2001-02 enrollment: 80 students, grades K-8. Serves children of diverse cultural, racial, and ethnic backgrounds. Leanne Schertz, board chair (309-383-2451)

Christopher Dock Mennonite High School *
cdock@christopherdock.org, www.christopherdock.org
215-362-2675, fax 215-362-2943
1000 Forty Foot Rd, Lansdale PA 19446
Founded: 1952. Sponsor: Franconia Mennonite
Conference (F).
   Elaine A. Moyer, principal. 2001-02 enrollment: 427
students, grades 9-12. Accredited by MSA. John M.
Goshow, board chair (215-257-6551)

Clinton Christian School #
clinton@npcc.net
574-642-3940, fax 574-642-3674
61763 County Road 35, Goshen IN 46528
Founded: 1950. Sponsor: Michiana area churches of the
CM Conference.
   Conrad Showalter, principal. 2001-02 enrollment:
120 students, grades K-12. Affiliated with ACSI. Ken
Miller, board chair (574-642-3940)

Conestoga Christian School *#^
info@cc-school.org
610-286-0353, fax 610-286-0350
2760 Main St, Morgantown PA 19543-9623
Founded: 1952. Sponsor: Rockville, Conestoga, and
Hopewell congs. (AC).
   Susan Yoder, administrator. 2001-02 enrollment: 90
students, grades 9-12; 198 students, grades K-8.
Affiliated with ACSI, MACSA, NILD; accredited by MSA.

Eastern Mennonite High School *
emhs@emhs.net, www.emhs.net
540-432-4500, fax 540-432-4528
801 Parkwood Dr, Harrisonburg VA 22802
Founded: 1917. Sponsor: Virginia Mennonite
Conference (V).
   J. David Yoder, principal. 2001-02 enrollment: 227
students, grades 9-12; 105 students, grades 6-8.
Affiliated with MACSA; accredited by SACS. Jackie
Hartman, board chair

Ephrata Mennonite School #^
ems@ephms.com
717-738-4266, fax 717-738-4266
598 Stevens Rd, Ephrata PA 17522
Founded: 1946.
   David L. Sauder, principal. 2001-02 enrollment: 213
students, grades K-9. Affiliated with MSA and MACSA.
Lynn Zimmerman, board chair

Freeman Academy *
www.freemanacademy.pvt.k12.sd.us
605-925-4237, fax 605-925-4271
748 S Main St, PO Box 1000, Freeman SD 57029
Founded: 1900. Sponsor: Independent.
   Marlan Kaufman, principal. 2001-02 enrollment: 32
students, grades 9-12. Everett Waltner, board chair
(605-925-7766)

Gateway Christian School
610-682-2748, fax 610-682-9670
245 Fredericksville Rd, Mertztown PA 19539

Founded: 1978. Sponsor: Living Word Christian
Fellowship (F).

Gehmans Mennonite School #^
gms@dejazzd.com
717-484-4222, fax 717-484-4222
650 Gehman School Rd, Denver PA 17517
Founded: 1952. Sponsor: Patrons.
   Melvin L. Weaver, administrator. 2001-02 enrollment: 184 students, grades K-8. Affiliated with MACSA.
Irvin Weaver Jr, board chair (717-445-6791)

Greenwood Mennonite School #
302-349-4131 and 302-349-5130, fax 302-349-5076
12802 Mennonite School Rd, Greenwood DE 19950
Founded: 1928. Sponsor: Cannon and Greenwood
Mennonite churches (CM).
   Paul E. Isaacs, administrator. 2001-02 enrollment:
204 students, grades 9-12; 93 students, grades K-8.
Affiliated with MACSA.

Hinkletown Mennonite School #^
office@hms.pvt.k12.pa.us, www.hms.pvt.k12.pa.us
717-354-6705, fax 717-354-8438
272 Wanner Rd, Ephrata PA 17522
Founded: 1981. Sponsor: Patron families.
   Tom Burnett, administrator. 2001-02 enrollment:
195 students, grades K-8. Accredited by MSA. Lorna
Stoltzfus, board chair

Hopi Mission School
HMS@hopimissionschool.org,
www.hopimissionschool.org
928-734-2453, fax 928-734-2453
PO Box 39, Kykotsmovi AZ 86039-0039
Founded: 1951. Sponsor: Mennonite and American
Baptist Churches USA.
   William R. Zuercher, administrator; Ray Peters, prin-
cipal. 2001-02 enrollment: 45 students, grades K-6.
Staffed primarily by MVS volunteers. Laverne Dallas,
president (928-734-2302), ldallas83@hotmail.com

Iowa Mennonite School *
ims@iamenno.pvt.k12.ia.us,
www.iamenno.pvt.k12.ia.us
319-656-2073 and 319-683-2586, fax 319-656-2073
1421 540th St SW, Kalona IA 52247
Founded: 1945. Sponsor: Central Plains Mennonite
Conference (CPMC).
   Wilbur D. Yoder, principal. 2001-02 enrollment: 174
students, grades 9-12. Mike Brenneman, board chair
(319-683-2661)

Juniata Mennonite School #^
jms@tricountyi.net
717-463-2898
PO Box 278, McAlisterville PA 17049-0278
Founded: 1980. Sponsor: Juniata Mennonite School
Association.
   Andrew R. Meiser, principal. 2001-02 enrollment:
131 students, grades K-8. Affiliated with ACSI and
MACSA. Doug Meiser, board chair (717-535-5363)

ORGANIZATIONAL INDEX

3

Kraybill Mennonite School #^
kms@supernet.net
717-653-5236, fax 717-653-7334
598 Kraybill Church Rd, Mount Joy PA 17552
Founded: 1949.
    John S. Weber, principal. 2001-02 enrollment: 410
students, grades K-8. Affiliated with MACSA. Rose Baer,
board chair (717-361-0431)

Lake Center Christian School *#
lccsprincipal@yahoo.com, www.lccs.com/tech
330-877-2049, fax 330-877-2040
12893 Kaufman Ave NW, Hartville OH 44632
Founded: 1947. Sponsor: Cornerstone, Hartville &
Maple Grove Menn churches.
    Matthew R. McMullen, administrator. 2001-02
enrollment: 400 students, grades K-8. Member of ACSI
and NILD. Chris Ramsburg, board chair (330-877-9351)

Lancaster Mennonite School *#^
thomasjr@lancastermennonite.org,
www.lancastermennonite.org
717-299-0436, fax 717-299-0823
2176 Lincoln Hwy E, Lancaster PA 17602
Founded: 1942. Sponsor: Atlantic Coast (AC) and
Lancaster (L) conferences.
    J. Richard Thomas, superintendent. 2001-02 enroll-
ment: 775 students, grades 9-12; 325 students, grades
K-8. Lancaster Mennonite School consists of New
Danville Mennonite School, Lancaster Mennonite
Middle School, and Lancaster Mennonite High School.
Accredited by MSA. Connie F. Stauffer, board chair.

Linville Hill Mennonite School #^
linvillehill@juno.com
717-442-4447, fax 717-442-9283
295 S Kinzer Rd, Paradise PA 17562
Founded: 1944. Sponsor: Atlantic Coast (AC) and
Lancaster (L) conferences.
    Dwilyn Beiler, administrator. 2001-02 enrollment:
151 students, grades K-8. Affiliated with MACSA. Dale
Hess, board chair (717-548-2573)

Lititz Area Mennonite School #^
lams@dejazzd.com
717-626-9551, fax 717-626-0430
1050 E Newport Rd, Lititz PA 17543
Founded: 1978. Sponsor: LAMS patrons.
    Kay Predmore, interim administrator. 2001-02
enrollment: 262 students, grades K-8. Affiliated with
MACSA; accredited by MSA. Nelson Zimmerman, board
chair (717-738-0184)

Locust Grove Mennonite School #^
jodyw@lgms.pvt.k12.pa.us, www.lgms.pvt.k12.pa.us
717-394-7107, fax 717-394-4944
2257 Old Philadelphia Pike, PO Box 37, Smoketown PA
17576
Founded: 1939.
    David M. Helmus, principal. 2001-02 enrollment:
387 students, grades K-8. Accredited by ACSI, MSA, and
NILD. G. Roger Rutt, board chair

Manheim Christian Day School #^
cypeachey@dejazzd.com, www.mcdsschool.com
717-665-4300 and 717-664-2638, fax 717-664-4253
686 Lebanon Rd, Manheim PA 17545
Founded: 1952. Sponsor: Manheim Mennonite District.
    Crist Peachey, administrator. 2001-02 enrollment:
155 students, grades K-8. Affiliated with MACSA. Julie
Good, board chair (717-664-4717)

Mount Pleasant Christian School #
mpcs4kids@assure.net
757-482-9557 and 757-482-3447, fax 757-482-3447
1613 Mount Pleasant Rd, Chesapeake VA 23322
Founded: 1941. Sponsor: Mount Pleasant Mennonite
Church (V).
    Ken Platt, principal. 2001-02 enrollment: 125 stu-
dents, grades K-8. Affiliated with ACSI, NILD, and
Hampton Roads Association of Christian Schools.
Dennis Conrad, board chair

New Covenant Christian School *#^
NCCS@nccspa.org, www.nccspa.org
717-274-2423, fax 717-274-9830
452 Ebenezer Rd, Lebanon PA 17046
Founded: 1982. Sponsor: Association school under
Lebanon District (L).
    Neal J. Eckert, administrator. 2001-02 enrollment: 57
students, grades 9-12.

Penn View Christian School #
brutt@pennview.org, www.pennview.org
215-723-1196, fax 215-723-0148
420 Cowpath Rd, Souderton PA 18964
Founded: 1945. Sponsor: Franconia Menn Conference
(FCMC).
    Robert D. Rutt, executive director. 2001-02 enroll-
ment: 594 students, grades K-8. Affiliated with MACSA;
accredited by MSA. Ken Hochstetler, board chair (215-
723-5236)

Philadelphia Mennonite High School *
phms@verizon.net, www.philamennonitehs.org
215-769-5363, fax 215-769-4063
860 N 24th St, Philadelphia PA 19130
Founded: 1996. Sponsor: Philadelphia Mennonite
Council.
    Barbara Moses, principal. 2001-02 enrollment: 74
students, grades 9-12. Affiliated with ACSI and MACSA.
Mark Garis, board chair (215-769-5363)

Quakertown Christian School #
qcsajgeosits@netcarrier.com,
www.Quakertownchristian.org
215-536-6970, fax 215-536-2115
50 E Paletown Rd, Quakertown PA 18951
Founded: 1951. Sponsor: Franconia Menn Conference
(FCMC).
    Alma J. Geosits, administrator. 2001-02 enrollment:
284 students, P-8. Accredited by MSA. Jeff Naugle,
board chair (215-536-0845)

Sarasota Christian School *#
admissions@sarasotachristian.org,
www.sarasotachristian.org
941-371-6481, fax 941-371-0898
5415 Bahia Vista St, Sarasota FL 34232
Founded: 1958. Sponsor: Sarasota area Menn churches
(SE and CM).
    Eugene Miller, administrator; Jean Martin, elementary and middle school principal; Robert Hovde, high school principal. 2001-02 enrollment: 170 students, grades 9-12; 315 students, grades K-8.

Shalom Christian Academy *
shalom@shalomca.com,shalomca.com
717-375-2223, fax 717-375-2224
126 Social Island Rd, Chambersburg PA 17201
Founded: 1976. Sponsor: Shalom Christian Academy
Association.
    Conrad Swartzentruber, administrator. 2001-02 enrollment: 140 students, grades 9-12; 245 students, grades K-8. Affiliated with ACSI, MACSA, MSA, and NILD. Gary Harnish, board chair (717-264-5091)

Warwick River Christian School #
GorZook@yahoo.com, www.wrcs.baweb.com
757-877-2941, fax 757-877-6510
252 Lucas Creek Rd, Newport News VA 23602-6251
Founded: 1942. Sponsor: Warwick River, Huntington,

Providence congs. (V).
    Gordon D. Zook, administrator; Susan Yoder
Ackerman, principal. 2001-02 enrollment: 285 students, grades P-8. Affiliated with ACSI. Lynn Showalter, board chair (757-877-1932)

West Fallowfield Christian School #^
WFCS279@epix.net, www.wfcsonline.com
610-593-5011 and 610-593-7150, fax 610-593-6041
795 Fallowfield Rd, PO Box 279, Atglen PA 19310-0279
Founded: 1941.
    Elvin Kennel, principal. 2001-02 enrollment: 193 students, K-8. Affiliated with NILD and MACSA. Ed Engle, board chair.

Western Mennonite High School *
wmsoffice@teleport.com, www.westernmennonite.org
503-363-2000, fax 503-370-9455
9045 Wallace Rd NW, Salem OR 97304-9716
Founded: 1945. Sponsor: Pacific Northwest Menn
Conference (PNMC).
    Eric D. Martin, principal. 2001-02 enrollment: 122 students, grades 9-12; 49 students, grades 6-8. Accredited by NASC; affiliated with Oregon Federation of Independent Schools, Salem Area Association of Christian Schools, and National Honor Society of Secondary Schools. Linwood Rush, board chair (503-282-3497)

Schowalter Foundation Inc.
316-283-3720, fax 316-283-2039
900 N Poplar St, Ste 200, Newton KS 67114

STAFF
Willis Harder, president and manager

INFORMATION
Founded 1954. Seeks to encourage and stimulate outreach and witness locally and through the two sponsoring Mennonite denominations: Mennonite Church USA and Church of God in Christ, Mennonite.

Secondary Schools
—see Schools

Seminaries
—See specific listings for Associated Mennonite Biblical Seminary and Eastern Mennonite Seminary earlier in this section.

Service Adventure
—see Mennonite Mission Network in section 1: Churchwide Agencies

Service Opportunities
—see Mennonite Mission Network in section 1: Churchwide Agencies

Shalom Foundation Inc.
rbenner833@aol.com,
www.churchoutreach.com
888-833-3333 and 540-433-5351,
fax 540-434-0247
1251 Virginia Ave, Harrisonburg VA 22802

STAFF
Richard L. Benner, executive director
    (rbenner833@aol.com)
Melodie M. Davis, editor
    (melodie@mennomedia.org)

INFORMATION

Publishes two every-home full-color, outreach-oriented quarterlies: *Together* for congregations and *Living* for local communities. Partner with New Life Ministries. Subscribers to *Together* are predominantly Mennonite, Church of the Brethren and Brethren congregations, but it is open to any congregation, affiliated, or independent with evangelism goals. Shalom was founded in 1991 to advance Christian values and to cultivate the development of faith in Christ through the production and dissemination of quality, easy to utilize communication tools.

BOARD

Robert Kettering, chair (bobket@juno.com), 1043 W Elizabethtown Rd, Manheim PA 17545 (717-664-2620); Peggy Landis, vice-chair; Jonas Borntrager, treasurer; Terry White, secretary; Myron S. Augsburger, Jerry Engle, Rhoda Oberholtzer, Nathan D. Showalter

PUBLICATIONS

Together and *Living*, Melodie M. Davis, editor (same address as above)

Short-term Service Opportunities

—see Mennonite Mission Network in section 1: Churchwide Agencies

SOOP (Service Opportunities for Older People)

—see Mennonite Mission Network in section 1: Churchwide Agencies

South Central Mennonite Conference

—see section 2: Conferences and Congregations

Southeast Mennonite Conference

—see section 2: Conferences and Congregations

Special Days and Church Year

—see pages 8 and 9

Stewardship University

—see MMA in section1 : Churchwide Agencies

Story Friends

—see Mennonite Publishing House in section 1: Churchwide Agencies

T

Ten Thousand Villages

—see Mennonite Central Committee U.S.

The Mennonite

editor@themennonite.org,
www.themennonite.org
800-790-2498 and 574-535-6051 (Goshen)
and 316-283-5155 (Newton)
fax 574-535-6050(Goshen) and 316-283-0454
(Newton)
1700 S Main St, Goshen, IN 46526 and
722 Main St, PO Box 347, Newton, KS 67114

STAFF

Everett J. Thomas, editor
   (Everett@TheMennonite.org)
Gordon Houser, associate editor
   (GordonH@TheMennonite.org)
Rich Preheim, associate editor
   (RichP@TheMennonite.org)
Marla Cole, marketing and secretary
   (MarlaC@TheMennonite.org)
Melanie Mueller, advertising
   (MelanieM@TheMennonite.org)
J. Lorne Peachey, editor emeritus
   (lorne@mennonitefinancial.com)

INFORMATION

The Mennonite, the magazine of Mennonite Church USA, seeks to serve the church by helping its readers glorify God, grow in faith, and become agents of healing and hope in the world.

The Mennonite was founded in 1998 as a merger of the General Conference Mennonite Church periodical, *The Mennonite*, and the Mennonite Church periodical, *Gospel Herald*.

BOARD

Cheryl Zehr Walker, chair (cheryl@advanassociates.com), 219 Brookwood Drive, Bluffton, OH 45817 (419-358-0701); Kerry Strayer, vice-chair; Larry Miller, treasurer; Levina Huber, secretary; Joe Manickam, Miriam Martin, Joe Roos

Thrift Shops

—see Mennonite Central Committee U.S.

TourMagination

office@tourmagination.com, www.tourmagination.com
215-723-8413, fax 215-723-8351
1011 Cathill Rd, Sellersville PA 18960

STAFF

Wilmer Martin, president and managing partner (martin@tourmagination.com)

INFORMATION

Founded 1970. TourMagination is owned and operated by Mennonites from Ontario and Pennsylvania who love to create educational travel experiences. TourMagination's mission statement is "Building bridges among Mennonites and other Christians around the world through custom-designed travel."

TourMagination plans custom-designed tours for groups to their destination of choice. Besides custom-designed tours, TourMagination also plans service tours for those who want to make a difference while they are on vacation. TourMagination also offers a roster of tours to many destinations, including the European Heritage Tour upon which TourMagination was founded, the Bible Lands, Alaska, South America, North American tours.

BOARD

Henry D. Landes, chair (hlandes@dvfambus.com), 1011 Cathill Rd, Sellersville PA 18960 (215-723-8413); Wilmer Martin, president and managing partner

PUBLICATION

Discovery (4 times a year), David Beckerson, editor, 9 Willow St, Waterloo, ON N2J 1V6, Canada (800-565-0451 and 519-885-2522; fax: 519-885-0941)

U

United Native Ministries

—see also Mennonite Indian Leaders Council
574-295-530, fax 574-293-1892
2121 Hawthorne Dr, Elkhart IN 46517

STAFF

Ray E. Horst, executive secretary

INFORMATION

Founded 1987. United Native Ministries is an organization of representatives from Native American Mennonite congregations. The council meets semiannually for work on issues related to Native American Ministries, promotes leadership training, assists with congregational resources, and serves as an advocate with conference and churchwide agencies. UNM sponsors the intertribal assembly every two years and is a channel of relationship with other churchwide programs.

BOARD

Olivette McGhee, president (olivettemcghee@hotmail.com), 1675 Poarch Rd, Atmore AL 36502 (251-368-5938); Elizabeth Detweiler, vice-president; Vina Steel, secretary; CLC rep: Deborah Whetzel

TRIBAL GROUPS, CONGREGATIONS AND COUNCIL MEMBERS

Choctaw: Nanih Waiya Mennonite Church, Bobbie Frazier; Pearl River Mennonite Church, Lena Willis. Creek: Poarch Community Church, Olivette McGhee; Gospel Light Church. Ojibway: Morson Community Bible Fellowship, Elizabeth Detweiler, Deborah Whetzel. Navajo: Upper Room Mennonite Church, Frank James; Light of Life Mennonite Church, Priscella Wero; Black Mountain Mennonite Church, Mary Mitchell Trejo. Houma (Biloxi-Chitimacha): Native Christian Fellowship, Steve Cheramie Risingsun. Lakota Sioux: Lakota Gospel Church, Vina Steele.

PUBLICATION

United Native Ministries Newsletter (semian-nual), Ruth B. Horst, editor (same address as above)

V

Victim Offender Reconciliation Program (VORP)

—see Mennonite Central Committee U.S. Crime and Justice Office

Virginia Mennonite Board of Missions

info@vmbm.org, www.vmbm.org
800-707-5535 and 540-434-9727,
fax 540-434-7627
901 Parkwood Dr, Harrisonburg VA 22802

STAFF

Loren E. Horst, president
Lois E. Maust, assistant to president
Galen Lehman, Caribbean regional director
Gloria Lehman, public relations director and regional assistant
Willard K. Eberly, Mediterranean regional director

Joseph Bontrager, USA regional director
Kenneth Horst, director of Partners in Mission and Mediterranean associate

INFORMATION

Founded in 1919 as the mission agency of Virginia Mennonite Conference. International work began in 1949 in Sicily. VMBM works in collaboration with the districts of Virginia Mennonite Conference in USA ministries. Internationally, VMBM also works in collabora-tion with other Mennonite-affiliated churches and agencies in the countries of Albania, Italy, Jamaica and Trinidad. Short-term teams serve through Partners in Missions. Constituent churches and individuals sponsor VMBM min-istries through contributions, including estate bequests and endowments.

BOARD

Marvin Slabaugh, chair (mcslabaugh@aol.com), 540-879-9288; James Foster, vice-chair; Milton Heatwole, treasurer; Philip Borntrager, secretary; Ed Bontrager, Jonathan Bowman, Lori Green, Beth Jarrett, Janine Kanagy, Merna Kindy, John Kreider, Kenneth Kurtz, Basil Marin, Phyllis Martin, Phyllis Miller, Carol Rhodes, Daniel Witmer

PUBLICATION

Connections (Monthly), Gloria Lehman, editor (lehmang@vmbm.org), Rachel Smith, assistant editor (smithra@vmbm.org); *Update* (Monthly) to congregational mission communicators

Virginia Mennonite Conference

—see section 2: Conferences and Congregations

Vision: Healing & Hope

—see page 4

ORGANIZATIONAL INDEX

3

W

Washington DC Area Mennonite Workers Fellowship

STAFF

Steve Ramer, group facilitator
(rameregan@yahoo.com)
Chet Miller-Eshleman, host
(chetmiller-eshleman@capitalchristian.org)
Lewis Jones, representative to MCC East Coast,
(cormdc@erols.com)

INFORMATION

Founded 1995. Meets monthly (except July, August, and December) at noon on the third Wednesday at Washington Community Fellowship (907 Maryland Ave NE, Washington DC 20002) for fellowship, prayer and a speaker. Includes pastors from Baltimore and Washington, MCC's Washington office, the International Guest House, MMN's VS unit, MCC's VS unit, and Washington Study Service Year.

West Coast Mennonite Men's Chorus

mrke@juno.com,
www.geocities.com/mmchorus
559-251-3345
267 S Armstrong Dr, Fresno CA 93727

INFORMATION

The West Coast Mennonite Men's Chorus is organized to minister through music, promote male singing, cultivate common bonds of the Mennonite tradition, and support the work of Mennonite Central Committee. It is supported by Mennonite Central Committee constituent churches in the San Joaquin Valley of California. The West Coast Mennonite Men's Chorus was organized in 1977. The chorus of 150 lay volunteers presents three benefit concerts each year.

BOARD

Randy Toews, chair, 240 Elm, Shafter CA 93263 (661-746-2771); Ken Elrich, financial officer and contact person (mrke@juno.com); Bill Braun, secretary; Bob Buxman, Wink Farrand, Paul Flaming, Al Fleming, Walt Goertzen, Amos Kleinsasser, Arnold Liesch, Don Loewen, Lola Penner, Marvin Regier, Ben Warkentin

Western District Mennonite Conference

—see section 2: Conferences and Congregations

WITH

—see Mennonite Publishing House in section 1: Churchwide Agencies

Y

Youth Venture

—see Mennonite Mission Network in section 1: Churchwide

Mennonite World Conference

4

Mennonite World Conference (MWC) is an international fellowship of Christian churches who trace their beginning to the 16th-century Radical Reformation in Europe, particularly to the Anabaptist movement. Today more than 1,200,00 believers belong to this faith family; at least 55 percent are African, Asian, or Latin American. Mennonite Church USA is one of 87 Mennonite and Brethren in Christ (BIC) national churches from 48 countries on five continents that MWC represents.

Creating a "space" is a primary ministry of MWC—where member churches experience communion, interdependence, solidarity, and mutual accountability. MWC provides occasions and networks, publications and exchanges where Mennonites and Brethren in Christ members can experience fellowship and be encouraged to live and act more faithfully.

The worldwide MWC assembly, Africa 2003, will be held August 11-17, 2003, in Bulawayo, Zimbabwe. For more information, go to the website www.mwc-cmm.org or contact Dumisinkosi Dothan Moyo, National Coordinator Africa 2003 (bulawayo@mwc-cmm.org).

MWC serves as a global congregation. With MWC, Mennonite Church USA believes that the church is a worldwide body where people of different cultures and nations are "no longer strangers ... but members of God's household ..." (Ephesians 2:19).

SECRETARIAT
www.mwc-cmm.org

Strasbourg office
8 rue du Fossé des Treize, 67000 Strasbourg, France
tel (33) 3 88-15-27-50, fax (33) 3 88-15-27-51 (strasbourg@mwc-cmm.org)

Kitchener office
50 Kent Ave, Kitchener, ON N2G 3R1, Canada
tel (1) 519-571-0060, fax (1) 519-571-1980 (kitchener@mwc-cmm.org)

Fresno office
2529 Willow Ave, Clovis CA 93612, USA
tel (1) 559-291-2125, fax (1) 559-291-2065 (fresno@mwc-cmm.org)

Bulawayo office
212-213 Lutheran House, L Takawira/H Chitepo, Bulawayo, Zimbabwe
tel (263) 4-720-192 (bulawayo@mwc-cmm.org)

Executive Staff
Larry Miller, executive secretary (larrymiller@mwc-cmm.org), Strasbourg office
Pakisa Tshimika, associate executive secretary, Networks and Projects (pakisatshimika@mwc-cmm.org), Fresno office

Ray Brubacher, associate executive secretary, Events and Administration (raybrubacher@ mwc-cmm.org), Kitchener office

Dumisinkosi Dothan Moyo, National Coordinator Africa 2003 (bulawayo@ mwc-cmm.org), Bulawayo office

EXECUTIVE COMMITTEE
Officers

Mesach Krisetya, president (krisetya@indo.net.id), Jl. Merbabu No. 3, Salatiga 50724, Indonesia

Nancy Heisey, president-elect (nancyheisey@mwc-cmm.org), 556 Lee Ave, Harrisonburg VA 22802, USA

Bedru Hussein, vice-president (husseinb@ telecom.net.et), PO Box 18997, Addis Ababa, Ethiopia

Larry Miller, executive secretary (larrymiller@mwc-cmm.org), Conférence Mennonite Mondiale, 8, rue du Fossé des Treize, 67000 Strasbourg, France

Paul Quiring, treasurer (pquiring@quiring.com), 2207 W Spruce Ave, Fresno CA 93711-0456, USA

Members
Africa

Dieudonné Fimbo Ganvunze, B.P. 4081, Kinshasa II Dem. Rep. of Congo (mcc@ecc-sn.org)

Joram Mbeba, PO Box 21, Magu, Tanzania (rdmbeda@africaonline.co.tz)

Asia

Miwako Katano, Room 211, Toyohira 3-6-1-7, Toyohira-Ku, Sapporo 062-0903, Japan (hiromiwako@bd.wakwak.com)

Ambrocio Porcincula, 177 Tabia Street, Barangay Salac, Lumban, Laguna 4014, Philippines (alporcin@mozcom.com)

Caribbean, Central and South America

Nicolás Largaespada Alvarez, Apartado 3305, Managua, Nicaragua

Hugo Moreira, Iglesia Evangelica Menonita, Cno. Mendoza 4000, 12300 Montevideo, Uruguay (hugomore@adinet.com.uy)

Europe

Stefan van Delden, Amelandsweg 50A, 48599 Gronau, Germany (st.v.d@t-online.de)

G.A.Ineke Reinhold-Scheuermann, Vechtensteinlaan 63, 3601 CN Maarssen, The Netherlands (i-p.reinhold@planet.nl)

North America

Justina Heese, 187 Waverley St, Winnipeg MB, R3M 3K4, Canada, (jheese@mennonitechurch.ca)

COMMUNICATIONS, COUNCILS, AND PROJECTS STAFF

Rainer Burkart, secretary, Faith & Life Council, Torneystr. 90a, 56567 Neuwied, Germany (1114-631@online.de)

Ferne Burkhardt, news editor, copy editor, regional editor—North America, RR # 2, Petersburg ON N0B 2H0, Canada (fburkhardt@golden.net)

Doris Dube, regional editor—Africa, 212-213 Lutheran House, Bulawayo, Zimbabwe, (mccz@mweb.co.zw)

Ricardo Esquivia Ballestas, central communicator, GAPJN, Av calle 32 No 14-42 Piso 1, Bogotá, Colombia (justapaz@colnodo.apc.org)

Nancy Heisey, secretary, Connecting Theological Educators on Five Continents, 556 Lee Ave, Harrisonburg VA 22802, USA (nancyheisey@mwc-cmm.org)

Miwako Katano, regional editor—Asia, Room 211, Toyohira 3-6-1-7, Toyohira-Ku, Sapporo 062-0903, Japan (hiromiwako@bd.wakwak.com)

John A. Lapp, coordinator, Global Mennonite History Project, 13 Knollwood Dr, Akron PA 17501, USA (jalapp@lancnews.infi.net)

Eleanor Miller, communications assistant, MWC Strasbourg office, France (eleanormiller@mwc-cmm.org)

Lorne Peachey, *Courier* managing editor, 800 Walnut Ave, Scottdale PA 15683-1999, USA (lornepeachey@mwc-cmm.org)

Milka Rindzinski, *Courier* general editor and regional editor—Central and South America, 3 de Febrero 4381, 12900 Montevideo, Uruguay, (milkarindzinski@mwc-cmm.org)

Liesa Unger, director, YAMEN!, Gottesauerstrasse 35, 76131 Karlsruhe, Germany (liesaunger@mwc-cmm.org)

Ed van Straten, regional editor—Europe, Eksterlaan 24, 2261 EL Leidschendam, The Netherlands, (e.van.straten.wxs.nl)

Paulus Widjaja, secretary, Peace Council, Fakultas Theologia, Universitas Kristen Duta Wacana, Jalan Dr. Wahidin 5-19, Jogjakarta, Indonesia (pauluswidjaja@ukwd.ac.id)

Judy Zimmerman Herr, associate secretary, Peace Council, Mennonite Central Committee, 21 South 12th St, PO Box 500, Akron PA 17501-0500, USA (jzh@mcc.org)

PUBLICATIONS

Courier/Correo/Courrier, a quarterly publication available in three languages (English, Spanish, French) that provides news, feature articles, essays and testimonies as a means to promote community, communication, and cooperation in the worldwide Mennonite and Brethren in Christ faith family. Larry Miller, publisher; Milka Rindzinski, editor; J. Lorne Peachey, managing editor; Sylvie Gudin Poupaert, French edition editor.

CTEFC Link, a newsletter available in three languages (English, Spanish, French) to connect theological educators on five continents.

Gift Sharing Newsletter, semi-annual newsletter produced by MWC Global Gifts Sharing staff which provides a forum for news, ideas, thoughts, and stories about the sharing of gifts among members of the worldwide Mennonite/Brethren in Christ family.

All publications are available on the MWC web site (www.mwc-cmm.org). Paper editions of *Courier, Correo or Courrier* and *CTEFC Link* are available by request from MWC, 8, rue du Fossé des Treize, 67000 Strasbourg France; e-mail: Strasbourg@mwc-cmm.org

MEMBERSHIP SUMMARY

The statistical information is based on the *2000 Mennonite and Brethren in Christ Directory*. *Membership statistics indicate baptized members in all Anabaptist-Mennonite churches worldwide, not only MWC member churches. Some statistics are estimates. New data will be available in 2003.

Africa
Members 405,979
Countries 14
Organized Bodies 22

Asia and Pacific
Members 184,049
Countries 9
Organized Bodies 22

Caribbean, Central and South America
Members 112,128
Countries 25
Organized Bodies 98

Europe
Members 57,921
Countries 13
Organized Bodies 21

North America
Members 443,918
Countries 2
Organized Bodies 34

World Total*
Members 1,203,995
Countries 63
Organized Bodies 197

MENNONITE WORLD CONFERENCE

4

MWC Member Churches

AFRICA

Angola
Igreja da Comunidade Menonita em Angola, CX. P. N. 232-C, LUANDA
fax (244) 2-39-37-46, e-mail icma@angonet.org

Igreja Evangélica Irmãos Mennonitas em Angola, 21 de Janeiro/Rocha Pinto, CP 20066, Luanda
tel (244) 2-330-415, fax (244) 2-393-746, e-mail ieima@angonet.org

Democratic Republic of Congo
Communauté des Eglises de Frères Mennonites au Congo, B.P. 81, Kikwit
e-mail mcc-congo@maf.org

Communauté Evangélique Mennonite, B.P. 440, Mbuji Mayi/Kasai Oriental

Communauté Mennonite au Congo, B.P. 18, Tshikapa, Kasai Occidental
tel MCC-Congo, fax MCC-Congo, e-mail MCC-Congo

Ethiopia
Meserete Kristos Church, PO Box 24227, Addis Ababa
tel (251) 1-534-758, fax (251) 1-513-310, e-mail meserete_kristos@telecom.net.et

Ghana
Ghana Mennonite Church, PO Box 5485, Accra-North
tel (233) 21-310113, fax (233) 21-227125, e-mail michael@fidcc.online.com.gh

Kenya
Kenya Mennonite Church, PO Box 39, Suna-Migori

Nigeria
Mennonite Church Nigeria, PO Box 123, Uyo, Akwa Ibom State
fax (234) 85-203840, e-mail mccnigeria@hisen.org

South Africa
Grace Community Church of South, 42 DuPlessis Street, 8795 Philipstown
tel (27) 53-665-0458

Tanzania
Kanisa la Mennonite Tanzania, PO Box 1040, Musoma
tel (255) 2-620143, fax (255) 2-622826, e-mail kmtbaraza@online.co.tz

Zambia
Brethren in Christ Church (Zambia), Box 630115, Choma
tel (260) 32-20127, fax (260) 32-20127, e-mail bicm@zamnet.zm

Zimbabwe
Brethren in Christ Church, Ibandla Labazalwane ku Kristu e Zimbabwe, PO Box 711, Bulawayo
tel (263) 9-62839, fax (263) 9-42193, e-mail bicchu@acacia.samara.co.zw

ASIA AND PACIFIC

Australia
Australian Conference of Evangelical Mennonites, 9 Brougham Avenue, Fennell Bay 2283 N.S.W.
tel (61) 02 4959 3847

India
Bharatiya Jukta Christa Prachar Mandali (United Missionary Church), Hastings Chapel, 10 St. Georges Gate Road, Calcutta 700 022
tel (91) 33-223 0609

Bhartiya General Conference Mennonite Church, Mission Compound, Jhilmila, PO Saraipali, Raipur, M.P. 493 558

Bihar Mennonite Mandli, Mennonite Mission Compound, PO Chandwa, Dist. Palamau, Bihar 829 203

Brethren in Christ Church Society, Bharatiya Khristiya Mandali, Box 6, Purnea, Bihar 854 301
tel (91) 64-54-22926

Conference of the Mennonite Brethren Churches in India, MB Medical Centre, Jadcherla, A.P. 509 302
tel (91) 8544-32-488

Mennonite Church in India (Bharatiya Mennonite Church in India ki Pratinidhi Sabha), Mennonite Centre, Dhamtari 493 773, Chhatisgarh

Indonesia
Gereja Injili di Tanah Jawa, Jl. Diponegoro No. 33, Pati 59112 Jateng
tel (62) 295-385337, e-mail hendrosp@telkom.net

Persatuan Gereja-Gereja Kristen Muria Indonesia, Jl. Sompok Lama 60, Semarang 50249, Jateng
tel (62) 24-312795, fax (62) 24-442644, e-mail sinodemi@idola.net.id
ed777dd@cbn.net.id

Sinode Jemaat Kristen Indonesia, Jl. Permata Hijau Blok BB-25A, Pondok Hasanudin, Semarang-50176 Jawa Tengah
tel (62) 24-557300, fax (62) 24-557300, e-mail sutantoadi@worldnet.att.net

Japan
Nihon Kirisuto Keiteidan, 4-12-6 Hanakoganei, Kodaira-shi, Tokyo 187-0002
tel (81) 424-63-7295, fax (81) 424-63-7295,

Nihon Menonaito Kirisuto Kyokai Kaigi, 2-3-2
Atago-cho, Nobeoka-shi, Miyazaki-ken 882-0872
tel (81) 982-33-2218,
e-mail ck-atago@sun-net.ne.jp

Nihon Menonaito Kirisuto Kyokai Kyogikai
(Japan Mennonite Christian Church Conference),
c/o Mennonite Fukuzumi Center, Fukuzumi 2-3-6-1,
Toyohira-ku, Sapporo, 062-0042
tel (81) 155-24-3285, e-mail kirai@comco.ne.jp

**Nippon Menonaito Burezaren Kyodan (Japan
Mennonite Brethren Conference),** 1-12, 2 chome,
Soen, Ikeda-shi, Osaka-Fu 563-0038
tel (81) 727-62-5731, fax (81) 727-62-5731

Tokyo Chiku Menonaito Kyokai Rengo, 2-1-17
Honan, Suginami, Tokyo, 168-0062
tel (81) 3-3311-4277, fax (81) 3-3313-1201,
e-mail anabap@gol.com

Philippines
Integrated Mennonite Churches, Inc., 177 Tabia
Street, Barangay Salac, Lumban, Laguna 4014
tel (63) 49-808-4363, fax (63) 49-808-0524,
e-mail alporcin@mozcom.com

Taiwan
Fellowship of Mennonite Churches in Taiwan,
PO Box 27-50, Taipei 10098
tel (886) 2-2503-9618, fax (886) 2-2501-6497,
e-mail fomcit@ms18.hinet.net

CARIBBEAN, CENTRAL AND SOUTH AMERICA

Argentina
Iglesia Evangélica Menonita Argentina, De la
Libertad 164, 8360 Choele Choel (RN)
tel (54) 011-4671 6207, fax (54) 011-4671 6207,

Belize
Belize Evangelical Mennonite Church, PO Box 30,
Orange Walk Town
tel (501) 3-22044, e-mail bemc@btl.net

Brazil
Associação das Igrejas Menonitas do Brasil,
Rua Lamenha Lins, 1839, 80220-080 Curitiba -
Paraná
tel (55) 41-332-7624, fax (55) 41-332-7624,
e-mail aimb@super.com.br

Associação Evangélica Menonita, Rua Venezuela
318, 13036-350, Campinas-SP
tel (55) 19-278-4152, fax (55) 19-278-4152,
e-mail celep@correionet.com.br

Colombia
**Asociación de Iglesias Hermanos Menonitas de
Colombia,** Apartado Aéreo 4172, Cali
tel (57) 2-551-4322, fax (57) 2-552-6375,
e-mail adihm@emcali.net.co

Iglesia Cristiana Menonita de Colombia,
Ave. 32#14-42 P.2, Bogotá
tel (57) 1-287-2927, fax (57) 1-288-2452,
e-mail imcol@latino.net.co

Costa Rica
**Convención de Iglesias Menonitas de Costa
Rica,** Apartado 116-3000, Heredia
tel (506) 237-7130, fax (506) 237-0520,
e-mail convemen@sol.racsa.co.cr

Cuba
Sociedad Misionera Hermanos en Cristo, Calle
102 No. 10307, Cuatro Caminos, Cotorro, La Habana
19340

Dominican Republic
Concilio Nacional Menonita Faro Divino, Avenida
Libertad 128, Apartado 3, Bonao
tel (1809) 525-3057, fax (1809) 525-2530

Conferencia Evangélica Menonita Dominicana,
Apartado 21408, Santo Domingo
tel (1809) 536-6669, fax (1809) 684-9724,
e-mail desarrollo.com@codetel.net.do

Guatemala
Iglesia Evangelica Menonita de Guatemala,
Apartado 1779, 19 Avenida 5-94, Zona 11 Mirador I,
Ciudad de Guatemala
tel (502) 471-89-87, fax (502) 471-89-87,
e-mail willih@intelnet.net.gt

**Iglesia Nacional Evangélica Menonita
Guatemalteca,** Apartado 1, 16909 San Pedro Carchá,
Alta Verapáz
tel (502) 951-6385, fax (502) 951-6041,
e-mail menonita@amigo.net.gt

Honduras
Iglesia Evangelica Menonita Hondureña,
Apartado Postal 77, La Ceiba Atlantida

Amor Viviente, Apartado 978, 511 Toncontin,
Tegucigalpa
tel (503) 551-5511, fax (503) 551-5522,
e-mail misiones@viviente.sdnhon.org.hn

Jamaica
Jamaica Mennonite Church, 28 Upper Waterloo
Rd, PO Box 358, Kingston 10
tel (876) 92-50878

Mexico
**Conferencia de Iglesias Evangélicas
Anabautistas Menonitas de México,**
Calle 12 # 173, Col. Juárez Pantitlán, Edo. de México
tel (015) 701-22-13, fax (015) 701-22-13,
e-mail cieamm@mail.internet.com.mx

Conferencia Menonita de Mexico, Campo 22,
Apartado 518, Cuauhtémoc, Chih. 31500
tel (52) 158-1-0109, fax (52) 158-1-2323,
e-mail petstoesz@terra.com.mx

MENNONITE WORLD
CONFERENCE

4

Nicaragua
Convención de Iglesias Evangélicas Menonitas de Nicaragua, Km. 8 Carr. sur, Apartado 3305, Managua
tel (505) 2-651-367, fax (505) 2-651-229

Fraternidad de Iglesias Evangélicas Menonitas de Nicaragua, Apartado 3163, Managua
tel (505) 266-30-78, fax (505) 266-30-78, e-mail fiemn@ibw.com.ni

Misión Hermanos en Cristo de Nicaragua, Bello Horizonte L-I-17, Managua
tel (505) 2891627

Panama
Iglesia Evangélica Unida Hermanos Menonitas de Panamá, Apartado 812-0025, Zona 12, Panamá
tel (507) 220-6801, fax (507) 220-6801, e-mail ieu@sinfo.net

Paraguay
Convención de las Iglesias Evangélicas Nivaclé, Filadelfia ASCIM, c.d.c. 984, Chaco 9300
tel (595) 21-91-231, fax (595) 21-91-453, e-mail conven@uninet.com.py

Convención de las Iglesias Evangélicas Unidas, c/o Menno Indianer Mission, Casilla 883, Loma Plata
tel (595) 918-301

Convención Evangélica de Iglesias Paraguayas Hermanos Menonitas, C.D. 1154, Juan Diaz de Solis 2150, Asunción
tel (595) 21-0423-891, fax (595) 21-0423-891, e-mail Conven@uninet.com.py

Convención Evangélica Mennonita Lengua, c/o Luz a los Indígenas, Filadelfia 40, C.d.c. 984, Chaco 9300
tel (595) 91-2231, fax (595) 91-2231

Convención Evangélica Menonita Paraguaya, c.c. 2475, Av. Venezuela 1464, Asunción
tel (595) 21-296284, fax (595) 21-293054, e-mail comenpar@rieder.net.py

Evangelische Mennonitische Bruderschaft, Filadelfia-Chaco, Pf. 119, c.d.c. 984, Asunción
tel (595) 91-2456

Vereinigung der Mennoniten Brüdergemeinden Paraguays, c.d.c. 1154, Asunción
tel (595) 21-481-081, fax (595) 21-481-081, e-mail mbverein@uninet.com.py

Vereinigung der Mennonitengemeinden von Paraguay, Colonia Menno, C.d.c. 883, Asunción
tel (595) 918-552

Uruguay
Consejo de las Congregaciones de los Hermanos Menonitas, C. Correo 122, Código Postal 11.000, Montevideo
tel (598) 2-305-5675, fax ,
e-mail hmcons@adinet.com.uy

Convención de Iglesias Evangélicas Menonitas en Uruguay, 3 de Febrero 4381, C.P. 12.900, Montevideo
tel (598) 2-39-32-74, e-mail edithm@adinet.com.uy

Konferenz der Mennonitengemeinden in Uruguay, c.d.c. 400, Montevideo
tel (598) 2 2094170 or 2 605067

EUROPE

France
Association des Eglises Evangéliques Mennonites de France, 3, route de Grand-Charmont, F - 25200 Montbéliard
tel (33) 381-94-59-14, fax (33) 381-95-56-30, e-mail editions.mennonites@wanadoo.fr

Germany
Arbeitsgemeinschaft Mennonitischer Gemeinden in Deutschland, Ringstrasse 3, D-67677 Enkenbach
tel (49) 6303 3883, fax,
e-mail Rwrc.Funck@t-online.de

Italy
Chiesa Evangelica Mennonita Italiana, Via R. d'Aquino, 9, Palermo
tel (39) 91-213084, fax (39) 091-422498, e-mail ocemi@telegest.it

Netherlands
Algemene Doopsgezinde Sociëteit, Singel 454, 1017 AW Amsterdam
tel (31) 20-6230914, fax (31) 20-6278919, e-mail info@ads.nl

Switzerland
Konferenz der Mennoniten der Schweiz (Alttäufer), Conférence Mennonite Suisse (Anabaptiste), Bugnon 19, CH-2316 Les Ponts de Martel.
tel (41) 32 937 11 54,
e-mail thomas.gyger@bluewin.ch

NORTH AMERICA

Canada
Canadian Conference of the Mennonite Brethren Churches, 3-169 Riverton Avenue, Winnipeg R2L 2E5 MB
tel (1) 204-669-6575, fax (1) 204-654-1865, e-mail admin@mbconf.ca

Evangelical Mennonite Conference (Canada), Box 1268, Steinbach R0A 2A0 MB
tel (1) 204-326-6401, fax (1) 204-326-1613

Evangelical Mennonite Missions Conference, Box 52059, Niakwa PO, Winnipeg R2M 5P9 MB tel (1) 204-253-7929, fax (1) 204-256-7384, e-mail emmc@mb.sympatico.ca

Mennonite Church Canada, 600 Shaftesbury Blvd., Winnipeg R3P 0M4 MB tel (1) 204-888-6751, fax (1) 204-831-5675

Canada/USA
Brethren in Christ General Conference (North America), 431 Grantham Road, PO Box 290, Grantham 17027 PA tel (1) 717-697-2634, fax (1) 717-697-7714, e-mail bic@messiah.edu

Evangelical Mennonite Missions Conference, Box 52059, Niakwa PO, Winnipeg R2M 5P9 MB tel (1) 204-253-7929, fax (1) 204-256-7384, e-mail emmc@mb.sympatico.ca

USA
Conservative Mennonite Conference, 9910 Rosedale-Milford Center Rd., Irwin 43029 OH tel (1) 740-857-1234, fax (1) 740-857-1605

Mennonite Church USA, Box 1245, 500 S Main St, Elkhart IN 46515-1245 tel (1) 574-294-7523

U.S. Conference of Mennonite Brethren Churches, 315 S Lincoln St, Box 220, Hillsboro 67063-0220 KS tel (1) 316-947-3151, fax (1) 316-947-3266, e-mail usconf@southwind.net

Associate Member Churches

AFRICA

Burkina Faso
Eglise Evangélique Mennonite du Burkina Faso, B.P. 85, Orodara tel (226) 96-01-29

ASIA AND PACIFIC

China
Conference of Mennonite Churches in Hong Kong, Hong Kong Mennonite Centre, 76 Waterloo Road 1/F, Kowloon, Hong Kong tel (852) 2-713-4271, fax (852) 2-714-2852, e-mail cmchkltd@netvigator.com

CARIBBEAN, CENTRAL AND SOUTH AMERICA

Bolivia
Iglesia Evangélica Menonita Boliviana, Casilla 3086, Santa Cruz tel (591) 3-46-0401, fax (591) 3-37-0675, e-mail mcc.bolivia.ca@scbbs-bo.com

Colombia
Hermandad en Cristo, Apartado Aéreo 100655, Santa Fé de Bogotá tel (57) 258-2586, fax (57) 1-612-9204, e-mail book505@latino.net.co

El Salvador
Iglesia Evangélica Menonita de El Salvador, Apartado postal #20, Metapán Santa Ana fax (503) 400-0564, e-mail iemes@saltel.net

Mexico
Iglesia Evangélica Menonita del Noroeste de México, Apartado 38, Ahome, Sinaloa tel (52) 686-30429, fax (52) 686-30429, e-mail

Trinidad and Tobago
Mennonite Church of Trinidad and Tobago, 10, Dinoo Road, Charliesville tel (868) 671-9250, e-mail paulest@carib-link.net

Venezuela
Concilio de Iglesias Evangélicas Menonitas en Venezuela, Apartado 28, Charallave 1210, Edo. Miranda tel (58) 2-578-22-06, fax (58) 2-578-22-06

EUROPE

Belgium
Conseil Pastoral des Assemblées Mennonites de Belgique, c/o Robert Otto, Chaussée de Waterloo 1143, B-1180 Bruxelles tel (32) 2374 6652, e-mail robert_wilda@compuserve.com

Austria/Germany
Bund der Europäisch-Mennonitischen Brüdergemeinden, Falkenstr. 24, D-32791 Lage tel (49) 5232 61770, e-mail gemeinde@mbg-lag.de

Spain
Asociación de Menonitas y Hermanos en Cristo en España, C/ Estrella Polar, 10, E-09197 Quintanadueñas (Burgos) tel (34) 947-292-618

United Kingdom
British Conference of Mennonites, c/o London Mennonite Centre, 14 Shepherds Hill, London N6 5AQ tel (44) 181-340-8775, fax (44) 181-341-6807

MENNONITE WORLD CONFERENCE

4

Sister Denominations

5

Canada

Mennonite Church Canada

office@mennonitechurch.ca,
www.mennonitechurch.ca
1-866-888-6785 or 204-888-6781,
fax 204-831-5675
600 Shaftesbury Blvd, Winnipeg MB, R3P 0M4,
Canada

General Secretary Dan Nighswander
(dnighswander@mennonitechurch.ca)
Witness (includes International Ministries,
National Ministries, and Congregational
Partnerships); Executive Secretary: Robert J.
Suderman
(rjsuderman@mennonitechurch.ca)
Formation (includes Publishing and
Resources, Youth and Young Adults,
Christian Education and Nurture, and
Ministerial and Congregational Leadership);
Executive Secretary: Justina Heese
(jheese@mennonitechurch.ca)
Support Services (includes Communications,
Resource Development, Human Resources,
and Finance); Executive Secretary: Pam
Peters-Pries
(ppeters-pries@mennonitechurch.ca)
Denominational Minister Henry Paetkau
(hpaetkau@mennonitechurch.ca)

ANNUAL ASSEMBLY
An elected program committee, together with
staff, plans and coordinates annual assemblies.
Pam Peters-Pries, executive secretary, Support
Services, is the lead contact.

PUBLICATION
Canadian Mennonite
editor@canadianmennonite.org,
www.canadianmennonite.org
519-884-3810, fax 519-884-3331
490 Dutton Dr, Unit C5, Waterloo ON N2L 6H7,
Canada
Ron Rempel, editor/publisher; Margaret Loewen
Reimer, managing editor

GENERAL BOARD
The General Board includes 18 members of
whom 5 are on the Executive Committee. Henry
Krause, Mennonite Church Canada moderator
(hkrause@uniserve.com); Joy Kroeger, assistant
moderator (kroegerj@sdh.sk.ca); Sam Steiner,
secretary, (steiner@uwaterloo.ca); Bruno
Friesen, treasurer (bafriese@cadvision.com).

PROFILE
Mennonite Church Canada represents over
36,000 members in 250 congregations across
Canada. Five area conferences (Mennonite
Church British Columbia, Mennonite Church
Alberta, Mennonite Church Saskatchewan,
Mennonite Church Manitoba, and Mennonite

Church Eastern Canada) represent the regional bodies of Mennonite Church Canada. Northwest Mennonite Conference, with 1300 members in 18 congregations, is a provisional member until March 31, 2003.

Mennonite Church Canada Witness and Formation seek to lead, motivate, and offer resources to the church to participate in holistic witness to Jesus Christ in a broken world. MC Canada is a co-owner of Canadian Mennonite University and Associated Mennonite Biblical Seminary and is affiliated with Conrad Grebel University College and Columbia Bible College. Resources are at work in 42 overseas countries, supporting 117 workers. An additional 40 Canadian workers are actively ministering in North America. A Resource Centre, Ministerial and Congregational Lay Leadership office, Congregational Partnerships office, Support Services office, and activities in Publishing and Resources, Youth and Young Adults, Christian Education and Nurture, and Peace and Justice combine with National and International Ministries to form a vital and energized Mennonite Church Canada, striving to do together what we cannot do alone, from across the street to around the world.

United States

Brethren in Christ General Conference (North America)

bic@messiah.edu, www.bic-church.org
717-697-2634, fax 717-691-7714
431 Grantham Rd, PO Box A, Grantham PA
    17027
Warren L. Hoffman, moderator; Kenneth O. Hoke, general secretary; Elizabeth Brown, general treasurer; John Allen Brubaker, executive director, Board for World Missions

MESSIAH COLLEGE

One College Ave
Grantham PA 17027
717-766-2511
Rodney J. Sawatsky, president

PUBLICATION

Visitor
visitor@messiah.edu
574-773-3164, fax 574-773-5934
2000 Evangel Way, PO Box 166, Nappanee IN
46550-0166
Ron Ross, editor

Church of the Brethren

GENERAL BOARD
info@brethren.org, www.brethren.org/genbd
800-323-8039 or 847-742-5100, fax 847-742-6103
1451 Dundee Avenue, Elgin IL 60120
Judy Mills Reimer, general secretary

ANNUAL CONFERENCE
annualconf@aol.com, www.brethren.org/ac
800-323-8039 or 847-742-5100, fax 847-742-3998
1451 Dundee Ave, Elgin IL 60120
  Lerry Fogle, executive director

BRETHREN SERVICE CENTER
www.brethren.org/genbd/BSC/index.html
410-635-8710, fax 410-635-8789
500 Main St, PO Box 188, New Windsor MD
  21776-0188

WASHINGTON OFFICE
washofc@aol.com,
  www.brethren.org/genbd/washofc/index.htm
202-546-3202, fax 202-544-5852
337 North Carolina Ave SE, Washington DC 20003

ASSOCIATION OF BRETHREN CAREGIVERS
abc@brethren.org, www.brethren.org/abc
800-323-8039 or 847-742-5100, fax 847-742-5160
1451 Dundee Ave, Elgin IL 60120
Steve Mason, executive director

BETHANY THEOLOGICAL SEMINARY
bethanysem@aol.com,
  www.brethren.org/bethany
765-983-1800, fax 765-983-1840
Main Campus, 615 National Rd W, Richmond IN
  47374
Eugene F. Roop, president

BRETHREN BENEFIT TRUST
www.brethrenbenefittrust.org
800-746-1505 or 847-695-0200,
  fax 847-742-0135

1505 Dundee Ave, Elgin IL 60120-1619
Wilfred E. Nolen, president

ON EARTH PEACE
oepa_oepa@brethren.org,
  www.brethren.org/oepa/index.html
410-635-8704, fax 410-635-8707
500 Main St, PO Box 188, New Windsor MD
  21776-0188
Barbara Sayler and Bob Gross, co-executive
  directors

PUBLICATION
Messenger
ffarrar_gb@brethren.org, www.brethren.org
847-742-5100, fax 847-742-6103
1451 Dundee Ave, Elgin IL 60120
Fletcher Farrar, editor; Wendy McFadden,
  publisher

The Church of the Brethren General Board is
the primary ministry arm of the Church of the
Brethren Annual Conference, the denomination's highest elected authority. The General
Board's ministries demonstrate Brethren beliefs
and values to the world through word and deed.
  General Board ministries include congregational life ministries; Brethren Volunteer
Service; publishing and communications; youth
and young adult ministries; serving pastors and
districts; global partnerships in Brazil, the
Dominican Republic, Nigeria and Sudan; and
peace, justice, and ecological advocacy.
  The General Board maintains a Washington,
D.C., office; has a disaster response network of
coordinators, workers, and child care providers
ready to respond at a moment's notice; offers
refugee resettlement services and ships material
aid for places in need abroad.
  The Church of the Brethren is headquar-
tered in Elgin, IL with offices and a conference
and service center in New Windsor, Md.; an
office in Geneva, Switzerland; and field staff
placed throughout the United States, Brazil, the
Dominican Republic and Nigeria.

Conservative Mennonite Conference

cmcrosedale@juno.com, www.cmcrosedale.org
740-857-1234, fax 740-857-1605
9910 Rosedale Milford Center Rd, Irwin OH
43029

Administration and contact: David I. Miller,
general secretary, at the above address. Steve
Swartz after September 1, 2003.
Executive Board: Philip Stutzman, moderator;
Steve Swartz, moderator-elect; James Kropf,
recording secretary; Scott Hochstedler,
recording secretary-elect; Carl Wesselhoeft,
Luke Yoder
Treasurer: Lynford Schrock

Committees related to categories of procedure
or concern and which may be contacted at or
through the above address are Nominating,
Ministerial, Music and Worship, Peace Witness,
Publication and Literature, Stewardship, and
Youth. Representatives serve on the boards of
Mennonite Central Committee, (bi-national,
U.S., and regional), Mennonite Disaster Service,
Mennonite Stewardship Consortium, and
Mennonite World Conference.

ROSEDALE BIBLE COLLEGE

An accredited junior Bible college
info@rosedalebible.org, www.rosedalebible.org
740-857-1311, fax 740-857-1577
2270 Rosedale Rd, Irwin OH 43029

Administration: Leon Zimmerman, president;
Jon Showalter, academic dean; Mark Miller,
director of students; Alfred Yoder, business
manager. Board of Trustees: Levi Sommers,
chairman; Eli Gingerich, vice chairman; Sheldon
Swartz, secretary, Gerald Yoder, treasurer; Joe
Byler, Lester Diller, and Phil Swartzentruber

ROSEDALE MENNONITE MISSIONS

info@rmmoffice.org,
www.rosedalemennonitemissions.org.
740-857-1366, fax 740-857-1605
9920 Rosedale Milford Center Rd, Irwin OH
43029

Administration: Joseph Showalter, president;
Bob Stauffer, general secretary; Keith Scheffel,
treasurer. Board of Directors: Adin Miller,
chairman; Dale Keffer, vice chairman; Harold
Delagrange, recording secretary; Tom Beachy,
Robert Fisher, Elmer Miller, Edward Roggie

PUBLICATION

Brotherhood Beacon
cmcrosedale@juno.com, www.cmcrosedale.org.
740-857-1234, fax 740-857-1605
9910 Rosedale Milford Center Rd, Irwin OH
43029

ANNUAL EVENTS

The annual conference is held from Thursday to
Sunday of the weekend of the first Sunday of
August (with possible shifts to a week earlier or
a week later when necessitated by local circum-
stances). Projected locations: Hartville OH,
2003; Beaver Falls NY, 2004; Greenwood DE,
2005; Rosedale OH, 2006; Goshen IN, 2007.

Ministers' Fellowship, planned especially for
ministers, is held annually in February.
Projected locations and dates: Sarasota FL,
February 17-21, 2003; Berlin OH, February 16-
20, 2004; Kalona IA, February 14-18, 2005.

SISTER DENOMINATIONS

5

Mennonite Brethren Churches, U.S. Conference

U.S. CONFERENCE OFFICE
usconf@southwind.net, www.usmb.org
620-947-3151, fax 620-947-3266
315 S Lincoln, PO Box 220, Hillsboro KS
    67063-0220

PUBLICATION
Christian Leader
christianleader@usmb.org
620-947-5543, fax 620-947-3266
315 S Lincoln, PO Box 220, Hillsboro KS
    67063-0220
Connie Faber, associate editor

editor@usmb.org
334-834-3338, fax 253-369-9423
101 N Capitol Pkwy, Montgomery AL 36107
Carmen Andres, editor

CONFERENCE MINISTER
loyalfunk@aol.com
805-474-9290, fax 805-474-9161
330 Sunrise Dr, Arroyo Grande CA 93420-4412
Loyal Funk, interim executive minister

MENNONITE BRETHREN BIBLICAL SEMINARY
mbseminary@aol.com, www.mbseminary.com
559-251-8628, fax 559-251-7212
4824 E Butler Ave, Fresno CA 93727-5097
Henry J. Schmidt, president

TABOR COLLEGE
www.tabor.edu
620-947-3121, fax 620-947-2607
400 S Jefferson, Hillsboro KS 67063
Larry Nikkel, president

FRESNO PACIFIC UNIVERSITY
admissions@fresno.edu, www.fresno.edu
559-453-2000, fax 559-453-2007
1717 S Chestnut Ave, Fresno CA 93702
D. Merrill Ewert, president

MENNONITE BRETHREN FOUNDATION
mbfoundation@usmb.org
800-551-1547 or 620-947-3151,
    fax 620-947-3266
315 S Lincoln, PO Box 220, Hillsboro KS
    67063-0220
Jon C. Wiebe, president/CEO

MBMS INTERNATIONAL
mbmsi@mbmsinternational.org,
    www.mbmsinternational.org
888-866-6267 or 559-4546-4600,
    fax 559-251-1432
4867 E Townsend, Fresno CA 93727-5006
Harold Ens, general director

The Mennonite Brethren are a people of faith, history, and mission. In 1860, spiritual renewal among Russian Mennonites resulted in groups of believers meeting together for fellowship and Bible study. A close spiritual kinship resulted and the group became known as "brethren," and eventually, "Mennonite Brethren." Mennonite Brethren are now found in over 20 countries around the world.

The U.S. Conference of Mennonite Brethren Churches is made up of five district conferences which serve the more than 180 churches in the United States. The Conference consists of ministries including National Youth Commission, Peace Commission, cross-cultural ministries, church planting, discipleship, evangelism, mission both at home and abroad, education (Christian schools, two four-year liberal arts colleges and a seminary), a denominational magazine, and stewardship resources and education. The Mennonite Brethren also participate in the relief and caring ministries of Mennonite Central Committee. The national headquarters is located in Hillsboro, Kansas, which is also home to Tabor College. On the west coast, Fresno Pacific University, Mennonite Brethren Biblical Seminary, and the headquarters for the mission agency, MBMS International, are all located in Fresno, California.

MENNONITE CHURCH USA 2003 DIRECTORY

5

Ministers

Ministerial information for this section is provided by the Mennonite Church USA Executive Board Office of Ministerial Leadership (see contact information under Executive Board in section 1) in cooperation with area conferences. Ministerial names included are those who have been credentialed by Mennonite Church USA area conferences. These records are complete as of July 2002.

SAMPLE LISTING

Name (name of spouse)
Ahlgrim, Ryan Jeffrey (Laurie Ann Silver)

Home (or preferred) address
4831 Manning, Indianapolis IN 46228

Telephone, e-mail address
317-299-8368, ahlgrim@juno.com

[Area conference holding credential], ministerial role, [credential status]
[IM] IIB1 [AC] (Note: Conference codes are listed on page 10)

Title, name of congregation, congregation's location
Pastor, First Menn Ch, Indianapolis IN

For example
Ahlgrim, Ryan Jeffrey (Laurie Ann Silver) 4831 Manning, Indianapolis IN 46228, 317-299-8368, ahlgrim@juno.com [IM] IIB1 [AC] Pastor, First Menn Ch, Indianapolis IN

Credential status
AC–(Active)
AW–(Active without charge)
RE–(Retired)

Ministerial role
I–Oversight ministries
IA–Licensed toward ordination for oversight ministry
IB1–Ordained and serving in a denominational ministerial leadership office
IB2–Ordained and serving as a conference minister
IB3–Ordained and serving as an overseer or bishop
IC–Licensed/commissioned for a specific ministry within oversight

II Church and pastoral ministries
IIA–Licensed toward ordination
IIB1–Ordained and serving as a lead pastor or co-pastor in a congregation
IIB2–Ordained and serving as an associate/assistant pastor, youth minister
IIB3a Ordained and serving as a chaplain/pastoral counselor
IIB3b–Ordained and serving in a missions or service assignment
IIB3c–Odained and serving as a conference or church administrator, conference youth minister
IIB3d–Ordained and serving as a teacher in a church educational institution
IIC–Licensed/commissioned for a specific ministry

III Lay ministries
III–Elders, deacons, lay ministers

A

Acosta, Eusebio, Colonia Union, Tijuana, Baja Calif, Mexico, 619-232-1385 [PSW] IIB1 [AC] Pastor, Casa de Oracion Menonita, San Diego CA

Adams, Jesse U. (Martha Elizabeth) 145 Dover Chester Rd, Randolph NJ 07869, 201-927-1362 [FRC] IIB1 [AC] Pastor, Garden Chapel, Dover NJ

Adams, Ronald W. (Marilou) 320 Abbeyville Rd, Lancaster PA 17603, 717-397-9882 [LAN] IIB1 [AC] Pastor, East Chestnut Street Menn Ch, Lancaster PA

Adi, Sutanto, 2472 White Dove Ln, Chino Hills CA 91709, 909-465-9211 [PSW] IIB1 [AC] Pastor, Jemaat Kristen Indonesia Bethel, Chino CA

Aguado, Gamaliel, 1312 Ridgeland Ave, Berwyn IL 60402, 708-795-4738 [IL] IIB2 [AC] Associate Pastor, Centro Cristiano Vida Abundante, Cicero IL

Aguilar, Guadalupe, 6711 Tallowood Circle, Brownsville TX 78521 [SC] IIA [AC] Pastor, Iglesia Menonita Rey de Gloria, Brownsville TX

Aguilera, Euclides, Shalom Mennonite (Spanish), Venezuela [LAN] IIA [AC] Associate Pastor, Shalom Mennonite, Venezuela

Ahanonu, George, 812 E La Brea Dr #11, Inglewood CA 90301, 310-671-5672, aebere@earthlink.net [PSW] IIA [AC] Pastor, Great Commission Deliverance Ch, Inglewood CA

Ahlgrim, Ryan Jeffrey (Laurie Ann Silver) 4831 Manning, Indianapolis IN 46228, 317-299-8368, ahlgrim@juno.com [IM] IIB1 [AC] Pastor, First Menn Ch, Indianapolis IN

Albrecht, Wayne L. (Annette) 1010 Cardinal Ln, Richardson TX 75080-4707, 214-235-8449 [WDC] IIB3a [AC] Executive Director, Pastoral Counseling & Ed Center, Dallas TX

Alcantara, Antonio P. (Paula) 2231 Buttonwood Rd, Berwyn PA 19312, 610-407-4668 [LAN] IIB1 [AC]

Alderfer, Edwin, 1214 Berkey Ave, Goshen IN 46526, 574-533-3572 [IM] [RE]

Alderfer, Wellington K. (Betty) Apt G75 3250 State Rd, Sellersville PA 18960, 215-257-8492 [FRC] IIB3a [RE]

Alger, John Paul (Retha) 512 Bird Song Lane, Broadway VA 22815, 540-896-5909 [VA] [RE]

Allaby, Gordon K. (Leslie Ann) PO Box 167, 800 S Randall Ave, Moundridge KS 67107, 620-345-2566, goles@midusa.net [WDC] IIB1 [AC] Pastor, First Menn Ch of Christian, Moundridge KS

Almodovar, Felipe (Iris) 1101 Arnold Dr, Corpus Christi TX 78412, 512-985-2790 [SC] IIB1 [AC] Pastor, Prince of Peace Menn Ch, Corpus Christi TX

Althouse, Daniel P. (Linda) 422 S 7th St, Reading PA 19602-2413, 610-376-3854, lindanalt@hotmail.com [LAN] IIB1 [AC] Pastor, South Seventh Street Menn Ch, Reading PA

Alwine, Clarence (Turie) 24 Apple House Rd, Belleville PA 17004, 717-935-2720 [ALL] [RE]

Amador, Victor S. (Carolina) 616 Jamaica Ave, Brooklyn NY 11208, 718-235-7249, victoramador2001@aol.com [LAN] IIA [AC] Pastor, International Christian Community Ch, Brooklyn NY

Amstutz, Anita F., 3530 Anderson SE, Albuquerque NM 87106, 505-265-9418, afadreamer@aol.com [RM] IIA [AC] Pastor, Albuquerque Menn Ch, Albuquerque NM

Amstutz, James S. (Lorraine J.) 1135 Main St, Akron PA 17501-1615, amstutz@fast.net [ACC] IIB1 [AC] Lead Pastor, Akron Menn Ch, Akron PA

Amstutz, Myron J., 13887 Jericho Rd, Dalton OH 44618, 330-857-1293 [OH] [RE]

Amstutz, Neil B. (Janette Amstutz) 520 S Maple, McPherson KS 67460, 620-241-0652, neilafmc@earthlink.net [WDC] IIB1 [AC] Pastor, First Menn Ch, McPherson KS

Amstutz, Vilas, 4195 Old Delphos Rd, Elida OH 45807, 419-339-6807 [OH] [RE]

Anders Jr, Earl N. (Elaine) 91 Allentown Rd, Elroy PA 18964, 215-799-0864 [FRC] IIB1 [AC] Pastor, Providence Menn Ch, Collegeville PA

Angerman, Rob L., 34816 Spicer Dr SE, Albany OR 97321, 541-924-0679, pastorrob@plainview.org [PNW] IIB1 [AC] Pastor, Plainview Menn Ch, Albany OR

Angstadt Sr, Paul D., 85 E College Ave, Wernersville PA 19565, 610-678-3812 [LAN] [RE]

Angustia, Nicolas (Caroline) 1346 Dekalb Ave #1, Brooklyn NY 11221, 718-919-1588, unitedrevival@aol.com [LAN] IB3, IIB1 [AC] Pastor, Iglesia Unida de Avivamiento, Brooklyn NY

Arana, Salvador, 3119 Liberty Blvd, Southgate CA 90280, 323-569-2029 [PSW] IIB1 [AC] Pastor, Iglesia Monte Sinai, South Gate CA

Araujo, David (Sonia) 506 Liberty St, East Chicago IN 46312, 219-397-9936 [IL] IIA [AC] Pastor

Araujo, Sonia N. (David) 506 Liberty St, East Chicago IN 46312, 219-397-9936 [IL] IIA [AC] Co-Pastor

Arbaugh II, John Joseph (Sharon Rose) 286 Cider Barn Ln, Stuarts Draft VA 24477, 540-337-1975, joearbaugh@juno.com [VA] IIB2 [AC] Minister of Missions, Waynesboro Menn Ch, Waynesboro VA

Arbuckle, Brian (Gwen) PO Box 163, Shipshewana IN 46565, 260-768-7762, barbuck@ligtel.com [IM] IIA [AC] Pastor, Marion Menn Ch, Shipshewana IN

Arevalo, Jesus Antonio (Elsa Marlen) 4215 Rockford Dr, Dallas TX 75211-8438, 214-337-2200 [SC, WDC] [RE]

Argueta, Jorge, PO Box 338, Upland CA 91785, 909-987-9594 [PSW] IIA [AC] Pastor, Iglesia Fuente de Vida, Upland CA

Arias, Salomon (Betty) 9 Kew Gardens Apt 102, Jamaica NY 11415, 718-261-4752 [ACC] IIB1 [AC] Pastor, Ephesians Menn Ch, Jamaica NY

Armstrong, James R., 3603 Engel Dr, Valparaiso IN 46383, 219-464-8101, larmstro@niia.net [IM] IB3, IIB3a [AC] Overseer, Burr Oak Menn Ch, Rensselaer IN

Arn Jr, John Willard (Sarah E.) 102 Highland Ave, Lansdale PA 19446-3207, 215-855-4584, twinoaks7@juno.com [EDC] [AW]

Asante, Albert, 1243 W 46th St, Los Angeles CA 90037, 323-292-8139 [PSW] IIC [AC] Pastor, Labor for Christ Ministry, Los Angeles CA

Assefa, Dagne (Carol Sue Weaver) 2613 Astro Ct, Indianapolis IN 46229, 317-895-6756, dcassefa@sprynet.com [IM] IIB1 [AC] Pastor, Shalom Menn Ch, Indianapolis IN

Assis, Nilson (Mary Jane) 105 Eric Avenue, Shillington PA 19607-2811, 610-796-2776, nilsassis@aol.com [ACC] [AW]

Atwood, Tim, PO Box 12976, Fort Wayne IN 46866, 260-420-6175 [IM] [AW]

Augsburger, A. Don (Martha Kling Augsburger) 1632 College Ave, Harrisonburg VA 22802-5541 [LAN] [RE]

Augsburger, David, 135 N Oakland Ave, Pasadena CA 91101, 909-621-1126 [PSW] IIB3d [AW]

Augsburger, Fred E., 32035 State Route 643, Fresno OH 43824, 216-897-1075 [OH] [RE]

Augsburger, Larry, 848 Runkle St, West Liberty OH 43357, 937-465-4314, augsburg@bright.net [OH] IIB1 [AC] Pastor, Oak Grove Menn Ch, West Liberty OH

Augsburger, Myron S. (Esther) 1549 Hillcrest Dr, Harrisonburg VA 22802, 540-433-2151 [VA] IB3 [AC]

Aukamp, James Arnold (Jean) 2212 Bald Eagle Rd, Drumore PA 17518, 717-548-3477 [LAN] IIC [AC] Evangelist, Living Stones Fell, Peach Bottom PA; Chaplain, Evangelism & Prison Ministry, PA

B

Baccam, Ha (La) 121 SE Emma Ave, Des Moines IA 50315, 515-285-7057, HaBaccam@aol.com [CP] IIB2 [AC] Associate Pastor, Des Moines Menn Ch, Des Moines IA

Baer, Abram M., 1425 Philadelphia Ave #119, Chambersburg PA 17201-1391, 717-261-4018 [FRK] [RE]

Baer, Dale T. (Susan E.) 207 Sherwood Dr, Lexington OH 44904, 419-884-1128 [EDC] III [AC]

Baer, Darrell (Sharon) 3715 Clay Hill Rd, Waynesboro PA 17268, 717-762-4041 [FRK] [RE] Conference Minister, Franklin Mennonite Conference, Chambersburg PA

Baer, Harold J. (Gail M.) 5347 Acre, Mapleton IL 61547, 309-697-0715 [IL] IIC [AC] Pastor, First Norwood Menn Ch, Peoria IL

Bair, Ray, 937 Oxford St, Elkhart IN 46516, 574-522-3743 [IM] [RE]

Baker, Ronald, 7200 Briar Spring Farm, Schuyler VA 22969, 804-831-2593, rrbak@juno.com [VA] IIB3a [AC]

Bal, Joan C. (Martin L.) 3023 Kenross St, Houston TX 77043, 713-460-2338, jbal@houston.rr.com [WDC] IIB3a [AC] Chaplain, Houston TX

Baldwin, Robert B. (Edea Anne) PO Box 508, Quitman MS 39355, 601-776-6407 [GS] IIC [AC]

Ball, Torrey D., 402 S Elm, So Hutchinson KS 67505, 620-669-8979, tball@ourtownusa.net [SC] IIB2 [AC] Youth Pastor, South Hutchinson Menn Ch, South Hutchinson KS

Bame, Bradlee T. (Kristi) 513 East Ave, Pandora OH 45877, 419-384-3841, raddisguy@juno.com [CDC] IIB2 [AC] Associate Pastor, St John Menn Ch, Pandora OH

Banks, Michael (Addie) 1114 Sherman Ave, Bronx NY 10456, 718-538-9156, kgtbronx@aol.com [LAN] IB3, IIB1 [AC] Pastor, King of Glory Tabernacle, Bronx NY; Assistant Bishop for the New York District, Lancaster Mennonite Conference, New York NY

Banks, Otis M. (Carlett) 1606 Ivy Hill Rd, Philadelphia PA 19150, 215-247-8825, revitalization@juno.com [LAN] IIB1 [AC] Pastor, Diamond Street Menn Ch, Philadelphia PA

Bapst, Rodney, 13249 SR 104, Lucasville OH 45648, 740-259-5712, rjbapst@zoomnet.net [OH] IIB1 [AC] Pastor, Owl Creek Menn Ch, Lucasville OH

Barahona, Rafael H. (Maria del Pilar Lillo) 1314 S 11th Street, Goshen IN 46526, 574-534-4569, rafaeleb@goshen.edu [IM] IIB3c [AC] Director, Hispanic Ministries Dept. Goshen College, Goshen IN; Congregational Development Resource person, Hispanic Mennonite Convention, USA & Canada

Bardell, Larry (Linda L.) 1708 Springhill Dr NW, Albany OR 97321, 541-928-0747, lbdesigns@attbi.com [PNW] IIA [AC] Interim Pastor, Prince of Peace Menn Ch, Corvallis OR

Bare, Donald (Arlene) 12467 Millertown Rd, Fulks Run VA 22830, 540-896-1149 [VA] IIB1 [AC] Pastor, Hebron Menn Ch, Fulks Run VA

Barge, Melvin K., 136 Lepore Dr, Lancaster PA 17602 [LAN] [RE]

Barkema, David M. (Regina) 5067 Indian Mound St, Sarasota FL 34232, 941-378-3999 [SE] IIC [AC] Youth Pastor, Bay Shore Menn Ch, Sarasota FL

Barrett, Lois Yvonne (Thomas Bruce Mierau) 1508 Fairview, Wichita KS 67203-2634, 316-264-3686, mierau@onemain.com [WDC] IIB3c [AC] Director, Associated Mennonite Biblical Seminary-Great Plains Extension, North Newton KS

Bartel, Floyd G. (Justina Neufeld) 2916 Wildwood Way, North Newton KS 67117, 316-283-7890, fgbjdn@ourtown.net [WDC] [RE]

Bartholomew, James E., 733 W Maple St, North Canton OH 44720, 330-499-9708, jpbart@juno.com [OH] IIB1 [AC] Pastor, Dayspring Christian Fell, North Canton OH

Bartholomew, Maxine (Richard Carl Sr) 12759 Blosser Rd, North Lima OH 44452, 330-549-3389, rbarth1@aol.com [OH] IIB1 [AC] Co-Pastor, Maple Grove Menn Ch, New Castle PA

Bartholomew, Rebecca J., 1508 Lincoln, Columbus OH 43212, 614-488-4377, agoracf@aol.com [CDC, OH] IIB1 [AC] Co-Pastor, Agora Christian Fell, Columbus OH

Bartholomew, Richard (Maxine Fay) 12759 Blosser Rd, North Lima OH 44452, 330-549-3389, rbarth1@aol.com [OH] IIB1 [AC] Co-Pastor, Maple Grove Menn Ch, New Castle PA

Bartholomew Jr, Richard, 1508 Lincoln Rd, Columbus OH 43212-2722, 614-488-4377, agoracf@aol.com [CDC, OH] IIB1 [AC] Co-Pastor, Agora Christian Fell, Columbus OH

Bartow, David W. (Rebecca J.) Box 115, Zionsville PA 18092-0115, 610-965-3899, DavWinB@aol.com [EDC] IIB1 [AC] Interim Pastor, Oley Menn Ch, Oley PA; Associate Chaplain, Frederick Mennonite Community, Frederick PA

Bauer, Royal H., 1440 Greencroft Dr, Goshen IN 46526, 574-533-6931, RoEvBauer@juno.com [IM] [RE]

Bauman, Brian Charles (Nancy Brubaker) 1 West Campbell Ave Ste K59, Campbell CA 95008-1039, 408-866-1415, brian@pacificsouthwest.org [PSW] IB2 [AC] Mission Associate, Center for Anabaptist Leadership

Bauman, Harold E. (Carolyn Hertzler) 1418 Hampton Cr, Goshen IN 46526, 574-533-6526, hbauman@maplenet.net [IM] IB3 [AC] Overseer for Olive Menn, Elkhart IN; Overseer for Yellow Creek Menn, Goshen IN; Overseer for Faith Menn, Goshen IN

Bauman, John (Susan E. Ebersole) 50 Maple Ave, Hastings Hdsn NY 10706, 212-665-3577 [LAN] IIB1 [AC]

Bauman, Lester B. (Carol Ann) 405 N Main St, Hesston KS 67062-9163, lcbauman@northnet.org [NY] [RE]

Baumgartner, Beverly, 200 W Cedar St, Hesston KS 67062-8100 [WDC] IIA [AC] Chaplain

Beachey, Duane, 424 Addax Dr, San Antonio TX 78213 [SC, WDC] IIA [AC] Lead Pastor, San Antonio Menn Ch, San Antonio TX

Beachy, Daniel (Emma) 4040 Main St, Conestoga PA 17516, 717-871-0320, dan@goldrule.net [LAN] IIC [AC] Staff, Life Ministries, Conestoga PA

Beachy, Edward E. (Louise) 35 Country Ln, Honey Brook

PA 19344, 610-273-2555 [LAN] IIB1 [AC]

Beachy, Eleanor Jeanette (Perry J.) 221 E Spruce, Hesston KS 67062, 620-327-4211 [WDC] [RE]

Beachy, James K. (Pamela Annette) 134 Kutz Rd, Fleetwood PA 19522, pastorjim@hopecomm.org [ACC] IIB1 [AC] Pastor, Hope Community Ch, Fleetwood PA

Beachy, John E., 1739 Wildwood Ct, Goshen IN 46526, 574-533-6198 [IM] [RE]

Beachy, Marvin J. (Dorothy) 815 Cloverleaf Rd, Elizabethtown PA 17022, 717-367-6267 [LAN] [RE]

Beachy, Moses, 716 E Jackson, Goshen IN 46526, 574-533-5832 [IM] [RE]

Beachy, Perry J. (Eleanor J.) 221 E Spruce, Hesston KS 67062, 620-327-4211 [WDC] [RE]

Bean, Heather Ann Ackley, 8404 Frankfort Ave, Fontana CA 92335-4113, 909-822-8715, heathrbean@aol.com [PSW] IIB1, IIB3d [AC] Associate Professor, Azusa Pacific University, Azusa

Bechler, Leroy (Irene) 1213 Camden Ct, Goshen IN 46526, 574-537-8698, lBechler@juno.com [IM] [AW]

Bechtel, Lowell B. (Peggy) RD 3 Box 49D, Greenwood DE 19950, 410-896-3451 [ALL] IIB1 [AC] Pastor, Tressler Menn Ch, Greenwood DE

Bechtold, J. Nelson (Connie) 2563 Bainbridge Rd, Bainbridge PA 17502, 717-367-1938, jnbechtold@dejazzd.com [LAN] IIB1 [AC] Pastor, Goods Menn Ch, Bainbridge PA

Beck, Bill (Sherry) 589 S 300 WPO Box 316, Hebron IN 46341, 219-477-4776, billsherrykids@juno.com [IM] IIB1 [AC] Co-Pastor, Hopewell Menn Ch, Kouts IN

Beck, Carl, Akishma Shi, Tokyo 196, Japan [OH] [RE]

Beck, Duane E. (Lois A.) 56939 Pearl Ann Dr, Elkhart IN 46516, 574-294-3016, duaneb@maplenet.net [IM] IIB1 [AC] Pastor, Belmont Menn Ch, Elkhart IN

Becker, Palmer Joseph (Ardys) 221 Kingsway, Hesston KS 67062, 620-327-4355, palmerb@southwind.net [SC, WDC] IIB3c [AC] Director of Pastor Ministries Program, Hesston College, Hesston KS

Bedsworth, Curtis C., Box 107, Berne IN 46711-0107, 574-589-3795 [CDC] [RE]

Beidler, Luke (Dorothy) 606 Swede St, Norristown PA 19401, 610-270-0636, Lukdot@juno.com [FRC] IIB1 [AC] Associate Pastor, Norristown New Life Menn Ch, Norristown PA

Beidler, S. Ken, 1641 Derwen Dr, Iowa City IA 52246, kbeidler@avalon.net [CP] IIA [AC] Pastor, First Menn Ch of Iowa City, Iowa City IA

Beiler, Calvin D. (Lillian) 5166 Mine Rd, Kinzers PA 17535-9762, 717-442-4842 [LAN] IIB1 [AC] Pastor, Millwood Menn Ch, Kinzers PA

Beitzel, Leroy P. (Mary) 51 Hossler Rd, Manheim PA 17545, 717-664-4000 [LAN] IIC, III [AC] Licensed Deacon, Kauffman Menn Ch, Manheim PA

Bender, John A. (Jean) 134 E Mohler Church Rd, Ephrata PA 17522, 717-733-4258 [LAN] III [AC] Ordained Deacon, Millport Menn Ch, Leola PA

Bender, John Paul (Marilyn Handrich Bender) 2300 Lora Ln, Raleigh NC 27604-2216, 919-833-5299, jbender770@aol.com [VA] IIB1 [AC] Co-Pastor, Raleigh Menn Ch, Raleigh NC

Bender, L. Roy (Connie Kreider) 808 E Jefferson Ct, Lancaster PA 17602, 717-293-1513, whmc2270@aol.com [LAN] IIB1 [AC] Pastor, Witmer Heights Menn Ch, Lancaster PA

Bender, Marilyn Handrich (John Paul) 2300 Lora Ln, Raleigh NC 27604-2216, 919-833-5299, jbender770@aol.com [VA] IIB1 [AC] Co-Pastor, Raleigh Menn Ch, Raleigh NC

Bender, Paul E. (Leona) 3464 W Main St, Belleville PA 17004, 717-935-2598 [ALL] IB3 [AC]

Bender, Ralph N., PO Box 123, Morris Run PA 16939, 717-638-2453 [LAN] IIB1 [AC] Associate Pastor, Calvary Menn Fell, Morris Run PA

Bender, Ross T., 1444 Hampton Cr, Goshen IN 46526, 574-534-9010 [IM] [RE]

Benner, David K. (Priscilla) PO Box 216, Pennsburg PA 18073, 215-679-6590 [FRC] [AW]

Benner, Kenneth, 2285 N Kemp Rd, Elida OH 45807, 419-339-8505 [OH] IIB2 [AC] Associate Pastor, Kalida Family Outreach Center, Kalida OH

Benner, Mary Elizabeth (Darin S.) 704 Quail Cr, Hatfield PA 19440, 215-721-6466 [FRC] IIB2 [AC] Pastor, Plains Menn Ch, Hatfield PA

Benner, Millard (Lura) RR 3 Box 51C, Greenwood DE 19950, 302-349-4734 [ALL] IB3 [AC]

Benner, Paul K. (Faith) PO Box 288, Morris PA 16938, 717-353-2019, pbmorris@epix.net [FRC] IIB1 [AC] Pastor, Menn Bible Fell, Morris PA

Benner, Robert H. (Betsy) 506 Meeting House Rd, Gap PA 17527, 717-768-7612, bbbenner@wjtl.net [LAN] IIA [AC] Associate Pastor, Old Road Menn Ch, Gap PA

Benner, Marvin Y. (Kathryn) 841 Allentown Rd, Earlington PA 18918, 215-723-9519 [FRC] [RE]

Benner, Scott Springer (Angela B.) 17B Franklin Ave, Souderton PA 18964, 215-723-6918, socialmisfits@enter.net [EDC] IIA [AC] Associate Pastor-Youth, Zion Menn Ch, Souderton PA

Bentch, Timothy, 2401 Eutaw Pl, Baltimore MD 21217 [CDC] IIB3b [AC]

Bentzinger, Richard Alvin (Marian Ruth) 504 University, Box 83, Donnellson IA 52625, 319-835-9124 [CP] IIB1 [AC] Pastor, Zion Menn Ch, Donnellson IA

Berg, Terry Lawrence (Cathy Beery) 627 S 7th St, Goshen IN 46526, 574-533-1196, terryb@maplenet.net [CDC] IIB3a [AC]

Bergen, Wesley (Deborah R.) 107 W 27th, N Newton KS 67117, 316-283-0369, wbergen@southwind.net [WDC] IIA [AC] Associate Pastor, New Creation Fell, Newton KS; Visiting Assistant Professor, Wichita State University, Wichita KS

Bergey, Curtis L. (Esther) 207 W Summit Apt A365, Souderton PA 18964, 215-723-4924 [FRC] [RE]

Bergey, J. Harold (Rose) 2041 Mount Pleasant Rd, Chesapeake VA 23322, 757-482-4379, bergey@arilion.com [VA] IIB1 [AC] Pastor, Mount Pleasant Menn Ch, Chesapeake VA

Bergey, James H. (Mary Bergey) 405 Maxwell St, Chesapeake VA 23322, 757-482-4711, 10777s.474@compuserve.com [VA] [RE]

Bernhard, Carlos (Karl) Enrique (Marlene S.) 3500 Edenborn St Apt 209, Metairie LA 70002, 504-780-0663, ceb.05@gnofn.org [GS] IIB1 [AC] Pastor, Iglesia Amor Viviente, Metairie LA

Berthold, Josef V. (Brenda Wert) 516 S Queen St, Lancaster PA 17603, 717-299-3228, josefberthold@aol.com [LAN] IIB1 [AC] Pastor, West End Menn Fell, Lancaster PA

Bertrand, Lesly (Bernadette) 11650 NW 10th Ave,

Miami FL 33168 [SE] IIC [AC]

Bertsche, Jim, 57770 Roys Ave, Elkhart IN 46517, 574-522-7916 [CDC] [RE]

Beyer, E. Eugene (Linda) 3924 Oregon Pike, Leola PA 17540, 717-859-5626, millport@email.com [LAN] IIB1 [AC] Pastor, Millport Menn Ch, Leola PA

Bianchi, Tony (Zenobia Sowell Bianchi) PO Box 6357, Chicago IL 60680, 312-922-5333 [IL] IIB1 [AC] Pastor, Bethel Menn Community Ch, Chicago IL

Biandudi, Celestin Hill (Brenda J.) 2701 13th St S, St. Petersburg FL 33705, 727-823-0346 [SE] IIC [AC] Pastor, New Beginning Community Ch, St Petersburg FL

Binder, Neil (Anna Margaret) 321 Broad St, Port Allegany PA 16743, 814-642-9275, bindluse@penn.com [ACC] IIB1 [AC] Pastor, Birch Grove Menn Ch, Port Allegany PA

Birkey, Marlin Keith (Cherie Lynn) 3701 Aster Dr, Sarasota FL 34233, 941-926-4615, Birkma@juno.com [SE] IB3, IIB1 [AC] Pastor, Ashton Menn Ch, Sarasota FL; District Minister, Southeast Menn Conf, Sarasota FL; Moderator, Southeast Menn Conf, Sarasota FL

Birky, Chris (Melissa) 527 E SR 8, Kouts IN 46347, 219-766-3270, birky@netnitco.net [IM] IIB1 [AC] Co-Pastor, Hopewell Menn Ch, Kouts IN

Birky, Glen I. (Erma) 35272 State Hwy 34, Detroit Lakes MN 56501-8000, 218-847-4988 [NC] IB3 [AC]

Birky, Mervin R. (Venita King Birky) 1015 Bowser Dr, Colorado Springs CO 80909, 719-596-5776, mervenita@juno.com [RM] IIB1 [AC] Pastor, Beth-El Menn Ch, Colorado Springs CO

Bishop, Michael Scott (Brenda Lee) 2 Woodlawn Dr, Blooming Glen PA 18911 [FRC] IIA [AC]

Bitikofer, Phares (Helen) 5535 Patton Rd, Greencastle PA 17225, 717-597-9566 [FRK] IIC [AC] Licensed Minister

Blackburn, Jeffrey D. (Lori) 310 W Pennsylvania St, Greensburg KS 67054, 620-723-2478 [SC] IIB1 [AC] Pastor, Greensburg Menn Ch, Greensburg KS

Blackburn, Richard G. (Arlee) 101 W Washington, Lombard IL 60148, 630-627-2597 [IL] IIB3c [AC] Director, Lombard Mennonite Peace Center, Lombard IL

Blank, Bill D. (Glenda) 160 McHenry Road, Parkesburg PA 19365, 610-593-7315, mgchurch@juno.com [ACC] IIA [AC] Associate Pastor, Maple Grove Menn Ch of Atglen, Atglen PA

Blank, Keith W., 49 Brandt Blvd, Landisville PA 17538, 717-892-1047 [LAN] IIC [AC] Director of Discipleship Ministries, Eastern Mennonite Missions, Salunga PA

Blank, Lester A. (Mary Lou Lauver Blank) 126 N Christiana Ave, Gap PA 17527, 610-593-5790, lablank@epix.net [LAN] [RE]

Blosser, Donald W. (Carolyn Brooks Blosser) 65241 County Rd 27, Goshen IN 46526, 574-533-8147 [IM] IIB3d [AC] Prof of Bible, Goshen College, Goshen IN

Blosser, Eugene (Elsie) 510 14th St, Wellman IA 52356, 319-646-2615 [CP] [RE]

Blosser, Floyd G. (Janet Keller Blosser) 1281 Mt Clinton Pike, Harrisonburg VA 22802, 540-434-8474, FJBlosser@aol.com [VA] [AW]

Blosser, Gary S. (Judith Brunk Blosser) 725 Ann Ave, Wauseon OH 43567, 419-446-7457 [OH] IIB1 [AC] Lead Pastor, North Clinton Menn Ch, Wauseon OH

Blosser, Glendon L. (Dorothy) 1513 Mount Clinton Pike, Harrisonburg VA 22802, 540-434-0657,

gblosser@aol.com [VA] IB3 [AC]

Blough, Ronald L. (Rhoda M.) 6977 Paris Ave NE, Louisville OH 44641, 330-875-4953, bloughr@sssnet.com [OH] IIB1 [AC] Pastor, Beech Menn Ch, Louisville OH

Bogard, Marlene (Michael) 7732 NW 12th, Newton, KS 67114, 316-284-2183 [SCC, WDC] IIC [AC] Minister of Christian Nurture, SCC/WDC, North Newton, KS

Bohn, Ernest Stanley (Anita Pannabecker Bohn) 333 E 9th St, Newton KS 67114, 316-284-2176 [WDC] [RE]

Bolanos Sr, Israel (Alma Marina) 2020 Baker Dr, Allentown PA 18103, 610-791-1469 [FRC] [RE]

Boll, John E. (Anna Lois) 96 Olive St, Bolivar NY 14715, 716-928-2380 [LAN] IIB1 [AC] Pastor, Kossuth Community Chapel, Bolivar NY

Bolanos Sr, Israel (Alma Marina) 2020 Baker Dr, Allentown PA 18103, 610-791-1469 [FRC] [RE]

Boll, Mark B. (Roseanna E.) 823 Pine Hill Rd, Lititz PA 17543, 717-626-8685 [LAN] IIB1 [AC] Pastor, Derry Menn Ch, Lititz PA

Bonham, Rusty (Mary Lou Schmidt Bonham) 2526 N Webb Rd, Newton KS 67114, 620-837-5673, Rbonham@southwind.net [WDC] IIB2 [AC] Pastor of Youth and Caregiving, First Menn Ch, Newton KS

Bontrager, Brent (Diana) 1381 E Phelps, Kalkaska MI 49646, 616-258-2339, bbontrager@hotmail.com [IM] IIB1 [AC] Pastor, Coldsprings Menn Ch, Kalkaska MI

Bontrager, Eugene, 11846 County Road 16, Middlebury IN 46540, 574-825-9284 [IM] [AW]

Bontrager, G. Edwin (Edith) 2 E Spur Ct, Hampton VA 23666, eebontrag@aol.com [VA] IIB1 [AC] Pastor, Huntington Menn Ch, Newport News VA

Bontrager, Jonas, 1707 E Longview Rd, Hutchinson KS 67501-8411, 620-662-2500 [SC] [AW]

Bontrager, Joseph E. (Gloria B.) 3551 Apple Tree Dr, Harrisonburg VA 22802, 540-867-0529 [VA] IIB3c [AC]

Bontrager, Marion (Buetta) PO Box 3000, Hesston KS 67062, 620-327-4472 [SC] IIB3d [AC] Professor, Hesston College Bible Department, Hesston KS

Bontrager, Orvan, 1945 S 600 W, Topeka IN 46571, 260-593-2060 [IM] [RE]

Bontrager, Willard L., 7517 County Rd 751 NE, Mancelona MI 49659, 616-587-8190 [IM] [RE]

Bontreger, Kenneth, 1006 E Kercher Rd, Goshen IN 46526, 574-533-3671, kenb@maplenet.net [CDC] IIB1 [AC] Senior Pastor, Silverwood Menn Ch, Goshen IN

Bontreger, Myron (Fran) 1408 S 15th St, Goshen IN 46526, 574-534-6791, myron@firstmennonite.net [IM] IIA [AC] Associate Pastor and Minister of Youth, First Menn Ch, Middlebury IN

Bontreger, Vernon E., 1420-6 Kentfield Way, Goshen IN 46526, 574-533-7068 [IM] [RE]

Bontreger, Wes J. (Cheryl) 63630 County Road 111, Goshen IN 46526-8101, 574-862-2849 [IM] IIB1 [AC] Pastor, Yellow Creek Menn Ch, Goshen IN

Book, David (Martha) RR 1 Box 48C, Frazee MN 56544, 218-847-3914 [NC] IIB1 [AC] Pastor, Lake Region Menn Ch, Frazee MN

Book, Miriam F. (James M. Lapp) 443 Penn Oak Ct, Harleysville PA 19438, 215-513-4115, miriamfbook@juno.com [FRC] IIB2 [AC] Associate Pastor, Salford Menn Ch, Harleysville PA

Borg, Jeffrey A., 219 West St, Ft Collins CO 80521, 970-416-1687, revjborg@juno.com [RM, WDC] IIB1 [AC]

Pastor, Fort Collins Menn Fell, Fort Collins CO

Borjas, Jose Franscisco (Irma) 7810 Clark Rd C-2, Jessup MD 20794, 410-799-1461 [VA] IIB2 [AC] Associate Pastor, Iglesia del Evangelio Completo Alpha y Omega, Washington DC

Borkholder, CarolSue Hostetler, 10713 East U Ave, Vicksburg MI 49097, 616-649-4348, borker@concentric.net [CDC] IIB3a [AC] Chaplain, Battle Creek Health Systems, Battle Creek MI

Born, Floyd E. (Bertha Toews Born) 505 N Main, PO Box 68, Elbing KS 67041, 620-799-2593, zion@iwichita.com [WDC] IIB1 [AC] Pastor, Zion Menn Ch, Elbing KS

Boshart, David W. (Shana) 3382 305th St, Parnell IA 52325, 319-646-2842, dboshart@netins.net [CP] IIB1 [AC] Pastor, West Union Menn Ch, Parnell IA

Boshart, Shana Peachey (David W. Boshart) 3382 305th St, Parnell IA 52325, 319-646-2842, shana@netins.net [CP] IIA [AC]

Bowman, Edwin S. (Minerva) 106 Sunset Rd, New Holland PA 17557-9618, 717-354-9478 [LAN] [RE]

Bowman, James C. (Lois) 433 Linden Rd, East Earl PA 17519, 717-445-5339 [LAN] IIB2 [AC] Associate Pastor, Lichty Menn Ch, New Holland PA

Bowman, Leroy H. (Lydia Ann) 3001 Lititz Pike, PO Box 5093, Lancaster PA 17606-5093, 717-560-4747 [LAN] [RE]

Bowman, Nelson L. (Mary Ann) 658 Wentzel Rd, East Earl PA 17519, 717-445-7790 [LAN] IB3 [AC]

Bowman, Paul K., 1520 Harrisburg Pike, Lancaster PA 17601-2632, 717-392-6596 [LAN] [RE]

Bowman, R. Todd, 105 Lambert Dr, Newport News VA 23602, 757-874-9163, faiththinker@hotmail.com [VA] IIA [AC] Pastor, Providence Menn Ch, Newport News VA

Bowman, Richard L. (Elsie C.) 937 College Ave, Harrisonburg VA 22802, 540-434-0892, rbowman@bridgewater.edu [VA] IIB3c [AC]

Boyer, Claude F. (Mary M.) 205 Diller St, Pandora OH 45877-9709, 419-384-3508, boyer@wcoil.com [CDC] [AC]

Boyer, H. Wesley (Lois A.) 2153 East Cedarville Rd, Pottstown PA 19465, 610-705-8836, vincentmennonite@juno.com [FRC] IIB1 [AC] Pastor, Vincent Menn Ch, Spring City PA

Brandenberger, Martin, 6925 Black Rd, New Haven IN 46774, 260-749-9045 [IM] [RE]

Brandt, LeRoy (Linda) 40 Cadbury St, Pottsville PA 17901-3921, 570-628-4992 [LAN] [AW]

Breckbill, Willis L. (Ina Ruth) 1521 Kentfield Way #7, Goshen IN 46526, 574-534-8370, 105060.2416@compuserve.com [CDC, IM] [RE]

Breeden, Diana (Marlon (Marty)) 10709 Indian Trail Rd, Harrisonburg VA 22802, 540-574-4007 [VA] IIA [AC] Associate Pastor, Grace Menn Fell, Lacey Spring VA

Breeden, Marlon W. (Diana J.) 10709 Indian Trail Rd, Harrisonburg VA 22802, 540-574-4007 [VA] IIA [AC] Associate Pastor, Grace Menn Fell, Lacey Spring VA

Breeze, Cynthia Massanari (Clark) 1310 Old Farm Rd, Champaign IL 61821, 217-356-2471, cbreeze4@aol.com [CDC, IL] IIB2 [AC] Associate Pastor, First Menn Ch of Champaign-Urbana, Urbana IL

Breneman, Janet M., Apartado 371-I, Montserrat, Zona 7, Guatemala City, Guatemala, janetb@intelnet.net.qt [LAN] IIC [AC] Overseas Mission Worker, EMM, Belize,

South America

Breneman, Robert A. (Mabel) 620 Sandstone Rd, Strasburg PA 17579, 717-786-3823 [LAN] [RE]

Brenneman, Diane Zaerr (Douglas Joseph Brenneman) 1061 480th St SW, Parnell IA 52325, 319-646-2371, DianeZB@mennoniteusa.org [CP] IB1 [AC] Denom. Minister, Office of Ministerial Leadership, Mennonite Church USA, Parnell IA

Brenneman, Donald L. (Marilyn) 4899 Chaucer Dr, Greensboro NC 27407, 919-299-1369 [VA] [RE]

Brenneman, James E. (Terri J. Plank Brenneman) 1915 Mill Rd, South Pasadena CA 91030, 626-799-6340, JEBrenneman@aol.com [PSW] IIB1 [AC] Pastor, Pasadena Menn Ch, Pasadena CA; Professor of OT, Episcopal Theological School at Claremont, Claremont CA

Brenneman, John K. (Lois) 258 Brenneman Rd, Lancaster PA 17603, 717-872-5183 [LAN] [RE]

Brenneman, Todd, 215 Smithfield St, Johnstown PA 15905, 814-288-5036 [ALL] IIC1 [AC]. Pastor, Carpenter Park Menn Ch, Davidsville PA

Brenneman, Virgil J., 516 E Waverly Ave, Goshen IN 46526-4726, 574-534-3345, vjbren@bnin.net [CDC, IM] [RE]

Brewer, Douglas W. (Marla) RR 1 Box 30A, Birch Tree MO 65438-9606, 314-292-3553 [SC] IIB1 [AC] Pastor, Berea Menn Community Ch, Birch Tree MO

Brooks, Dennis R. (Sheri) Lithuanian Christian Fund College, Kretingos 36a, Lt5808 Klaipeda, Lithuania [LAN] IIB3b [AC]

Brown, Cora L. (Jonathan) 56564 Woodbine Ln, Elkhart IN 46516, 574-522-1832, coralbrown@juno.com [IM] IIB1 [AC] Co-Pastor, Church Without Walls, Elkhart IN

Brown, Jonathan (Cora L.) 56564 Woodbine Ln, Elkhart IN 46516, 574-522-1832, jonbrown@juno.com [IM] IIB1 [AC] Pastor, Church Without Walls, Elkhart IN

Brown, Lena H. (Michael R.) PO Box 112, Grantham PA 17027, 717-766-3985 [LAN] IIC [AC] Associate Pastor, Slate Hill Menn Ch, Camp Hill PA

Brown, Mitchell C. (Deborah) 1334 Elmwood Ave, Wilmette IL 60091, 847-256-3985, mcb9476@aol.com [CDC, IL] IIB1 [AC] Pastor, Evanston Menn Ch, Evanston IL

Brown, Steven Lavonne, 81 Michaels Woods Dr, Hampton VA 23666-5614, 757-826-9140, minsbrown@aol.com [VA] IIB2 [AC]

Brubacker, John S. (Rachel) 1629 Hancock Blvd, Reading PA 19607-2921, 610-796-9331 [LAN] IIC [AC] Co-Pastor, Shiloh Menn Ch, Reading PA

Brubaker, Cliff, 11794 Clark Rd, Hillsdale MI 49242, 517-254-4643, brubaker@powersupply.net [OH] IIB1 [AC] Interim Pastor, Central Menn Ch, Archbold OH

Brubaker, Dean M., 1801 Greencroft Blvd, Goshen IN 46526, 574-534-4955 [IM] [RE]

Brubaker, Doane (Sharon) 212 S Baltimore, Morton IL 61550, 309-263-7306 [IL] IIB1 [AC] Pastor, First Menn Ch of Morton, Morton IL

Brubaker, Donald L. (Lyndell) 634 Lincoln Rd, Lititz PA 17543, 717-626-4833 [LAN] III [AC] Ordained Deacon, Hess Menn Ch, Lititz PA

Brubaker, Glenn E. (Josephine T.) 1580 Co Rd 22, Whitesville NY 14897, 607-356-3379, g-jbrubaker@juno.com [NY] IIB1 [AC] Co-Pastor, West Union Menn Ch, Rexville NY

Brubaker, J. Donald (Marian) 460 Stony Battery Rd, Landisville PA 17538-1032, 717-898-2517, donmarb@juno.com [LAN] III [AC] Ordained Deacon, Chestnut Hill Menn Ch, Columbia PA

Brubaker, James C. (Naomi) 269 Meetinghouse Ln, Lewisburg PA 17837, 717-524-2838 [ALL] IB3, IIB3a [AC]

Brubaker, Roy L. (Anita Hope) RR 1 Box 209, Mifflintown PA 17059, 717-436-9477, hoperoy@pa.net [LAN] [RE] Bishop/Overseer, LAN - Community Menn Fell, Milton PA

Brubaker, Sharon L. (Gregg) Lithuania Christian College, Kretingos gatve 36, Klaipeda LT 5808, Lithuania, gsbrubaker@emm.org [LAN] IIC [AC] Chaplain, EMM, Klaipeda Lithuania

Brubaker, Shirley Yoder (Kenton K.) 1222 Parkway Dr, Harrisonburg VA 22802, 540-434-0473, kkbrubaker@juno.com [VA] IIB2 [AW]

Brubaker, Verle Alden (Maralee Ann) 906 Chelsea, Washington IL 61571, 309-444-8474, verleb@mtco.com [CDC] IIB1 [AC] Pastor, Calvary Menn Ch, Washington IL

Brunk, Kenneth S. (Twila) 5420 Riverview Rd, Williamsburg VA 23188, 757-566-1619 [VA] [RE]

Brunk, Lawrence (Dorothy) 41 Hausman Rd, Lenhartsville PA 19534, 610-756-3601 [ACC] [RE]

Brunk, Nathan W. (Diane) 107 Garris Rd, Dowingtown PA 19335, 610-269-9602, NWBrunk@cs.com [LAN] IIB1 [AC] Pastor, Downing Hills Christian Fell, Downingtown PA

Brunk, William A. (Nancy) 8568 Shupps Ln, Coopersburg PA 18036, 610-965-8849 [FRC] IIB1 [AC] Pastor, Swamp Menn Ch, Quakertown PA

Brunk III, George R., 983 Summit Ave, Harrisonburg VA 22802, 540-434-1583 [VA] IIB3d [AC]

Brunk Jr, Truman H. (Betty) 1066 Blue Mountain Ct, Harrisonburg VA 22801, 540-801-0918, btrubet@aol.com [VA] IB3, IIB2 [AC] Associate Pastor, Harrisonburg Menn Ch, Harrisonburg VA

Brunner, David D. (Jo Ann) 2219-15th Ave NW, Rochester MN 55901-1569, 507-529-7910, brunnerd@prodigy.net [CP] IIB1 [AC] Pastor, Rochester Menn Ch, Rochester MN

Brunner, Grace (Paul) 441 S Main St, Hesston KS 67062, 620-327-2157 [SC] [RE]

Brunner, Paul D. (Grace) 441 S Main St, Hesston KS 67062, 620-327-2157 [SC] [RE]

Brunstetter, Charles E. (Miriam) 736 Centre St, Easton PA 18042, 610-252-5351, charb@entermail.net [FRC] IIB1 [AC] Pastor, River of God Fell, Easton PA

Brutus, Dieudonne (Lunie) PO Box 380386, Miami FL 33238, 305-756-5101 [SE] IIC [AC] Pastor, Tabernacle of Bethlehem, Miami-Dade FL

Bryant, B. Elaine (Clarence C.) 8636 S Wolcott, Chicago IL 60620-4730, 773-779-6566, elainebryant@prodigy.net [IL] IIB1 [AC] Pastor, Englewood Menn Ch, Chicago IL

Buch, Richard E., 120 S 10th St, Akron PA 17501, 717-859-2660, richardbuch@juno.com [LAN] IIB1 [AC] Pastor, Metzler Menn Ch, Akron PA

Buchen, Curvin R. (Lois) 178 Forest Hill Rd, Leola PA 17540, 717-656-6905 [LAN] [RE]

Bucher, Kenneth A. (Evelyn) 2474 Wisgarver Rd, Manheim PA 17545, 717-665-6411, kebucher@juno.com [LAN] IIB1 [AC] Pastor, Manheim Menn Ch, Manheim PA

Bucher, Richard Wayne (Carol A.) 113 W Columbia, Box 22, Danvers IL 61732, 309-963-6323, rbucher@frontiernet.net [CDC] IIB1 [AC] Pastor, North Danvers Menn Ch, Danvers IL

Bucher, Roy C. (Betty Jane Ruppert Bucher) 1001 E Oregon Rd, Lititz PA 17543, 717-519-2658, roybucher@juno.com [ACC] [RE]

Buckwalter, A. David (Marian) 1957 Drexel Ave, Lancaster PA 17602-3363, 717-397-3605 [LAN] [RE]

Buckwalter, Albert S. (Lois Miriam Litwiller) 1432 Greencroft Dr, Goshen IN 46526, 574-537-4380 [SC] [RE]

Buckwalter, Henry L. (Millie) 462 Willow Rd, Lancaster PA 17601, 717-295-7125, henrymillieb@juno.com [LAN] IB3 [AC] Interim Bishop/Overseer, LMC - New England District; Missionary/Church Worker, LMC, Belize South America

Buckwalter, J. Harold (Twila) 453 Wenger Rd, Chesapeake VA 23322-1612, 804-482-4918 [VA] IIB3c [AC]

Buckwalter, Kyle D. (Rachelle) 36 Front St, Lititz PA 17543, 717-626-7559, skarbucks4@netzero.net [LAN] IIA [AC] Associate Pastor, Hess Menn Ch, Lititz PA

Buckwalter, Matthew R. (Norene) 170 King Rd, Cochranville PA 19330-9794, 717-940-2331, pastormatt@wjtl.net [LAN] IIA [AC] Pastor, Old Road Menn Ch, Gap PA

Buckwalter, Richard B. (Sara) 433 S Kinzer Ave, Apt #339, New Holland PA 17557, 717-355-6844 [LAN] [RE]

Buckwalter, Richard L. (Deborah) 124 Skyline Dr, New Holland PA 17557, 717-355-2725, rlbuck@lancnews.infi.net [LAN] IB3 [AC] Bishop/Overseer, LMC - Pequea Valley, PA

Bulford, Charles (Nadine G. Smith-Bulford) 3015 Midvale Ave, PO Box 43174, Philadelphia PA 19129-3306, 215-438-0293, cmercies@aol.com [LAN] IIB1 [AC] Pastor, New Mercies Menn Ch, Philadelphia PA

Bulford, Nadine G. Smith (Charles) 3015 Midvale Ave, PO Box 43174, Philadelphia PA 19129-3306, 215-438-0293, cmercies@aol.com [LAN] IIC [AC] Associate Pastor, New Mercies Menn Ch, Philadelphia PA

Buller, Charles (Tracy Marble Buller) 405 N Constitution Ave, Goshen IN 46526-1464, 574-534-4714, cbuller@communionfellowship.org [IM] IIB1 [AC] Pastor, Communion Fell, Goshen IN

Buller, Eric, Rt 1, Box 69, Ransom KS 67572, 785-731-2283, buller@gbta.net [WDC] IIB1 [AC] Pastor, First Menn Ch, Ransom KS

Buller, Harold W. (Anne W.) 1108 Monroe St, Beatrice NE 68310, 402-228-3004 [WDC] [RE]

Buller, Jane Stoltzfus (Jim) 2711 S Main St, Goshen IN 46526, 574-533-1353, jsb53@hotmail.com [IM] IIB2 [AC] Pastor, Walnut Hill Menn Ch, Goshen IN

Buller, Jeannette, 3018 W Rose Ln, Phoenix AZ 85017-1641, 602-246-7237, JBuller@CoachNet.org [IM] IIB3b [AC] Coach-Consultant, CoachNet, Phoenix AZ; Missionary - Coach, Strategic Ministries Inc, Phoenix AZ

Buller, Peter (Gladys E.) 15 Fairfield Park, Goshen IN 46526, 574-534-4158, pwbuller@juno.com [CDC, IM] [RE]

Burdette, Rob (Patty) 17823 Carson Rd, Butler OH

MINISTERS

6

44822-9427, 740-694-1759 [OH] IIA [AC] Interim Pastor, Moorhead Menn Ch, Millersburg OH

Burke, John H. (Mamie R.) 9435 South Green St, Chicago IL 60620-2715, 312-233-2892 [CDC] IIB1 [AC] Pastor, First Menn Ch, Chicago IL

Burkhalter, Sheldon Wayne (Janis Sprunger Burkhalter) 1622 Sutton Ct, Goshen IN 46526, 574-534-5892, sheldonwb@goshen.edu [IM] IIB3c [AC] Director of Church Relations, Goshen College, Goshen IN

Burkhart, Larry E. (Carol J.) 277 Black Rd, Quarryville PA 17566, 717-529-2227, MTHLRTL@juno.com [LAN] IIB1 [AC] Associate Pastor, Living Stones Fell, Peach Bottom PA

Burkholder, David H. (Edna) 803 Burky Ln, Ephrata PA 17522, 717-733-3210 [LAN] IIB3a [AC] Associate Pastor, Carpenter Community Ch, Talmage PA

Burkholder, Galen E. (Marie) 165 Cooper Ave, Salunga PA 17538, 717-898-0335 [LAN] IIB3c [AC]

Burkholder, Isaac R. (Rosanna) 745 Twin Bridge Rd, Chambersburg PA 17201, 717-369-4185 [FRK] IIB3a [AC] Chaplain, Franklin County Prison, Chambersburg PA

Burkholder, James A. (Marian G.) 13 Montadale Dr, Dillsburg PA 17019, 717-502-1216, jimburk@mail.cvn.net [ACC] [RE]

Burkholder, John Richard (Sue) 1508 S 14th St, Goshen IN 46526-4546, 574-533-1326 [CDC, IM] [RE]

Burkholder, Leonard G. (Anna Mary) 7332 Bunting Pl, Philadelphia PA 19153, 215-365-0670 [LAN] IIB2 [AC] Associate Pastor, Indonesian Fell, Philadelphia PA

Burkholder, Marlin S. (Katie) 254 Morris Rd, Harleysville PA 19438 [LAN] [RE]

Burkholder, Nelson D. (Dorothy) 234 Lakewood Park Dr, Newport News VA 23602, 757-877-4606 [VA] [RE]

Burkholder, Owen E. (Ruth Ann Augsburger) 1585 College, Harrisonburg VA 22802-5550, 540-433-2138, oweneb@juno.com [VA] IB2 [AC] Conference Minister, Virginia Mennonite Conference, Harrisonburg VA

Burkholder, Paul G. (Miriam) 1001 E Oregon Rd, Lititz PA 17543, 717-581-3964, pburkholder@juno.com [ACC] [RE]

Burkholder, Raymond (Naomi) Grand Anse Valley PO, St George's, Grenada, 473-444-4762, rayburkholder@anabaptist.org [LAN] IIB1 [AC]

Burkholder, Samuel S. (Naomi) 112 Apple Blossom Cr, Lititz PA 17543, 717-627-2222 [LAN] IIB1 [AC] Associate Pastor, Hammer Creek Menn Ch, Lititz PA

Burkholder Jr, Lewis (Helen) 1125 Rocky Ford Rd, Powhatan VA 23139, 804-598-3643 [VA] IIB3a [AC]

Burrus, Rennie W., 6442 Road R, Columbus Grove OH 45830, 419-384-3131, rennie@wcoil.com [CDC] IIB1 [AC] Pastor, St John Menn Ch, Pandora OH

Busenitz, Willis Herman (Nadine Faye) PO Box 50, Busby MT 59016-0050, 406-592-3643 [CP] IIB1 [AC] Pastor, White River Cheyenne Menn Ch, Busby MT

Bushi, John, 888 S Roselle Rd, Schaumburg IL 60193-3965, 847-895-1022, johnbushi@yahoo.com [CDC, IL] IIA [AC] Minister of Evangelism, Christ Community Menn Ch, Schaumburg IL

Bustos, Mario (Shirley A. Bustos) 5406 4th Ave, Valparaiso IN 46383, 219-462-0526, mbustos@earthlink.com [IM] IIB1 [AC] Pastor, Valparaiso Menn Ch, Valparaiso IN

Byler, J. (Jesse) **Daryl** (Cynthia Ann (Lehman)) 110 Maryland Ave, NE Ste 502, Washington DC 20002, 301-386-4024, J._Daryl_Byler@mcc.org [GS] IIB3c [AC] Director, Washington Office, Mennonite Central Committee, Washington DC

Byler, Jayne M., 338 Haven, Barberton OH 44203, 330-753-9737, jkejbyler@juno.com [OH] IIB1 [AC] Pastor, Summit Menn Ch, Barberton OH

Byler, Jonathan Jesse (Loice N.) Box 3431, Thika, Kenya, East Africa, JonByler@maf.org [GS] IIB3b [AC] Director, Centre for Christian Discipleship, Thika, Kenya East Africa

C

Caceros, Serapio Antonio, 5526 Reiger Ave #221, Dallas TX 75214 [WDC] IIA [AC] Pastor, Iglesia Cristiana Menonita de Dallas, Dallas TX

Caes, Elizabeth Werenfels, 3562 E Kerckhoff, Fresno CA 93702, 559-495-1731, libbycaes@juno.com [PSW] [AW]

Cahill, Robert D. (Tara Jean) c/o FUNDAMENO, Apartado 1, 16909 San Pedro Carcha, Av 49506-5061, GUATEMALA, rtcahill@yahoo.com [ACC] IIB3b [AC] Missionary, MCC, San Pedro Carcha Guatemala

Calderon, Armando J. (Sara) RR 4 Box 64L, Mathis TX 78368, 512-547-3727 [SC] IIB1 [AC] Pastor, Calvary Menn Ch, Mathis TX

Caldwell, G. Darrell (Susan) 1315 Southern Rd, Norwich OH 43767, 614-872-4111 [LAN] IIB3b [AC]

Callahan, Charles W. (Linda) 212 A Hibiscus St, Honolulu HI 96818, 808-836-5651 [LAN] IIA [AC] Pastor, New Life Christian Fell, Honolulu HI

Callejas, Gabriel F. Licona, c/o Amor Viviente, 3893 SW 133rd Pl, Miami FL 33133, 305-447-8364 [SE] IIC [AC] Pastor, Iglesia Amor Viviente/Ft Lauderdale, Tamarac FL

Campbell Jr, Walter A. (Ester Arline) 386 West Ave, Plain City OH 43064, 614-873-1324, wacamp@juno.com [OH] IIB1 [AC] Pastor, Cornerstone Menn Fell, Plain City OH

Campoz, Jose, 763 18th St NE, Salem OR 97301, 503-363-8687 [PNW] IIB1 [AC] Pastor, Jerusalem Iglesia, Salem OR

Cañon, Angel M. (Elcira) 2520 S Lawndale Ave, Chicago IL 60623, 773-277-6665 [IL] IIB1 [AC] Pastor, Lawndale Menn Ch, Chicago IL

Cantu, Felipe (Maria) 1208 14 1/2 St, Rock Island IL 61201, 309-788-2941 [CP] IIB1 [AC] Pastor, Templo Alabanza Menonita, Moline IL

Carlson, Robert Joel (Phyllis Hershey Carlson) 9730 Reeder, Overland Park KS 66214-2577, 913-894-9408, grandpa1@ix.netcom.com [WDC] [RE]

Carmona, Juan C. (Sonia) 2151 N Howard St #2NDFL, Philadelphia PA 19122-1712, 215-455-0263 [LAN] IIB1 [AC] Pastor, Arca de Salvacion, Philadelphia PA

Carpenter, James J. (Faith) 5676 E 99th Ave, Anchorage AK 99516, 907-346-2909, barniejc@alaska.net [PNW] [RE]

Carrasco, Ruben Duenas (Haydee) Apartado 708, Cusco, Peru [LAN] IIB3b [AC] Missionary/Church Worker, Cusco Peru

Chapman, Christine Fowle (Daniel E.) 112 Main St, North Springfield VT 05150, 802-886-2142, cfnier@hotmail.com [FRC] IIA [AC]

Chapman, Daniel Ernest (Christine) 112 Main St, North

Springfield VT 05150, 802-886-2142, creekbird@hotmail.com [FRC] IC [AC]

Charles, Abram H. (Ruth) 449 S Centerville Rd, Lancaster PA 17603, 717-872-7478, abecharles@juno.com [LAN] [RE]

Charles, Dwight G. (Lynette) 1147 Stone Mill Dr, Elizabethtown PA 17022, 717-361-7298 [LAN] III [AC] Ordained Deacon, East Hanover Menn Ch, Palmyra PA

Charles, Mervin (Laurel F.) 546 Leaman Ave, Millersville PA 17551, 717-626-4716 [LAN] IIB1 [AC]

Charles, Paul K. (Dorothy) 125 S Donerville Rd, Lancaster PA 17603, 717-285-4251 [LAN] [RE]

Charles, Sylvia Shirk, 904 College Ave, Goshen IN 46526, 574-534-0142 [IM] IIB3a [AC] Campus Minister, Goshen College, Goshen IN

Chen, Mark (Susan Chuang) 30129 Third Place South, Federal Way WA 98003-3139, 253-946-9553 [PNW] [RE]

Cheramie Risingsun, Steve W., 6210 Jack Springs Rd, Atmore AL 36502, 251-368-0280 [GS] IIB1 [AC] Pastor, Poarch Community Ch, Atmore AL; Pastor, Native Christian Fell, Atmore AL

Cheung, Paul (Alice) 14 Leland St, Malden MA 02148, 781-397-1092 [LAN] IIB1 [AC] Pastor, Chinese Christian Ch of Malden, Malden MA

Childs, Evelyn E., 18948 Monte Vista, Detroit MI 48221, 313-345-5615 [IM] IIB1 [AC] Pastor, Peace Community Menn Ch, Detroit MI

Chiles, Lawrence F. (Nereida) 150 City Mill Rd, Lancaster PA 17602-3808, 717-393-2654, lawrencech@juno.com [LAN] IIB3c [AC] Global Ministries Representative to USA, Eastern Mennonite Missions, Salunga PA

Choi, Bong-Gi (Young-Hee) 16205 Redland Rd, Rockville MD 20855 [VA] IIB1 [AC]

Choi, Sang Jin (Jin Son Park) 40-1 Hearthstone Ct, Annapolis MD 21403, 410-295-7059, appasc@aol.com [VA] IIB3b [AC]

Christophel, James L., 1702 S MacGregor Rd, South Bend IN 46614, 574-291-4228 [IM] [RE]

Chupp, Ruben (Idella) 1002 Beechwood Dr, Nappanee IN 46550, 574-773-2963, ruberc@juno.com [IM] IIB1 [AC] Pastor, North Main Street Menn Ch, Nappanee IN

Cius, David (Theanard) PO Box 255532, Dorchester MA 02125, 781-396-6009 [LAN] IIA [AC] Pastor, Boston Bethel Missionary Ch, Dorchester MA

Claassen, Arlin G. (Helen) 1229 Camden Ct, Goshen IN 46526, 574-534-0407 [CDC, IL] [RE]

Claassen, Curt Albert (Olga Rose [Schultz]) 218 W Franklin St, Berne IN 46711-2132, 260-589-8148 [CDC] [RE]

Clark, Benjamin L. (Mary Esther) 43 S Kinzer Rd, Kinzers PA 17535, 717-442-4865, bmeclark@juno.com [LAN] III [AC] Ordained Deacon, Kinzer Menn Ch, Kinzers PA

Clark, Kevin A. (Susan) 3484 Mt Clinton Pike, Harrisonburg VA 22802, 540-867-0409 [VA] IIB1 [AC] Pastor, Big Spring Menn Ch, Luray VA

Clark, Paul L. (Faye) 2552 S Cherry Ln, Ronks PA 17572, 717-687-8870, paul.clark@fandm.edu [LAN] IIB1 [AC] Pastor, Kinzer Menn Ch, Kinzers PA

Claudio Sr, Samuel (Ana) 240 Tenth Ave, Bethlehem PA 18018, 610-865-5602, samclaudio@lehighcounty.org [EDC] IIA [AC] Hispanic Pastor, Grace Menn Ch, Lansdale PA

Clemens, Donella M. (R. Wayne) 401 Leidy Rd, PO Box 439, Souderton PA 18964, 215-723-2223, DonellaC@FMC-online.org [FRC] IC [AC] Conference Minister, Franconia Mennonite Conference, Souderton PA

Clemens, Philip K. (Nancy M.) 11716 Rte 89, Corry PA 16407, 814-664-9102, PNClemens@tbscc.com [OH] IIB1 [AC] Pastor, Beaverdam Menn Ch, Corry PA

Clements, Ryan, 326 Elm Dr, Wooster OH 44691, 330-264-0093, woostermc@sssnet.com [OH] IIA [AC] Youth Pastor, Wooster Menn Ch, Wooster OH

Clemmer, Gerald A. (Lydia M.) 59 W Chestnut St, Souderton PA 18964, 215-721-0356 [FRC] IIB1 [AC] Co-Pastor, Souderton Menn Ch, Souderton PA

Clinton, Walter Ray (Janice I.) 1406 16th St S, Fargo ND 58103, 701-298-0783, clintonwjmc@gateway.net [CP] [AC]

Clugston, Dale Eugene (Ethel) 6072 Olde Scotland Rd, Shippensburg PA 17257, 717-263-1518 [FRK] III [AC] Ordained Deacon, Cedar Street Menn Ch, Chambersburg PA

Coblentz, Glenn Dale (Viola Elaine) 16329 Harrison Rd, Navarre OH 44662, 330-359-7181, revc@sssnet.com [OH] IIB1 [AC] Pastor, Longenecker Menn Ch, Winesburg OH

Coblentz, Randy, 9301 Barnes Rd, Toano VA 23168 [VA] IIC [AC]

Collins, Ronald C. (Betty Lou) 1504 S 13th Street, Goshen IN 46526, 574-533-5269, roncoll@juno.com [IM] [AW]

Colliver, Kathy, 607 3rd St, Fort Wayne IN 46808, 260-422-1649, kathycolliver@hotmail.com [IM] IIA [AC] Pastor, First Menn Ch, Fort Wayne IN

Combs, Jeff (Joyce) 1555 S Limestone St, Springfield OH 45505, 937-322-9130, jeffcombs@mics.net [OH] IIB1 [AC] Co-Pastor, Southside Christian Fell, Springfield OH

Combs, Joyce (Jeff) 1555 S Limestone St, Springfield OH 45505, 937-322-9130, jeffcombs@mics.net [OH] IIB1 [AC] Co-Pastor, Southside Christian Fell, Springfield OH

Conn, Jay, 5325 PR 382, Millersburg OH 44654, 330-893-8109 [OH] IIA [AC] Associate Pastor, Martins Creek Menn Ch, Millersburg OH

Conrad, Paul E. (S. Ann Burkholder) 820 Bellows Dr, New Carlisle OH 45344, 937-849-9778 [OH] [RE]

Conrad, Paul G. (Rhonda Rae) 12550 Lake Village Dr, Gulfport MS 39503, 228-547-5884, conradpr@juno.com [GS] IIB1 [AC] Lead Pastor, Gulfhaven Menn Ch, Gulfport MS

Conrad, Willard D. (Hettie M.) 359 W Cedar, Hesston KS 67062, 620-327-2782 [SC] [RE]

Coon, Robert Russell, 214 Morrow Ave #503, Topeka IN 46571, 260-593-3443 [CDC] [RE]

Cooper, Robert D., 398 Geigel Hill Rd, Upper Black Eddy PA 18972, bjcooper@epix.net [FRC] [AC] Assistant Pastor, Rocky Ridge Menn Ch, Quakertown PA

Corbin, Jonathan, 1725B Graceland Ct, Goshen IN 46526, 574-534-1738, jonc@maplenet.net [CDC] IIA [AC] Associate Pastor, Silverwood Menn Ch, Goshen IN

Cordell, Irvin E. (Margaret) 57 E Grandview Ave, Mercersburg PA 17236, 717-328-2746 [FRK] [RE] Licensed Deacon, Mercersburg Menn Ch, Mercersburg PA

Cordell, Merle G. (Beulah) 8979 Grindstone Hill Rd, Chambersburg PA 17201, 717-597-7415 [FRK] [RE]

MINISTERS

6

Cosden, David T. (Charlotte) 1552 Virginia Ave, Folcroft PA 19032, teachtruth@juno.com [LAN] IIB1 [AC] Pastor, Delaware County Fell, Folcraft PA

Coss, Lewis M. (Mary) 13505 Olde Mystic Cr, Hagerstown MD 21742, 301-733-2147 [FRK] IIB1 [AC] Pastor Emeritus, Community Menn Ch, Hagerstown MD

Crable, David (Betty) 23 S Water St, Masontown PA 15461, 724-583-7464 [ALL] IIA [AC]

Cragan, Daniel J., 1070 A CR 411, Westerloo NY 12193 [LAN] IIB3a [AC]

Crawford, Walter Lewis (Hattie) 8910 Blue Ridge Dr, Tampa FL 33619, 813-623-6010 [SE] IIB1 [AC] Pastor, Newtown Gospel Chapel, Sarasota FL

Crockett, Robert (Maria) 1704 DeCamp, Elkhart IN 46516, 574-293-5118 [IM] IIB1 [AC] Pastor, House of Power, Elkhart IN

Croegaert, James Charles (Janalee) 827 Monroe St, Evanston IL 60202, 847-475-2749, jcroegae@mcs.com [IL] IIB3a [AC] Chaplain, Resurrection Medical Center, Chicago IL

Croyle, Ellis B. (R. Charlotte [Hertzler]) 1112 Spring Brooke Dr, Goshen IN 46528, 574-533-2248 [IM] [RE]

Crugnale, Joseph M. (Linda J.) 235 East Fairwood Dr, Chalfont PA 18914 [FRC] IIC [AC] Chaplain, Neshaminy Manor Nursing Home, Warrington PA

Cruz, Justiniano (Mabel) 5327 16th St NW, Washington DC 20011, 202-726-8161 [VA] IIB1 [AC] Pastor, Iglesia del Evangelio Completo Alpha y Omega, Washington DC

Cruz, Miriam R. (Jesus) 441 Surrey Dr, Lancaster PA 17601, 717-5817816, jcruz1225@aol.com [LAN] IIC [AC] Chaplain, Mennonite Home, Lancaster PA

Cubbage, R. Matthew (Glenda) 6101 Monaco Court, Hickory NC 28601, 828-267-5754 [VA] IIC [AC]

Culver, Wes, 422 N Constitution Ave, Goshen IN 46526, 574-533-6300, wesculver@wesculver.com [IM] IIA [AC] Associate Pastor, Pleasant View Menn Ch, Goshen IN

Custar, Deanna (Daniel Lamar Custar) 11261 US Rt 127, West Unity OH 43570, 419-924-5158 [OH] IIA [AC] Preaching Minister, Salem Menn Ch, Waldron MI

Cutipa, Celestino Santa Cruz (Inez) Apartado 708, Cusco, Peru [LAN] IIA [AC] Missionary/Church Worker, Cusco Peru

Cyster, Graham James (Dorcas) 15 Savo Ave, Lancaster PA 17601, 717-519-0315 [LAN] [AW]

D

Dagen, Paul L. (Lois) 1001 E Oregon Rd, Lititz PA 17543, 717-581-3965 [LAN] [RE]

Dalellew, Tesfatsion, 2233 Bobwhite Ln, Lancaster PA 17601 [PSW] IIB3b [AW]

Dalke, Herbert M. (Bertha) 33 6th Avenue SE, Oelwein IA 50662, 319-283-9211 [CDC, IL] [RE]

Dalke, Robert Eugene (Flauretta Faye) 645 North Wall, PO Box 38, Buhler KS 67522-0038, 620-543-6623, flbob@ourtownusa.net [WDC] IIB1 [AC] Pastor, Buhler Menn Ch, Buhler KS

Danner, Michael (Melissa) 201 W Cleveland, Roanoke IL 61561, 309-923-7702, mikemmc@mtco.com [IL] IIB1 [AC] Lead Pastor, Metamora Menn Ch, Metamora IL

Darling, Timothy E. (Dawn M.) 177 Almond Rd, Pittsgrove NJ 08318, 856-692-7441, nmpastor@juno.com [LAN] IIB1 [AC] Pastor, Norma Menn Ch, Norma NJ

Daught, Gary, 925 N Desert Ave Apt C, Tucson AZ

85711-2044, 520-881-8834, gfdaught@cox.net [PSW] IIB1 [AC] Minister of Teaching and Preaching, Shalom Menn Fell, Tucson AZ

Daux, Simon, 1110 NW 126th St, Miami FL 33168, 305-687-3949 [SE] IIC [AC] Pastor, Eglise du Nouveau Testament, Miami FL

Davis, Richard Douglas (Marla Janice) 10007 Dale Crest Dr, Dallas TX 75229-5841, 214-350-5244, pmc@airmail.net [WDC] IIB1 [AC] Pastor, Peace Menn Ch, Dallas TX

Dawson, Daryl (Sandy) 176 Chalybeate Rd, Bedford PA 15522-9801, 814-623-7792 [ALL] IB3, IIB1 [AC] Pastor, Canan Station Menn Ch, Altoona PA

Dayton, Philip, Rt 2 Box 647, Ridgeley WV 26753, 304-726-4380 [ALL] IIA [AC] Pastor, Pinto Menn Ch, Pinto MD

De Jesus, Artemio, 13411 Misti Loop, Lakelnd FL 33809 [SE] IIC [AC] Pastor, Luz y Verdad, Lakeland FL

De Leon, Neflali, c/o Neflali De Leon, 130 3rd Ave Apt 18G, Brooklyn NY 11217, 718-522-5029 [LAN] IIA [AC] Pastor, Menn Evangelical Tabernacle, Brooklyn NY

Deal, Michael (Christine) 12 N Fourth St, Hughesville PA 17737, 717-584-3881 [LAN] IIB1 [AC] Pastor, Agape Fell, Williamsport PA

Dean, Michael Richard (Tonya) Po Box 520, Fisher IL 61843, 217-897-1365 [IL] IIB1 [AC] Pastor, East Bend Menn Ch, Fisher IL

Deckert, Eric R., PO Box 172, Wellman IA 52356 [CP] IIA [AW]

Deiter, Raymond L. (Elizabeth) 595 Cinder Rd, New Providence PA 17560, 717-786-3890, rldaed@juno.com [LAN] IIB1 [AC] Pastor, Living Stones Fell, Peach Bottom PA

DeLeon, Seferina Garcia, 712 S 12th St, Goshen IN 46526, 574-34-0362, seferina.deleon@lacasagoshen.org [IM] IIA [AC] Pastor, Iglesia Menonita del Buen Pastor, Goshen IN

Delp, Earl R. (Emma) 1309 Woodland Dr, Harrisonburg VA 22802, 540-564-3778 [VA] [RE]

Delp, James S. (BJane) 115 Green Hill Ln, Churchville VA 24421-2521, 540-337-8883, jdelp@cfw.com [VA] IIB1 [AC] Pastor, Staunton Menn Ch, Staunton VA

Delp, Lowell H. (Brenda) 2828 Woodview Dr, Hatfield PA 19440, 215-822-0235 [FRC] IIB1 [AC] Pastor, Line Lexington Menn Ch, Line Lexington PA

Delp, Melvin B., 1007 Haverhill Rd, Baltimore MD 21229, 410-644-8343 [LAN] IB3 [AC]

Delp, R. Lee (Ruth) 840 Keeler Rd, Lansdale PA 19446, 215-368-8019, ldelp@voicenet.com [EDC] III [AC]

Delp, Willard B. (Arlene) 7186 Iron Stone Hill Rd, Dallastown PA 17313, 717-428-1709 [LAN] [RE]

Dengler, Lee (Susan) 611 S 8th St, Goshen IN 46526, 574-534-7552, lee@collegemennonite.org [IM] IIC [AC] Pastor, College Menn Ch, Goshen IN

Dengler, Susan (Lee) 611 S 8th St, Goshen IN 46526, 574-534-7552, susan@collegemennonite.org [IM] IIC [AC] Pastor, College Menn Ch, Goshen IN

Denlinger, Garry L. (Ruth Helen) Box 3703, 31036 Haifa, Israel, garuden@aol.com [LAN] IIB3b [AC]

Denlinger, Glen M. (Marilyn J.) 2475 E Burr Oak Ct, Sarasota FL 34232, 941-371-7550 [SE] IIC [AC] Minister of Adult Christian Educ & Family Life, Bahia Vista Menn Ch, Sarasota FL; Counselor/Director, Charis Center, Sarasota FL

Denlinger, Jason (Ann) RR 3 Box 250, Canton PA 17724, 717-243-9983 [LAN] IIB1 [AC]

Denlinger, John H. (Deborah) 2062 Millstream Rd, Lancaster PA 17602, 717-396-0031, jhdenlinger@juno.com [ACC] IIB1 [AC] Pastor, Ridgeview Menn Ch, Gordonville PA

Denlinger, Lester K. (Marian) 388 Baumgardner Rd, Willow Street PA 17584, 717-464-4317, lesmarian@juno.com [LAN] IIB1 [AC] Pastor, Rossmere Menn Ch, Lancaster PA

Denlinger, Wilmer B. (Bertie) 400 Park Ave, Quakertown PA 18951-1638, 215-536-2900 [EDC] [RE]

Dennis, James (Kathleen) 2045 N Carlisle St, Philadelphia PA 19121, 215-765-2911 [LAN] IIB1 [AC] Pastor, Christian Life Menn Fell, Philadelphia PA

Derstine, James L., 3628 Weightman St, Philadelphia PA 19129-1621, 215-848-4935 [FRC] [RE]

Derstine, John L. (Mary) 577 Westwood Dr, Downingtown PA 19335, 610-363-2662, cornerstonecel@bee.net [LAN] IIB3b [AC] Pastor, Cornerstone CELLebration Ch and Ministries, Downingtown PA

Derstine, Kenton Trost, 146 Belmont Dr, Harrisonburg VA 22801, derstine@emu.edu [VA] IIB3a [AC] Staff, Eastern Mennonite Seminary, Harrisonburg

Derstine, Lorene B., 332 Homestead Dr, Harleysville PA 19438, 215-256-8320, 104105.3575@compuserve.com [FRC] IIA [AC]

Derstine, Michael L. (Dawn Frankenfield Derstine) 130 S Main St, Telford PA 18969, 215-723-8511, mikedawn@juno.com [FRC] IIB1 [AC] Pastor, Plains Menn Ch, Hatfield PA

Derstine, Norman (Virginia) 1285 Shank Dr Apt 220, Harrisonburg VA 22802, 540-433-1193 [VA] [RE]

Derstine Jr, David F. (Maxine) 215 Dock Dr, Lansdale PA 19446, 215-362-6410 [FRC] [RE]

Derstine, Samuel N, 112 8th St, Souderton PA 18964, 215-723-3151 [FRC] [RE]

Desalegn, Sisay (Yodit Alemu) 4048 S 148th St, Seattle WA 98168, 206-244-4892, sisayd@msn.com [PNW] IIB3b [AC] Pastor, Seattle African Ministries, Seattle WA

Detweiler, Alvin F. (Kass) 285 Mill St, Boyertown PA 19512, 610-367-0602 [FRC] [RE]

Detweiler, Bill, PO Box 11, Kidron OH 44636, 330-857-3151 [OH] [RE]

Detweiler, Randy (Joy) 4763 N 700 E, Kokomo IN 46901, 765-628-2865, pastor-randy@juno.com [IM] IIB1 [AC] Pastor, Howard-Miami Menn Ch, Kokomo IN

Detweiler, Rudy, 9652 Akron Rd, Rittman OH 44270, 330-927-3613 [OH] [RE]

Detweiler, Russell M. (Evelyn) 224 Detweiler Rd, Sellersville PA 18960, 215-257-7021 [FRC] IIB1 [AC] Pastor of Visitation, New Eden Fell, Schwenksville PA

Detweiler, Timothy R. (Carol) 2675 230th St, Washington IA 52353, 319-653-4109, tdetweiler@hotmail.com [CP] IIB1 [AC] Pastor, Washington Menn Ch, Washington IA

Detweiler, Wally (Liz) RR 1, Sleeman ON P0W 1M0, Canada, 807-488-5620 [NC] IIB1 [AC] Pastor, Morson Community Bible Fell, Sleeman ON

Detweiler, Wilton (Delores) PO Box 165, Shickley NE 68436, 402-627-4155, dee@inebraska.com [CP] IIB1 [AC] Pastor, Salem Menn Ch, Shickley NE

Detwiler, R. Blaine (Connie) RR 1 Box 55, Susquehanna PA 18847, 717-756-2793 [FRC] IIB1 [AC] Pastor, Lakeview Menn Ch, Susquehanna PA

Dey, John Michael (Susan Elizabeth) 504 E Main St, PO Box 387, Pandora OH 45877, 419-384-3421, gracemenchurch@juno.com [CDC] IIB1 [AC] Pastor, Grace Menn Ch, Pandora OH

Dick, Jane (Mervin) 2881 E Huntington Blvd, Fresno CA 93721, 559-497-0198, janeldick@worldnet.att.net [PSW] IIB1 [AC] Co-Pastor, Menn Community Ch, Fresno CA

Dick, Mervin (Jane) 2881 E Huntington Blvd, Fresno CA 93721, 559-497-0198, mervdick@worldnet.att.net [PSW] IIB1 [AC] Co-Pastor, Menn Community Ch, Fresno CA

Diener, Edward, 3252 CR 19, Archbold OH 43502, 419-445-5796 [OH] [RE]

Diener, Joe (Elizabeth [Liz]) 13580N CR 300E, Humboldt IL 61931, 217-234-8709 [IL] [RE]

Diener, Ronald (Marilee) 58794 CR 19 N, Goshen IN 46528, 574-875-3594, rdiener@maplenet.net [IM] IIB1 [AC] Pastor, Pleasant View Menn Ch, Goshen IN

Diener, Terry (Julie) 14411 CR 28, Goshen IN 46528, 574-825-3222, diener2@juno.com [IM] IIB2 [AC] Assist. Pastor/Min. of Pastoral Care & Counseling, Clinton Frame Menn Ch, Goshen IN; Associate Pastor/Youth Ministry Overseer, Clinton Frame Menn Ch, Goshen IN

Diener Jr, Andrew S. (Jean Marie) 2464 Creek Hill Rd, Lancaster PA 17601, 717-656-8341 [LAN] IIA, III [AC] Licensed Deacon, Stumptown Menn Ch, Bird-in-Hand PA

Diller, Aden K. (Ruth) 12635 Williamsport Pike, Greencastle PA 17225, 717-597-2765 [FRK] [RE]

Diller, Donavin Wayne (June Elizabeth) 1812 Jefferson, Beatrice NE 68310, 402-223-2340 [WDC] [RE]

Diller, Dwight H. (Mary Elaine) PO Box 148, Hillsboro WV 24946, 304-653-4397 [VA] IIB3b [AC]

Dintaman, Pamela R. (Larry Gingrich) 116 Swarthmore Dr, Lititz PA 17543, 717-627-3649, pamlarry@dejazzd.com [LAN] IIB1 [AC] Co-Pastor, Community Menn Ch of Lancaster, Lancaster PA

Dintaman, Steve F. (Betsy) 1190 Parkway Dr, Harrisonburg VA 22802, 540-434-5148 [VA] IIB3d [AC]

Dombach, J. Eric (Deborah) 344 Morgan Dr, Lancaster PA 17601-6012, ericdom@juno.com [LAN] IIB2 [AC] Associate Pastor, ACTS Covenant Fell, Lancaster PA

Dominguez, Mario, 4148 NW 45 Terrace, Lauderdale Lakes FL 33319 [SE] IIC [AC] Pastor, Evangelical Garifuna Ch, Lauderdale Lakes FL

Dove, Otis W. (Lottie) 7081 Porch Swing Ln, Dayton VA 22821, 540-828-4864 [VA] [RE]

Dow, Leonard M. (Rosalie Rolon) 19 West Phil-Ellena St, Philadelphia PA 19119, 215-991-5805, ldow@mcc.org [LAN] IIB1 [AC] Pastor, Oxford Circle Menn Ch, Philadelphia PA

Drescher, John M., 2265 Esten Rd, Quakertown PA 18951, 215-804-0248 [FRC] IIB3b [AC]

Driver, Daryl S. (Kay) 345 Hanover St, Elizabethtown PA 17022, 717-367-8499, daryldriver@juno.com [LAN] [AW]

Duerksen, Norma B. (Philip K.) 2595 Paradise Rd, Orrville OH 44667-9161, 216-682-1465, ogsmthvll@aol.com [CDC, OH] IIB1 [AC] Pastor, Oak Grove Menn Ch, Smithville OH

Dula, Mary Ellen (Mamo) 47 W Roseville Rd, Lancaster

MINISTERS

6

PA 17601, 717-519-2495, dulamm@desupernet.net [LAN] IIC [AC] Chaplain, Community Hospital of Lancaster, Lancaster PA

Dunigans, Jesse (Portia) Jesse Dunigans, 2518 Arden St, St Louis MO 63121, 314-385-5877 [IL] IIB2 [AC] Associate Pastor, Bethesda Menn Ch, St Louis MO

Dunn, George B., 13735 Equestrian Dr, Burton OH 44021, 440-834-9317 [OH] IIB3a [AC]

Dunn, James L. (Ann Suderman Dunn) 8611 N Hesston Rd, Hesston KS 67062, 620-327-2185 [WDC] IIB1 [AC] Pastor, Alexanderwohl Menn Ch, Goessel KS

Dunn, Kathy Neufeld (Michael J. Dunn) 2106 Pauline Blvd, # 203, Ann Arbor MI 48103, 734-930-0176, dunfeld@juno.com [CDC, IM] IIB3a [AC] Chaplain, Glacier Hills Retirement Center, Ann Arbor MI

Dutchersmith, Teresa (Kent) 515 S 5th St, Goshen IN 46526, 574-535-1103, dutchersmith@hotmail.com [CDC, IM] IIA [AC] Pastor, Faith Menn Ch, Goshen IN

Dyck, Arthur P. (Suzanne Ruth [Nix]) 914 Pinetree Way, Lancaster PA 17601-6608, 717-285-7678, artdyck@msn.com [ACC] IIA [AC] Minister of Music, Neffsville Menn Ch, Lancaster PA

Dyck, Cornelius John, 1252 Westbrooke Ct, Goshen IN 46528-5065, 574-533-2677 [CDC] [RE]

Dyck, Edna Margaret (George) 1505 Hillcrest Rd, Newton KS 67114-1340, 316-283-7774, gdyck@kscable.com [WDC] [RE]

Dyck, Gordon R. (Judy Beechy) 2212 Wakefield Rd, Goshen IN 46528, 574-533-5909, grdjab@aol.com [IM] IB3 [AC] Overseer for Parkview Menn, Kokomo IN; Overseer for Southside Fell, Elkhart IN; Overseer for Bonneyville Menn, Bristol IN

Dyck, Mary, 107 W 23rd, PO Box 485, North Newton KS 67117, 316-283-0115, mdyck@southwind.net [WDC] [RE]

Dyck, Peter Henry (Sheryl) 202 W Clark St, PO Box 354, Thomasboro IL 61878-0354, 217-643-2789 [CDC, IL] IIB3a [AC] Chaplain, Provena Covenant Medical Center, Urbana IL

Dyck, Peter J., 1 Woodcrest Circle #209, Scottdale PA 15683-9500, 412-887-3924 [ALL] [RE]

E

Early, Richard K. (Kay) 5379 Klines Mill Rd, Linville VA 22834, 540-896-3423 [VA] IIB1 [AC] Pastor, Grace Menn Fell, Lacey Spring VA

Eash, Brent (Heidi) 15485 CR 4, Bristol IN 46507, 574-848-4589, baeash@hotmail.com [IM] IIB2 [AC] Pastor, Shore Menn Ch, Shipshewana IN

Eash, Theodore M., 16038 CR 4, Bristol IN 46507, 260-848-7089 [IM] [AW]

Eberly, Ben (Martha) 5923 Corinth Dr, Colorado Springs CO 80918, 719-265-9478, beneberly@juno.com [RM] IIB1 [AC]

Eberly, Harold B. (Ruth Ann) 616 Sawmill Rd, East Earl PA 17519, 717-445-5543 [LAN] III [AC] Licensed Deacon, Bowmansville Menn Ch, Bowmansville PA

Eberly, Kenneth B. (Betty Lou) 816 N 13th St, Reading PA 19604, 610-378-1017, servantken@juno.com [LAN] IIB1 [AC] Associate Pastor, Hampden Menn Ch, Reading PA

Ebersole, Lee E. (Connie Joy [Graber]) 951 Chestnut Dr, Harrisonburg VA 22801, 540-434-6065, leencon@rica.net [VA] IIB2 [AC] Pastor, Ridgeway

Menn Ch, Harrisonburg VA

Ebersole, Marlin E. (Doris) 6495 Olde Pine Dr, Chambersburg PA 17201, 717-352-2135, mdebersole@pa.net [FRK] IIB1 [AC] Pastor, Pond Bank Menn Ch, Chambersburg PA

Ebersole, Myron L. (Geraldine Ann Hartman Ebersole) 2001 Harrisburg Pike, Apt B 407, Lancaster PA 17601, 717-735-2564, mgebersole@aol.com [ACC] [RE]

Eby, Edwin R. (Sue) 9401 Raintree Rd, Burke VA 22015, 703-426-2549 [VA] IIB2 [AC]

Eby, J. Herbert (Marian) RR 3 Box 332, Canton PA 17724-9317, 570-924-3260 [LAN] IIC [AC] Associate Pastor, Mountain View Fell, Trout Run PA

Eby, J. Wilmer (Anna) 24 Creekside Dr, Millersville PA 17551, 717-872-5924, wilann62@juno.com [LAN] IIB1 [AC] Pastor, Masonville Menn Ch, Washington Boro PA

Eby, Kathryn Weaver (J. Harold) 198 Delp Rd, Lancaster PA 17601, 717-569-1290 [LAN] IIC [AC] Chaplain, Prison, and Landis Homes, Lititz PA

Eby, Paul H. (Barbara) 12 Mary Dr, Gap PA 17527, 717-442-9050 [LAN] [RE]

Eby, Wilmer M., 1001 East Oregon Rd, Lititz PA 17543-9205, 717-509-5426 [LAN] [RE]

Ediger, Darrell Lee (Deadra J.) 225 N Wenger Rd, Dalton OH 44618, 330-828-8186, d_ediger@bigfoot.com [CDC] IIB1 [AC] Pastor, Salem Menn Ch, Kidron OH

Ediger, George Roland (Margaret Irene) 426 West Ave, Kelowna BC V1Y 4Z2, Canada, 250-712-9383, Mediger@silk.net [WDC] [RE]

Ediger, Margaret Irene (George Roland) 426 West Ave, Kelowna BC V1Y 4Z2, Canada, 250-712-9383, Mediger@silk.net [WDC] [RE]

Edwards, Dennis Robert (Susan Steele Edwards) 636 Lexington Pl NE, Washington DC 20002 [VA] IB1 [AW]

Egli, James Walter (Vicki Sue) 3214 Brentwood, Champaign IL 61821 [CDC] [AW]

Egli, Marian, 406 2nd St, PO Box 411, Hopedale IL 61747, 309-449-5479, Egli_2@hotmail.com [IL] IIC [AC] Chaplain, St. Joseph's Hospice Program, Bloomington IL

Eglinton-Woods, Bruce (Nancy) 307 4th St, East Greenville PA 18041, 215-679-3380, salempastor@netcarrier.com [FRC] IIB1 [AC] Pastor, Salem Menn Ch, Quakertown PA

Ehst, Abram M., HC Box 11, Bally PA 19503, 610-845-2529 [FRC] [RE]

Ehst, John M. (Beverly Meyers Ehst) 507 Schoolhouse Rd, Harleysville PA 19438, 215-721-7498 [FRC] IIB1 [AC] Pastor, Franconia Menn Ch, Franconia PA

Eisele, Randy, 115 Judd Rd, Siletz OR 97380, 541-444-9063 [PNW] IIA [AC] Pastor, Logsden Neighborhood Ch, Logsden OR

Elias, Jacob W. (Lillian) 602 W Hively Ave, Elkhart IN 46517, 574-293-6657, jelias@ambs.edu [IM] IIB1 [AC] Intentional Interim, Parkview Menn Ch, Kokomo IN

Elias, Lillian (Jacob) 602 W Hively Ave, Elkhart IN 46517, 574-293-6657, lillianelias@juno.com [IM] IIA [AC] Intentional Interim, Parkview Menn Ch, Kokomo IN

Elizalde, Jose (Deena) 4811 Baring Ave, East Chicago IN 46312, 574-392-3299, DJElizalde@cs.com [IL] IIA [AC]

Emery, Brian L. (Kelly) 149 Ebersole Rd, Ephrata PA 17522, 717-336-2206, brianemmanuel@dejazzd.com [EDC] IIA [AC] Associate Pastor, Emmanuel Menn Ch,

Reinholds PA

Encarnacion, Ambrosio (Jennie) 2591 Apache St, Sarasota FL 34231, 941-926-0843 [SE] IB3 [AC] Hispanic Advocate, Southeast Mennonite Conference, Sarasota FL

Engbrecht, Robert L. (Joan) 618 East 7th St, Box 67, Freeman SD 57029, 605-925-7410 [CP] IIB1 [AC] Pastor, Salem-Zion Menn Ch, Freeman SD

Engel, Harold R. (Anna Mae) 145 Doe Run Rd, East Fallowfield PA 19320, 610-593-6464 [LAN] IIB1 [AC] Pastor, Newlinville Menn Ch, Coatesville PA

Engle, George W. (Betty) RR 1 Box 1690, Pineville MO 64856, 501-636-1645, gengle@leru.net [SC] III [AC] Elder, Rogers Menn/Ch of the Brethren, Pea Ridge AR

Engle, Jesse, 8973 Wieneck Rd, Streetsboro OH 44241, 330-422-0829, jessengle@juno.com [OH] IIA [AC] Co-Pastor, Aurora Menn Ch, Aurora OH

Engle, Naomi, 8973 Wiencek Rd, Streetsboro OH 44241, 330-442-0829, jessengle@juno.com [OH] IIA [AC] Co-Pastor, Aurora Menn Ch, Aurora OH

Epp, Arlen, 51892 CR 11, Elkhart IN 46514-8558, 574-293-8100, repp@juno.com [CDC] IIB3a [AC]

Epp, Charlene, 1292 NW Fall Ave, Beaverton OR 97006-4031, 503-533-5654, lenakaye@hotmail.com [PNW] IIC [AC]

Epp, Eldon John, 710 Mission, Manhattan KS 66502, 785-587-8256 [WDC] IIB3a [AC] Chaplain, Community Hospital, Manhattan KS

Epp, Rosella E. (Raymond Reimer) 3916 E Ronning Dr, Sioux Falls SD 57103 [CP] IIB1 [AC] Pastor, Sermon on the Mount Menn Ch, Sioux Falls SD

Erb, Leroy H. (Rachel) 925 Strick Rd, Milton PA 17847, 570-437-3773 [LAN] IIA [AC] Associate Pastor, Derry Menn Ch, Lititz PA

Ernest, Dennis Wayne (Rosalind Dawn) 165 E Front St, Lititz PA 17543, 717-626-8237, lmchurch@dejazzd.com [LAN] IIB1 [AC] Pastor, Lititz Menn Ch, Lititz PA

Esau, John A. (Bernice A. [Klaassen]) Box 117, 9 Emerald Court, North Newton KS 67117-0117, 316-283-4624, jae@southwind.net [WDC] [AW]

Esbenshade, Adam (Alta) 626 S Kinzer Ave, New Holland PA 17557, 717-354-9509 [LAN] [RE]

Esh, Robert E., 45565 Erie County Line Rd, Corry PA 16407, 814-664-7892, ree0817@aol.com [OH] IIA [AC] Pastor, Valley View Menn Ch, Spartansburg PA

Esh, Stephen S., 2655 Valley View Rd, Morgantown PA 19543, 610-286-8892 [LAN] [RE]

Eshleman, Allen R. (Mary Ellen) 13239 Buchanan Trail West, Mercersburg PA 17236, 717-328-0058 [FRK] IIB1 [AC] Pastor, Mercersburg Menn Ch, Mercersburg PA

Eshleman, D. Rohrer (Mabel) 46 Country Ln, Landisville PA 17538, 717-898-2593 [LAN] [RE]

Eshleman, J. David (Helen) 8806 Eastbourne Ln, Laurel MD 20708, 301-725-5692 [LAN] IIB1 [AC] Pastor, Capital Christian Fell, Laurel MD

Eshleman, J. Leon (Melba) 570 Fruitville Pike, Manheim PA 17545, 717-665-6690 [LAN] III [AC] Ordained Deacon, Chestnut Hill Menn Ch, Columbia PA

Eshleman, J. Lester (Lois) 1001 E Oregon Rd, Lititz PA 17543, 717-581-3968 [LAN] [RE]

Eshleman, Mahlon D. (Mary) 450C Menno Village, Chambersburg PA 17201, 717-263-1082 [FRK] [RE]

Estes, Steven Ralph (Jackie) 31429 Center St, Chenoa IL 61726, 309-747-2878, sjestes@gridcom.net [CDC, IL]

IIB3a [AC] Chaplain, Meadows Mennonite Retirement Community, Chenoa IL

Estrada, Gilberto, 1765 Tomlin Ave, Woodburn OR 97071, 503-982-5731 [PNW] IIA [AC] Pastor, Comunidad Cristiana de Vida Nueva, Woodburn OR

Ewert, David Darrel (Karen L.) 2111 E Luther Rd, Janesville WI 53545, 608-754-6942, loudarew@juno.com [CDC, IL] [RE]

Ewert, Linda, 868 N Maize Rd, Wichita KS 67212, 316-722-0903, lewert@hopemennonite.com [WDC] IIA [AC] Associate Pastor, Hope Menn Ch, Wichita KS

Ewert, Marvin H. (Alma L.) 1328 W 9th St, Newton KS 67114-1620, 316-283-8520 [WDC] [RE]

F

Fahnestock, James R. (Nancy) 7 Audubon Cr, Stevens PA 17578, 717-336-8263, jnfahnestock@dejazzd.com [LAN] IIB1 [AC] Pastor, Blainsport Menn Ch, Stevens PA

Fahrer, Walfred J. (Susan R.) 16 Despard Rd, Upper Holloway, London N195 NW, Great Britain [IM] IIB3b [AC]

Faler, Brad, 21636-20A, Archbold OH 43502, 419-445-4408, brad.faler@northclinton.org [OH] IIB2 [AC] Associate Pastor, North Clinton Menn Ch, Wauseon OH

Falla, Amanda (Gamaliel) Apartado 24226, Cali, Colombia, 011-572-3331 ext 521, cindy@ colombianet.net [SE] IIB3b [AC] Mission Service, Encuentro de Renovacion, Colombia, South America

Falla, Gamaliel (Amanda) Apartado 24226, Cali, Colombia, 011-572-3331 ext 521, cindy@ colombianet.net [SE] IIB3b [AC] Mission Service, Encuentro de Renovacion, Colombia, South America

Farmer, Roger Alan (Mary Lou Swartzendruber Farmer) 2830 Coppock Rd, Washington IA 52353, 319-653-2547, rfarmer1@juno.com [CP] IIB1 [AC] Pastor, Sugar Creek Menn Ch, Wayland IA

Farmwald, Kevin Dale (Susie Kay) 217 Main St, Box 250, Sugarcreek OH 44681, 330-852-2894, farmwald@adelphia.net [CDC] IIB1 [AC] Pastor, First Menn Ch, Sugarcreek OH

Farrell, William, 182 Ark Ln, Schoharie NY 12157, 518-295-7891, wfarrell@midtel.net [NY] IIA [AC] Pastor, Grace Fell, Schoharie NY

Farrow, Frank E. (Susan B.) 115 Bunker Hill Rd, Rogersville TN 37857-6049, 423-345-9165, farrowfs@ntelos.net [VA] [RE]

Fatunmbi, Olwfemi A., 6503/6505 S Normandie Ave, Los Angeles CA 90043, 323-779-4363 [PSW] IIB1 [AC] Mission Associate, Center for Anabaptist Leadership; Founding Pastor, Royal Dominion Family Chapel, Los Angeles CA

Feliciano, Rogelio, 1116 Kittatinny St, Harrisburg PA 17014 [LAN] [AW]

Feliz, Jose, 426 Highlawn Ave, Elizabethtown PA 17022, 717-367-3966 [LAN] IIB2 [AC]

Fellenbaum, Robert E. (May) 508 N Plum St, Mount Joy PA 17552, 717-653-1278 [LAN] III [AC] Ordained Deacon, Elizabethtown Menn Ch, Elizabethtown PA

Ferreras, Juan (Maritza) PO Box 50870, Cicerio IL 60804, sonidodealabanza@earthlink.net [IL] IIB1 [AC] Pastor, Sonido de Alabanza, Cicero IL

Fetterly, Tim (Candy) PO Box 368, Grantsville MD 21536, 301-895-4054, tcfetterly@earthlink.net [ALL] IIB1 [AC] Pastor, Oak Grove Menn Ch, Grantsville MD

MINISTERS

6

Fisher, J. Herbert (Ruth) 117 Weaver Rd, Lancaster PA 17603, 717-394-8159 [LAN] [RE]

Fisher, Orlo J. (Dorothy M.) 9365 Vest-Talcum Rd, Talcum KY 41722, 606-251-3303 [IM] IIB1 [AC] Pastor, Talcum Menn Ch, Talcum KY

Fisher, Rachel S. (Robert) 1724 S 12th St, Goshen IN 46526, 574-533-0669, fisher915@bnin.net [IM] [RE]

Fisher Jr, Menno (Sallie) 2523 Old Philadelphia Pk, Bird-In-Hand PA 17505-9797 [LAN] IIB2 [AC] Associate Pastor, Millwood Menn Ch, Kinzers PA

Flaming, Ron (Patrice Stucky) 125 Broad St, Akron PA 17501 [WDC] IIB3c [AC]

Flinner, Matt, 5337 PR 382, Millersburg OH 44654, 330-893-3923 [OH] IIA [AC] Associate Pastor, Martins Creek Menn Ch, Millersburg OH

Flores, Gilberto, PO Box 347, 722 Main, Newton KS 67114-0347, 316-283-5100, GilbertoF@MennoniteUSA.org [WDC] IIB3c [AC]

Flowers, Claude, 10634 Navajo Rd, Apple Valley CA 92308, 760-247-5713 [PSW] IIB1 [AC] Pastor, Family Menn Ch, Los Angeles CA

Foncannon, David (Brenda) 408 Morrison, Pueblo CO 81005, 719-561-1609, blindpossum@juno.com [RM] IIB1 [AC] Pastor, Pueblo Menn Ch, Pueblo CO

Foote, Ralph Wayne (Eloise Christine) PO Box 337, Carlock IL 61725-0337, 309-376-4014, ralphfoote@mac.com [CDC] IIA [AC] Pastor, Carlock Menn Ch, Carlock IL

Forestal, Ducois, 300 NW 117th St, Miami FL 33168, 305-953-9703 [SE] IIC [AC] Pastor, Unity Pentecostal Ch of God, Miami FL

Forrey, K. Eugene (Nancy) 312 Druid Hill Dr, Mountville PA 17554, 717-285-4046 [LAN] IIB2 [AC] Associate Pastor, East Petersburg Menn Ch, East Petersburg PA

Forry, Nevin (Fanny) 3500 Oxford Rd, New Oxford PA 17350, 717-624-4263 [LAN] IIA [AC] Associate Pastor, Life Menn Fell, Conestoga PA

Foss, Richard Gordon (Sarah) Rt 2 Box 2A, Tiskilwa IL 61368, 815-646-4264, richfoss@theramp.net [CDC, IL] IIC [AC] Lay Minister, Plow Creek Menn Ch, Tiskilwa IL

Foster, Brent Edwin (Sandra L.) 2710 W Kasas, Peoria IL 61604, 309-685-0213 [CDC, IL] [AW]

Foster, Sandra S. (James) 204 Busbee Rd, Knoxville TN 37920, 423-573-4089 [VA] IIB3a [AC]

Fox, Randy (Arlene) 15 S Ridge Rd, Reinholds PA 17569-9692, 717-336-2471 [LAN] III [AC] Deacon, Red Run Menn Ch, Denver PA

Francisco, Karla (Steven) 4507 Lear Close, Chesapeake VA 23321, 757-686-0049 [VA] IIB2 [AC] Associate Pastor, Calvary Community Ch, Hampton VA

Francisco, Natalie A. (Leslie W. III) 4505 McRae Close, Chesapeake VA 23321, 757-483-3784 [VA] IIB2 [AC] Associate Pastor, Calvary Community Ch, Hampton VA

Francisco, Steven H. (Karla Kirstina) 4507 Lear Close, Chesapeake VA 23321-4264, 757-686-0048 [VA] IIB2 [AC] Associate Pastor, Calvary Community Ch, Hampton VA

Francisco III, Leslie W. (Natalie) 4505 McRae Close, Chespeake VA 23321, 757-483-3784, pastor@ calvarycommunity.org [VA] IB3, IIB1, IIB3c [AC] Pastor, Calvary Community Ch, Hampton VA

Franco, Eliseo, 6226 Colfax Ave, North Hollywood CA 91606, 818-508-6467 [PSW] IIB1, IIB3b [AC] Pastor, Iglesia Evangelica Bethel, Sun Valley CA

Frank, Richard H. (Naomi) 3104 Bossler Rd, Elizabethtown PA 17022, 717-367-3242 [LAN] IIB3a [AC] Chaplain, Mennonite Home, Lancaster PA

Frankenfield, Marlene F., 428 Turnberry Way, Souderton PA 18954-2071, 215-723-5857, MarleneF@FMC-Online.org [FRC] IC [AC] Conference Youth Minister, Franconia Conference, Souderton PA; Campus Pastor, Christopher Dock Mennonite High School, Lansdale PA

Franz, Delton W., 6151 3lst St NW, Washington DC 20015-1515, 202-966-5271 [ALL] [RE]

Frederick, Duane, 1034 O'Brien Rd, Swanton MD 21561, 301-387-2763, revfrederick@hotmail.com [ALL] IB3, IIB1 [AC] Pastor, Meadow Mountain Menn Ch, Swanton MD

Frederick, Elmer S., 37 E 8th St, Pennsburg PA 18073, 215-679-9368 [FRC] IIB1 [AC] Pastor, Covenant Community Fell, Lansdale PA

Frederick, Franklin M. (Naomi) 778 Morwood Rd, Telford PA 18969, 215-723-7351 [FRC] [RE]

Frederick, Jacob W. (Anna) 906 Pine Hill Rd, Lititz PA 17543, 717-626-7464 [LAN] [RE]

Frederick Jr, J. Mark (Emma) San Nic/Del Tla cp 14100, Mexico DF, Mexico [FRC] IIB3b [AC]

Freed, Glenn W. (Ella Mae) 3312 Pruss Hill Rd, Pottstown PA 19464, 610-326-5478 [FRC] [AW]

Freed, Floyd W., Box 109, Putnam Station NY 12861 [FRC] [RE]

Fretz, J. Herbert (Helen Habegger Fretz) 625 South 7th St, Goshen IN 46526, 574-533-1961 [CDC] [RE]

Frey, Adin L. (Janet) 1838 Falling Spring Rd, Chambersburg PA 17201, 717-267-3654 [FRK] [RE]

Frey, Harold R. (Ruth) 1930 Colebrook Rd, Lebanon PA 17042, 717-274-3394 [LAN] [RE]

Frey, Preston M. (Lorraine) 3492 Glen Eagles Dr, Chambersburg PA 17201-8190, 717-352-3600 [FRK] IIB1 [AC] Associate Pastor, Chambersburg Menn Ch, Chambersburg PA

Frey, Vincent J. (Marcella) 890 Blind Brook Dr, Columbus OH 43235, 614-436-9615, freyv@juno.com [ACC] [AW]

Friesen, Ben K. (RaeVella) 1004 Old Farm Est, Hutchinson KS 67502, 620-665-9868 [WDC] [RE]

Friesen, Delores (Stanley) 3014 N 8th St, Fresno CA 93703, 559-229-3645 [PSW] [AW] Associate, Mennonite Board of Missions, Fresno

Friesen, Dorothy Nickel (Richard Allen) 130 Garmatter, Bluffton OH 45817-7557, 419-358-7557, rfriesen@wcoil.com [CDC] IIB1 [AC] Pastor, First Menn Ch, Bluffton OH

Friesen, Elmer R. (Lois M.) 11003 SE Home, Milwaukie OR 97222, 503-786-0289 [PNW] [RE]

Friesen, Ivan D. (Rachel Hilty) PO Box 30, Freeman SD 57029, 605-925-7186 [CP] IIB1 [AC] Co-Pastor, Hutterthal Menn Ch, Freeman SD

Friesen, J. Stanley (Delores) 3014 N 8th St, Fresno CA 93703, 559-229-3645 [PSW] [AW] Teacher, Fresno College, Fresno CA

Friesen, Jacob Toews (Lola M.) Box 133, North Newton KS 67117, 316-283-8064 [WDC] [RE]

Friesen, John A., 1558 Greencroft Dr, Goshen IN 46526, 574-537-4392 [IM] [RE]

Friesen, Matthew Charles (Terisa Lyn) 1935 21st Ave SE, Apt 99, Albany OR 97321, 541-791-9604, amcpastor@proaxis.com [PNW] IIB1 [AC] Pastor, Albany Menn Ch, Albany OR

Friesen, Patty Jo (Patrick Charles Preheim) 2211 28th Ave S, Minneapolis MN 55406, 612-724-0733, faithmc@juno.com [CP] IIB1 [AC] Pastor, Faith Menn Ch, Minneapolis MN

Friesen, Philip E. (Kim Vu) 1781 Hamline Ave N, St Paul MN 55113-6221, 651-644-6406, fries009@tc.umn.edu [CP] IIB3a [AC] Chaplain, International Student & Family Center, Minneaplis MN

Friesen, Rachel (Ivan Dan) PO Box 30, Freeman SD 57029, 605-925-7186 [CP] IIB1 [AC] Co-Pastor, Hutterthal Menn Ch, Freeman SD

Friesen, Todd K. (Dennette Alwine) 536 E Madison St, Lombard IL 60148, 630-889-8701, tkfriesen@aol.com [IL] IIA [AC] Lead Pastor, Lombard Menn Ch, Lombard IL

Friesen, Walter S. (Carol M.) 2009 Clover Ln, Newton KS 67114, 316-283-5250 [WDC] IIB3a [AC] Chaplain, Bethesda Home, Goessel KS

Friesen, Wilbert (Will) James, 3643 E Kerckhoff Ave, Fresno CA 93702-2809, 559-255-4185 [PSW] IIC [AW]

Fry, Donald William (Katherine P.) 5 Audubohn Cr, Stevens PA 17578, 717-336-6849, rdonfry@juno.com [EDC] IIB1 [AC] Pastor, New Eden Fell, Schwenksville PA

Funk, Melvin F., 118 Mallard Ln, Goshen IN 46526, 574-537-1991 [CDC] [RE]

Fyffe, Direl (Polly) 52 Fyffe Ct, West Liberty KY 41472, 606-743-4389 [VA] [RE]

G

Gabbert, Darren (Denise) 400 E Small Ln, Columbia MO 65202, 314-874-1190 [SC] IIA [AC]

Gaeddert, John W. (Mary Lou [Voran]) Box 186, 108 W 24th St, North Newton KS 67117-0186, 316-283-7660 [WDC] [RE]

Gaiotti, Michael C., RR 3 Box 255, Canton PA 17724-9771 [LAN] IIB1 [AC] Pastor, Wheelerville Menn Ch, Canton PA

Gallardo, Andres (Lilia) 1323 S Austin Blvd, Cicero IL 60804-1026, 708-863-6495, CCVIDA@aol.com [IL] IIB1 [AC] Pastor, Centro Cristiano Vida Abundante, Cicero IL

Garber, Fred M., 1614 Bossler Rd, Elizabethtown PA 17022, 717-367-5215, fgarb@juno.com [LAN] IIB1 [AC] Pastor, Bossler Menn Ch, Elizabethtown PA

Garber, Gerald B. (Jewel) 208 Long Rifle Rd, Willow Street PA 17584, 717-464-0640, gjgarber@juno.com [LAN] IIB1 [AC] Associate Pastor, Willow Street Menn Ch, Willow Street PA

Garber, Jay C. (Lois) 2275 New Danville Pike, Lancaster PA 17603-9667, 717-872-6298, garberlj@juno.com [LAN] [RE]

Garber, Joe C. (Yvonne) 242 Stoney Ln, Lancaster PA 17603, 717-872-6922, jygarber@juno.com [LAN] IIA [AC] Pastor, Byerland Menn Ch, Willow Street PA

Garber, Leonard (Veva Roine Hershberger) 1301 Somerset Ct, Goshen IN 46528, 574-534-9622, lvgarber@peoplepc.com [IM] IB3 [AC] Overseer for Waterford Menn, Goshen IN

Garber, Robert E., 17500 Northside Blvd, Nampa ID 83687, 208-466-5081 [PNW] [RE]

Garber, Robert H. (Alta Mae) 1001 W Oregon Rd, Lititz PA 17543, 717-581-1623 [LAN] [RE]

Garber, S. David, 300 S High St, Scottdale PA 15683, 724-887-9407 [ALL] IB3 [AC]

Garcia, Hugo E., 1019 N 27th St, Camden NJ 08105, 609-365-9236 [LAN] IIA [AC] Pastor, Iglesia Manantial de Vida, Camden NJ; Supervisor, Spanish District, Camden NJ

Garrett, Millard P. (Priscilla) 1145 Kenneth Dr, Lancaster PA 17601, 717-397-4593, millardg@emm.org [LAN] IIB3c [AC] Director of Finance, Eastern Mennonite Missions, Salunga PA

Gary, Joe (Lucy) 731 Wagner Ave, Elkhart IN 46516, 574-293-0776 [IM] IIC [AC] Other, Church Without Walls, Elkhart IN

Gascho, Harry (Elva) 1425 Greencroft #265, Goshen IN 46526, 574-534-2190 [IM] [RE]

Gaskins, Paul (Belinda) PO Box 60923, Washington DC 20039, 301-868-1519, powell.dorthy@hq.navy.mil [VA] IIB1 [AC] Pastor, Christian Conquest Fell, Washington DC

Gatlin, Joe (Nancy) 1700 Morrow, Waco TX 76707, 254-754-5942, Joe_Gatlin@habitat.org [SC, WDC] IIB1 [AC] Co-Pastor, Hope Fell, Waco TX

Gatlin, Nancy (Joe) 1700 Morrow, Waco TX 76707, 817-754-5942 [SC, WDC] IIB1 [AC] Co-Pastor, Hope Fell, Waco TX

Gautsche, Charles H. (Marjorie Ann) 820 Ringenberg Dr, Archbold OH 43502-3248, 419-445-6451, cmgautsc@fulton-net.com [OH] IIB3a [AC]

Gaytan, Gilberto (Gloria) 134 S Braintree Ct, Schaumburg IL 60193, 847-534-7242 [CDC] IIB1 [AC] Pastor, Iglesia Menonita Comunidad de Fe, Schaumburg IL

Gehman, Brooke L. (Dana) PO Box 347, Downingtown PA 19335, 610-873-5429 [LAN] IIA [AC] Associate Pastor, Downing Hills Christian Fell, Downingtown PA

Gehman, Dale Lee (Brenda) 314 Millway Rd, Ephrata PA 17522, 717-859-4246 [LAN] IIB1 [AC]

Gehman, David L. (Lois W.) 562 Octorara Trl, Parkesburg PA 19365, 610-857-1641, dlgehman@chesco.com [LAN] IIB1 [AC] Pastor, Parkesburg Menn Ch, Parkesburg PA

Gehman, John W. (Susan Marie) RR2 Box 1435, Mcalisterville PA 17049-9716, 717-463-9378, johnwg@nmax.net [LAN] IIB1 [AC] Pastor, Lauver Menn Ch, Richfield PA

Gehman, Paul H. (Edith) 351 E Farmersville Rd, Ephrata PA 17522, 717-354-9725 [LAN] III [AC] Deacon, Red Run Menn Ch, Denver PA

Gehman Jr, Lester W. (Ruth Ann) 565-A Schoeneck Rd, Ephrata PA 17522, 717-738-1235,[LAN] IIB2 [AC] Youth Pastor, Village Chapel Menn Ch, New Holland PA

Gehring, Barbara Krehbiel (Richard) 221 S 8th, Manhattan KS 66502, 785-770-8816, rbgehring@juno.com [SC, WDC] IIB1 [AC] Co-Pastor, Manhattan Menn Ch, Manhattan KS

Gehring, Richard L. (Barbara Krehbiel Gehring) 221 S 8th, Manhattan KS 66502, 785-770-8816, rbgehring@juno.com [SC, WDC] IIB1 [AC] Co-Pastor, Manhattan Menn Ch, Manhattan KS

Geib, Daniel R. (Cheryl) 73 Sun Ln, Millersville PA 17551, 717-871-8775, dcgeib@juno.com [LAN] IIC [AC] Licensed Deacon, Lyndon Menn Ch, Lancaster PA

Geib, David (Linda) 112 Longfellow Rd, Dagmar MT 59219, 406-483-5307 [NC] IIB1 [AC] Pastor, Coalridge Menn Ch, Dagmar MT

Geigley, Ray M. (Dorothy) 3459 Church St, Chambersburg PA 17201, 717-264-9490 [FRK] IIB3a

MINISTERS

6

[AC] Chaplain, Menno Haven Retirement, Chambersburg PA

Geiser, Elmer, 16306 State Rt 160, Vinton OH 45686, 614-388-9809 [OH] [RE]

Geissinger, Carl (Sherry) 1329 Ertley Rd, Mc Clure PA 17841, 717-543-5130 [ALL] IIB1 [AC]

Geissinger, Norman A., 460B Menno Village, Chambersburg PA 17201, 717-267-1050 [EDC] [RE]

Gerber, James (Barbara) PO Box 526, Brutus MI 49716, 616-529-6276, bjgerber@freeway.net [IM] IB3, IIB1 [AC] Pastor, Maple River Menn Ch, Brutus MI; Interim Pastor, Hilltop Menn Fell, Petoskey MI

Gerber, Lowell Keith (Lois Shank Gerber) 14264 Hackett Rd, Apple Creek OH 44606-9774, 330-857-5243 [OH] IIB3a [AC]

Gerber, Robert (Fran) 5373 W Summy, Leesburg IN 46538-9253 [IM] IIB3b [AC] Assistant to the Director, China Educational Exchange, Harrisonburg VA

Gerig, Virgil M., 1801 Greencroft Blvd #214, Goshen IN 46526, 574-537-4577 [CDC] [RE]

Gering, William M., 624 W Mishawaka Ave, Mishawaka IN 46545-6013, 574-255-3296 [CDC] [RE]

Gibbs, Elizabeth Anne, 250 Lucas Creek Rd, Newport News VA 23602, 757-874-0794, stephenbethgibbs@aol.com [VA] IIA, IIC [AC] Associate Pastor of Youth and Worship, Warwick River Menn Ch, Newport News VA

Gibbs, Stephen H. (Elizabeth (Beth)) 118 Binnacle Dr, Newport News VA 23602-6239, stephenbethgibbs@aol.com [VA] IIB1 [AC] Pastor, Warwick River Menn Ch, Newport News VA

Giersch, William E. (Carol Tobin) 1400 E King St, Lancaster PA 17602, 717-396-8928, wgiersch@yahoo.com [LAN] IIA [AC] Pastor, Beaver Run Menn Ch, Watsontown PA

Gilot, Marie, 1707 6th Ave, Immokalee FL 34142 [SE] IIC [AC] Associate Pastor, Assemblee de la Grace, Immokalee FL

Ginder, Ralph G. (Margaret) 1958 Cloverleaf Rd, Mount Joy PA 17552, 717-653-5042 [LAN] [RE]

Gingerich, Dennis D. (Linda) 502 SE 17th Ave, Cape Coral FL 33990, 941-574-8382 [SE] IIB1 [AC] Senior Pastor, Cape Christian Fell, Cape Coral FL

Gingerich, Emanuel, Rt 1 Box 357M, Glenfield NY 13343, 315-376-7126, margeman@northnet.org [NY] IIC [AC] Overseer, Northern District of the New York Conference, Glenfield

Gingerich, Firman (Susan) 64542 Orchard Dr, Goshen IN 46526, 574-534-7365, firman@collegemennonite.org [IM] IIB1 [AC] Pastor, College Menn Ch, Goshen IN

Gingerich, James Daniel (Roberta S.) PO Box 48, Moundridge KS 67107-0048, 620-345-2130 [WDC] [RE]

Gingerich, Ray C. (Wilma) 1018 Waterman Dr, Harrisonburg VA 22802, 540-434-4465 [VA] IIB3d [AC]

Gingrich, Beth, 100 S Strong Dr, Gallup NM 87301 [IM] IIB3a [AC] Chaplain, Rehobeth McKinnley Hospital, Gallup NM

Gingrich, Byron, 7857 Lavender Ln, Turner OR 97392, 541-363-2662 [PNW] IIB3a [AC]

Gingrich, James M. (Joan) 128 Langley Sq, Lancaster PA 17603, 717-295-7150 [LAN] IIC [AC] Licensed Deacon, Landisville Menn Ch, Landisville PA

Gingrich, Lloyd W. (Rachel) 12357 Orchard Cr, Mercersburg PA 17236, 717-328-5389,

lorae1@juno.com [FRK] IIB2 [AC] Minister of Visitation, Mercersburg Menn Ch, Mercersburg PA

Gingrich, Mervin M. (Janet) 1 Valley View Ct, Lititz PA 17543, 717-626-6111 [LAN] III [AC] Ordained Deacon, Hammer Creek Menn Ch, Lititz PA

Gingrich, Paul M. (Ann) 1903 Maywood Ct, Goshen IN 46526, 574-534-9762, gingrichp@juno.com [IM] IB3 [AC] Overseer for Prairie Street Menn, Elkhart IN

Glanzer, Paul J. (Eva) 1820 Glanzer Ct, Harrisonburg VA 22801, 540-433-8234 [VA] [RE]

Glick, Del, 19889 Peach Ridge Rd, Goshen IN 46526, 574-534-5545, delglick@yahoo.com [IM] IIB1 [AC] Interim Pastor, Washington Community Fell, Washington DC

Glick, Elam H., 234 Hartzler Dr, Belleville PA 17004, 717-935-5495 [ALL] [RE]

Glick, Herman N. (Mary) 1603 Swan Rd, Atglen PA 19310, 610-593-5757 [ACC] [RE]

Glick, Jesse B., 371 W Main St, Amston CT 06231 [IM] IIB3b [AC] Service Assignment, Church World Service, Colchester CT

Glick, Karl G. (Charlotte) 2724 W Philadelphia Ave, Oley PA 19547, 610-987-0429, kglick@juno.com [ACC] IIB1 [AC] Pastor, Ark Bible Chapel, Boyertown PA

Gochnauer, Paul H. (Jean) 720 Centerville Rd, Lancaster PA 17601, 717-898-8361 [LAN] [RE]

Godoy, Filemon B. (Tammy) 529 A Analu St, Honolulu HI 96817, 808-595-6906 [LAN] IIA [AC] Associate Pastor, New Life Christian Fell, Honolulu HI

Godoy, Ronald (Joyce) PO Box 4424, Kaneohe HI 96744-8424, 808-236-2540 [LAN] IIA [AC] Associate Pastor, New Life Christian Fell, Honolulu HI

Godshall, Edward M. (Evelyn Pauline) 5253 W NC, 10 Hwy, Hickory NC 28602, 704-462-1707, edwardgo@aol.com [VA] IB3, IIB1 [AC]

Godshall, Ernest M. (Martha) 14 Elowro Dr, Newport News VA 23602, 757-877-2007 [VA] [RE]

Godshall, Leroy G., 64 Morris Rd, Harleysville PA 19438, 215-256-9968 [FRC] [RE]

Godshall, Paul (Catherine) 3203 Hursey St, Durham NC 27703, 919-598-7533 [VA] IIB1 [AC] Pastor, Durham Menn Ch, Durham NC

Godshall, Stanley G., 5132 McLean Station Rd, Green Lane PA 18054, 215-679-2834 [FRC] [RE]

Godshall, Susan E. (Dr Stanley M.) 1891 Mt Pleasant Rd, Mount Joy PA 17552, 717-653-6191 [LAN] IIC [AC] Associate Pastor, EMM—Africa, Africa

Goering, Paul Louis, 505 Carter Rd, Goshen IN 46526-5209, 574-533-3762 [CDC] [RE]

Goering, Steven William (Susan Ortman Goering) 820 Hawthorn Ave, Boulder CO 80304, 303-443-1236, swgoering@aol.com [WDC] IB2, IIB1 [AC] Co-Pastor, Boulder Menn Ch, Boulder CO; Colorado Conference Minister, Western District Conference, North Newton KS

Goering, Susan Ortman (Steven William) 820 Hawthorn, Boulder CO 80304, 303-443-1236, sogoering@aol.com [WDC] IIB1 [AC] Co-Pastor, Boulder Menn Ch, Boulder CO

Goertz, Charles G. (Beverly) 966 South Bluebird Ln, Homestead FL 33035, 305-242-4543, Goertz@Bellsouth.net [SE] IB3, IIB1 [AC] Pastor, Homestead Menn Ch, Homestead FL; Urban Minister Director, Southeast Menn Conf, Miami FL

Goertzen, Kevin T. (Denise F.) PO Box 368, Goessel KS

67053, goesselchurch@juno.com [WDC] IIB1 [AC]
Pastor, Goessel Menn Ch, Goessel KS
Goldfus, Ross H. (Ruth) 580 Hiview Dr, Lititz PA 17543,
717-664-4613, rgoldfus@aol.com [ACC] [RE]
Gonzalez, Juan (Mercedes) 625 Harrison St, Lancaster
PA 17602, 717-396-0346 [LAN] IIB1 [AC] Pastor, El
Buen Pastor, Lancaster PA
Good, Alice, 215 Wile Ave, Souderton PA 18964, 215-
723-9094 [FRC] IIC [AC]
Good, Charles E. (Susie) 1001 E Oregon Rd #K13, Lititz
PA 17543-9205, 717-687-6714 [LAN] [RE]
Good, Charles S. (Mary Jane) 1001 E Oregon Rd, Lititz
PA 17543 [ACC] [RE]
Good, Clair Bennett (Geraldine) 992 Dry Tavern Rd,
Denver PA 17517, 717-445-4107 [LAN] IIB1 [AC]
Pastor, Churchtown Menn Ch, East Earl PA
Good, Clair E. (Beth) RR 1 Box 71, Canton PA 17724,
717-673-8153 [LAN] IIB3b [AC]
Good, Claude, 215 Wile Ave, Souderton PA 18964, 215-
723-0904 [FRC] [RE]
Good, Daniel D. (Lois) 1334 N 14th St, Reading PA
19604-1936, 610-375-0208, dan.lois@juno.com [LAN]
IIB2 [AC] Associate Pastor, Alsace Christian Fell, Temple
PA
Good, Dennis M. (Dorcas Lady) PO Box 118, North
Newton KS 67117-0118, 316-284-2648,
dmgood@southwind.com [WDC] IIB3c [AC]
Good, Donald W., 3713 Nolt Rd, Landisville PA 17538,
717-898-2500 [LAN] IIB2 [AC]
Good, E. Richard (Wanda) 317 Weavers Rd,
Harrisonburg VA 22802, 540-434-4086 [VA] [RE]
Good, Ethan Joseph (Shirley [Harman]) 4651 Hwy 490,
Preston MS 39341-9345, 662-726-5577 [GS] IIB1 [AC]
Retiring Pastor, Nanih Waiya Indian Menn Ch,
Philadelphia MS
Good, Harley D. (Irene) 1813 Park Rd, Harrisonburg VA
22802, 540-434-0896 [VA] IIB3a [AC]
Good, Harold, 6135 Billymack Rd, Elida OH 45807, 419-
339-1906 [OH] [RE]
Good, Harry S. (Alta Mae) 336 W Broad St, New Holland
PA 17557-1239, 717-354-2219 [LAN] [RE]
Good, Jacob H. (Elaine) 424 S 7th St, Reading PA 19602,
610-375-9223 [LAN] [RE]
Good, John W. (Phoebe) 1415 Lime Valley Rd, Lancaster
PA 17602-1815, 717-687-6360, pgood@desupernet.net
[LAN] III [AC] Ordained Deacon, Strasburg Menn Ch,
Strasburg PA
Good, Linford L. (Velma) 1690 Wheatland School Rd,
Lancaster PA 17602, 717-687-0704, lllgood@aol.com
[LAN] IIA [AC] Licensed Deacon, Mellinger Menn Ch,
Lancaster PA
Good, Linford W. (Terri) 424 Park Ave, Milton PA 17847,
717-742-4485, lgood@ptd.net [LAN] IB3 [AC]
Bishop/Overseer, LAN—Williamsport-Milton, PA
Good, Melvin S. (Irene) RR 1 Box 71, Canton PA 17724,
717-673-8153 [LAN] IIC [AC] Chaplain, Prison Ministry,
PA
Good, Merlin, 3535 N Grubb Rd, Elida OH 45807, 419-
339-1998 [OH] [RE]
Good, Randy (Carolyn) RR 1 Box 218, Woodstock VT
05091, 802-457-5838, jrccgood@valley.net [FRC] IIA
[AC] Pastor, Taftsville Chapel Menn Fell, Taftsville VT
Good, Roy F. (Kathryn Louise) 16 Grandview Dr,
Harrisonburg VA 22802, 540-433-8584 [VA] [AC]

Associate Pastor, Gospel Hill Menn Ch, Harrisonburg VA
Good, Stephen J. (Carol) 347 S 7th St, Reading PA
19602-2442, 610-374-8590, scjjgood@juno.com [LAN]
IIC [AC] Licensed Deacon, South Seventh Street Menn
Ch, Reading PA
Good, Steven Joe (Pamela Liby) 9835 N 7th St, Phoenix
AZ 85020, 602-997-7171 [CP] IIB1 [AC] Pastor,
Sunnyslope Menn Ch, Phoenix AZ
Good, Warren S., 1884 Division Hwy, Ephrata PA 17522-
9803, 717-354-9113 [LAN] [RE]
Good, Wilmer Z. (Barbara) 6010 Carters Ln, Riverdale
MD 20737, 301-864-8798 [LAN] IIB2 [AC] Associate
Pastor, Capital Christian Fell, Laurel MD
Good Jr, Lewis C. (Helen) 9326 Dubarry Ave, Lanham
MD 20706-3108, 301-577-3554, lewgood@
pressroom.com [LAN] IB3 [AC] Bishop/Overseer, Capital
Christian Fell (Wash.-Baltimore), Laurel MD
Goossen, Henry William (Edna Marie) Box 372, North
Newton KS 67117-0372, 316-283-5963 [WDC] [RE]
Goossen, Paul Franz, 4209 V St, Homestead IA 52236,
319-622-6410 [CDC] [RE]
Gordon, Andrew T (Randi) 9 Jefferson Ave, Marlton NJ
08053, 609-988-9419, atgoodnews@aol.com [LAN]
IIB1 [AC] Pastor, Crossroads Christian Community,
Marlton NJ
Gordon, Winston E. (Ingrid) 245 Pixlee Pl, Bridgeport CT
06610, 203-335-1548 [LAN] IIC [AC] Associate Pastor,
Gospel Light Community Ch, Bridgeport CT
Gorno, Timothy M. (Phyllis) 13 Silver Creek Rd, Lititz PA
17543, 717-738-2918 [LAN] [AW]
Goshow, Henry, 207 W Summit St Apt 180, Souderton
PA 18964, 215-721-3011 [FRC] [RE]
Graber, Dan (Rose Elaine [Waltner]) 3069 Mill Rd,
Norristown PA 19403, danrose70s@aol.com [FRC] IIB1
[AC] Pastor, Methacton Menn Ch, Norristown PA
Graber, Daniel J. (Mary M.) 29129 Johnston Rd Apt
2619, Dade City FL 33523-6128, 352-588-4865 [CDC]
[RE] Interim Pastor, Deep Run West Menn Ch, Perkasie
PA
Graber, David J., PO Box 117, Montgomery IN 47558,
812-486-3451 [IM] [RE]
Graber, Donovan Roy (Jill Rae) 724 Park Ln, RR 1, Box
172, Moundridge KS 67107, 620-345-6424 [WDC]
[AW]
Graber, Eddie, RR 3 Box 317, Loogootee IN 47553, 812-
636-4181 [IM] IIB1 [AC] Pastor, Berea Menn Ch,
Loogootee IN
Graber, Glen D., 1300 Greencroft Dr #67, Goshen IN
46527, 574-537-3527 [CDC] [RE]
Graber, Harold (Gladys C.) 805 W 17th, Newton KS
67114, 316-283-7516 [WDC] [RE]
Graber, Larry E. (Bonnie) 1653 Lestercove, Springdale
AR 72764, 501-631-3904 [SC] III [AC] Minister, Rogers
Menn/Ch of the Brethren, Pea Ridge AR
Graber, Melvin Lynn, 311 Wollmann St, Box 894,
Moundridge KS 67107 [WDC] IIC [AC]
Graber, Rose Elaine (Waltner) (Dan) 3069 Mill Rd,
Norristown PA 19403, 610-222-3973,
danrose70s@aol.com [EDC] IIB1 [AC] Pastor, Upper
Milford Menn Ch, Zionsville PA
Grace, Donald R., 102 N Railroad St, Martinsburg PA
16662-1328 [EDC] [RE]
Graham, Reginald C. (Andrea Lynette) 822 E 14th St,
Chester PA 19013 [LAN] III [AC] Ordained Deacon, Way

MINISTERS

6

Through Christ, Chester PA

Gray, Albert (June) RD 2 Box 110, Mifflintown PA 17059, 717-436-8585, lighthouse@tricountyi.net [EDC] IIC [AC] Pastor, Cornerstone Community Menn Ch, Mifflintown PA

Gray, John, 20191 Kentville Rd, Tiskilwa IL 61368, 815-646-4620, grayone74@hotmail.com [IL] IIB2 [AC] Associate Pastor, Willow Springs Menn Ch, Tiskilwa IL

Graybill, Carl E. (Sharon) HC 63 Box 38, Cocolamus PA 17014, 717-694-3725 [LAN] [AW]

Graybill, Douglas C. (Leona) RR 1 Box 178A, Granville Summit PA 16926, 570-673-3418, dgraybil@sosbbs.com [LAN] IIB1 [AC] Pastor, Canton Menn Ch, Canton PA

Graybill, Earl R. (Miriam) 5841 Zook Ln, Gap PA 17527-9650 [LAN] [RE]

Graybill, J. Lester (Eileen) 324 Hilltop Dr, Leola PA 17540, 717-656-8267, lgraybil@mindspring.com [ACC] IIB3a [AC] Chaplain, Garden Spot Retirement Community, New Holland PA

Greaser, Lawrence, 1411-7 Kentfield Way, Goshen IN 46526, 574-534-3934 [IM] [RE]

Green, Stanley W., 203 Mount Vernon Dr, Goshen IN 46526, 574-533-4251 [IM] IIB3c [AC] Executive Director, Mennonite Mission Network, Elkhart IN

Green, Tim (Karen) 2502 Ridgedale Rd, Harrisonburg VA 22801, 540-433-1566 [VA] IIB2 [AC] Pastor, New Beginnings Ch, Bridgewater VA

Greene, William F. (Cynthia) 475 Northglen Ln, Harrisonburg VA 22802, 540-434-5696 [VA] IIB1 [AC] Pastor, Crossroads Menn Ch, Broadway VA

Greer, Doris J., 5400 S 11th Ave, Los Angeles CA 90043, 323-292-8503, faithnlovecc@aol.com [PSW] IIB1 [AC] Senior Pastor, Faith and Love Christian Center, Los Angeles CA

Greiser, David (Anita Nussbaum) 116 W Chestnut St, Souderton PA 18964, 215-723-7490 [FRC] IIB1 [AC] Co-Pastor, Souderton Menn Ch, Souderton PA

Grimsrud, Theodore Glenn (Kathleen Temple) 1150 Lincolndale Dr, Harrisonburg VA 22801 [VA] IIB3d [AC]

Groff, Clarence V., 5026 Strasburg Rd, Kinzers PA 17535, 717-442-4385 [LAN] [RE]

Groff, Dwight L., 35 S Kinzer Rd, Kinzers PA 17535, 717-442-4901 [LAN] IIA [AC] Associate Pastor, Kinzer Menn Ch, Kinzers PA

Groff, Elias H. (Elizabeth) 1520 Harrisburg Pike, Lancaster PA 17601, 717-295-7464 [LAN] [RE]

Groff, Galen (Phyllis) Fray Bartolome de Las Casas, Alta Verapaz 16015, Guatemala, gpgroff@ns.intelnet.net.gt [LAN] IIC [AC] Minister, EMM, Alta Verapaz Guatemala

Groff, Gwendolyn M. (Robert) Box 145, Bridgewater VT 05035, 802-672-2140, bethanym@sover.net [FRC] IIB1 [AC] Pastor, Bethany Menn Ch, Bridgewater Corners VT

Groff, J. Wesley (Wanda) RR1 Box 131-G, Mt Pleasant Mills PA 17853, 570-539-2575 [LAN] IIB2 [AC] Pastor, Susquehanna Menn Ch, Mt Pleasant Mills PA

Groff, Leonard L. (Anna Mary) 756 Bellevue Ave, Gap PA 17527, 717-442-8394, lgroff1460@earthlink.net [LAN] IIB1 [AC] Pastor, Coatesville Menn Ch, Coatesville PA

Groff, Philip M. (Sharon) 1640 S Cocalico Rd, Denver PA 17517, 717-336-0198 [LAN] IIC [AC] Martindale District - Youth Pastor,

Groff, Weyburn W., 1432 Bradford Ct, Goshen IN

46528-5052, 574-533-8554 [IM] [RE]

Groh, David (Mary) PO Box 55, Kalona IA 52247, 319-656-5221 [CP] [RE]

Grosh, Jeffrey A. (Christine Ann) 52 Main St, Yorkanna PA 17402, 717-755-8756, jcgrosh@aol.com [LAN] IIB3 [AC] Pastor, Stony Brook Menn Ch, Yorkanna PA

Grove, Mary (Stan) 20063 CR 46, New Paris IN 46553-9210, 574-831-2266, stanng@goshen.edu [IM] IIC [AC] Chaplain, Greencroft, Inc, Goshen IN

Guengerich, Owen, PO Box 198, Springs PA 15562, 814-662-2884 [ALL] [RE]

Guengerich, Ronald D., 1100 Lindau St, Archbold OH 43502, 419-446-1002, rgueng1@bnnorth.net [OH] IIB1 [AC] Pastor, Zion Menn Ch, Archbold OH

Guengerich, Vernard E. (Florence) 25231 SR 119, Goshen IN 46526, 574-862-2521 [IM] IIB2 [AC] Associate Pastor, Holdeman Menn Ch, Wakarusa IN

Guete, Marco A. (Sandra L.) 815 Parkside Dr, Cedar Hill TX 75104-3147, 972-293-2761, marcoguete@sbcglobal.net [WDC] IB2 [AC] Associate Conference Minister, Western District Conference, Dallas TX

Gullman, David J. (Deborah) 2336 Mayland Rd, Broadway VA 22815, 540-896-7529, gullman4@juno.com [VA] IIB3a [AC]

Gundy, James Ralph (Marjorie Ann) Box 227, Burrton KS 67020-0237, 620-463-3415 [WDC] IIB1 [AC] Pastor, Burrton Menn Ch, Burrton KS

Gustafson-Zook, Gwen Ann (Les) 1608 S 8th St, Goshen IN 46526-4704, 574-534-1173, gustazook@aol.com [CDC, IM] IIB1 [AC] Pastor, Faith Menn Ch, Goshen IN

Gutierrez, Luis (Nancy Salazar) Tio Av: Jorge Chavez M-1-1, san francisco 138 interior, Cusco 708, Peru, 239905, luisgu@latinmail.com [LAN] IIA [AC]

Guyton, Cynthia A. (Glen) 223 Bryant Dr, Hampton VA 23663, 757-722-0238 [VA] IIA [AC]

Guyton, Glen A. (Cynthia) 223 Bryant Dr, Hampton VA 23663, 757-722-0238 [VA] IIA [AC]

Guzman, Byron (Melida) 604 Monroe Dr, Harleysville PA 19438, 215-368-4836, byme1@juno.com [EDC] [AW]

H

Haar, Randall, 3639 W Monte Cristo Ave, Phoenix AZ 85023, 602-843-4545 [PSW] IIA [AC]

Haarer, Charles, 605 Woodbridge Ct, Middlebury IN 46540, 574-825-5339 [IM] [RE]

Haarer, Lowell W. (Miriam) 8997 Mt Zion Rd, Linville VA 22834, 540-833-4753, lowellhaarer@juno.com [VA] IIB1 [AC] Pastor, Zion Hill Menn Ch, Singers Glen VA

Haarer, Sylvester R., 0905 N 850 W, Shipshewana IN 46565, 260-768-4546 [IM] [RE]

Haarer, Verlin (Doris) 16901 Hand Rd, Huntertown IN 46748, 260-637-2309, dove9@juno.com [IM] IIB1 [AC] Pastor, Carroll Community Worship Center, Ft Wayne IN

Habegger, David Luther (LaVeta Loganbill) 6929 Hillsboro Ct, Ft Wayne IN 46835-1818, 260-486-4291, DLHabegger@aol.com [CDC] [RE]

Habegger, Howard J., 613 S Main, Hesston KS 67062, 620-327-5092 [CDC] [RE]

Habegger, Loris A. (Evelyn J.) Box 250, North Newton KS 67117-0250, 316-283-7498 [WDC] [RE]

Hackman, Arthur K., 207 W Summit St Apt A227, Souderton PA 18964, 215-723-1759 [FRC] [RE]

Hackman, Floyd, 691 Souder Rd, Souderton PA 18964, 215-723-6621 [FRC] [RE]

Haines, Joseph M. (Elaine) 563 Broxton Ct, Harleysville PA 19438, 215-631-9949, pastorjoe@enter.net [EDC] IIB1 [AC] Pastor, Zion Menn Ch, Souderton PA

Hall, David L. (Carol A.) 1322 Edison St NW, Hartville OH 44632, 330-877-4385 [OH] IIB1 [AC] Pastor, Hartville Menn Ch, Hartville OH

Hall, Michael D. (Marsha Hall) 15 East Third St, Quarryville PA 17566, 717-786-2934 [ACC] IIA [AC] Pastor, Quarryville Community Fell, Quarryville PA

Hamilton, Eldon L. (Jesse) 1280 Greystone St, Harrisonburg VA 22802, 540-434-0823 [VA] [RE]

Hampton, Timothy S. (Chris) 9506 Highlander Cr, Walkersville MD 21793, timh98@juno.com [FRK] IIC [AC] Pastor, Faith Community Menn Ch, Walkersville MD

Hamsher, Bruce Allen (Jocelyn Marie) General Delivery, Berlin OH 44610-9999, 330-893-2320, brujoc@aol.com [OH] IIB2 [AC] Associate Pastor, Berlin Menn Ch, Berlin OH

Hamsher, Don, 169 N Walnut, Davidsville PA 15928, 814-479-2702, hamsher@valkyrie.net [ALL] IIB1 [AC] Pastor, Kaufman Menn Ch, Davidsville PA

Hamsher, Matthew W. (Kristina Zendt Hamsher) 850 Geneva St, Sugarcreek OH 44681, 330-852-1086 [OH] IIB2 [AC] Associate Pastor, Walnut Creek Menn Ch, Walnut Creek OH

Handojo, Virgo, 1632 Locust St, Pasadena CA 91106, 626-564-9869, vhandojo@calbaptist.edu [PSW] IIB1 [AC] Pastor, Jemaat Kristen Indonesia Anugrah, Pasadena CA

Handrich, Bruce, PO Box 25, Germfask MI 49836, 906-586-9738 [IM] [RE]

Handrich, Ellsworth, PO Box 215, Fairview MI 48621, 517-848-2322 [IM] [RE]

Handrich, Willard D., PO Box 271, Grand Marais MI 49839, 906-494-2547 [IM] [RE]

Hang, Tong, 7827 Rimbley Rd, Woodbury, MN 55125, 651-501-0836 [CP] IIB1 [AC] Pastor, United Hmong Menn Ch, St Paul MN

Hange, Maren Tyedmers (Roy) 102 Linda Ct, Charlottesville VA 22901, 434-296-5289, pastorcmc@earthlink.net [VA] IIB1 [AC] Co-Pastor, Charlottesville Menn Ch, Charlottesville VA

Hange, Roy (Maren Tyedmers Hange) 102 Linda Ct, Charlottesville VA 22901, 434-296-5289, pastorcmc@earthlink.net [VA] IIB1 [AC] Co-Pastor, Charlottesville Menn Ch, Charlottesville VA

Hanger, T. Kirk, Aptdo Postal 39-105, Aeropuerto Internacional, Mexico City 15621, Mexico [FRC] IIB3b [AC]

Hannanoto, Buddy, 12051 Havelock Ave, Los Angeles CA 90230, 626-579-4802 [PSW] IIA [AC] Pastor, Indonesian Menn Ch, Los Angeles CA

Harder, Keith R. (Judy) 951 190th, Hillsboro KS 67063-8019, 620-947-2510 [WDC] IB1 [AC] Co-Director, Office of Ministerial Leadership, Mennonite Church USA, Newton KS

Harder, Leland David (Bertha F.) PO Box 363, North Newton KS 67117-0363, 316-283-0186 [WDC] [RE]

Harder, Lois, 868 Vandalia Rd, Morgantown WV 26505, 304-328-5510 [ALL] IIB3a [AC]

Harder, Lois Marie (Thomas Lee) 654 S Chautauqua,

Wichita KS 67211, 316-687-4151, lamcpastor2@prodigy.net [WDC] IIB1 [AC] Co-Pastor, Lorraine Avenue Menn Ch, Wichita KS

Harder, Milton J. (Katharine Moyer Harder) Rt 1, Box 66, Deer Creek OK 74636, 580-267-3544 [WDC] [RE]

Harder, Thomas L. (Lois M.) 654 S Chautauqua, Wichita KS 67211, lamcpastor@prodigy.net [WDC] IIB1 [AC] Co-Pastor, Lorraine Avenue Menn Ch, Wichita KS

Harder, Willmar Toews, 47 13th Ave, Inman KS 67546, wtharder@hotmail.com [WDC] IIA [AC] Pastor, Hoffnungsau Menn Ch, Inman KS

Harding, Dorothy, 5218 Goldcrest Trace, Stone Mountain GA 30088 [SE] IIC [AC] Minister of Urban Evangelism, Berea Menn Ch, Atlanta GA

Harms, Dawn Yoder (Douglas) 226 W Main St, Ephrata PA 17522, 717-733-4522, dyharms@akronmench.org [ACC] IIB2 [AC] Pastor, Akron Menn Ch, Akron PA

Harnish, John Henry (Judy) 3731 Blue Rock Rd, Washington Boro PA 17582, 717-872-4450, jhh1346@aol.com [LAN] III [AC] Ordained Deacon, Millersville Menn Ch, Millersville PA

Harnish, Paul K. (Anna) 2000 Franklin Rd, Washington Boro PA 17582, 717-684-8691 [LAN] [RE]

Harnish, Robert A. (Marian N.) 2179 Beaver Valley Pike, New Providence PA 17560-9605, 717-872-6704, bobharnish@prodigy.net [LAN] IIB1 [AC] Pastor, New Providence Menn Ch, New Providence PA

Harnish, Robert Brunk (Carol) 1609 Carnavon Pl, Colorado Springs CO 80919, 719-277-7086 [RM] [AW]

Harnish, Robert L. (Ruth) 611 E Center St, Eureka IL 61530, 309-467-4452, Bob@Maple-Lawn.com [IL] IIB1, IIB3a [AC] Director of Pastoral Care, Maple Lawn Homes, Eureka IL

Harnish, Sr, John H. (Ruth) 156 Victoria Rd, Millersville PA 17551-9762, 717-872-8680 [LAN] [RE]

Harnly, Lester M. (Mary) 7 Central Pk Dr Ste 110, Manheim PA 17545, 717-665-3104 [LAN] [RE]

Harris, Doug, 404 LaVista, Dodge City KS 67054, 620-846-2663, faithmenno@juno.com [SC, WDC] IIA [AC] Pastor, Faith Menn Ch, Dodge City KS

Harrison, Daniel, Leadership Development Internation, PO Box 4152, Evergreen CO 80437 [IM] IIB3b [AC] President, Leadership Development International, PO Box 4152 CO

Hartman, Darwin, 6035 Poling Rd, Elida OH 45807-9492 [OH] [AW]

Hartman, Gene A. (Cynthia (Cindy) A.) Gene Hartman, PO Box 502, Topeka IN 46573, 260-593-3726, genhart@maplenet.net [IM] IIA [AC] Pastor, Emma Menn Ch, Topeka IN

Hartman, Peter E. (Marilyn) 706 Wheat Ln, Hesston KS 67062 [SC] [RE]

Hartman, Wilmer J. (Lois) 1013 Olds Ln, Archbold OH 43502, 419-445-6329, whartman@juno.com [OH] IIB1 [AC] Interim Pastor, Salem Menn Ch, Waldron MI

Hartshorn, C. Leo (Iris DeLeon) 202 S Ann St, Lancaster PA 17602, 717-391-6512, cleohart@aol.com [EDC] IIB3c [AC] Minister of Peace and Justice, Mennonite Mission Network, Elkhart IN

Hartshorn, Iris DeLeon (Leo) 202 S Ann, Lancaster PA 17602, 717-391-6512, idh@mccus.org [EDC] IIB3c [AC] Director of Peace & Justice Ministries, MCC, US, Akron PA

Hartwell, Bill, 3105 Maplewood Blvd No 73, Omaha NE

MINISTERS

6

68134, 402-573-5601 [CP] IIB3a [AC] Chaplain, Nebraska Prisons, Omaha NE

Hartzler, Robert Lee (Phyllis Jean [Freyenberger]) 605 Northridge Ct, Wayland IA 52654, 319-256-4494, rhartz@farmtel.net [CP] IIB1 [AC] Interim Pastor, Wellman Menn Ch, Wellman IA

Harwood, Bret (Leonora) 34 Cottage Ave, Lancaster PA 17602-3212, 717-295-4555, mednetbrett@juno.com [LAN] IIC [AC]

Haryono, Petrus, 7707 White Oak Ave, Reseda CA 91335, 818-342-6777 [PSW] IIB1 [AC] Pastor, Jemaat Kristen Indonesia Maranatha, Reseda CA

Hatfield, Maria (Jason) 819 West Russell St, Peoria IL 61606, 309676-2772, pastoraMariaH@aol.com [CDC, IL] IIA [AC] Pastor, Living Love Ministries, Peoria IL

Hathaway, Melvin R. (Dottie B.) 3935 Allentown Rd, Elida OH 45807, 419-331-4971, hathaway@wcoil.com [OH] IIB1 [AC] Pastor, Salem Menn Ch, Elida OH

Hatter, William W. (Becky) 79 Hickory Hunt Ln, Lyndhurst VA 22952, 540-943-9697 [VA] [AW]

Hauder, Larry (Rebecca S.) 2102 N 20th St, Boise ID 83702-0831, 208-336-5646, lhauder@earthlink.net [PNW] IB2 [AC]

Haupert, Stephen Andrew (Phoebe) 239 Slacks Run Rd, Trout Run PA 17771, 570-995-5620, bighouse@uplink.net [LAN] IB3 [AC] Bishop/Overseer, North Penn District, PA

Hayes, Benjamin R. (Christine) RR 3 Box 221, Mifflinburg PA 17844, 570-966-9636, bhayes@sunlink.net [LAN] IIB2 [AC] Pastor, Buffalo Menn Ch, Mifflinburg PA

Heacock, Randy E. (Nancy J. [Gehman]) 2193 Winterberry Ct, Warrington PA 18976, 215-343-7099, randy.heacock@doylestownmc.org [FRC] [AC] Pastor, Doylestown Menn Ch, Doylestown PA

Headings, Richard L. (Dorothy) 2390 Meadow Ct, Harrisonburg VA 22801, 540-433-8421, richardheadings@aol.com [VA] IIB1 [AC] Pastor, Ridgeway Menn Ch, Harrisonburg VA

Headrick, Don, 2202 Chatalet Ln, Pueblo CO 81005, 717-564-0649 [RM] IIB3a [AC] Prison Chaplain, Colorado State Prison, Canon City CO

Heatwole, Edwin M. (Eileen K.) 8735 Union Springs Rd, Dayton VA 22821, 540-867-5216, eheatwole@yahoo.com [VA] IIB1 [AC] Pastor, New Beginnings Ch, Bridgewater VA

Heatwole, Steven Jay (Bonnie) PO Box 127, Springs PA 15562, 814-662-2507 [ALL] IB3, IIB1 [AC] Pastor, Springs Menn Ch, Springs PA

Hedrick, Merlin, 605 Rte 113, Sellersville PA 18960, 215-723-6878 [FRC] IIB3a [AC] Chaplain, Dock Woods Community, Lansdale PA

Hege, Nathan B. (Arlene) 655 Church St, Landisville PA 17538, 717-898-0463 [LAN] [RE]

Heimbach, Albert W. (Mary) 521 Mill Rd, Selinsgrove PA 17870, 570-374-1713 [LAN] IIB1 [AC] Pastor, Susquehanna Menn Ch, Mt Pleasant Mills PA

Heinlein, Chris (Carol) RR 2 Box 147, Mount Union PA 17066, 814-543-7269 [ALL] IIB1 [AC]

Heiser, Don J., 19093 Rock Rd, New Paris IN 46553, 574-831-3427 [CDC] [RE]

Heisey, Dean (Tacy) 13060 Jackson Rd, Mishawaka IN 46544, 574-254-1554 [IM] IIB3c [AC] Chaplain, Memorial Hospital, South Bend IN; Director, New

Ministry Formation, Mennonite Church USA, Elkhart IN

Heistand, Gerald M., 329 Trail Rd S, Elizabethtown PA 17022, 717-367-8587, g-heistand@juno.com [LAN] IIB1 [AC] Pastor, Risser Menn Ch, Elizabethtown PA

Heller, Fred G. (Julie) 250 Keener Rd, Lititz PA 17543-9604, 717-626-2649 [LAN] IIB1 [AC] Associate Pastor, Hammer Creek Menn Ch, Lititz PA

Heller, Parke M. (Charity) 228 Keener Rd, Lititz PA 17543, 717-626-5146 [LAN] [RE]

Helmuth, Carl (Lanadell) RR 1 Box 2740, Adair OK 74330, 918-785-2160 [SC] IIB1 [AC] Pastor, Oak Grove Menn Ch, Adair OK

Helmuth, David (Naomi) 1118 S 7th St, Goshen IN 46526, 574-534-2576, helmuthdavid@hotmail.com [CDC, IM] IB3 [AC] Overseer for Iglesia Menonita del Buen Pastor, Goshen IN

Helmuth, Noah B. (Edna) 711 14th St, Kalona IA 52247, 319-656-4467 [CP] [RE]

Helton Jr, Ova, 8753 Daly Rd, Cincinnati OH 45231, 513-522-1882, ohelton@fuse.net [OH] IIB1 [AC] Pastor, Springdale Chapel, Cincinnati OH

Henderson, Eric B. (Marilyn) 52 Grandview Dr, Harrisonburg VA 22802, 540-433-3730 [LAN] [AC] Interim Pastor, Holly Grove Menn Ch, Westover MD

Henderson, Richard, 16205 Glendale Ave, Cleveland OH 44128, 216-561-0637 [OH] IIC [AC]

Henderson, Scott Anthony (Melissa Dawne) 212 Faith St, Jefferson OR 97352, 541-327-3554, pastorscott@plainview.org [PNW] IIA [AC] Youth Pastor, Plainview Menn Ch, Albany OR

Hendricks, Melvin E., Box 197, Carlock IL 61725, 309-376-7281 [CDC] [RE]

Hernandez, Martha (Ramiro) 29725 SW Rose Ln #139, Wilsonville OR 97070, 503-682-9116 [PNW] IIA [AW]

Hernandez, Ramiro (Martha Corpus) 29725 SW Rose Ln, Apt 139, Wilsonville OR 97070, 503-682-9116 [PNW] IIB1 [AC] Hispanic Ministries Pastor, Calvary Menn Ch, Aurora OR

Hernández Jr, José R. (Rinna E.) 16130 SW 304 Terrace, Homestead FL 33033, 305-248-1279, Joseram@bellsouth.net [SE] IIC [AC] Associate Pastor, Homestead Menn Ch, Homestead FL

Herr, H. Eugene (Mary) 708 Normandy Rd, Newton KS 67114-1257 [IM] IIB3c [AC]

Herr, Mary (H. Eugene) 708 Normandy Rd, Newton KS 67114-1257 [IM] IIB3c [AC]

Herrera, Gerardo (Sandra) 12028 Bluhill Rd, Wheaton MD 20902, 301-933-8929 [VA] IIB2 [AC] Associate Pastor, Iglesia del Evangelio Completo Alpha y Omega, Washington DC

Herschberger, Philip J. (Janelle) 1228 Silver Spring Rd, Holtwood PA 17532, 717-284-6022, campandrews@pa.freei.net [LAN] III [AC] Ordained Deacon, Nickel Mines Menn Ch, New Providence PA

Hershberger, Cheryl, 22 Pheasant Run Rd, Hesston KS 67062-9123, 620-327-4768, cherylh@prairieinet.net [SC] IIB2 [AC] Associate Pastor, Hesston Menn Ch, Hesston KS

Hershberger, Delvin (Michele) 22411 Fireside Dr, Goshen IN 46528, 574-875-7852, Dmhersh@aol.com [SC] [AC]

Hershberger, Duane (Ruth Ann) 403 E Third St, Boyertown PA 19512, 610-367-2879, DHershberger@hfhi.org [FRC] IIA [AC] Pastor, Shalom

Christian Fell, Pennsburg PA

Hershberger, Ernest, PO Box 217, Berlin OH 44610, 330-893-2098 [OH] IIB1 [AC] Pastor, Berlin Menn Ch, Berlin OH

Hershberger, Gregory L. (Lois I.) 524 S 16th St, Columbia PA 17512, 717-684-5935, ghershberg@aol.com [LAN] IIB1 [AC] Pastor, Columbia Menn Ch, Columbia PA

Hershberger, James L., 5647 Wengers Mill Rd, Linville VA 22834, 540-833-8033, hershbergl@aol.com [VA] IIB1 [AC] Pastor, Beldor Menn Ch, Linville VA

Hershberger, John K., 1706 S 13th St, Goshen IN 46526, 574-533-9982 [IM] IIB3a [AC] Counselor, Oaklawn, Inc, Goshen IN

Hershberger, Marc (Jennifer) 1472 260th St, Mount Pleasant IA 52641, 319-986-6162 [CP] IIB1 [AC] Pastor, Pleasant View Menn Ch, Mount Pleasant IA

Hershberger, Mervin (Judith) 3711 Metropolitan Ave, Kansas City KS 66106, 913-677-0249 [SC] IIB1 [AC] Pastor, Argentine Menn Ch, Kansas City KS

Hershberger, Virgil S. (Margaret) 1549 N Abbe Rd Box 100, Fairview MI 48621, 517-848-2417 [IM] [RE]

Hershey, Carl E. (Doris) 25 Main St, Landisville PA 17538, 717-898-1737, dhersh48@aol.com [LAN] IIB1 [AC] Pastor, Chestnut Hill Menn Ch, Columbia PA

Hershey, Clair J. (Dorothy) 2090 Jarvis Rd, Lancaster PA 17601, 717-393-7077 [LAN] [RE]

Hershey, Glenn C. (Helen) 121A N New Holland Rd, Gordonville PA 17529, 717-354-9951, glennhelen@juno.com [LAN] [AW]

Hershey, J. Kenneth (Joanne Campbell Hershey) 24 Hawthorne Cr, Willow Street PA 17584, 717-284-3841 [LAN] IIB2 [AC] Associate Pastor, New Providence Menn Ch, New Providence PA

Hershey, J. Robert (Eva) 17500 Lime Stone Rd, Oxford PA 19363, 610-932-5691 [ACC] [RE]

Hershey, John O. (Dorothy) 1001 E Oregon Rd, Lititz PA 17543 [LAN] [RE]

Hershey, Leonard D., 772 Mount Eaton Rd, Wadsworth OH 44281, 330-334-0966 [OH] [RE]

Hershey, Lester T., PO Box 1160, Fort Ashby WV 26719, 304-298-4452 [ALL] IIB1 [AC] Associate Pastor, Pinto Menn Ch, Pinto MD

Hershey, Melvin L. (Anna) 152 Iris Dr, Lancaster PA 17602, 717-392-1558 [LAN] [RE]

Hershey, Nelson H. (Thelma) 420 Rohrer Rd, Mountville PA 17554-1818, 717-285-5030 [LAN] III [AC] Ordained Deacon, Rohrerstown Menn Ch, Lancaster PA

Hershey, Noah L. (Alta Mary Metzler Hershey) 8875 N Moscow Rd, Parkesburg PA 19365-9802, 717-442-4629 [LAN] [RE]

Hershey, Phoebe, 27877 Old Valley Pike, Toms Brook VA 22660, 540-436-9481 [VA] IIB3a [AC]

Hershey, Sanford E. (Mae) 3728 Ridge Rd, Gordonville PA 17529, 717-768-8602 [LAN] [RE]

Hershey, William E. (Diane) 26 Ferncrest Rd, Quarryville PA 17566, 717-548-3757 [LAN] IIC [AC] Associate Pastor, Mechanic Grove Menn Ch, Peach Bottom PA

Hertzler, Daniel (Mary) RR 1 Box 576, Scottdale PA 15683, 724-887-7598 [ALL] IB3 [AC]

Hertzler, Joseph, 2731 Pleasant Plain Ave, Elkhart IN 46517, 574-293-8358 [IM] [RE]

Hess, Donald W. (Diane) 27 Cherokee Rd, Willow Street PA 17584, 717-464-4506, ddhess71@juno.com [LAN]

IIC, III [AC] Licensed Deacon, New Danville Menn Ch, Lancaster PA

Hess, Ernest M. (Lois) 1709 Newport Dr, Lancaster PA 17602-1309, 717-464-3505, elhess@infi.net [LAN] IB3 [AC] Bishop/Overseer, LMC - New Danville District, PA

Hess, J. Brent (Julie) 1068 Central Manor Rd, Lancaster PA 17603-9484, brenthess@onemain.com [LAN] IIB1 [AC] Associate Pastor of Youth, Mountville Menn Ch, Mountville PA

Hess, James R. (Beatrice) 77 Highland Dr, Lancaster PA 17602, 717-393-7348 [LAN] [RE]

Hess, James R. (Helen Keener Hess) 445 Yeagley Rd, Meyerstown PA 17067-1786, 717-933-8470, helenjimhess@juno.com [LAN] [RE]

Hess, John C. (Anna Mary) 5834 Country Rd 2B, Belmont NY 14813, 716-268-7415 [LAN] III [AC] Ordained Deacon, Kossuth Community Chapel, Bolivar NY

Hess, Mahlon M. (Mary Harnish Hess) 1001 E Oregon Rd, Lititz PA 17543, 717-509-5883, mahlonhess@juno.com [LAN] [RE]

Hess, Marshall (Karen) 2317 Conley Ln, Lancaster PA 17603, 717-872-9749 [LAN] IIC, III [AC] Licensed Deacon, New Danville Menn Ch, Lancaster PA

Hess, Thomas A. (Janice) 9310 Old 22, Bethel PA 19507, 717-933-8434, phess@ptd.net [LAN] IIB1 [AC] Pastor, Schubert Menn Ch, Bethel PA

Heusinkveld, David Scott (Gail Patricia) PO Box 19, Wakarusa IN 46573, 574-862-1413, dagaheu@earthlink.net [IM] IIB1 [AC] Pastor, Holdeman Menn Ch, Wakarusa IN

Heyerly, John Ernest (Jeanne) 24955 Church St, Chenoa IL 61726-9391, 309-747-3256, heyerly@gridcom.net [CDC] IIB1 [AC] Pastor, Meadows Menn Ch, Chenoa IL

Hicks, Richard Douglas (Elaine K.) 1109 Springfield Rd, East Peoria IL 61611, 309-694-4035, doug@maple-lawn.com [IL] IIC [AC] Pastor, Maple Lawn Fell, Eureka IL

Hickson, Mark C. (Deanna) 625 Walnut St, Coatesville PA 19320, 610-383-1921 [LAN] IIA [AC] Associate Pastor, Coatesville Menn Ch, Coatesville PA

Higgins, William S., 19510 NE Glisan, Portland OR 97230, 503-667-9115, peacemennonite@juno.com [PNW] IIB1 [AC] Pastor, Peace Menn Ch, Portland OR

High, Jeffery L. (Janet) 705 Hopeland Rd, PO Box 142, Hopeland PA 17533, 717-733-4390, jhigh5@juno.com [LAN] IIA [AC] Leadership Team, Ephrata Menn Ch, Ephrata PA

High, Levi G. (Elizabeth) 3454 Bimini St, Sarasota FL 34239-7421 [LAN] [RE]

High Jr, David F. (Rebecca) 995 N Penryn Rd, Manheim PA 17545-8515, 717-665-7967 [LAN] IIC [AC] Licensed Deacon, Erb Menn Ch, Lititz PA

Himes, Kevin S. (Jennifer Janene) 982 Marilyn Dr, Wooster OH 44691, 330-262-8369, himesks@hotmail.com [CDC] IIA [AC] Minister of Music, Salem Menn Ch, Kidron OH

Hinojosa, Conrado (Esther) 2408 Fern Dr, San Juan TX 78589-3879, conrado_hinojosa@hotmail.com [SC] IB3 [AC] Pastor, Iglesia Menonita Buenas Nuevas, San Juan TX

Hochstedler, Jarvis (Ruby Lee) 505 Fraiser Ave, PO Box 1, Beemer NE 68716 [CP] IIB1 [AC] Pastor, Beemer Menn Ch, Beemer NE

MINISTERS

6

Hochstedler, Kathryn J. (Wayne) 2440 Ebersole Rd, Harrisonburg VA 22802, 540-438-9454, kjhoch@aol.com [VA] IIB2 [AC] Associate Pastor, Harrisonburg Menn Ch, Harrisonburg VA

Hochstetler, David (Anna) W1216 CR B, Stone Lake WI 54876, 715-865-5403 [NC] IIB1 [AC] Pastor, Sand Lake Menn Chapel, Stone Lake WI

Hochstetler, Dean, 13684 N SR 19, Nappanee IN 46550, 574-773-4915 [IM] [RE]

Hochstetler, Emery (Audry) 755 Elliott Ct, Iowa City IA 52246, 319-628-4174 [CP] [RE]

Hochstetler, Harold, 4721 Becker Cr Se, Albany OR 97321, 541-928-9474, harold@transport.com [PNW] [RE]

Hochstetler, Lois (Wayne C.) 1324 E Vernon Ave, Normal IL 61761-3266, 309-862-9061, lohoch@mindspring.com [CDC, IL] IIB3a [AC] Pastoral Counselor, BroMenn Counseling Center, Bloomington IL

Hochstetler, M. Clair, 603 Gra-Roy Dr Apt 4, Goshen IN 46526, 574-537-1907, clairh7777@aol.com [CDC] IIB3a [AC]

Hochstetler, Noah, Box 34, Dangriga, Belize [IM] IIB3b [AC] Missionary, Mennonite Mission Agency, Belize Central America

Hochstetler, Ritch (Char) 104 E Lincoln, Hesston KS 67062, 620-327-3052 [SC] IB2 [AC] Conference Youth Minister, South Central and Western District Conferences, Newton KS

Hochstetler, Roger L. (Glennis) 6173 W 75th Ave, Arvada CO 80003, 303-403-4280 [RM] [RE]

Hochstetler, Wayne C. (Lois King Hochstetler) 1324 E Vernon Ave, Normal IL 61761-3266, 309-862-9061, ilconmin@mindspring.com [CDC, IL] IB2 [AC] Other, Conference Minister, Illinois Churches, Bloomington IL

Hockman, John Edward (Joan Lattimore Hockman) 425 S Hillcrest Ct, PO Box 297, Topeka IN 46571, 260-593-3701, hockman@kuntrynet.com [CDC] IIB1 [AC] Pastor, Topeka Menn Ch, Topeka IN

Hoffer, Jeffrey W. (Jan) 340 N George St, Millersville PA 17551, 717-872-5540, Jjhoffer@aol.com [LAN] IIB1 [AC] Pastor, First Deaf Menn Ch, Lancaster PA

Hoffman, Philip (Edna) RR 1 Box 136, Gulliver MI 49840, 906-283-3117 [IM] IIB1 [AC] Pastor, Maple Grove Menn Ch, Gulliver MI

Hoffman, Verle, 23675 River Manor Blvd, Elkhart IN 46516, 574-875-7715 [IM] [RE]

Hollinger, Aaron H. (Marian) 118 Crestview, New Holland PA 17557, 717-354-7572 [LAN] [RE]

Hollinger, Dennis P. (Mary Ann) 441 N 25th St, Camp Hill PA 17011-2102, dphmah@aol.com [LAN] [AW]

Hollinger, J. Clair (Lois) 265 E Noble St, Lititz PA 17543, 717-626-0517 [LAN] [RE]

Hollinger, L. Kenneth (Rosene) 4 Crestview Dr, Akron PA 17501, 717-859-4593 [LAN] III [AC] Ordained Deacon, Ephrata Menn Ch, Ephrata PA

Hollinger, Lloyd L. (Edith Marie) 1001 East Oregon Rd, Lititz PA 17543 [LAN] [RE]

Hollinger, Philip R. (Linda) 1732 Weaverland Rd, East Earl PA 17519, 717-445-5486 [LAN] III [AC] Ordained Deacon, Churchtown Menn Ch, East Earl PA

Holsopple, Elvin (Rena) 648 Sugar Maple Ave, Hollsopple PA 15935, 814-479-4638 [ALL] [RE]

Hoober, Kristen, 916 S 7th St, Goshen IN 46526, 574-535-0610, kristen@collegemennonite.org [IM] IIA [AC]

Youth Pastor, College Menn Ch, Goshen IN

Hooley, Daniel, 1939 3rd St SE, Canton OH 44707, 330-453-1015, danhooley@netzero.net [OH] IIB1 [AC] Pastor, First Menn Ch, Canton OH

Hooley, Gary Dean (Miriam J.) 945 Catalpa St, Sweet Home OR 97386, 541-367-5657 [PNW] IIB1 [AC] Pastor, River of Life Fell, Sweet Home OR

Hooley, William D. (Edith) 68286 CR 29, New Paris IN 46553, 574-831-4708 [IM] IB3 [AC] Overseer for Emma Menn, Topeka IN; Overseer for College Menn, Goshen IN; Overseer for Shore Menn, Shipshewana IN

Hoover, Abram N. (Jean) 710 Horseshoe Pk, Lebanon PA 17042-4842, 717-867-4495 [LAN] [RE]

Hoover, Daryl L., 2765 Den Mil Dr, Lancaster PA 17601-1713, dnjhoover@juno.com [LAN] IIC [AC] Youth Pastor, Carpenter Community Ch, Talmage PA

Hoover, Glenn A. (Virginia) 78 N Church St SW, Ephrata PA 17522, 717-859-2347, glennhoo@juno.com [LAN] IIB1 [AC] Pastor, Carpenter Community Ch, Talmage PA

Hoover, Jon R. (Jacqueline Y.) Dar Comboni, 6 Ahmed Sabri St, Zamalek, Cairo 11211, Egypt, 20-2-335-8612, jonhoover@hotmail.com [ACC] IIB3b [AC] Missionary, Eastern Mennonite Mission, Cairo Egypt

Hoover, Lester M. (Anna) 1001 E Oregon Rd, Lititz PA 17543-9205, 717-560-3506, hoover_lm@juno.com [LAN] [RE]

Hoover, Lloyd E. (Elaine) 30 Hoover Ln, Leola PA 17540, 717-656-3464 [LAN] IB3 [AC]

Hoover, Pearl Ann, 3918 Penderview Dr #432, Fairfax VA 22033-4797, 703-246-9124, nvmc1@juno.com [VA] IIB1 [AC]

Hoover, Saralee M. (Thomas R.) 915 Washington St, Reading PA 90601, 610-374-7842, smartinhoover@aol.com [LAN] IIC [AC] Associate Pastor, South Seventh Street Menn Ch, Reading PA

Hoover, Thomas R. (Saralee M.) 915 Washington St, Reading PA 19601, 610-374-7842, TomRHoover@aol.com [LAN] IIC [AC] Associate Pastor, South Seventh Street Menn Ch, Reading PA

Hopson, Helen M., 2317 S Pleasant Valley Rd #536, Austin TX 78741, 512-445-2536, hm.hopson@mailcity.com [WDC] IIB3a [AC] Associate Director, Dept. of Pastoral Care, Austin State Hospital, Austin TX

Horiuchi, Paul Tadashi, 1720 Huna Apt 205, Honolulu HI 96817, 808-521-4838 [LAN] IIA [AC] Associate Pastor, New Life Christian Fell, Honolulu HI

Horner, Carl (Stephanie R.) 29484 CR 36, Wakarusa IN 46573, 574-862-1403, carlhorner@juno.com [IM] IIB1 [AC] Pastor, Shore Menn Ch, Shipshewana IN

Horner, Glen A. (Thelma Elaine) 128 Cherry St, Orrville OH 44667, 330-682-5804, g2horner@aol.com [OH] IIB1 [AC] Interim Pastor, Orrville Menn Ch, Orrville OH

Horner, Thelma (Glen A.) 128 Cherry St, Orrville OH 44667, 330-682-5804, g2horner@aol.com [OH] IIB1 [AC] Interim Pastor, Orrville Menn Ch, Orrville OH

Horning, Alvin B. (Roberta) 2680 Conestoga Creek Rd, Morgantown PA 19543, 610-286-9851, alvin107@juno.com [ACC] IIB1 [AC] Pastor, Conestoga Menn Ch, Morgantown PA

Horning, Carl E. (Erma) 595 Wedgewood Dr, Lebanon PA 17042-8832, 717-949-3314, chorning@redrose.net [LAN] IB3 [AC] Assistant Moderator, Lancaster Mennonite Conference, Lancaster PA; Bishop/Overseer,

LMC- Lebanon District, PA

Horning, James S. (Jean) 425 W Metzler Rd, Ephrata PA 17522, 717-869-4320, jimhorning@juno.com [LAN] III [AC] Ordained Deacon, Carpenter Community Ch, Talmage PA

Horning, Kevin E. (Melanie) 219 Country Ln, Denver PA 17517, 717-445-5548, nlfephrata@juno.com [LAN] IIB2 [AC] Pastor, New Life Fell, Ephrata PA

Horning Sr., Kenneth L. (Selena) 5 St Paulia Ln, Oley PA 19547, 610-987-9833, kshorning@enter.net [ACC] IB3 [AC] Interim Pastor, Red Run Menn Ch, Denver PA

Horsch, James E. (Ruth A. Emerson) 1404 Pembroke Cr Apt 3, Goshen IN 46526, 574-534-4609, jrhorsch@Maplenet.net [ALL] IIB3c [AC]

Horst, Aaron M., Garden Spot Village Apt 338, 433 S Kinzer Ave, New Holland PA 17557, 717-355-6843 [LAN] [RE]

Horst, Aaron Z. (Loretta) 270 Panorama Dr, Denver PA 17517, 717-445-4189 [LAN] III [AC] Ordained Deacon, Lichty Menn Ch, New Holland PA

Horst, Aden, 56864 Pinecrest Dr, Elkhart IN 46516, 574-293-2199 [IM] [RE]

Horst, Eric E., 1453 West Broad St, Quakertown PA 18951, 215-538-9061, Ehorst@juno.com [FRC] IIB2 [AC]

Horst, Frank Kenneth, Box 884, Warden WA 98857, 509-349-2001 [PNW] [RE]

Horst, Glenn R. (Velma) 511 Lester St, Christiansburg VA 24073, 540-381-2486, glenn.horst@juno.com [VA] IIB1 [AC] Pastor, Christiansburg Menn Fell, Christiansburg VA

Horst, J. Alton (Dorothy) 18345 1250 N Ave, Tiskilwa IL 61368, 815-646-4363, adhorst@TheRamp.net [IL] [RE]

Horst, Jeffrey S. (Julia) 3720 Yost Rd, Gordonville PA 17529, 717-354-6075, jsjshorst@juno.com [LAN] IIB1 [AC] Pastor, Village Chapel Menn Ch, New Holland PA

Horst, Jere A. (Doreen) 4290 Black Gap Rd, Chambersburg PA 17201, 717-263-0561 [FRK] IIB2 [AC] Associate Pastor, Chambersburg Menn Ch, Chambersburg PA

Horst, John A. (Linda) 13526 Big Pool Rd, Clear Spring MD 21722, 301-842-3282, horstjlj@intrepid.net [FRK] III [AC] Ordained Deacon, Mercersburg Menn Ch, Mercersburg PA

Horst, Kenneth R. (Sue) 1037 Smith Ave, Harrisonburg VA 22802, 540-433-6584 [VA] IIB1 [AC] Pastor, Gospel Hill Menn Ch, Harrisonburg VA

Horst, Kurt M. (Elaine (Kauffman)) 327 West Race St, Somerset PA 15501, 814-445-9006, KurtHorst@Compuserve.com [ALL] IB2, IB3 [AC]

Horst, Lauren B. (Betty) 3920 Scar Hill Rd, Greencastle PA 17225, 717-597-4681 [FRK] IIB2 [AW] Associate Pastor, Bethel Community Ch, Warfordsburg PA

Horst, Laurence, 1414 Greencroft Dr # 4D, Goshen IN 46526, 574-537-4371 [IM] [RE]

Horst, Lloyd R. (Elverta.) 72 Hillside Dr, Maurertown VA 22644-0161, 540-436-8012 [VA] [RE]

Horst, Loren (Earlene) 845 College Ave, Harrisonburg VA 22802, 540-432-1038 [VA] IIB3c [AC] President, Virginia Mennonite Board of Missions, Harrisonburg VA

Horst, Luke L. (Ruth) 1001 E Oregon Rd, Lititz PA 17543-9205, 717-509-5849 [LAN] [RE]

Horst, Nevin L. (Blanche) 360 E Church St, Stevens PA 17578, 717-721-3413, bhnh@juno.com [LAN] [RE]

Horst, Reuben W. (Ruth Ann [Swartz]) 860 Farmdale Rd, Mount Joy PA 17552, 717-684-2063, reuben@horst.net [LAN] IIB1 [AC] Pastor, Marietta Community Chapel, Marietta PA

Horst, Thomas A. (Thelma) 110 Savo Ave, Lancaster PA 17601, 717-560-3999, tomhorst@peoplepc.com [LAN] IIB1 [AC] Pastor, Landis Valley Menn Ch, Lancaster PA

Horst, Thomas E. (Nancy L.) 17803 Alpine Dr, Maugansville MD 21767, 301-797-0746, thorst@juno.com [ACC] IIC [AC] Chaplain, Marketplace Ministries, Inc, Hagerstown MD

Horst, Tina Stoltzfus (Gary) 59900 CR 21, Goshen IN 46528, 574-534-1953, GTSHorst@juno.com [IM] IIC [AC] Associate Pastor, Communion Fell, Goshen IN

Hosler, Glenn D. (Judy) RR1, Box 65H, Thompsontown PA 17094-9713, geehoss@juno.com [LAN] IIA [AC] Pastor, Delaware Menn Ch, Thompsontown PA

Hostetler, Darrel M. (Marian) 627 S 3rd St, Goshen IN 46526, 574-533-9456 [IM] [RE]

Hostetler, David E. (Rose) 209 Newcomer Dr, Scottdale PA 15683-9510, 724-887-4401 [ALL] [RE]

Hostetler, Donnita J. Payne (Marvin) 1666 N Womer Ave, Wichita KS 67203, 316-943-4102 [WDC] IIB3a [AC] Chaplain, Hospice Care of Kansas, Wichita KS

Hostetler, John H., Summer Inst Linguistics, Brasilia Df, Brazil [OH] IIB3b [AC]

Hostetler, Joseph B. (Dorothy) 1001 E Oregon Rd, Lititz PA 17543-9205, 717-519-2686 [LAN] [RE]

Hostetler, Marvin E., 333 E Sassafras Apt 503, Orrville OH 44667, 330-683-5445 [OH] [RE]

Hostetler, Merle (Mary) 2041 Nathan Ln, Goshen IN 46528, 574-533-5540, merle@eastgoshenmc.org [IM] IIB1 [AC] Pastor, East Goshen Menn Ch, Goshen IN

Hostetler, Michael (Virginia A.) PO Box 11 16100, Nazareth, Israel [ALL] IIC [AC]

Hostetler, Richard, 1307 Wilson Ave, Goshen IN 46526, 574-533-7343 [IM] [RE]

Hostetler, Samuel, 1401 S 13th St, Goshen IN 46526, 574-534-4548 [IM] [RE]

Hostetler, Sheri, 2825 Kingsland, Oakland CA 94619, 415-695-2812, sherihoss@aol.com [PSW] IIA [AC] Pastor, First Menn Ch of San Francisco, San Francisco CA

Hostetler, Tony (Ada T. Troyer) 3326 SE 15th Pl, Cape Coral FL 33904, 941-549-4894 [SE] IIB2 [AC] Pastor of Visitation, Cape Christian Fell, Cape Coral FL

Hostetler, Virginia A. (Michael) PO Box 11 16100, Nazareth, Israel [ALL] IIC [AC]

Hostetter, A. Clyde (Edna) 1001 E Oregon Rd, Lititz PA 17543, 717-560-0115 [LAN] [RE]

Hostetter, Darrel M. (Sherill Louise King Hostetter) 735 Emerald Dr, Lancaster PA 17603-5823, 717-672-0655, growinjc@aol.com [LAN] IIB3c [AC] Co-Director Human Resources, Eastern Mennonite Missions, Salunga PA

Hostetter, G. Hershey (Evelyn) 220 Millwood Rd, Gap PA 17527, 717-442-4569 [LAN] IIB1 [AC]

Hostetter, Isaac E. (Elizabeth) 2540 Noble Rd, Kirkwood PA 17536, 717-529-2852 [LAN] III [AC] Ordained Deacon, Mechanic Grove Menn Ch, Peach Bottom PA

Hostetter, J. Martin (Lena) 720 Wide Hollow Rd, East Earl PA 17519, 717-445-4775 [LAN] III [AC] Ordained Deacon, Martindale Menn Ch, Ephrata PA

Hostetter, Sherill Louise King (Darrel) 735 Emerald Dr, Lancaster PA 17603, 717-672-0655,

MINISTERS

6

growinjc@aol.com [LAN] IIC [AC] Co-Director Human Resources, Eastern Mennonite Missions, Salunga PA

Hostetter Jr, B. Charles (Joyce) 4208 Hickory Lincolnton Rd, Newton NC 28658-8691 [VA] IIB2 [AC]

Howe, Allan H. (Jeanne C.) 723 Seward St, Evanston IL 60202, 708-475-5041, ahhowe@aol.com [IL] IIB3b [AC] Mission and Service Director, Illinois Mennonite Conference, Evanston IL

Hoy, Edmond (Kay) 507 Wentworth Dr, Winchester VA 22601, 540-662-1981 [VA] [AW]

Huber, Allan (Anna Mae) 724 Spruce Rd, New Holland PA 17557, 717-354-8482 [LAN] IIB3a [AC]

Huber, B. Landis (Anna) 8 Bomberger Rd, Lititz PA 17543, 717-626-6439 [LAN] [RE]

Huerta, Ismael, 201 E Mechanic St, Archbold OH 43502, 419-446-7458 [OH] IIA [AC] Associate Pastor, Iglesia Menonita del Buen Pastor, Archbold OH

Huffman Jr, Robert, 3782 Candia Ave, North Port FL 34286 [SE] IIA [AC] Minister of Youth, Peace Christian Fell, North Port FL

Hunsberger, Paul A., 1804 S 13th St, Goshen IN 46526, 574-533-2843 [IM] [RE]

Hunsberger, Walter I., PO Box 214, Worcester PA 19490, 610-584-9385 [FRC] [RE]

Hunsecker, Wilmer A. (Dorothy) 7 Kenneth Dr, Walkersville MD 21793, 301-845-2280 [LAN] [RE]

Hunsicker, Ronald Jay (Kendall Keech-Hunsicker) 501 Randolph Dr, Lititz PA 17543, 717-560-3553 [ACC] IIB3a [AC]

Hunt, Dion, 2895 B Ashton Rd, Sarasota FL 34231 [SE] IIA [AC] Minister of Youth, Ashton Menn Ch, Sarasota FL

Hurst, George M., 2870 Oregon Pike, Lititz PA 17543, 717-656-7305, gmchurst@yahoo.com [LAN] IIB1 [AC] Pastor, Hernley Menn Ch, Manheim PA

Hurst, J. Nevin (Melissa) 1569 Briertown Rd, East Earl PA 17519-9706, 717-355-5566, nevmelis@juno.com [LAN] IIC [AC] Youth Pastor, Weaverland Menn Ch, East Earl PA

Hurst, Leon R. (Rosella) 570 Snapper Dr, Ephrata PA 17522, 717-656-3224 [LAN] IIB2 [AC] Associate Pastor, Weaverland Menn Ch, East Earl PA

Hurst, Levi M., 1001 E Oregon Rd, Lititz PA 17543, 717-569-8326 [OH] [RE]

Hurst, Noah S., 1026 Pinehill Rd, Lititz PA 17543, 717-626-8773 [LAN] [RE]

Hurst, Ray N. (Brenda Martin Hurst) 1591 Dinkel Ave, Bridgewater VA 22812-9803, 540-828-6578, rayhurst@ntelos.net [VA] IIB1 [AC] Co-Pastor, Community Menn Ch, Harrisonburg VA

Hurst, Raymond S. (Ruth) 1089 Rock Rd Apt #1, Schuylkill Haven PA 17972 [LAN] [RE]

Hutchings, Michael D. (Roxanne L.) 1901 S 4th St, Morton IL 61550, enest@mtco.com [IL] IIA [AC] Pastor, Trinity Menn Ch, Morton IL

Huyard, Alvin M. (Rose) 103 Cherry Ave, Grottoes VA 24441, 540-249-0331 [VA] IIB1 [AC] Co-Pastor, Mount Vernon Menn Ch, Grottoes VA

Huyard, David S. (Anna Mary) 541 New York Ave, Harrisonburg VA 22801, 540-433-9481 [VA] [RE]

Huyard, Elvin R. (Linda) 46 Meadow View Dr, Leola PA 17540, 717-656-2505, erh.nh.pa@juno.com [LAN] IIB1 [AC] Pastor, Hess Menn Ch, Lititz PA

Huyard, Rose (Alvin) 103 Cherry Ave, Grottoes VA

24441, 540-249-0331 [VA] IIB2 [AC] Co-Pastor, Mount Vernon Menn Ch, Grottoes VA

I

Imchen, Ramoktoshi, 1096A Rettew Mill Rd, Ephrata PA 17522, Imchen@earthlink.net [LAN] IIB1 [AC] Pastor, Hershey Menn Ch, Kinzers PA

Intagliata, Stephen, 7727 N 34th Dr, Phoenix AZ 85051, tig7@juno.com [PSW] IIB2 [AC] Associate Pastor, Trinity Menn Ch, Glendale AZ

Irvin, William J., 1654 Hi Point St, Los Angeles CA 90035, 213-939-6478 [PSW] IIB1 [AC] Pastor, Prince of Peace Anabaptist Fell, Los Angeles CA

Isaac, Gary Orrin (Jean Elizabeth) 307 Sutton, Newton KS 67114 [WDC] IIB3b [AC]

Isaacs, Alvin, 718 E 121st St, Los Angeles CA 90059, 213-754-7376 [PSW] IIB1 [AC] Pastor, Calvary Christian Fell, Inglewood CA

Isaacs, Brenda, 9711 Rancho Verde Dr, Bakersfield CA 93311-3018 [PSW] IIB3b [AW] Co-Pastor, Bakersfield Anabaptist Ministries, Bakersfield CA

Isaacs, James M. (Brenda D.) 9711 Rancho Verde Dr, Bakersfield CA 93311-3018 [PSW] IIB3b [AC] Co-Pastor, Bakersfield Anabaptist Ministries, Bakersfield CA

Isaak, Paul J. (Beryl Berdeen (Jantz)) 201 S Lee St, PO Box 66, Deer Creek OK 74636, 580-267-3376, pji201@aol.com [WDC] IIB1 [AC] Pastor, Deer Creek Menn Ch, Deer Creek OK

Isner, Vernon D. (Gail) 24 Clover Cr, Chambersburg PA 17201, 717-267-0870 [FRK] IIB3a [AC] Chaplain, Menno Haven, Chambersburg PA

Ivy, Clifford Dale (Diane) PO Box 916, Blountstown FL 32424, 850-674-4516, twodivys@gtcom.net [SE] IC, IIA [AC] Pastor, Oak Terrace Menn Ch, Blountstown FL; Assistant Moderator, Southeast Mennonite Conference, FL

J

Jachin, Stephen M. (Cathrine June) 3360 Punta Del Este Dr, Hacienda Heights CA 91745, 626-333-2033, stevejachin@juno.com [PSW] IIB1 [AC] Pastor, Jemaat Kristen Indonesia Imanuel, Downey CA

Jackson, Warner, 24580 Ridgeline Dr, Bedford Heights OH 44146, 440-232-2519 [OH] IIB1 [AC] Pastor, University Euclid Christ New Testament, Bedford Heights OH

Jacobs, Donald R. (Anna Ruth) 715 Southview Dr, Landisville PA 17538, 717-898-0329 [LAN] [RE]

Jaime, Celso C. (Zulma) 1419 Zerega Ave A, Bronx NY 10462, 718-792-5455, jaime4ever@aol.com [LAN] IIB1 [AC] Pastor, Evangelical Garifuna, Bronx NY

James, Frank, PO Box 2401, Chinle AZ 86503, 520-674-3402 [PSW] IIA, IIC [AC] Pastor, Upper Room Menn Ch, Chinle AZ

James, Nehemiah, 382 N 6th Ave, Upland CA 91786, 909-946-7453, chigoji@aol.com [PSW] IIA [AC]

Jantz, Wallace (Sylvia) 736 Random Rd, Hesston KS 67062, 620-327-2059 [SC] [RE]

Jantzen, Lubin W. (Matilda M.) 217 Vista Cr, Hesston KS 67062 [WDC] [RE]

Jantzi, Beryl M. (Margo M.) 825 Sugar Maple Ln, Harrisonburg VA 22801, 540-574-4348, bjantzi@aol.com [VA] IIB1 [AC] Lead Pastor,

Harrisonburg Menn Ch, Harrisonburg VA

Jantzi, Denton R. (Kathleen M.) 918 N 12th St, Beatrice NE 68310, 402-228-6997, bm84101@alltel.net [WDC] IIB1 [AC] Pastor, Beatrice Menn Ch, Beatrice NE

Jantzi, Donald, 1330 Greencroft Dr, Goshen IN 46526, 574-537-4345 [IM] [RE]

Janzen, Anna S. (Milton) 318 Lucas Creek Rd, Newport News VA 23602, 757-988-1797 [VA] [AW]

Janzen, Bernard Henry (Marie J.) c/o Kidron Bethel Home, 3000 Ivy Dr, North Newton KS 67117-0002, 316-283-0683 [WDC] [RE]

Janzen, Dorothea Marie (Heinz Daniel) Box 529, North Newton KS 67117, 316-283-4729, dorheinz@ourtownusa.net [WDC] [RE]

Janzen, Harold Henry (Margie Lois) 714 Highland, Newton KS 73703, 316-282-2123 [WDC] [RE]

Janzen, Heinz Daniel (Dorothea Marie) Box 529, North Newton KS 67117, 316-283-4729, dorheinz@ourtownusa.net [WDC] [RE]

Janzen, J. Melvin, 1929 Mt Vernon St, Waynesboro VA 22980-2240, 540-942-2471 [VA] IIB3a [AC]

Janzen, Lester E. (Eileen D.) 3035 Ivy Ct, North Newton KS 67117-8072, 316-283-6763 [WDC] [RE]

Janzen, Samuel R. (Lila Mae) 1256 Shank Dr, Harrisonburg VA 22802, 540-732-7241 [VA] [RE]

Janzen, Susan E., 4441 N 80th St, Omaha NE 68134, 402-573-6084, sejanzen@aol.com [CP] IIB1 [AC] Pastor, New Hope Menn Ch, Omaha NE

Jarrett, Harry (Mary Elizabeth) 1672 Sunny Slope Lane, Harrisonburg VA 22801, 540-442-8089, hjarrett7@cs.com [VA] IIB2 [AC] Associate Pastor, Harrisonburg Menn Ch, Harrisonburg VA

Jefferson, Nathaniel L. (Pamela) 2108 Briarcliff Rd, Richmond VA 23225, 804-232-9987 [VA] IIB3b [AC]

Jewell, Gary Lee, 210 South F St, Spokane WA 99204, 509-456-4973, mrglj@juno.com [PNW] IIB1 [AC] Pastor, Shalom Ch, Spokane WA

Johns, Galen (Edith M.) 18166 CR 48, New Paris IN 46553, 574-831-4019, gijohns@maplenet.net [IM] IB3 [AC] Overseer for Mennonite Church of Warsaw, Warsaw IN

Johns, Loren L. (Rachel Ann Leaman Johns) 3003 Benham Ave, Elkhart IN 46517, 574-295-3726, ljohns@ambs.edu [CDC] IIB3d [AC]

Johnson, Arlee (JoAnn) 1313 N College, Cordell OK 73632, 580-832-3435, awjohnson@itlnet.net [WDC] IIB1 [AC] Pastor, Herold Menn Ch, Cordell OK

Johnson, Cornelius, 856 W 84th St, Los Angeles CA 90044, 323-971-5449 [PSW] IIA [AC] Associate Pastor, Los Angeles Faith Chapel, Inglewood CA

Johnson, James (Sheri) 7108 St 64 SW, Motley MN 56466, 218-397-2543, JohnsonJam@tyson.com [NC] IIA [AC]

Johnson, Janeen Bertsche (Barry Lee) 64382 Limberlost Dr, Goshen IN 46526, 574-533-3608, jbjohnson@ambs.edu [CDC] IIB3d [AC]

Johnson, Morton H. (Katherine) 1533 Siegfried St, Bethlehem PA 18017, 610-868-1241, adriene3@aol.com [LAN] IIC [AC] Chaplain, Prison Ministry, Bethlehem PA

Johnson, Norma J. (Vern Preheim) 127 S Main, Newton KS 67114, 316-283-4018, normaj@southwind.net [WDC] IIB1 [AC] Associate Pastor, Bethel College Menn Ch, North Newton KS

Johnson Jr, Joseph, 830 Keefer Rd, Girard OH 44420, 330-539-2059 [OH] [RE]

Johnston, Daniel R. (Michelle) 15606 L St, Omaha NE 68135, 402-896-4132 [CP] IIB3a [AC] Healthy Ministries Coordinator, Methodist Health System, Omaha NE

Johnston, Ruth Marie (Shuji Moriichi) 2704 41st Ave S, Minneapolis MN 55406, 612-721-7068, shujiruth@juno.com [CP] IIB3a [AC]

Jones, Jeff J. (Christianna L.) 24 Devon Dr, Hollidaysburg PA 16648, 814-695-8935, Revjjj@aol.com [ALL] IIB1 [AC] Pastor, Cornerstone Fell Menn Ch, Hollidaysburg PA

Jones, Rick, 402 West St, Archbold OH 43502, 419-445-2612, yfcjones@hotmail.com [OH] IIB1 [AC] Pastor, Inlet Menn Ch, Wauseon OH

Jones, Willie J. (Bettina) 1553 Snug Harbor Rd, Shadyside MD 20764, 410-867-2755 [LAN] IIA [AC] Associate Pastor, Peabody Street Menn Ch, Washington DC

Jurisson, Enno (Angela) 21 Swan Rd, Atglen PA 19310, 610-593-0313, jurisson@ccis.net [ACC] IIB1 [AC] Pastor, Maple Grove Menn Ch of Atglen, Atglen PA

K

Kahila, Chris C. (Kerri Ann) 5 Sunset Ct, Hesston KS 67062, ckahila@prairieinet.net [SC] IIB2 [AC]

Kaiser, Jerry Lee (Allene Grace) 305 S Walnut, PO Box 236, Inman KS 67546, 620-585-2333 [WDC] IIB1 [AC] Pastor, Inman Menn Ch, Inman KS

Kalous, Charles, 3775 Susanna Dr, Cincinnati OH 45251, 513-385-8462 [OH] [RE]

Kampen, John I., 507 Greding St, Bluffton OH 45817, 419-358-0033, kampenj@bluffton.edu [CDC] IIB3c [AC]

Kanagy, Conrad L. (Heidi) 423 S Spruce St, Elizabethtown PA 17022-2549, ckanagy@earthlink.net [LAN] IIB1 [AC] Pastor, Elizabethtown Menn Ch, Elizabethtown PA

Kanagy, Curtiss Lee (Robin L.) 2106 S 5th Ave, Lebanon PA 17042, 717-295-7359, cr_kanagy@juno.com [LAN] IIB1 [AC] Pastor, New Danville Menn Ch, Lancaster PA

Kanagy, Fred (Lila) 753 Road 523, Bloomfield MT 59315, 406-583-7782, KanagyF@midrivers.com [NC] IIB1 [AC] Pastor, Red Top Menn Ch, Bloomfield MT

Kanagy, Irene, 5838 E 19th St, Indianapolis IN 46218 [IM] IIC [AC] Chaplain/Pastoral Counselor, Community Hospital, Indianapolis IN

Kanagy, Lee H. (Adella) 19 Edgewood Ln, Bellville PA 17004, 717-483-6520 [LAN] [RE]

Kanagy, Nanette M. (Kevin L.) 2200 Bahia Vista St B2, Sarasota FL 34239, 941-366-1286, nanbvmenno@comcast.net [SE] IC, IIC [AC] Assistant Moderator, Southeast Mennonite Conference, FL; Minister of Children and Youth, Bahia Vista Menn Ch, Sarasota FL; Conference Youth Minister, Southeast Mennonite Conference, Sarasota FL

Kanagy, Philip C. (Janine) 17091 Timberview Rd, Timberville VA 22853, 540-896-4439, kanagyspad@juno.com [VA] IIB1 [AC] Pastor, Trissels Menn Ch, Broadway VA

Kanagy, Wilfred (Charleen) 18872 CR 40, Goshen IN 46526, 574-534-4878, willie@collegemennonite.org [IM] IIC [AC] Pastor, College Menn Ch, Goshen IN

Kandel, Homer, PO Box 198, Berlin OH 44610, 330-893-2622 [OH] [RE]

Kanski, David K. (Linda) RR 5 Box 383, Jersey Shore PA 17740, 570-398-3455, DavidKanski@aol.com [LAN] IIB1 [AC] Pastor, Praise Center, Jersey Shore PA

Kao, Nelson Kuang-Daw, 60 Grant, Irvine CA 92620, 949-653-2785, jtancpa@aol.com [PSW] IIB1 [AC] Pastor, Trinity Chinese Menn Ch, Irvine CA

Kauffman, Aaron W. (Anna) 651 Steelville Rd, Cochranville PA 19330, 610-593-5665 [LAN] [RE]

Kauffman, Allen L. (Susie) RR 1 Box 295-A, Loysville PA 17047-9767, 717-789-9671 [LAN] [RE]

Kauffman, Alvin, 1801 Greencroft Blvd, Goshen IN 46526, 574-537-4638 [IM] [RE]

Kauffman, E. Elaine, 315 N 7th St, PO Box 473, Mountain Lake MN 56159, 507-427-2212, seekfrst@rconnect.com [CP] IIB1 [AC] Pastor, First Menn Ch, Mountain Lake MN

Kauffman, Earnest (Lois) 544 E Park, West Point NE 68788, 402-372-5027 [CP] [RE]

Kauffman, Edward John (Gay Lee [Geartz]) 2204 E Edgewood Rd, Sioux Falls SD 57103, 605-334-2778, egkauff@amerion.com [CP] IB2 [AC] Conference Minister, Central Plains Mennonite Conference, Freeman SD

Kauffman, Galen E. (Betty Jean) PO Box 190, Surrey ND 58785-0236, 701-852-4957, galenkauffman@hotmail.com [NC] IIB1 [AC] Pastor, Prairie Peace Fell, Surrey ND

Kauffman, Glenn R. (June Louise) 76 Waterloo Rd, Kowoloon, Hong Kong [LAN] IIB3b [AC]

Kauffman, J. Brent, 3020 Oak Terrace Dr, Lebanon OR 97355, 541-259-2127, kauffmanb@compuserve.com [PNW] IIB1 [AC] Pastor, Lebanon Menn Ch, Lebanon OR

Kauffman, J. Fred, 816 S 48th St, Philadelphia PA 19143, 215-727-8136, JFKauffman@mennonite.net [FRC] IIB1 [AC] Pastor, West Philadelphia Menn Fell, Philadelphia PA

Kauffman, J. Robert (Mary Etta) 686 Meetinghouse Rd, New Holland PA 17557, 717-354-2533, tchrmrk@aol.com [LAN] IIA [AC] Pastor, Welsh Mountain Menn Ch, New Holland PA

Kauffman, Melvin L. (Erma) 1001 E Oregon Rd, Lititz PA 17543-9205 [LAN] [RE]

Kauffman, Richard Alan (Nancy Jane) 891 Beachy Rd, Accident MD 21550, 301-245-4041 [ALL] IIB1 [AC]

Kauffman, Ron, 850 Burr Rd, Wauseon OH 43567, 419-335-3212 [OH] IIC [AC]

Kauffman, Sherman W. (Betty L. [Yoder]) 2420 S Main, Goshen IN 46526, 574-533-2461, sherm@ im.mennonite.net [IM] IB2 [AC] Executive Conference Minister, Indiana-Michigan Mennonite Conference, Goshen IN

Kauffman, Stanlee D. (Marcia) 1703 Goose Creek Rd, Waynesboro VA 22980, 540-943-1324, pastork@ntelos.net [VA] IIB1 [AC] Senior Pastor, Waynesboro Menn Ch, Waynesboro VA

Kauffman, Thomas E. (Julia) 981-A Summit Ave, Harrisonburg VA 22802, 540-801-8920 [VA] [RE]

Kauffman, Tom (Amy Gerber Kauffman) 2303 Maryann Place, Toledo OH 43614-2113, 419-382-3816, tekauffman@sev.org [OH] IB2 [AC]

Kauffmann, Ivan J., 1725 Wildwood Ct, Goshen IN 46526, 574-534-0232 [IM] [RE]

Kauffmann, Nancy Lee (Joel Dean) 111 Carter Rd, Goshen IN 46526, 574-533-7252, nancy@im.mennonite.net [IM] IB2 [AC] Conference Regional Minister, Indiana-Michigan Mennonite Conference, Goshen IN

Kaufman, Calvin R. (Loretta) 901 Mervin Ave, Goshen IN 46526, 574-537-8002 [IM] [AW]

Kaufman, Douglas D.H. (Jill Hostetler Kaufman) 1101 S 8th St, Goshen IN 46526, 574-533-7625, kaufman@bnin.net [IM] IIB1 [AC] Pastor, Benton Menn Ch, Goshen IN

Kaufman, George K. (Naomi Marie Esau) PO Box 130, Henderson NE 68371-0130 [CP] IIB2 [AC] Associate Pastor, Bethesda Menn Ch, Henderson NE

Kaufman, Gordon D. (Dorothy W.) 6 Longfellow Rd, Cambridge MA 02138, 617-491-1771 [EDC] [RE]

Kaufman, Marvin L. (Ruth) 2968 Carpenter Park Rd, Davidsville PA 15928, 814-288-2167, kaufmanrm@ hotmail.com [ALL] IIB1 [AC] Pastor, Stahl Menn Ch, Johnstown PA

Kaufman, Orlo N. (Edna G.) 86 22nd Ave, Moundridge KS 67107, 620-345-2764 [WDC] [RE]

Kaufman, Robert (Krista) 7702 Garnett, Lenxa KS 66214, 913-248-0642 [SC, WDC] IIB1 [AC] Pastor, Rainbow Menn Ch, Kansas City KS

Kaufman, S. Roy (Lorretta) 28103 443rd Ave, Freeman SD 57029, 605-925-7106, lorokauf@gwtc.net [CP] IIB1 [AC] Pastor, Salem Menn Ch, Freeman SD

Kaufman-Frey, Cameron Blake (Dawn Renae) 501 Center St, Morgantown WV 26505, 304-296-1822, Camdawn@juno.com [ALL] IB3, IIB1 [AC] Pastor, Morgantown Ch of the Brethren, Morgantown WV

Kaufmann, Lois Johns (H. James) 18166 CR 48, New Paris IN 46553, 574-831-2072, loisjk@juno.com [CDC, IM] IIA [AC] Co-Pastor, Assembly Menn Ch, Goshen IN

Kautz, Delbert L. (Mary Ann Hosler) 475 Letort Rd, Millersville PA 17551, 717-872-2695, dellamark@prodigy.net [LAN] IIB1 [AC] Pastor, Millersville Menn Ch, Millersville PA

Keeler, Kendall Ray (Barbara Elizabeth) 379 Scotland Rd, Quarryville PA 17566, 717-786-8130 [LAN] IIA [AC] Associate Pastor, Mt Vernon Menn Ch, Kirkwood PA

Keeler, Randall S. (Karen Joan) 55 Crystal Pl, Bluffton OH 45817, 419-358-1932, keelerr@bluffton.edu [CDC] IIB3a [AC] Pastor, Bluffton College, Bluffton OH

Keeler, Richard Freed (Margaret) 6 Darcy Ave, Central Park, Balmain Village, Couva TRINIDAD, Trinidad, 868-679-7258, keeler2@att.net.tt [VA] IIB3b [AC]

Keener, Gerald, 731 Hempfield Hill Rd, Columbia PA 17512, 212-234-9539 [LAN] IIB3b [AC]

Keener, Robert E. (Rhoda) 5207 Heisey Rd, Shippensburg PA 17257, 717-532-9723 [FRK] IIB3a [AC] Chaplain, Menno Haven, Chambersburg PA

Keener, Walter L. (Martha) 2001 Harrisburg Pike, Apt 227, Lancaster PA 17601, 717-390-4176 [LAN] [RE]

Keeney, William Echard, 140 North Lawn Ave, Bluffton OH 45817-1275, 419-358-6017 [CDC] [RE]

Kehr, Anita Yoder (Bryan) 65719 SR 15, Goshen IN 46526, 574-535-1014 [IM] IIB1 [AC] Pastor, Berkey Avenue Menn Fell, Goshen IN

Keidel, Levi, 14430 Sunrise Ct, Leo IN 46765-9515 [IM] [RE]

Keim, Howard (Tami) 209 N Weaver, Hesston KS 67062 [SC] IIB3d [AC] Professor, Tabor College, Hillsboro KS

Keim, Ray, 880 Chalet Dr Apt 210, Berne IN 46711, 260-589-8596, craykeim@juno.com [CDC] IIB2 [AC] Pastor of Congregational Care, First Menn Ch, Berne IN

Keller, Frank Reller (Lorraine H.) 603 Bluestem St, PO Box 476, North Newton KS 67117, fkeller@alltel.net [WDC] [RE]

Keller, Lloyd B. (Eunice) 535 Fruitville Pike, Manheim PA 17545, 717-665-3137 [LAN] [RE]

Keller, Mark Haven (Darlene) 1018 Taliaferro Dr, Harrisonburg VA 22802, 540-434-4535, mkeller123@aol.com [VA] IIB2 [AC] Associate Pastor, Harrisonburg Menn Ch, Harrisonburg VA

Kelly, John, 16975 SR 93, Pedro OH 45659, 740-643-2731, shauna@bright.net [OH] IIC [AC] Pastor, Wayside Chapel, Pedro OH

Kennel, Leroy Eldon (Pauline) 888 S Roselle Rd, Schaumburg IL 60193-3965, 847-895-3654, lpkennel@msn.com [CDC, IL] IIB1, IIB3a [AC] Minister of the Word, Christ Community Menn Ch, Schaumburg IL

Kennel, Pauline (LeRoy Eldon) 888 S Roselle Rd, Schaumburg IL 60193-3965, 847-895-3654, lpkennel@msn.com [CDC, IL] IIB1 [AC] Pastor, Christ Community Menn Ch, Schaumburg IL

Kennel, Ronald L. (Judy) 2714 Evergreen Ln, Goshen IN 46526, 574-534-1385, rkennel@npcc.net [IM] IB3, IIB1 [AC] Pastor, Clinton Brick Menn Ch, Goshen IN

Kennel, Sharon, 1017 Rd V, Strang NE 68444-3027, 402-627-4375 [CP] IB2 [AC] West Regional Minister, Central Plains Mennonite Conference

Kennell, Dennis (Nelda) RR 2 Box 39, Roanoke IL 61561, 309-923-6621 [IL] IIB1 [AC] Pastor, Cazenovia Menn Ch, Roanoke IL

Kennell, Eldon W. (Mary Alice Ulrich Kennell) PO Box 801, Roanoke IL 61561, 309-923-7172 [IL] IIB3a [AC] Chaplain, Pontiac Correctional Center, Pontiac IL

Kennell, Timothy D. (Beverly Ann) 3250 Pineview Dr, Powhatan VA 23139, 804-598-9355, timbev2@yahoo.com [VA] IIB1 [AC] Pastor, Powhatan Menn Ch, Powhatan VA

Kern, Marilyn Ruth, 704 Charles Ave, Findley OH 45840-4515, 419-420-9927, kernmom@aol.com [CDC] [RE]

Kerner, David (Diane) 308 Dunbar Rd, Mundelein, IL 60060, 847-949-4119, dckerner@hotmail.com [CDC, IL] IIB1 [AC] Pastor, North Suburban Menn Ch, Mundelein, IL

Kiblinger, John D. (Catherine Anne) 1860 Glanzer Ct, Harrisonburg VA 22802, 540-433-6612 [VA] IB3 [AC]

Kimes, Steve (Diane) 17734 NE Glisan, Portland OR 97230, 503-492-1149, stevekimes@aol.com [PNW] IIA [AC] Pastor, Anawim Christian Community, Gresham OR

Kindy, David (Merna Jo) 2701 Griffith Rd, Winston Salem NC 27103, 910-760-4294 [VA] [AW]

Kindy, Erie, 1325 E Gordonville Rd, Midland MI 48640, 517-631-4637 [IM] [RE]

King, Aaron (Betty) 5975 Whippoorwill Ln, Harrisonburg VA 22802, 540-833-5135 [VA] IIB3a [AC]

King, Betty (Aaron) 5975 Whippoorwill Ln, Harrisonburg VA 22802, 540-833-5135 [VA] IIB3a [AC]

King, Calvin J. (Ardis J.) 17713 Hartman St, South Bend IN 46614-3619, 574-299-0351, Cking11941@aol.com [IM] IIB3c [AC] Constituent Information Manager, Mennonite Mission Network, Elkhart IN

King, Clifford E. (Mona Bebe) 7512 Los Banos Ct, Colorado Spring CO 80920, 719-260-7024, cliffmona@juno.com [RM] [RE]

King, Daniel L., PO Box 128, Kidron OH 44636, 330-857-0305 [OH] IIB3d [AC]

King, Donald G. (Barbara) 413 Alana Dr, Goshen IN 46526, 574-534-3778 [IM] [RE]

King, Doug D. (Paula M.) 204 N Monroe, Flanagan IL 61740, 540-574-0013, dpking@rica.net [CDC, IL] IIB1 [AC] Pastor, Prairieview Menn Ch, Flanagan IL

King, Eldon (Dorothy P.) 551 Tionesta Dr, Dalton OH 44618, 330-828-1004, eldor@sssnet.com [OH] IIB3a [AC]

King, John (Cynthia Joy (Bauman)) 167 N 2nd St, Souderton PA 18964, 215-721-6769, we5kings@yahoo.com [FRC] IIB2 [AC] Associate Pastor, Line Lexington Menn Ch, Line Lexington PA

King, John C., 1727 South 13th St, Goshen IN 46526, 574-533-1052, john@waterfordchurch.org [IM] [RE] Minister to Older Adults, Waterford Menn Ch, Goshen IN

King, Linford D. (Mary Etta) 311 North Lime St, Lancaster PA 17602, 717-391-6445, leking@supernet.com [ACC] IB3, IIB1 [AC] Pastor, Neffsville Menn Ch, Lancaster PA

King, Loren, PO Box K, West Liberty OH 43357, 937-465-4176 [OH] [RE]

King, Michael A. (Joan) 126 Klingerman Rd, Telford PA 18969, 215-721-7967, mking@netreach.net [FRC] IIB1 [AC] Pastor, Spring Mount Menn Ch, Spring Mount PA

King, Michael S. (Cindy) 312 S Mount St, Baltimore MD 21223, 410-566-3075, kingmike6@juno.com [LAN] IIA [AC] Pastor, Wilkens Avenue Menn Ch, Baltimore MD

King, Nicholas James (Ronda Suderman King) 1558 Fairview, Wichita KS 67203, 316-265-8568, Rondask@Juno.com [WDC] IIB2 [AC]

King, Phillip A. (Judy L.) 571 Linkville Rd, Johnstown PA 15906, 814-535-5203 [ALL] IB3 [AC]

King, Wayne D. (Clara) 418 North Elm, Arthur IL 61911, 217-543-3352, wcking@net.care-il.com [IL] [RE]

Kirk, Alfred Lee (Mary Dean Kirk) 819 Hill St Apt 3, Rocky Mount NC 27801, 252-212-0004 [VA] IIA [AC]

Kirk, Mary Dean (Alfred Lee Kirk) 819 Hill St Apt 3, Rocky Mount NC 27801, 252-212-0004, Tru1stlady01@aol.com [VA] IIA [AC]

Klaassen, Glendon J. (Reitha J.) 19 EMS D22C Lane, Syracuse IN 46567-9068, 574-658-3222, glendon.klaassen@gte.net [WDC] [RE]

Kleinsasser, Alvin D., PO Box 143, Mt Lake MN 56159, 507-427-2219 [WDC] [RE]

Klemm, Ulli M., 7241 Princeton Pl, Pittsburgh PA 15218, 412-241-5149 [ALL] IIB3a [AC]

Kliewer, Tim (Myrna) 301 S Main St, Hillsboro KS 67063, 620-947-2984, tkliewer@southwind.net [WDC] IIB1 [AC] Pastor, Trinity Menn Ch, Hillsboro KS

Kniss, Carl D. (Rochelle) 878 S College Ave, Harrisonburg PA 17522, 540-574-2779, crkniss@aol.com [LAN] IIA [AC]

Kniss, David L. (Esther Leaman Kniss) 4454 NW Dunn Dr, Arcadia FL 34266-5373, dkniss@aol.com [SE] IB3, IIB1 [AC] Interim Pastor, Pine Creek Chapel, Arcadia FL

Kniss, Paul G., 1549 Hillcrest Dr, Harrisonburg VA 22801, 540-432-0286 [OH] [RE]

Kniss, Philip L. (Irene Hershberger Kniss) 889 College Ave, Harrisonburg VA 22802, 540-564-1231, phil@pvmchurch@org [VA] IIB1 [AC] Pastor, Park View Menn Ch, Harrisonburg VA

Knowles, Michael (June) 256 8th Ave, PO Box 306,

Inman KS 67546, 620-585-6964, bethelch@southwind.net [WDC] IIB1 [AC] Pastor, Bethel Menn Ch, Inman KS

Koch, Roy, 204 S 6th St, Goshen IN 46526, 574-533-1798 [IM] [RE]

Kochert, Robert (Terri) 132 James Lee Dr, Chambersburg PA 17201, 717-263-3692 [FRK] IIB1 [AC]

Kochsmeier, David K. (Bev Goshow Kochsmeier) 1775 Creek Rd, Bethlehem PA 18015, 610-758-8156 [FRC] IIB1 [AC] Pastor, Steel City Menn Ch, Bethlehem PA

Koehn, Clifford E. (Anna Ruth) 111 NE 2nd St, Geary OK 73040-2005, 405-884-2705 [WDC] [AW]

Koehn, Melvin J., 2674 330th St, Wayland IA 52654, 319-256-2098, mdkoehn@farmtel.net [CP] IIB1 [AC] Pastor, Eicher Emmanuel Menn Ch, Wayland IA

Kolb, Elmer G., 207 W Summit St, Souderton PA 18964, 215-721-0599 [FRC] [RE]

Kolb, Matthew G., 592 Mennonite Rd, Royersford PA 19468, 610-948-6094 [FRC] [RE]

Kolb, Noah S. (Sara J.) 631 Melvins Rd, Telford PA 18969-2121, 215-723-7399, NoahK@FMC-online.org [FRC] IB2 [AC] Conference Minister, Franconia Mennonite Conference, Souderton PA

Kolb, Norman G., 1191 Peiffer Hill Rd, Stevens PA 17578 [FRC] [RE]

Kolb-Wyckoff, Martha (Ron) 257 W Reliance Rd, Souderton PA 18964, 215-799-2374, mkolbwyckoff@rcmm.org [FRC] IIB2 [AC]

Koop, Cleo H. (Faye A.) 1800 N Spencer Rd, Newton KS 67114, 316-283-2536 [WDC] IIB1 [AC] Pastor, First Menn Ch, Halstead KS

Kotva Jr, Joseph J. (Carol S.) 1514 Lehigh Parkway S, Allentown PA 18103, 610-791-3751, kotva@attglobal.net [EDC] IIB1 [AC] Pastor, First Menn Ch, Allentown PA

Kouns, Eric A. (Shirley Lorraine) PO Box 60, Irwin OH 43029, eakouns@rica.net [VA] IIB3a [AC]

Kouttjie, Frederik Jan, 14732 Dunnet Ave, La Mirada CA 90638, 714-521-5742, janasria@aol.com [PSW] IIB1 [AC] Pastor, Gereja Kristen Injili Indonesia Zion, La Mirada CA

Krabill, Gary L. (Eileen) PO Box 113, Mifflin PA 17058-0113, 717-436-2132 [LAN] IIB1 [AC] Pastor, Living Water Christian Fell, Mifflin PA

Krabill, Murray, 7348 Perry Twp Rd 95, Fredericktown OH 43019, 419-768-3278 [OH] [RE]

Krabill, Russell, 26221 Vista Ln, Elkhart IN 46517, 574-522-6869 [IM] [RE]

Kramer, Stacey, 209 N Main, Freeman SD 57029, estaceyk@hotmail.com [CP] IIA [AC] Associate Pastor, Salem Menn Ch, Freeman SD

Kratz, Clarice (Lawrence) N31 W28 795 Lakeside Rd, Pewaukee WI 53072, 262-691-0304, bfons@webtv.net [CDC, IL] IIB1 [AC] Co-Pastor, Maple Avenue Menn Ch, Waukesha WI

Kratz, Clyde G. (Eunice A.) 1737 G Buttonwood Ct, Harrisburg PA 22802, 540-438-7977 [VA] IIB1 [AC] Pastor, Zion Menn Ch, Broadway VA

Kratz, Dorothy, 54269 Old Mill Dr, Elkhart IN 46514, 574-266-5277 [IM] [RE]

Kratz, Lawrence M. (Clarice) N31 W28 795 Lakeside Rd, Pewaukee WI 53072, 262-691-0340, bfons@webtv.net [CDC, IL] IIB1 [AC] Co-Pastor, Maple Avenue Menn Ch, Waukesha WI

Kratz, Paul Leonard (Evelyn W.) 3226 Old Thirty-three Rd, Harrisonburg VA 22801, 540-432-9050 [VA] IB3 [AC]

Kratz, Wayne N., 114D Menno Home Dr, Souderton PA 18964, 215-723-2520 [FRC] [RE]

Kraus, C. Norman (Rhoda Hess) 1210 Harmony Dr, Harrisonburg VA 22802, 540-432-0828 [VA] [RE]

Kraybill, J. Nelson (Ellen Graber Kraybill) 26103 Vista Ln, Elkhart IN 46517, 574-293-2391, nkraybill@aol.com [IM] IIB3c [AC] President

Kraybill, John H. (Thelma) Harvest View 220, 1001 E Oregon Rd, Lititz PA 17543, 717-509-5861, johnkraybill@yahoo.com [LAN] [RE]

Kraybill, Simon P. (Mary Jean) 860 Maytown Rd, Elizabethtown PA 17022-9765, 717-367-2060, spkmaryjk@aol.com [LAN] [RE]

Krehbiel, Ronald Allen, 212 Kingsway, Hesston KS 67062, 620-327-4437 [WDC] [RE]

Krehbiel, Val R. (Consuelo) 837 E Wayne Ave, Apt 302, Salina KS 67401-6753 [SC, WDC] IIB1 [AC] Pastor, Salina Menn Ch, Salina KS

Kreider, Alan, 215 W Dinehart, Elkhart IN 46526 [IM] [AC]

Kreider, Andrew (Catherine (Katie)) 1726 Roys Ave, Elkhart IN 46516, 574-293-7354, psmcak@aol.com [IM] IIB1 [AC] Pastor, Prairie Street Menn Ch, Elkhart IN

Kreider, Barry R. (Erika Landes) 1119 Main St #1, Akron PA 17501-1615, 717-859-3147, berika@infi.net [LAN] IIA [AC] Pastor, Pilgrims Menn Ch, Akron PA

Kreider, Ellis D. (Amy) 171 Black Bear Rd, Quarryville PA 17566, 717-786-2626 [LAN] [RE]

Kreider, Harold, 24B Green Top Rd, Sellersville PA 18960, 215-257-7322 [FRC] [RE]

Kreider, Heidi Regier (David J.) PO Box 116, North Newton KS 67117, 316-284-0448, afn15812@afn.org [WDC] IIB1 [AC] Pastor, Bethel College Menn Ch, North Newton KS

Kreider, J. Robert, 1408-5 Kentfield Way, Goshen IN 46526, 574-533-5196 [IM] [RE]

Kreider, John T., 208 Flint Ave, Harrisonburg VA 22801, 540-433-6589, johnT2125@juno.com [VA] [RE]

Kreider, Philip (Lois) PO Box 447, Harrisonburg VA 22801, 540-433-8243 [VA] [RE]

Kreider, Wayne E. (Carla JoAnn) 1207 River Rd, Quarryville PA 17566, 717-548-2466 [LAN] IIB2 [AC] Associate Pastor, Mechanic Grove Menn Ch, Peach Bottom PA

Kriss III, Stephen F., 149 Old Tire Hill Rd, Johnstown PA 15905, 814-288-4251, Kriss1633@duq.edu [ALL] IIA [AC]

Kropf, Marlene Y. (Stanley E.) 337 E Beardsley Ave, Elkhart IN 46514, 574-262-8880 [IM] IIB3c [AC] Professor, Associated Mennonite Biblical Seminary, Elkhart IN

Kropf, Paul L. (June Louise) RR, Box 540, Lewisburg PA 17837, pjkropf@maf.net [LAN] IIC [AC] Minister, EMM, Lezhe Albania

Kuhns, Curtis (Carol) PO Box 627, Manson IA 50563, 712-469-2014, manson.menno@juno.com [CP] IIB1 [AC] Pastor, Manson Menn Ch, Manson IA

Kulp, Henry D., 161 W Cherry Ln, Souderton PA 18964, 215-723-3047 [FRC] [RE]

Kuniholm, Jason (Joanne) 53 Maple Linden Ln, Frazer PA 19355, 610-640-4075, jasonholm9@aol.com [LAN]

IIB1 [AC] Pastor, Frazer Menn Ch, Frazer PA

Kunkle, Albert B. (Vera Mae) 1297 Earl Ave, East Earl PA 17519, 717-354-5563 [LAN] III [AC] Ordained Deacon, Hinkletown Menn Ch, Ephrata PA

Kurtz, Calvin (Esther) 334 S Twin Valley Rd, Elverson PA 19520, 610-286-9574 [ACC] IIB3c [AC] Executive Director, Berks Co. Conference of Churches, Reading PA

Kurtz, Chester I. (Catherine) 3149 Parker Dr, Lancaster PA 17601, 717-898-0365, ckurtz0365@aol.com [LAN] IIB1 [AC]

Kurtz, Ira A. (Evelyn) 724 E End Ave, Lancaster PA 17602-3714, 717-293-0001, ikurtz@supernet.com [LAN] IIB1 [AC] Pastor, Sunnyside Menn Ch, Lancaster PA

Kurtz, Kathleen Weaver (Wayne David) 8914 Grant Ave, Manasses VA 22110, 703-361-7796 [VA] IIB3a [AC] Pastoral Counselor, Center for Pastoral Counseling of Virginia, McLean VA

Kurtz, Marilyn E. (Mervin) 655 Rawlinsville Rd, Willow Street PA 17584, 717-464-4427, kurtzme@juno.com [LAN] IIC [AC]

Kurtz, Omar A., 32 Furnace Road, Birdsboro PA 19508, 610-286-0159 [ACC] [RE]

Kusuma, Rina (Yusak) 1408 Forest Glen Dr #77, Hacienda Heights CA 91745 [PSW] IIB1 [AC]

Kusuma, Yusak (Rina) 1408 Forest Glen Dr #77, Hacienda Heights CA 91745 [PSW] IIB1 [AC]

Kuttab, George M., 8131 Washington Ln Apt 156, Wyncote PA 19095, 215-884-4839, gkkuttab@juno.com [LAN] IIB1 [AC] Pastor, Salam Menn Fell, Wyncote PA

Kym, Marlin (Betta) 621 South D St, Milford NE 68405, 402-761-3202, bell606@juno.com [CP] IIB1 [AC] Pastor, Bellwood Menn Ch, Milford NE

L

La Rue, Robin, 57019 Westlake Dr, Middlebury IN 46540, 574-825-1958, randrlarue@juno.com [CDC] IIB1 [AC] Pastor, Pleasant Oaks Menn Ch, Middlebury IN

Lahman, Harold H. (Evelyn M.) 14983 Model Rd, Elkton VA 22827, 540-298-8229 [VA] [RE]

Lanctot, Nina Bartelt (Donald) 1828 Roys Ave, Elkhart IN 46516, 574-295-6427, ninal@maplenet.net [IM] IIB1 [AC] Associate Pastor, Belmont Menn Ch, Elkhart IN

Landes, Craig Pelkey (Fortana May) 909 W Market St, Perkasie PA 18944, 215-453-6743 [FRC] IIB3c [AW]

Landes, R. Scott (Wendy Hange) 436 C Swamp Pk, Schwenksville PA 19473, 610-754-8865 [FRC] IIB1 [AC] Pastor, Frederick Menn Ch, Frederick PA

Landis, Abram K., Apt 272, Sellersville PA 18960, 215-453-9443 [FRC] [RE]

Landis, Betty (Elias) 1820 Rothsville Rd, Lititz PA 17543, 717-626-5741 [LAN] IIC [AC] Chaplain, Ephrata Community Hospital, Ephrata PA

Landis, Ira B. (Ruth) 2421 Camp Rd, Manheim PA 17545-8001, 717-664-2026 [LAN] [RE]

Landis, John G. (Eileen M. Hart) 1817 Thompson Ave, Lebanon PA 17046, 717-867-1517, jgl@mbcomp.com [LAN] IIB1 [AC] Pastor, Gingrichs Menn Ch, Lebanon PA

Landis, Keith L., 9150 Hite Rd, West Liberty OH 43357, 937-465-0312, kblandis@2access.net [OH] IIA [AC] Pastor, South Union Menn Ch, West Liberty OH

Landis, Mark (Elizabeth) 845 Quince Dr, Harrisonburg VA 22801, 540-801-8020 [VA] IIB2 [AC] Associate Pastor,

Grace Menn Fell, Lacey Spring VA

Landis, Mark G. (Alma) 881 Louser Rd, Annville PA 17003, 717-867-2028 [LAN] [RE]

Landis, Merrill B. (Betty Godshall Landis) 1009 Pine Cr, Telford PA 18969, 215-721-0152 [FRC] [RE]

Landis, Mervin L. (Rachel) 1045 Hunscker Rd, Lancaster PA 17601, 717-569-1334 [LAN] [RE]

Landis, Paul R. (Evelyn) RR 3 Box 676, Milton PA 17847, 717-742-4110 [LAN] [RE]

Landis, Paul S., 12 Church Landing Rd,, Pennsville NJ 08070, 856-678-3926 [LAN] IIB2 [AC] Visitation Pastor, Friendship Menn Chapel, Carney's Point NJ

Landis, Steven E. (Rosemary K.) 201 Maple Ave, Harleysville PA 19438, 215-513-0926 [FRC] IIB2 [AC] Minister of Pastoral Care, Franconia Menn Ch, Franconia PA

Lanting, Esther, 410 S Washington, Wakarusa IN 46573, 574-862-1910, elanting@maplenet.net [IM] IIB1 [AC] Pastor, Hudson Lake Menn Ch, New Carlisle IN

Lantz, Paul, 1804 College Manor, Goshen IN 46526, 574-533-1949 [IM] [RE]

Lapp, Cynthia, 3102 Webster St, Mt. Rainier MD 20712, 301-927-2983 [ALL] IIA [AC] Pastor for Music and Arts, Hyattsville Menn Ch, Hyattsville MD

Lapp, Ben F. (Geraldine D.) 2846 Little Rd, Perkiomenville PA 18074, 610-754-7258 [FRC] [RE]

Lapp, Dan L. (Anna Ruth) 11 Benjamin Green Rd, Pedricktown NJ 08067, 856-299-6589 [LAN] IIB1, IIB2 [AC] Associate Pastor, Friendship Menn Chapel, Carney's Point NJ

Lapp, Eugene M. (Marie) 53 Pequea Valley Rd, Kinzers PA 17535, 717-768-7550 [LAN] III [AC] Licensed Deacon, Millwood Menn Ch, Kinzers PA

Lapp, James M. (Miriam F. Book) 443 Penn Oak Ct, Harleysville PA 19438, 215-513-4115, jamesl@FMC-online.org [FRC] IB2 [AC]

Lapp, John H. (Floy) RD 2 Box 243, Port Allegany PA 16743, 814-642-9401, jflapp@usachoice.net [ACC] [RE]

Lapp, Ray (Edna) 109 Hershey Church Rd, Kinzers PA 17535, 717-768-3314, ridgeviewchurch@juno.com [ACC] IIB2 [AC] Associate Pastor, Ridgeview Menn Ch, Gordonville PA

Larson, Jonathan (Mary Kay) PO Box 17564, Atlanta GA 30316, 404-636-7915, JonPaull@aol.com [SE] IB3, IIB1 [AC] Pastor, Berea Menn Ch, Atlanta GA; District Minister, Southeast Mennonite Conference, GA/SC GA

Lasure, D. Wayne (Katie) 252 Keyser Rd, Boswell PA 15531, 814-629-7216 [ALL] IIB1 [AC]

Laureano, Juan (Amarillys) PO Box 573, Summit IL 60501, 773-889-7598 [IL] IIA [AC] Pastor, Iglesia Cristiana Peniel, Summit Argo IL

Lauver, J. Paul, 3910 N 760 W, Shipshewana IN 46565, 260-768-7073 [IM] [RE]

Lauver, Melvin H., 1001 E Oregon Rd, Lititz PA 17543, 717-581-7860 [LAN] [RE]

Lawton, Wayne D. (Mary Lou) 624 Groff Ave, Elizabethtown PA 17022, 717-361-8990, lawtonwd@aol.com [LAN] IIB1, IIB3a [AC] Pastor, Cedar Hill Community Ch, Elizabethtown PA

Lay, Sarin (Hun) 911 Washington Ave, Prospect Park PA 19076, 215-463-4677, cindy_lay@netzero.net [LAN] IIA [AC] Pastor, Philadelphia Cambodian Menn Ch, Philadelphia PA

Le, Can Ngoc (Lisa Pham) 3871 Scibilia Rd, Fairfax VA

22033, 703-802-0139 [VA] IIB1 [AC] Pastor, Vietnamese Christian Fell, Fairfax VA

Le Blanc, Marvin (Shirley Champagne) PO Box 144E, Des Allemands LA 70030, 504-758-2929 [GS] [AW]

Leaman, Daniel G. (Miriam) 2259 Seitz Dr, Lancaster PA 17601, 717-392-5950 [LAN] [RE]

Leaman, George W., 1001 E Oregon Rd, Lititz PA 17543, 717-569-0689 [LAN] [RE]

Leaman, Glenn (Mary Ann) 2392 Main St, Narvon PA 17555, 610-286-9112 [ACC] III [AC] Licensed Deacon, Conestoga Menn Ch, Morgantown PA

Leaman, Ivan B. (Mary Ellen) 109 N Decatur St, Strasburg PA 17579-1419, 717-687-7967 [LAN] III [AC] Licensed Deacon, Stumptown Menn Ch, Bird-in-Hand PA

Leaman, James R. (Elizabeth Ann Kling [Beth]) 157 Conestoga Blvd, Lancaster PA 17602-3811, 717-672-0970, leamanjb@juno.com [LAN] IIB1 [AC] Interim Pastor, Groffdale Menn Ch, Leola PA

Leaman, John M. (Nancy L. Gehman) 159 Glenbrook Rd, Bird-in-Hand PA 17505, 717-656-6612 [LAN] IIB2 [AC] Associate Pastor, Stumptown Menn Ch, Bird-in-Hand PA

Leaman, Mark M. (Brenda) 1284 Edgewood Dr, East Earl PA 17519, 717-354-8227 [LAN] IB3 [RE] Interim Bishop/Overseer, LAN - 2 churches, PA

Leaman, Paul G. (Erma L.) 3907 Lemonwood Dr, Sarasota FL 34232, 941-378-2793 [SE] [AW]

Leaman, Paul M. (Lillian) 1329 Union Grove Rd, Terre Hill PA 17581, 717-445-4431 [LAN] III [AC] Deacon, Welsh Mountain Menn Ch, New Holland PA

Leaman, Ray K. (Carol) 484 Willow Rd, Lancaster PA 17601, 717-392-7745, rleaman@epix.net [LAN] IIA [AC] Licensed Deacon, Mellinger Menn Ch, Lancaster PA

Leaman, Wilmer W. (Marie) 1342 Reading Rd, Denver PA 17517-9726, 717-445-4792 [LAN] [RE]

Leatherman, Andrew H. (Dorothy) 1551 Valley Rd, Coatesville PA 19320, 610-384-3678, dotandy@yahoo.com [ACC] IIB3a [AC] Chaplain, Einstein Medical Center, Coatesville PA

Lechlitner, Michael, 203 W Wilden Ave, Goshen IN 46526, 574-533-6532 [IM] IIB1 [AC]

Lederach, John M. (Naomi) 1326 Pebble Ct, Goshen IN 46528, 574-534-8395 [IM] [RE]

Lederach, Paul M. (Mary Slagell Lederach) 203 Woods Dr, Lansdale PA 19446, 215-393-8396 [FRC] [RE]

Ledford, Monty Dell (Elaine Joyce) 184 South 3rd West, Box 246, Aberdeen ID 83210-0246, 208-397-4202, mepluseight@juno.com [PNW] IIB1 [AC] Pastor, First Menn Ch, Aberdeen ID

Lefever, Harold H. (Mary) 16 S Mountain Rd, Harrisburg PA 17112, 717-545-1858 [LAN] IIB1 [AC] Pastor, Herr Street Menn Ch, Harrisburg PA

Lefever, Paul B. (Ellene) 714 W Brubaker Valley Rd, Lititz PA 17543, 717-626-5885 [LAN] [RE]

Lehman, Barbara Moyer (John Paul) 1023 Stuart St, Harrisonburg VA 22802, 540-432-6310, barbara@pvmchurch.org [VA] IIB2 [AC] Associate Pastor, Park View Menn Ch, Harrisonburg VA

Lehman, Dale E. (Ruby) 498 Cedar Flat Rd, Warfordsburg PA 17267, 717-294-3896, dlehman@pa.net [FRK] IIA [AC] Assistant Pastor, Bethel Community Ch, Warfordsburg PA

Lehman, Dean M. (Brenda) 4819 Guitner Rd,

Chambersburg PA 17201, 717-375-4586 [FRK] III [AC] Ordained Deacon, Pleasant View Menn Ch, Chambersburg PA

Lehman, Dorcas Miller (Glenn M.) 34 W Eby Rd, Leola PA 17540, 717-656-6226, lehmangd@hydrosoft.net [LAN] IIC [AC] Campus Pastor, Lancaster Mennonite School, Lancaster PA

Lehman, G. Irvin (Verna) 1592 Park Rd, Harrisonburg VA 22801, 540-434-3161 [LAN] [RE]

Lehman, Gerald D. (Joyce) 3729 Edenville Rd, Chambersburg PA 17201, 717-264-1576 [FRK] III [AC] Ordained Deacon, Marion Menn Ch, Chambersburg PA

Lehman, J. Allen (Laura) 1633 Elizabeth Dr, Chambersburg PA 17201, 717-263-3308 [FRK] IIB1 [AC] Pastor, Pleasant View Menn Ch, Chambersburg PA

Lehman, John Paul (Barbara Moyer Lehman) 1023 Stuart St, Harrisonburg VA 22802, 540-432-6310, jplomc@aol.com [OH] [AW]

Lehman, Larry (Helen) 750 Tallow Hill Rd, Chambersburg PA 17201, tallowhill@juno.com [FRK] IIB1 [AC] Pastor, Mount Zion Menn Ch, Boonsboro MD

Lehman, Mark N. (Pauline) 330 Kelley St, Harrisonburg VA 22802, 540-433-0020 [VA] IIB3a [AC]

Lehman, Martin W. (Rhoda) 5248 Manz Pl Apt 121, Sarasota FL 34232, 941-371-2750 x 503, MWLehman@iol14.com [IM] [AW]

Lehman, Maurice E., 1001 E Oregon Rd, Lititz PA 17543-9205 [LAN] [RE]

Lehman, Tim (Susan Marie Gotwals) 110 Pepperbush Dr, Bellefontaine OH 43311-2751, 937-592-8101, jubilee@2access.net [CDC, OH] IIB1 [AC] Pastor, Jubilee Menn Ch, Bellefontaine OH

Lehman, Todd A., 526 N Streeter, Hesston KS 67062, 620-327-2904, toddlehman@hotmail.com [WDC] IIA [AC] Youth Pastor, First Menn Ch, Hillsboro KS

Lehman, Verl, 66124 CR 27, Goshen IN 46526, 574-533-7943 [IM] [RE]

Lehman, Wilmer R. (Mary Louise (Rufenacht)) 4670 Mount Clinton Pk, Harrisonburg VA 22802, 540-867-5621, wmlehman@rica.net [VA] [RE]

Leichty, Paul D. (Nancy J.) 10877 Goldenrod Dr, Middlebury IN 46540-9240, 574-825-5649, PDLeichty@cresources.org [IM] IIB3c [AC] Community Relations & Special Events Manager, Goldenrod Community, Middlebury IN

Leichty, Philip D. (Virginia) 502 Jefferson St, Rensselaer IN 47978, 219-866-8404, bomc@netnitco.net [IM] IIB1 [AC] Pastor, Burr Oak Menn Ch, Rensselaer IN

Leidig, Melvin, 3212 7th St SW, Canton OH 44710, 330-455-5502 [OH] [AW]

Leinbach, Alan E. (Helen K. [Eby]) 5417 N 900 E, North Webster IN 46555, 574-834-4137, leinbaae@grace.edu [IM] IIB1 [AC] Pastor, Menn Ch of Warsaw, Warsaw IN

Leinbach, Etril J., 1801 Greencroft Blvd, Goshen IN 46526, 574-533-6550 [IM] [RE]

Leman, Robert, 2619 Coronado Dr, Fullerton CA 92635, 714-870-5766 [PSW] IIB2 [AC]

Lemon, J. Robert, 58 Gravel Hill Rd, Beaver OH 45613, 614-226-7635 [OH] [RE]

Lengel, C. Robert (Sylvia A.) 32 West Hilcrest Ave, Chalfont PA 18914, 215-822-6967, crl@bux.com [EDC] [AW]

Lentz, Wilbur A., 1001 E Oregon Rd, Lititz PA 17543-9205, 717 509-5823 [LAN] [RE]

Lepard, Alan, 516 N Duncan, Newton KS 67114, 316-284-9871, alepard@sbcglobal.net [WDC] IIA [AC] Youth and Young Adult Pastor, Faith Menn Ch, Newton KS

Leppert, George Earl (Yvonne) 226 North St, Filer ID 83328, 208-326-3288, gleppert@filertel.com [PNW] IIB1 [AC] Pastor, Filer Menn Ch, Filer ID

Lever, Lawrence Lee (Terri Lea) 201 N Wedel, PO Box 378, Moundridge KS 67107, 620-345-2629, leelever@hotmail.com [WDC] IIB1 [AC] Pastor, Eden Menn Ch, Moundridge KS

Lewman, Richard (Collene) 420 Thousand Acre Rd, Sellersville PA 18960, 215-257-5365, rlewman@p3.net [FRC] IIB1 [AC] Pastor, Finland Menn Ch, Pennsburg PA

Lichti, Tim (Carolyn) 1234 Westbrooke Ct, Goshen IN 46528-5065, 574-537-8826, tim@im.mennonite.net [IM] IB2 [AC] Conference Regional Minister, Indiana-Michigan Mennonite Conference, Goshen IN

Lilliston, Brenda Glanzer (Cecil Douglas Jr) 2200 S Rock Rd Apt 1308, Wichita KS 67207, 316-685-3951 [WDC] IIB3a [AC] Staff Chaplain, Via Christi-St. Joseph, Wichita KS

Linberger, Ray Charles (Carol J.) 2105 Mill Hill Rd, Quakertown PA 18951-2223, 215-536-5371, mplinberger@easy-pages.com [EDC] IIB1 [AC] Pastor, Grace Bible Fell of Huntingdon Valley, Huntingdon Valley PA

Lind, Millard (Mariam) 1123 S 8th St, Goshen IN 46526, 574-533-6098 [IM] [RE]

Lind, Ralph Irvin (Brenda Janzen Lind) 304 Spruce NE #1, Albuquerque NM 87106, 505-247-9753, rlind@flash.net [RM] IIB3a [AC]

Lind, Wilbert G. (Rhoda Hess) 1001 E Oregon Rd, Lititz PA 17543, 717-560-2922 [LAN] [RE]

Link, Gary L. (Lorene) 977 E Woodland Lake Rd, Morgantown IN 46160, 812-988-2189 [IM] IIB1 [AC] Pastor, Bean Blossom Menn Ch, Morgantown IN

Linsenmeyer, Dean A. (Rebecca K.) 644 Elridge St, Golden CO 80401, 303-238-5097, ghmenno@att.net [RM] IIB1 [AC] Pastor, Glennon Heights Menn Ch, Lakewood CO

Lisenmeyer, Rebecca (Dean A.) 644 Elridge St, Golden CO 80401, 303-238-5097, bdlinsemeyer@aol.com [RM] IIB3 [AC] Chaplain

Litwiller, Kenneth (Laura Dewey) 27 Kristi Ln, Lewistown PA 17044, 717-242-2439 [ALL] IIA [AC] Pastor, Lost Creek Menn Ch, Mifflintown PA

Litwiller, Kurt, 326 Madison St, Hopedale IL 61747, 309-449-3447, Kurt.Litwiller@bitwise1.com [CDC] IIA [AC] Pastor, Boynton Menn Ch, Hopedale IL

Litwiller, Richard A. (Cynthia A Valdez Litwiller) 418 S Wheatland, Goshen IN 46526, 574-534-2621 [IM] [AW]

Liu, Adam Chu-Tsun, 10084 Adriana, Cupertino CA 95014, 408-253-3638 [PSW] IIB1 [AC] Pastor, Cupertino Menn Ch, Cupertino CA

Livengood, Dwain D., 124 Herr Ave, Lancaster PA 17602, 717-390-8790 [LAN] IIC [AC] Associate Pastor, Lyndon Menn Ch, Lancaster PA

Livengood, Kenneth (Gale) 58214 SR 15, Goshen IN 46526, 574-533-9807, klivengood@elkhart.net [IM] IIB1 [AC] Pastor, Bonneyville Menn Ch, Bristol IN

Livengood, Paul T., Rt 6 Box 6640, Keyster WV 26726, 304-788-1882 [ALL] IIA [AC] Associate Pastor, Pinto Menn Ch, Pinto MD

Livermore Jr, J. D. (Debra K.) Rt 1 Box 215 Co Line Rd, Germfask MI 49836, 906-586-9978, dlivermore@portup.com [IM] IIA [AC] Pastor, Germfask Menn Ch, Germfask MI

Lloyd, Gary E. (Nancy) 419 E Vine St, Stowe PA 19464, 610-327-3109, clloyd98@juno.com [ACC] IIB1 [AC] Pastor, Hope Community Fell, Phoenixville PA

Logan, Peter L. (Tamalyn) 125 Meadow View Ln, Bainbridge PA 17502, 717-367-4091, ptlogan4@aol.com [LAN] IIA [AC] Pastor, Fountain of Life Ch, Middletown PA

Long, Clair R. (Barbara) 5334 Southview Dr, New Holland PA 17557, 717-355-2031 [LAN] IIB1 [AC] Pastor, Lichty Menn Ch, New Holland PA

Long, Paul W. (Esther) 250 N Spring Garden St, Ambler PA 19002 [FRC] IIA [AC]

Longacre, James C. (Ellen) 1387 Rt 100, Barto PA 19504, 610-845-7686 [FRC] IIB1 [AC] Pastor, Salford Menn Ch, Harleysville PA

Longenecker, Alvin (Ada) RR 3 Box 373A, Lewisburg PA 17837-9737, 717-568-4832 [LAN] III [AC] Deacon, Buffalo Menn Ch, Mifflinburg PA

Longenecker, Catherine S. (Daniel) 1580 College Ave, Harrisonburg VA 22802, 540-432-5549 [VA] [RE]

Longenecker, Daniel M. (Catherine) 1580 College Ave, Harrisonburg VA 22802, 540-432-5549 [VA] IIB3a [AC]

Longenecker, William P. (Rhoda) IIB3b [AC] Pastor, Morson Community Bible Fell, Sleeman ON

Loop, Barry W. (Sue) 2350 Staples Mill Rd, Richmond VA 23230, 804-355-4922, sloop@gardener.com [VA] IIB1 [AC] Pastor, First Menn Ch of Richmond, Richmond VA

Lopez, Samuel M. (Soledad) 573B E Main St, New Holland PA 17557-1406, 717-354-8867, smlopez573@juno.com [LAN] IB3 [AC] Spanish Supervisor (Overseer), LAN - Spanish District, PA

Louis, Laurent (Jasmine) 3511 22nd St SW, Lehigh Acres FL 33971, 941-369-7158 [SE] IIC [AC] Pastor, Assemblee de la Grace, Immokalee FL

Louis II, Peter K., 1521 A Kam IV Rd, Honolulu HI 96819 [LAN] IIA [AC] Associate Pastor, New Life Christian Fell, Honolulu HI

Lowery, Lee A. (Leona) 11624 S Hale St, Chicago IL 60643, 773-233-9699 [IL] [RE]

Ludwig, Jeffery A. (Maietta A.) 202 West St, PO Box 98, Pulaski IA 52584, jefflud@netins.net [CP] IIB1 [AC] Pastor, Pulaski Menn Ch, Pulaski IA

Luginbill, Douglas Ray (Paula Jean [Lehman]) Hope Mennonite Church, 868 N Maize Rd, Wichita KS 45817, pastor@hopemennonite.com [WDC] IIB2 [AC] Pastor, Hope Menn Ch, Wichita KS

Luu, Paul Quoccuong (Na) 1536 Pohaku St #306, Honolulu HI 96817-2854, 808-545-8318, pjhonuluu@juno.com [LAN] IIA [AC] Pastor, Vietnamese Christian Fell, Honolulu HI

Lyndaker, Milford E. (Carolyn June) HC 68, Box 113, Wardensville WV 26851, 504-874-4247, mclyndaker@citlink.net [VA] IIB1 [AC] Pastor, Crest Hill Community Ch, Wardensville WV

M

Mack, Ellis L., 487 Smokepipe Rd, Souderton PA 18964, 215-256-8422 [FRC] [RE]

Maclin, Janace (Rick) 13208 Matador, St Louis MO 63141, 314-542-2123 [IL] IIB2 [AC] Associate Pastor, Bethesda Menn Ch, St Louis MO

MINISTERS

6

Maclin, Phillip, 2918 W Montana St, Peoria IL 61605, 309-674-0529 [CDC, IL] IIC [AC] Pastor, Joy Fell Menn Ch, Peoria IL

Maclin, Rick (Janace) 13208 Matador, St Louis MO 63141, 314-542-2123 [IL] IIB1 [AC] Pastor, Bethesda Menn Ch, St Louis MO

MacMaster, Eve B. (Richard Kerwin MacMaster) 4130 NW 19th Pl, Gainesville FL 32605, gnvmenno@bellsouth.net [SE] IIA [AC] Pastor, Emmanuel Menn Ch, Gainesville FL

Maenza, Philip James, 123 South Main St, Athens PA 18810, 570-882-9366 [FRC] IIA [AC] Pastor, New Life Menn Ch, Athens PA

Maina, Gladys (Simon Mungai) 2104 W Bryden Dr, Muncie IN 47304, 317-289-5436, smungai@regenstrief.org [CDC, IM] IIB1 [AC] Pastor, Morning Star Ch, Muncie IN

Maldonado, Carlos M. (Adelaida) 473 Rockland St, Lancaster PA 17602 [LAN] IIA [AC] Pastor, Faro Ardiente, Vineland NJ

Maldonado, David (Madaline) 3225 4th Street W, Lehigh Acres FL 33971, 941-365-0568, DaveMady@aol.com [SE] IIB1 [AC] Pastor, Iglesia Menonita Arca de Salvacion, Fort Myers FL

Maldonado, Madeline (David) 3225 4th St W, Lehigh Acres FL 33971 [SE] IIA [AC] Associate Pastor, Iglesia Menonita Arca de Salvacion, Fort Myers FL

Malin, C. Ralph, 11 Sycamore Dr, Malvern PA 19355, 610-644-6726 [FRC] [RE]

Mamo, Mesfin (Lily Girma) 45 Marble Hill Ave #3D, Bronx NY 10463, 718-561-1250, Mesfinm@worldnet.att.net [LAN] IIA [AC] Associate Pastor, Emmanuel Worship Center, Bronx NY

Marchand, James C. (Donna) 732 Ashby Dr, Waynesboro VA 22980, 219-261-3401, marchand@ntelos.net [VA] IIB1 [AC] Pastor, Lynside Menn Ch, Lyndhurst VA

Margono, Harjono (Maria Ong) 12051 Havelock Ave, Culver City CA 90230, 310-745-0335, margono@juno.com [PSW] IIB2, IIB3b [AW]

Marin, Basil (Diane) 446 E Rock St, Harrisonburg VA 22802, 540-574-3344, basil@rica.net [VA] IIB1 [AC] Pastor, Immanuel Menn Ch, Harrisonburg VA

Marshall, Eric P. (Cheryl) 53 East Main St, Reinholds PA 17569, 717-336-0392, eric@gearlmartin.com [LAN] IIB2 [AC] Youth Pastor, Blainsport Menn Ch, Stevens PA

Martens, John, PO Box 113, Chester VT 05143, 802-875-3057 [FRC] [RE]

Martens, Rudolph (Elvina Neufeld Martens) 2114 Lane Ave, Elkhart IN 46517, 574-293-8612 [CDC, IL] [RE]

Martens, Weldon R. (Jenny Harms Martens) PO Box 342, Henderson NE 68371, 402-723-4878 [CP] IIB1 [AC] Pastor, Bethesda Menn Ch, Henderson NE

Martin, Alvin G. (Elva) 201 Wheat Ridge Dr, Ephrata PA 17522-8554, 717-445-6813 [LAN] [RE]

Martin, Brenda North (Stanley) 1616 Glengarry Dr, Cary NC 27561, 919-932-5206 [VA] IIB3a [AC]

Martin, Brian E. (Shirley) 5559 Division Hwy, Narvon PA 17555, 717-354-0784, bemartin@ptd.net [LAN] III [AC] Ordained Deacon, Weaverland Menn Ch, East Earl PA

Martin, Bruce (Jewell) 1100 College Ave, Harrisonburg VA 22802, 540-433-9926 [VA] IIB3c [AC]

Martin, C. Kenneth (Lois) 238 Reading Rd, East Earl PA 17519, 717-445-5736, kenc@epix.net [LAN] IB3 [AC]

Bishop, Weaverland-Northeast District PA

Martin, Carl W. (Margaret) 106 Furlow Rd, Reinholds PA 17569-9057, 717-484-4239 [LAN] [RE]

Martin, Chauncey L. (Gwen) 1400 Gloster Ave, Baltimore MD 21230, 410-646-4660 [LAN] IIC [AC] Associate Pastor, Wilkens Avenue Menn Ch, Baltimore MD

Martin, Chester L. (Linda) 1200 Kramer Mill Rd, Denver PA 17517, 717-445-7563, clmartin@epix.net [LAN] IIB2 [AC] Associate Pastor, Village Chapel Menn Ch, New Holland PA

Martin, Clifford L. (Carol) 83 S Reamstown Rd, Stevens PA 17578, 717-336-8239, ccmarfam@juno.com [LAN] IIA [AC] Leadership Team, Ephrata Menn Ch, Ephrata PA; Camp Administrator, Woodcrest Retreat Center, Ephrata PA

Martin, Curvin (Mary Ann) RR 2 Box 413A, Myerstown PA 17067, 717-949-2783 [LAN] [AW]

Martin, D. David (Robin) 603 Lititz Rd, Manheim PA 17545, 717-626-5295, ddavidmartin@juno.com [LAN] IIB2 [AC] Associate Pastor, Manheim Menn Ch, Manheim PA

Martin, Daryl G. (Doris) 16 Cherry St, Pine Grove PA 17963, 570-345-2552, dmartin@phfa.org [LAN] IIC [AC] Pastor, Roedersville Menn Ch, Pine Grove PA

Martin, David Henry (Janet) 85 Dogwood Ct, Shippensburg PA 17257, 717-264-8633 [FRK] III [AC] Ordained Deacon, Chambersburg Menn Ch, Chambersburg PA

Martin, Donald, 591 W Broad St, New Holland PA 17557, 717-354-8705 [LAN] [RE]

Martin, Edwin Ray (Janet) 105 S Blainsport Rd, Reinholds PA 17569-9714, 717-336-3596 [LAN] III [AC] Deacon, Blainsport Menn Ch, Stevens PA

Martin, Elmer G. (Grace) 105 New St Box 267, Blue Ball PA 17506-0267, 717-354-4000 [LAN] [RE]

Martin, Elmer M. (Joanne) 795 Durlach Rd, Stevens PA 17578, 717-738-0589 [LAN] III [AC] Ordained Deacon, Hershey Menn Ch, Kinzers PA

Martin, Emanuel (Lois Mumaw Martin) 228 N President Ave #3, Lancaster PA 17603, manlois57@cs.com [ACC] IB3 [AC] Interim Pastor, Bethel Menn Ch of Lancaster, Lancaster PA

Martin, Enos D. (Ruth) 595 Old Hershey Rd, Elizabethtown PA 17022-9409, 717-367-2628, enosd@desupernet.net [LAN] IB3 [AC] Bishop/Overseer, LAN - Elizabethtown District, PA

Martin, Ernest D. (Rosetta M.) 3005 Renkenberger Rd, Columbiana OH 44408, 330-482-3139 [OH] [RE]

Martin, Ernest W. (Nancy) 49 Hillside Rd, Pottsville PA 17901, 570-622-8743, enmartin@losch.net [LAN] IIB2 [AC] Associate Pastor, Palo Alto Menn Ch, Pottsville PA

Martin, Erwin G. (M. Arlene) 323 Hartings Park Rd, Denver PA 17517, 717-445-6546 [LAN] [RE]

Martin, Ezra M., 1415 Pleasant View Rd, Ephrata PA 17522, 717-733-4517 [LAN] [RE]

Martin, G. Joseph (Ruth Ann) 1539 Choxes Chase, Greencastle PA 17225, 717-593-0060 [FRK] IIB1 [AC] Pastor, Salem Ridge Menn Ch, Greencastle PA

Martin, Gary E. (Krista) 7 N Conestoga View Dr, Akron PA 17501, 717-859-5520, gkmartin1@yahoo.com [LAN] IIA [AC] Associate Pastor, Landis Valley Menn Ch, Lancaster PA

Martin, Gary E. (Patricia Mierau Martin) 1545 W Pratt #203, Chicago IL 60626-4215, gmartin1545@aol.com

[IL] IIB1 [AC] Interim Pastor, Arthur Menn Ch, Arthur IL

Martin, Glen D. (Mary) 119 Furlow Rd, Reinholds PA 17569-9143, 717-484-2162, glenmarymartin@juno.com [LAN] IIB1 [AC] Associate Pastor, Gehman Menn Ch, Adamstown PA

Martin, Glenn H. (Carolyn J.) 600 W Aberdeen Dr, Trenton OH 45067-1008, 513-988-1355 [CDC] IIB1 [AC] Pastor, Trenton Menn Ch, Trenton OH

Martin, Harold L. (Ellen) 3336 Teak Cr, Harrisonburg VA 22801, 540-432-0839 [VA] [RE]

Martin, Harold W. (Twila) 76 Reinholds Rd, Reinholds PA 17569, 717-336-5418 [LAN] [RE]

Martin, Irvin L., 1788 Bowmansville Rd, Mohnton PA 19540, 717-484-4439, IrvinM3@juno.com [LAN] IB3, IIB1 [AC] Pastor, Gehman Menn Ch, Adamstown PA

Martin Jr, Irvin S. (Rachel) 703 N Warfield Dr, Mount Airy MD 21771, 301-829-2312 [LAN] IIB1 [AC] Co-Pastor, Mount Airy Menn Ch, Mount Airy MD

Martin, J. Daniel (Cynthia) 14 W Main St Box 441, Richland PA 17087, 717-866-7911 [LAN] III [AC] Ordained Deacon, Meckville Menn Ch, Bethel PA

Martin Jr, J. Donald (Yvonne) 334 Pershing Ave, Lebanon PA 17042, 717-270-9918, donymartin@juno.com [LAN] IIB2 [AC] Pastor, Lebanon Christian Fell, Lebanon PA

Martin Sr, J. Donald (Mary Ann) 697 Prescott Dr, Lebanon PA 17042, 717-273-8797 [LAN] IIB1 [AC] Pastor, Meckville Menn Ch, Bethel PA; Chaplain, Lebanon County Prison, Lebanon PA

Martin, J. Elvin (Laverne) 100 Main St, Akron PA 17501, 717-859-3960 [LAN] [RE]

Martin, J. Leon (Katherine S.) 1725 Juniper Pl Apt #105, Goshen IN 46526, 574-537-3732 [EDC] [RE]

Martin, J. Nevin (Ruth Ann) 326 Broad St, PO Box 274, Terre Hill PA 17581, 717-445-5618, jnrmartin@juno.com [LAN] III [AC] Ordained Deacon, Weaverland Menn Ch, East Earl PA

Martin, J. Wilbur, 2525 Bolton Boone Dr Apt 1103, De Soto TX 75115-2033 [LAN] [RE]

Martin, James B. (Betty) 1642 Reading Rd, Mohnton PA 19540, 717-445-4313 [LAN] IIB3c [AC]

Martin, Jason S., 62249 Cedar Rd, Mishawaka IN 46544-9491, 574-633-4605 [IM] [RE]

Martin, Jerold R., 200 Speedwell Forge Rd, Lititz PA 17543, 717-626-9148 [LAN] IIB2 [AC] Associate Pastor, Hinkletown Menn Ch, Ephrata PA

Martin, Jewel (Bruce) 1100 College Ave, Harrisonburg VA 22802, 540-433-9926 [VA] IIB3c [AC]

Martin, John R. (Marian) 1504 Hawthorn Cr, Harrisonburg VA 22802, 540-432-7253 [VA] IIB2 [AC]

Martin, Kelly G. (Sherry) 496 Weaverland Valley Rd, East Earl PA 17519, 717-445-0930 [LAN] IIC [AC] Youth Pastor, Bowmansville Menn Ch, Bowmansville PA

Martin, Kenneth (Dawn) 622 Front St, PO Box 463, New Berlin PA 17855, 717-966-0003 [LAN] IIC [AC] Chaplain, Prison Ministry, PA

Martin, Lauren R. (Kimberly S.W.) 2401 Blake Ave, Glenwood Springs CO 81601-4326, 970-945-8851, llkmsplace@juno.com [RM] IIB1 [AC] Pastor, Glenwood Menn Ch, Glenwood Springs CO

Martin, Lee (Margaret) 4697 Mount Clinton Pike, Harrisonburg VA 22802, mcmchurch@juno.com [VA] IIB1 [AC] Pastor, Mount Clinton Menn Ch, Harrisonburg VA

Martin, Lee Roy M. (Ann) 53 Maple Farm Rd, Ephrata PA 17522-9582, 717-859-1526, lemars3@aol.com [LAN] III [AC] Ordained Deacon, Metzler Menn Ch, Akron PA

Martin, Leon Kurtz (Carolyn) 329 Smithville Rd, New Providence PA 17560, 717-786-1996 [LAN] IIB1 [AC] Pastor, Nickel Mines Menn Ch, New Providence PA

Martin, Lew K. (Kayleen) 30 S Whisper Ln, New Holland PA 17557, 717-354-3126, LewKayleeMartin@Paonline.com [LAN] IIC [AC] Youth Pastor, Meadville Menn Ch, Kinzers PA

Martin, Linford (Elaine) 12401 CR 20, Middlebury IN 46540, 574-825-3572, linford@firstmennonite.net [IM] IB3, IIB1 [AC] Pastor, First Menn Ch, Middlebury IN; Overseer for Forks Mennonite, Middlebury IN

Martin, Louis H. (Lois) 3795 Beagle Rd, Middletown PA 17057, 717-944-5677 [LAN] III [AC] Licensed Deacon, Herr Street Menn Ch, Harrisburg PA

Martin, Luke S. (Mary Kauffman Martin) 29 S Madison St, Allentown PA 18102, 610-434-9031, LSMKM@Enter.net [FRC] [RE]

Martin, Marlin E. (Linda) PO Box 202, Terre Hill PA 17581, 717-445-6697 [LAN] IIC [AC] Pastor, Cedar Lane Chapel, Terre Hill PA

Martin, Nelson L. (Janet) 90A Menno Village, Chambersburg PA 17201, 717-263-4502 [ACC] [RE]

Martin, Nelson R. (Carol) 6229 Mount Pleasant Rd, Honey Brook PA 19344, 610-273-3381, nrcdmartin@onemain.com [LAN] IIB1 [AC] Pastor, Goodville Menn Ch, Goodville PA

Martin, Nelson W. (Anna Mae) 7 Cindy Cr, Lititz PA 17543, 717-626-6301 [LAN] IB3 [AC]

Martin, Paul H. (Dorothy) 939 Main St Apt C-2, Akron PA 17501, 515-276-5753 [CP] [RE]

Martin, Philip, Alden Mennonite Church, 923 Two Rod Rd, Alden NY 14004, AMCpastor@juno.com [NY] IIA [AC] Pastor, Alden Menn Ch, Alden NY

Martin, Randall J., 3204 Hostetter Rd, Washington Boro PA 17582, 717-872-5910, giveitall@juno.com [LAN] IIB1 [AC] Pastor, Habecker Menn Ch, Lancaster PA

Martin, Raymond M. (Alice G.) 1212 Springwell Pl, Newport News VA 23608-7709, ralmar@worldnet.att.net [VA] IB3 [AC]

Martin, Rebecca, 303 Wertz Ave, Dalton OH 44618, 330-828-2928 [OH] IIB2 [AC] Youth Pastor, Pleasant View Menn Ch, North Lawrence OH

Martin, Richard B., RR 1 Box 248A2, Monroeton PA 18832-9622, 717-364-3974 [LAN] IIB1 [AC] Pastor, West Franklin Menn Ch, Monroeton PA

Martin, Richard E. (Beverly) 2030 S 050 W, LaGrange IN 46761, 260-463-2231 [IM] IIB1 [AC] Pastor, Plato Menn Ch, LaGrange IN

Martin, Robert A. (Sarah) 1460 Main St, East Earl PA 17519, 717-445-5101 [LAN] [AW]

Martin, Robert K. (Sandra) PO Box 212, Morris Run PA 16939, 570-638-2274, rkmartin@ptdprolog.net [LAN] IIB1 [AC] Pastor, Calvary Menn Fell, Morris Run PA

Martin, Robert S. (Mary) 2510 S 5th Ave, Lebanon PA 17042, 717-949-3586 [LAN] IIB2 [AC] Associate Pastor, Krall Menn Ch, Lebanon PA

Martin, Rodney A. (Angie) 63 Robinhill Dr, Lititz PA 17543-7301, 717-625-1706, rodmarmis@aol.com [LAN] IIA [AC] Youth Pastor, Lititz Menn Ch, Lititz PA

Martin, Roger I. (Dorothy) 117 S Valley Dr, Hagerstown

MD 21740, 301-790-3843 [FRK] [AW]

Martin, Roy B. (Grace) 17 Hilltop Dr, Ephrata PA 17522, 717-733-6351 [LAN] IIB2 [AC] Associate Pastor, Metzler Menn Ch, Akron PA

Martin, Roy D. (Ruth) RR 4 Box 236M, Waynesboro VA 22980, 540-943-8102 [VA] [RE]

Martin, Stephen L. (Betty) 875 Lincoln Garden Rd, Ephrata PA 17522, 717-733-3150, slm875@dejazzd.com [LAN] IIB1 [AC] Pastor, Indiantown Menn Ch, Ephrata PA

Martin, Todd, 303 Wertz Ave, Dalton OH 44618, 330-828-2928 [OH] IIB2 [AC] Youth Pastor, Pleasant View Menn Ch, North Lawrence OH

Martin, Warren W. (Verna) 416 Memorial Hwy, Fleetwood PA 19522, 610-944-0574 [LAN] [RE]

Martinez, Esther, 3701 Forest Lawn Rd, Balch Springs TX 75180, emartine@airmail.net [SC, WDC] IIA [AC] Co-Pastor, Many Peoples Menn Fell, Dallas TX

Martino, David (Susan) RR 1 Box 111, Winfield PA 17889, 717-743-0326, cmfmilton@hotmail.com [LAN] IIB1 [AC] Pastor, Community Menn Fell, Milton PA

Martz, Robert (Sherry) PO Box 164, 1941 Cleveland Ave, Comins MI 48619, 989-848-2909, Rmartz@yahoo.com [CDC] IIA [AC] Pastor, Comins Menn Ch, Comins MI

Martzall, Dorcas J. (Glenn) 316 S Railroad Ave, New Holland PA 17557, 717-354-8188 [LAN] IIC [AC] Chaplain, Mennonite Communities, Lancaster PA

Marvin, Ray (Mary) 28 Harrison Dr, Quarryville PA 17566, 717-786-9196, abcf@epix.net [ACC] IIA [AC] Pastor, Andrews Bridge Christian Fell, Christiana PA

Massanari, Eric, 912 S Pine St, Newton KS 67114 [WDC] IIB1 [AC] Pastor, Shalom Menn Ch, Newton KS

Mast, Conrad (Donna) 531 Scottdale Ave, Scottdale PA 15683, 724-887-5563 [ALL] IIB1 [AC] Co-Pastor, Kingview Menn Ch, Scottdale PA

Mast, Daniel Lamar (Lori) 818 North Octorara Trail, Parkesburg PA 19365, 610-857·3729, brtransport.com [LAN] IIA, III [AC] Licensed Deacon, Old Road Menn Ch, Gap PA

Mast, Donna (Conrad) 531 Scottdale Ave, Scottdale PA 15683, 724-887-5563 [ALL] IB3, IIB1 [AC] Co-Pastor, Kingview Menn Ch, Scottdale PA

Mast, Fremon E., 6193 Chestnut Ridge, Wooster OH 44691, 330-264-0945 [OH] [RE]

Mast, Galen, 62480 SR 13, Goshen IN 46528, 574-642-3941, mastg@westview.k12.in.us [IM] IIA [AC] Youth Pastor, Emma Menn Ch, Topeka IN

Mast, LeRoy J. (Sherry Lee) PO Box 91, Hammondsport NY 14840, 607-569-3651, lsmast2@juno.com [NY] IIB1 [AC] Pastor, Pleasant Valley Menn Ch, Hammondsport NY

Mast, Michael M. (Mattie Marie) 505 Smith Ave, Dalton OH 44618-9039, 330-828-0491, mmmast@juno.com [OH] IIB1 [AC] Pastor, Sonnenberg Menn Ch, Kidron OH

Mast, Moses (Sadie) 4708 Outpost Dr, Spencer OK 73084, 405-771-4743, mosesmast@aol.com [WDC] IIB1 [AC] Pastor, Joy Menn Ch, Spencer OK

Mast, Robert W. (Esther) 2314 Mount Pleasant Rd, Chesapeake VA 23322, 757-482-3435 [VA] [RE]

Mast, Russell Lowell, 2635 Walnut St, Box 59, Walnut Creek OH 44687-0059, 330-893-2356 [CDC] [RE]

Mast, Wesley S. (Elsie [Mack]) 532 Linden St, Bethlehem PA 18018-6215, 610-868-0780, wmast@juno.com [EDC] IIA [AC] Chaplain, Hospice of Lancaster County,

Lancaster PA

Matos, Eugenio (Sergia) 762 Centre St, Trenton NJ 08611, 609-396-1901 [LAN] IIA [AC] Pastor, Nueva Vida en Cristo, Trenton NJ

Matteson, F. Matthew (Mary Lou) 2720 Tsawsi Rd, Knoxville TN 37931, 865-691-5347, mlmatteson@compuserve.com [VA] IIB1 [AC] Pastor, Concord Menn Ch, Knoxville TN

Maust, Duane E. (Elaine L.) 135 Fairchild Rd, Meridian MS 39307, 601-485-2248, Duelchna@aol.com [GS] IIB1 [AC] Co-Pastor, Jubilee Menn Ch, Meridian MS

Maust, Elaine (Duane Earl) 135 Fairchild Rd, Meridian MS 39307, 601-485-2248, Duelchna@aol.com [GS] IIB1 [AC] Co-Pastor, Jubilee Menn Ch, Meridian MS

Maust, Ezra (Darlene), 7213 Honeybush Dr, Mount Airy MD 21771, 301-829-2556 [LAN] IIB2 [AC] Co-Pastor, Mount Airy Menn Ch, Mount Airy MD

Maust, Norman (Wilmetta) 57365 CR 23, Goshen IN 46528, 574-295-6511 [IM] IIB3c [AC] Ordained Deacon, Pleasant View Menn Ch, Goshen IN

Maven, G. Craig, 1326 Yoderstrasse, Berne IN 46711, 260-589-9911, craig@firstmennonite.org [CDC] IIB1 [AC] Pastor, First Menn Ch, Berne IN

McClintic, David (Terry) PO Box 328, Concord MI 49237, 517-524-7489, dtmcclin@modempool.com [IM] IIB1 [AC] Pastor, Liberty Menn Ch, Concord MI

McDorman, Lewis E., 326 SW 6th St, PO Box 1278, Premont TX 78375-1278, 361-348-2872 [SC] IIB1 [AC] Pastor, United Menn Ch, Premont TX

McFarland, John (Mabel) D-90 Kalkaji, New Delhi 110019, India [VA] IIB3b [AC]

McFarren, Patrick J. (Janet Elaine [Lehman]) 94 Hickory Tree Rd, Asheville NC 28805, 828-298-3233, avlmenno@juno.com [VA] IIB1 [AC] Pastor, Asheville Menn Ch, Asheville NC

McKinney, Karl (Kellie M.) 1628 W Columbia Ave, Chicago IL 60626-4111, 773-764-5871, pastorKAM@aol.com [IL] IIB3b [AC] Minister of Church Planting, Mennonite Mission Network, Elkhart IN

McKnight, Hugh (Joyce) 632 Menoher Blvd, Johnstown PA 15901, 814-539-0719 [ALL] IIB1 [AC]

McPhee, Art (Evelyn L. McPhee) AMBS, 3003 Benham Ave, Elkhart IN 46517, 574-296-6210, amcphee@ambs.edu [IM] IIB3c [AC] Professor, Associated Mennonite Biblical Seminary, Elkhart IN

McVay, Darrel, 48655 Center St, St Clairsville OH 43950, 740-695-0303 [OH] IIB1 [AC] Pastor, Fairpoint Menn Ch, Fairpoint OH

Meador, James B. (Judy Poole Meador) 2209 Silver Ln, Willow Street PA 17584-9613, 717-871-8210, JJ.Meador@verison.net [LAN] IIB1 [AC] Pastor, Willow Street Menn Ch, Willow Street PA

Mears-Driedger, June (Kevin) 2315 S Washington St, Lansing MI 48910, 517-346-7610, jmdriedger@mindspring.com [CDC, IM] IIB1 [AC] Pastor, MSU Menn Fell, East Lansing MI

Meck, Jay A. (Ruth) 5 Barr Ave, Gordonville PA 17529, 717-768-8119 [LAN] [RE]

Meck, John D. (Jane) 109 Snake Ln, Kinzers PA 17535, 717-768-8334, j6meck@dejazzd.com [LAN] IIB1 [AC] Pastor, Meadville Menn Ch, Kinzers PA

Meck, John Dwight (Deborah) 371 Walnut Run Rd, Willow Street PA 17584, 717-687-7120, jd.meck@juno.com [LAN] IIB1 [AC] Pastor, Strasburg

Menn Ch, Strasburg PA

Mejia, René, 1129 Ayersville St, Defiance OH 43512, 419-782-6761, reneme@defnet.com [OH] IIB1 [AC] Pastor, Primera Iglesia Menonita, Defiance OH

Melendrez, John, 11551 E 169th St, Artesia CA 90701-1706, 310-860-3464 [PSW] IIB1 [AC] Pastor, Bethel Community Ch, Santa Fe Springs CA

Mellinger, James (Ruth W.) 615 W Ames Pl, Williamsport PA 17701, 717-323-9779, agape@chilitech.net [LAN] IIB1 [AC] Youth Pastor, Agape Fell, Williamsport PA

Menard, Martin (Rosette) PO Box 381282, Miami FL 33238, 305-891-1651, PMenard@STIS.net [SE] IIC [AC] Pastor, Good Shepherd Evangelical, Miami FL

Mendoza, Irene (Rafael) 328 S Azusa Ave, La Puente CA 91744, 626-912-1983, holfmc1@juno.com [PSW] IIA [AC] Associate Pastor, House of the Lord Fell, La Puente CA; Staff Associate—Spanish Speaking Ministries, Center for Anabaptist Leadershiip, Pasadena CA

Meneses, Michael A. (Eloise Hiebert Meneses) 1109 Allentown Rd, Lansdale PA 19446, 215-393-9836, meneses1@juno.com [FRC] IIB1 [AC] Pastor, Wellspring Ch of Skippack, Skippack PA

Mengistu, Yeshitela (Ebebach) PO Box 16668, St Louis MO 63105, 314-725-63105 [IL] IIC [AC] Teacher/Director, Jesus-The Fountain Of Life Institute, Addis Ababa Ethiopia

Messenger, David, PO Box 150777, Cape Coral FL 33915-0777, 239-772-5683, DPMessage@juno.com [SE] IIA [AC] Worship Pastor, Cape Christian Fell, Cape Coral FL

Metzler, Duane L. (Kristine) 707 Millwood Rd, Willow Street PA 17584, 717-464-3361 [LAN] IIB1 [AC] Pastor, University Christian Fell, Willow Street PA

Metzler, Edgar J. (Ethel Yake Metzler) 1119 Main St, Akron PA 17501, 717-859-2133, etheled@juno.com [CDC, IM] IIB3c [AC] Director of International Programs, Mennonite Central Committee, Akron IN

Metzler, Everett G. (Margaret J.) 1311 Cosmo St, Goshen IN 46528, 574-534-5491, MetzlerUSA@aol.com [IM] [RE]

Metzler, Glenn D. (Betty) 2646 Pinewood Rd, Lancaster PA 17601, 717-581-5399 [LAN] IIC [AC] Chaplain, Landis Homes, Lititz PA

Metzler, Glenn E. (Esther) 26 Park St, Farmingdale ME 04344-2907, 207-377-8451, gmetzler@juno.com [LAN] IIB1 [AC] Pastor, Kennebec Menn Ch, Farmingdale ME

Metzler, John B., 266 Panorama Dr, Denver PA 17517, 717-445-6769 [LAN] [RE]

Meyer, Brenda Hostetler (Rich Meyer) 13416 CR 44, Millersburg IN 46543, 574-642-3963, brendam@maplenet.net [IM] IIA [AC] Pastor, Benton Menn Ch, Goshen IN

Michaels, Thomas L. (Cheryl D.) 5359 PR 382, Millersburg OH 44654, 330-893-3750 [OH] IIB1 [AC] Pastor, Millersburg Menn Ch, Millersburg OH

Middleton, Glenn (Ardis) 70245 Kime Rd, Sturgis MI 49091, 269-651-6046 [IM] IIB1 [AC] Pastor, Christian Fell Center, Sturgis MI

Mierau, Jake, 1478 Willow Ct Lot 45, Goshen IN 46526, 574-534-8102 [CDC] [RE]

Miller, Abner G. (Betty) 1001 E Oregon Rd, Lititz PA 17543, 717-509-5428 [LAN] [RE]

Miller, Alvin R., 28648 CR 38, Wakarusa IN 46573, 574-

862-4300 [IM] [RE]

Miller, Arthur H. (Ethel) 475 Church St, Landisville PA 17538, 717-898-7896 [LAN] [RE]

Miller, Beth (Marcus) Box 62, 914 5th St, Wellman IA 52356, 319-646-2856 [CP] IIC [AC] Chaplain, Parkview Nursing Home, Wellman IA

Miller, Chadwick, 1157 Yuma Circle Apt D, Hartville OH 44632, chad@hartvillemennonite.org [OH] IIA [AC] Youth Pastor, Hartville Menn Ch, Hartville OH

Miller, Corey Lee (Nancy Sue) 891 Chisholm Trail, Newton KS 67114, 620-367-4672, cnmiller@mteloo.net [WDC] IIB1 [AC] Pastor, Tabor Menn Ch, Newton KS

Miller, D. Richard (Marilyn M.) 1044 N 29th St, Fort Dodge IA 50501, 515-576-0285 [CP] [RE]

Miller, Daniel G. (Joyce Elaine) 1119 Chestnut St, Lebanon PA 17042, 717-270-1904, millers@paonline.com [LAN] IIB1 [AC] Pastor, Freedom in Christ Fell, Lebanon PA

Miller, Daniel Z. (Nadine) 62436 CR 17, Goshen IN 46526, 574-534-3229, SuspndrDan@aol.com [IM] [AW] Interim Pastor, Olive Menn Ch, Elkhart IN

Miller, David B. (Mary) 884 Bayberry Dr, State College PA 16801, 814-861-5612 [ALL] IB3, IIB1 [AC]

Miller, David F. (Martha) 231 Mockingbird Dr, Souderton PA 18964 [VA] [RE]

Miller, Edmond F. (Wendy) 11054 Phillips Store Rd, Broadway VA 22815, 540-896-5216 [VA] [AW]

Miller, Edward J., 16203 E Princeton Cr, Aurora CO 80013, 303-699-7510 [RM] [RE]

Miller, Eldo J., 315 W 6th, La Junta CO 81050, 719-775-2145 [RM] [RE]

Miller, Eli (Irene) RR 2 Box 2269, Seligman MO 65745, 417-341-1005 [SC] III [AC] Elder, Rogers Menn/Ch of the Brethren, Pea Ridge AR

Miller, Elsie, 179 Norwood Ct, Box 411, Smithville OH 44677, 216-669-2193 [CDC] [RE]

Miller, Eugene N. (Sharon) 3231 Palmer Rd, Wellsville NY 14895, 716-593-3287, Genemile@aol.com [NY] IIB1 [AC] Pastor, Yorks Corners Menn Ch, Wellsville NY; Camp Administrator, Penn-York Camp, Ulysses PA

Miller, Frederic A. (Judy) 13153 Hackett Rd, Orville OH 44667, 330-857-6521, bethmill@sssnet.com [OH] IIB3c [AC]

Miller, Freeman J. (Naomi) 2027 N Carlisle St, Philadelphia PA 19121, 215-765-3676, fjmiller@erols.com [LAN] IB3 [AC]

Miller, Gordon, 109 Mohican Ave, Orrville OH 44667, 330-683-9398, chpastor@neobright.net [OH] IIA [AC] Pastor, Crown Hill Menn Ch, Rittman OH

Miller, Harold N. (Karen A.) 280 Park Ave, Corning NY 14830, 607.937.4390, HNMiller@juno.com [NY] IB3, IIB1 [AC] Pastor, Community Menn Fell, Corning NY

Miller, Harold W., 604 Sumneytown Pike, PO Box 1001, North Wales PA 19454, 215-699-4227 [FRC] IIB3a [AC]

Miller, Howard I. (Carolyn) 4368 Zion Church Rd, Broadway VA 22815, 540-896-4614, howard@lindale.org [VA] IIB2 [AC]

Miller, Ira E. (Helen) 6519 Shelf Rd, Marshville NC 28103 [VA] [RE]

Miller, J. Brian (Heather) 115 N Pine St, Lancaster PA 17603, 717-399-9077 [LAN] IIC [AC] Associate Pastor, Sunnyside Menn Ch, Lancaster PA

Miller, J. Daniel, 5022 Avoca Ave, Ellicott City MD 21043, 410-465-1233 [LAN] IIB1 [AC] Pastor, First

MINISTERS

6

Menn Ch of Columbia, Ellicott City MD

Miller, J. John J. (Mabel) PO Box 305, Kalona IA 52247, 319-656-5457 [CP] [RE]

Miller, J. Robert (Irene) RR 1 Box 61, Liberty PA 16930-9757, 570-324-5405 [LAN] [RE]

Miller, James A. (Andrea) 41 Federal St, Bridgeport CT 06606, 203-335-0042 [LAN] IIB1 [AC]

Miller, John H. (Anna) 197 Quarry Hill Ln, Schuyler VA 22969, 804-831-2383 [VA] IIB1 [AC]

Miller, John M., 15297 Arnold Rd, Dalton OH 44618, 330-828-8593, johnmiller@nls.net [OH] IIB1 [AC] Pastor, Pleasant View Menn Ch, North Lawrence OH

Miller, Joseph S. (Julie Zimmerman) 1301 Sweet Clover Dr, Goshen IN 46526, 574-534-4448, joe@waterfordchurch.org [IM] IIB1 [AC] Pastor, Waterford Menn Ch, Goshen IN

Miller, Keith Allen Graber (Ann Maureen) 208 River Vista Dr, Goshen IN 46526, 574-534-3891 [IM] IIB3d [AC] Professor, Goshen College, Goshen IN

Miller, Kent E. (D. Jill) 806 E Waterford, Wakarusa IN 46573, 574-862-2512, miller1964@aol.com [IM] IIA [AC] Recruiter, Service, Learning & Discipleship, Mennonite Mission Network, Elkhart IN

Miller, Kenton Tod (Cynthia June [Schrock]) 10907 Market Ave, Uniontown OH 44685, 330-877-3217, k-cmiller@juno.com [OH] IIB2 [AC] Associate Pastor, Dayspring Christian Fell, North Canton OH

Miller, Lee E. (Vina) 2869 Wood St, Sarasota FL 34232, 941-316-0861 [SE] IIB2 [AC] Minister of Administration, Bay Shore Menn Ch, Sarasota FL

Miller, Leo J., 22470 Sandalwood Rd, Cleveland OH 44146, 216-439-3062 [OH] [RE]

Miller, Leo L. (Lola L.) 1906 Iris Village, Moundridge KS 67107-7008 [WDC] [RE]

Miller, Leon J. (Susan K.) 279 Black Oak Dr, Lancaster PA 17602-3477, 717-299-2709, miller1765@home.com [LAN] [AW]

Miller, Lester, 6190N 100E, Howe IN 46746, 260-562-2812 [IM] IIC [AC] Prison Ministry, LaGrange IN

Miller, Levi (Gloria) 903 Arthur Ave, Scottdale PA 15683, 724-887-5515 [ALL] IIC [AC]

Miller, Lewis B. (Lois) 250 Spring Beach Dr, Rome City IN 46784 [IM] IIB1 [AC] Pastor, Lake Bethel Menn Ch, Rome City IN

Miller, Lewis W. (Norma Jean [Sommers]) 719 7th St, Milford NE 68405 [CP] IIA [AC] Pastor, Milford Menn Ch, Milford NE

Miller, Lloyd L. (Joan Yoder Miller) 64308 CR 21, Goshen IN 46526, 574-534-4486, cdcllm@hoosierlink.net [CDC] IB2 [AC] Conference Minister, Central District Conference, Goshen IN

Miller, Lloyd R., 1425 Greencroft Apt 278, Goshen IN 46526, 574-537-4680 [IM] [RE]

Miller, Lynn Arthur (Linda J.) 11088 N Phillips Rd, Bluffton OH 45817, 419-358-2296, LynnAMiller@juno.com [CDC, OH] IIB3c [AC]

Miller, Lynn Roger (Janice Fay) 2758 South Shore Dr, Albany OR 97321, 541-926-3493, lynnjanicemiller@aol.com [PNW] IIB3a [AC] Chaplain, Albany Mennonite Home, Albany OR

Miller, Mahlon D. (Dorothy) 57377 CR 29, Goshen IN 46526 [IM] [RE]

Miller, Marilyn Ferne (Maurice Lee) 2000 Dartmouth Ave, Boulder CO 80305, 303-499-5229 [WDC] [RE]

Miller, Mark, 25392 CR F, Archbold OH 43502, 419-446-0012, pastorwm@powersupply.net [OH] IIB2 [AC] Associate Pastor, Lockport Menn Ch, Stryker OH

Miller, Mark G. (Debbie) 1222 S Owens, Lakewood CO 80226, 303-986-2969 [RM] [AW]

Miller, Mark R. (Joyce Moyer Miller) 2517 Proctor Ln, Baltimore MD 21234, 410-663-4554, mark.miller@mmyfc.org [ACC] IIC [AC] Staff, Metro-Maryland Youth for Christ, Baltimore MD

Miller, Marlin M. (Karen) 180 N Main St, Bolivar NY 14715, 716-928-1452 [LAN] IIB2 [AC] Associate Pastor, Kossuth Community Chapel, Bolivar NY

Miller, Merlin L. (Linda) 953 Bedford St, Chesapeake VA 23322, 757-482-4495 [VA] IIB1 [AC] Pastor, Landstown Community Ch, Virginia Beach VA

Miller, Mervin, 1802 E 37th St, Sterling IL 61085, 815-622-3049, sridge@cin.net [IL] IIB1 [AC] Pastor, Science Ridge Menn Ch, Sterling IL

Miller, Mervin R. (Mary) 9310 Old Route 22, Bethel PA 19507, 717-933-8434 [LAN] [RE]

Miller, Paul R., PO Box 44, Walnut Creek OH 44687, 330-893-2843 [OH] [RE]

Miller, Philip (Verna Mae) 728 Bedford St, Chesapeake VA 23322, 757-482-1836 [VA] [RE]

Miller, Raymond (Ruth) 803 Anderson Ferry Rd, Mount Joy PA 17552, 717-653-8762 [LAN] [RE]

Miller, Robert L. (Belinda) 9202 Cropper Island Rd, Newark MD 21841, 410-629-1233, bobbeem@hotmail.com [ACC] [AW]

Miller, Robin Dean (Cynthia Howell Miller) 3533 Hildana Rd, Shaker Heights OH 44120, 216-561-8142, RobinDeanMiller@hotmail.com [OH] IIB1 [AC] Pastor, Lee Heights Community Ch, Cleveland OH

Miller, Ross A., 844 Basel St, Sugarcreek OH 44681, 330-852-2575, rossamiller@juno.com [OH] IIB1 [AC] Pastor, Walnut Creek Menn Ch, Walnut Creek OH

Miller, S. Paul, 1300 Greencroft Apt 78, Goshen IN 46526, 574-537-3581 [IM] [RE]

Miller, Scott David (Wanda) 7204 N West Rd, Newton KS 67114-8933, 620-327-2822, scott.miller@prairieinet.net [SC, WDC] IIB1 [AC] Pastor, Hesston Inter-Menn Fell, Hesston KS

Miller, Sharon Wyse (Duane) 1204 Sioux St, Burlington IA 52601, 319-753-1516, swmission@lisco.com [CP] IIB1 [AC] Pastor, Peace Menn Ch, Burlington IA; Missions Minister, Central Plains Mennonite Conference

Miller, T. Lee (Marty) 3309 N 600 E, Kokomo IN 46901, 765-628-2984 [IM] IIB1 [AC] Co-Pastor, Howard-Miami Menn Ch, Kokomo IN

Miller, Terry L. (Arbo M.) PO Box 763, Stuarts Draft VA 24477, 540-337-3637, takkmiller@juno.com [VA] IIB1 [AC]

Miller, Thomas H. (Christine) 7 Greenwood Hills, Mountaintop PA 18707, 717-678-3010 [LAN] IIB1 [AC] Pastor, Cornerstone Christian Fell, Mountain Top PA

Miller, Timothy O. (Kathy) PO Box 127, 6097 Pearl St, Naubinway MI 49762, 906-477-8090, tomiller@portup.com [IM] IIB1 [AC] Pastor, Rexton Menn Ch, Naubinway MI; Pastor, Naubinway Menn Ch, Naubinway MI

Miller, Vern L., 2043 Sycamore Dr, Bedford Heights OH 44146, 440-735-1988, hmiller13@juno.com [OH] [AW]

Miller, Vernon U., 27727 CR 36, Goshen IN 46526,

574-862-2748 [IM] [RE]

Miller, Waldo E., 211 Lake Vista Cr, Hesston KS 67062, 620-327-2172 [WDC] [RE]

Miller, Walter Jay (Sonia) 2470 520th St SW, Kalona IA 52247, 319-683-3158 [CP] IIB1 [AC] Pastor, East Union Menn Ch, Kalona IA

Miller, Wendy, 25392 CR F, Archbold OH 43502, 419-446-0012, pastorwm@powersupply.net [OH] IIB2 [AC] Associate Pastor, Lockport Menn Ch, Stryker OH

Miller, Wendy J., 11054 Phillips Store Rd, Broadway VA 22815, 540-896-5216 [VA] IIB3d [AC]

Miller Jr, Albert E. (Diane) 1951 Racimo Dr, Sarasota FL 34240, 941-378-5536, RockyMiller@compuserve.com [SE] IIB2 [AC] Associate Pastor, Bay Shore Menn Ch, Sarasota FL

Miller Jr, Andrew G. (Naomi) 1728 Mount Joy Rd, Manheim PA 17545, 717-653-4848 [LAN] IIB2 [AC] Associate Pastor, Erisman Menn Ch, Manheim PA

Miller-Eshelman, Jon Chester (Holly) 12611 Kornett Ln, Bowie MD 20715-0444, 301-809-4246 [LAN] IIB2 [AC] Associate Pastor, Capital Christian Fell, Laurel MD

Miller, Willis A., 357 Main St, Harleysville PA 19438, 215-256-8240 [FRC] [RE]

Mininger, Gerald (Connie G.) 3901 Bahia Vista St #731, Sarasota FL 34232, 941-371-8335 [SE] [AW]

Mininger, Joseph H. (Eleanor) HC 70, Box 68, Harman WV 26270, 304-227-4370 [VA] [RE]

Mininger, Mary (Phil) 2589 N CR 100 W, Paoli IN 47454, 812-723-2414, mininger@blueriver.net [CDC, IM] IIA [AC] Co-Pastor, Paoli Menn Fell, Paoli IN

Mininger, Philip A. (Mary Kauffman Mininger) 2589 N CR 100 W, Paoli IN 47454, 812-723-2459, mininger@blueriver.net [CDC, IM] IIA [AC] Co-Pastor, Paoli Menn Fell, Paoli IN

Mininger, Richard Huber (Linda) 37 Sycamore Ave, Halifax PA 17032-9055, 717-896-2637, rlhm@pa.net [LAN] IIB1 [AC] Pastor, Halifax Community Fell, Halifax PA

Minino, Vincente (Carmen) 5799 Rayburn Ave #163, Alexandria VA 22311, vicarm1@juno.com [LAN] IIB1 [AC] Pastor, Iglesia Menonita Hispana Vida Nueva, Burke VA

Minnich, Abram D. (Marolyn J.) 30376 Charles Barnes Rd, Westover MD 21871, 410-957-3755 [ACC] [RE]

Minnich, H. Darrell (June) 9 Dale St, Needham MA 02194, 617-433-0940, darrell@gis.net [LAN] IIB1 [AC] Pastor, Good Shepherd Christian Fell, Needham MA

Minnich, R. Herbert (Shirley S.) 300 Nebraska Dr, Goshen IN 46526, 574-533-9965 [IM] [RE]

Mishler, David E. (Becky) 999 Blough Rd, Johnstown PA 15905, 814-288-3420 [ALL] IB3 [AC]

Mishler, Donald Paul (Catherine Yoder Mishler) 5793 US Hwy 340N, Rileyville VA 22650, 540-743-6972, pmishler@shentel.net [VA] [AW]

Mishler, Dorsa J., 1412-6 Pembroke Cr, Goshen IN 46526, 574-534-4998 [IM] [RE]

Mohler, David W. (Mildred) 220 Akron Rd, Ephrata PA 17522-2604, 717-733-4359, damohler@localnet.com [LAN] III [AC] Deacon, Gehman Menn Ch, Adamstown PA

Mohr, James R. (Roberta R.) 319 Simcox Ext, Wadsworth OH 44281, 330-336-2797, jraecroyle@cs.com [CDC] IIB1 [AC] Pastor, First Menn Ch, Wadsworth OH

Monroe, Earl B. (Joy Magdalene) 80 Lake Rd, Stuarts

Draft VA 24477, 540-337-1062, earlshome@rica.net [VA] IIB1 [AC] Pastor, Mountain View Menn Ch, Lyndhurst VA

Montanez, Emilio (Migdalea) 134 Guilford St, Lebanon PA 17042, 717-270-9512 [LAN] IIB1 [AC] Pastor, Cristo es la Respuesta, Lebanon PA

Montes, Juan V., PO Box 111, Reedley CA 93654, 559-638-8493, menno1st@mobynet.com [PSW] IIB2 [AC] Pastor, Primera Iglesia Menonita, Reedley CA; Associate Pastor, First Menn Ch, Reedley CA

Moore, Irene, 907 E 25th Ave, Tampa FL 33605, 813-223-1776 [SE] IIC [AC] Minister of Visitation, College Hill Menn Ch, Tampa FL

Moore, Jon E., 1939 West Page St, Philadelphia PA 19121-1513, 215-232-4579, Jonfeliciamoore@aol.com [FRC] IIA [AC] Pastor, New Beginnings Community Ch, Bristol PA

Morales, Eduardo P. (Lourdes) 419 2nd Rd Apt 3, Arlington VA 22203, 703-528-2417, peraza2@juno.com [LAN] IIB1 [AC] Pastor, Buenas Nuevas, Arlington VA

Moran, Samuel (Orflia R. Lopez) PO Box 68008, Oak Grove OR 97268, 503-653-4164 [PNW] IIB1 [AC] Pastor, Ministerios Restauracion, Oak Grove OR

Moreno, Justo, 717 Elsberry Ave, Valinda CA 91744, 818-336-7656, holfmc@juno.com [PSW] IIB1 [AC] Senior Pastor, House of the Lord Fell, La Puente CA

Morgan, Edward L. (Karen) HC 70 Box 250, Mountain View AR 72560, 501-591-6695 [SC] IIB1 [AC] Pastor, Bethel Springs Menn Ch, Mountain View AR

Morrow, David Marvin (Irene Schomus Morrow) 802 S Pine, PO Box 766, Warden WA 98857, 509-349-0577, dmmorrow@mennonite.net [PNW] IIB1 [AC] Pastor, Warden Menn Ch, Warden WA

Morton, Craig Daniel (Karla Crydermann) 2743 W Wave, Meridian ID 83642, 208-288-2378, ccdmort@velocitus.net [PNW] IIB1 [AC] Co-Pastor, , First Menn Ch, Nampa ID; Interim Pastor, Zion Menn Ch, Hubbard OR

Morton, Karla (Craig) 2743 W Wave, Meridian ID 83642, 208-288-2378, ccdmort@velocitus.net [PNW] IIA [AC]

Mosemann, Clyde R. (Anne) RR 1 Box 865, Warfordsburg PA 17267, 717-573-2504 [ACC] [RE]

Moser, David Palmer, 15406 Watercress Dr, Cassopolis MI 49031, 616-476-9989, moser@friedenswald.org [CDC] IIA [AC] Program Director, Camp Friedenswald, Cassopolis MI

Moser, Teresa (Phil Rempel) 4586 Geary St SE, Albany OR 97321, 541-812-1168, teresamoser@spearnet.net [PNW] IIB3a [AC] Chaplain, Mennonite Home of Albany, Albany OR

Motley, Alvin, 809 Glen Ter, Chester PA 19013, 610-872-5539 [LAN] IIB1 [AC] Pastor, Way Through Christ, Chester PA

Moua, Shoua (Chou Vang) 9980 W 59th Pl #1, Arvada CO 80004-5015, 303-463-0257 [RM, WDC] IIB1 [AC] Pastor, Hmong Menn Ch, Arvada CO

Moyer, Ann Bender, 4361 35th St, San Diego CA 92104-1504, 619-281-3240, ann.moyer@sharp.com [PSW] IIB1 [AC] Pastor, San Diego Menn Ch, San Diego CA

Moyer, Bradley Dean, 4361 35th St, San Diego CA 92104, 619-281-3240 [PSW] [AW]

Moyer, Jay (Cindy) 153 Lawndale Ave, Sellersville PA 18960, 215-453-8455, jmoyer@cc-fellowship.org [FRC]

MINISTERS

6

IIB1 [AC] Co-Pastor, Covenant Community Fell, Lansdale PA

Moyer, Larry G. (Loretta) 70 E Ridge Ave, Telford PA 18969, 215-723-5233, larrymoyer@juno.com [FRC] IIB1 [AC] Pastor, Rocky Ridge Menn Ch, Quakertown PA

Moyer, Norman W., RR 5 Box 78, Middleburg PA 17842-9805, 717-374-4266 [ALL] IB3 [AC]

Moyer, Richard A. (Fern) PO Box 504, Green Lane PA 18054, 215-234-8286, richfern@easy-pages.com [FRC] IIB1 [AC] Pastor, Shalom Christian Fell, Pennsburg PA

Moyer, Wellington (Evangeline) 6220 Greedy Hwy, Hickory NC 28602, 704-324-7652, wemoyer8@twave.net [VA] [RE]

Mull, Kenneth A. (Edna) 2345 Little Hill Rd, Narvon PA 17555, 610-286-9096 [LAN] IIB2 [AC] Associate Pastor, Churchtown Menn Ch, East Earl PA

Mullett, Isabel Margaret (S. James) 4181 State Rt 788, Wellston OH 45692, 740-384-3055 [OH] [RE]

Mullett, James, 4181 State Rt 788, Wellston OH 45692, 614-384-3055, jmullett@etrademail.com [OH] [RE]

Mummau, Ernest E., 1116 May Post Office Rd, Quarryville PA 17566, 717-786-7079 [LAN] IIB2 [AC] Associate Pastor, Nickel Mines Menn Ch, New Providence PA

Mungai, Simon (Gladys Maina) 2104 W Bryden Dr, Muncie IN 47304, 317-289-5436, smungai@regenstrief.org [CDC, IM] IIB2 [AC] Associate Pastor, Morning Star Ch, Muncie IN

Murray, John C. (Krista Anne Miller) 413 Rosewood, Hesston KS 67062, 620-327-0486, jcmurray@prairieinet.net [SC] IIB1 [AC] Pastor, Hesston Menn Ch, Hesston KS

Murray, John F. (Marilyn) 303 E Indiana, Kouts IN 46347, 219-766-3981 [IM] IB3 [AC] Overseer for Hopewell Mennonite, Kouts IN

Murray, Mick (Julie) 1136 Ginkgo Ave, Wellman IA 52356-9248, 319-646-6810, kmcmick@kctc.net [CP] IIB1 [AC] Pastor, Kalona Menn Ch, Kalona IA

Murray, Randy B. (Amy Justine [Yoder] Murray) 2522 Tannerville Rd, Orrville OH 44667, 330-683-0158 [OH] IIB1 [AC] Pastor, Martins Menn Ch, Orrville OH

Murti, Samuel, Indonesian Menn Church, 1419 S 3rd St, Alhambra CA 91803, 626-588-1665 [PSW] IIB2 [AC] Associate Pastor, Indonesian Menn Ch, Los Angeles CA

Musselman, Betty (Paul) 622 Morwood Rd, Telford PA 18969, 215-723-4922 [EDC] [RE]

Musselman, David L. (Brenda) 985 Sunset Ave, New Holland PA 17557, 717-354-2246, dlmusselman@juno.com [LAN] IIB2 [AC] Associate Pastor, Village Chapel Menn Ch, New Holland PA

Musselman, Glenn E., 1352 Greencroft Dr, Goshen IN 46526, 574-534-2275 [IM] IB3 [AC] Overseer for Liberty Mennonite, Somerset Center MI

Musselman, Henry S. (Lois L.) 114-D Menno Home Dr, Souderton PA 18964, 215-723-0145 [FRC] [RE]

Musselman, Steven Alan (April L.) 27 Park View Dr, Reinholds PA 17569, 717-336-2206, steveemmanuel@dejazzd.com [EDC] IIB1 [AC] Pastor, Emmanuel Menn Ch, Reinholds PA

Musser, David W. (Ella) 213 W Bahney Ave, Myerstown PA 17067-1202, 717-866-7787 [LAN] [AW]

Musser, Eric (Rebecca L.) 175-A Orchard Ln, Harleysville PA 19438, 215-256-0905, emusser@franconiamennonite.org [FRC] IIA [AC] Minister of Evangelism & Young Adults, Franconia Menn Ch, Franconia PA

Musser, James W., 5542 Valley Rd, Stephens City VA 22655, 540-868-0136 [VA] IIB1 [AC] Pastor, Stephens City Menn Ch, Stephens City VA

Musser, Roy W. (Joyce) 20 Union St, Pottsville PA 17901, 570-622-5681 [LAN] III [AC] Ordained Deacon, Palo Alto Menn Ch, Pottsville PA

Musser, Wilmer S. (Janelle) 510 S Farmersville Rd, Ephrata PA 17522, 717-354-4347 [LAN] IIB1 [AC] Pastor, Hammer Creek Menn Ch, Lititz PA

Myer, Landis E. (Esther) 2000 Temple Ave, Lancaster PA 17603, 717-299-6968 [LAN] [RE]

Myers, D. Glenn (Emma Bender Myers) 315 Northwood Dr, Philadelphia MS 39350, 601-656-3514, gemyers@nsimailbox.com [GS] IB3, IIB1 [AC] Pastor, Pearl River Menn Ch, Philadelphia MS

Myers, Herman F., 3363 Friendsville Rd, Wooster OH 44691-1237, 330-264-3404, hmyers@valkyrie.net [OH] IIB2 [AC] Associate Pastor, Kidron Menn Ch, Kidron OH

Myers, J. Vernon (Rebecca [Becky]) 145 Bethel Rd, Oxford PA 19363, 610-932-4429, bishopvern@juno.com [LAN] IB3 [AC] Bishop/Overseer, LMC - Willow Street - Strasburg, PA

Myers, John M. (Kimberly) 515 S Market St, Elizabethtown PA 17022, 717-361-2133, pastorjohnm@earthlink.net [LAN] IIA [AC] Associate Pastor, Elizabethtown Menn Ch, Elizabethtown PA

Myers, Ralph, 2415 Long St, Sweet Home OR 97386, 541-367-6617 [PNW] [RE]

N

Nachtigall, Ray (Karen) 626 W Marion, Elkhart IN 46516, 574-293-0347 [IM] [AW]

Nachtigall, Wilbur G. (Grace) 1921 S Ridge Dr, Coralville IA 52241-1058, 319-338-3839 [CP] [RE]

Nafziger, P. Melville (Esther) 1001 E Oregon Rd, Lititz PA 17543-9205, 717-519-2603, pmnaf@juno.com [ACC] IIB1 [AC] Interim Pastor, Ocean City Menn Christian Fell, Ocean City MD

Nafziger, Randall K. (Diane F.) 5175 CR 19, Wauseon OH 43567, 419-445-3486, parson@fulton-net.com [OH] IIB1 [AC] Pastor, Tedrow Menn Ch, Wauseon OH

Nafziger, Robert D. (Nadine) 6349 Springfield Rd, Delavan IL 61734, 309-244-7153 [IL] IIB1 [AC] Pastor, Menn Ch of Dillon, Delavan IL

Nafziger-Meiser, Linda E. (Gary) 5218 Castle Dr, Boise ID 83703, 208-331-8529, lindanm@mindsprng.com [PNW] IIB1 [AC] Pastor, Hyde Park Menn Fell, Boise ID

Naranjo, Luis E. (Ana) 812 Wedgewood Dr, Lansdale PA 19446, 215-368-5839, messiahisrael@aol.com [EDC] IIB1 [AC] Pastor, Comunidad de Amor, Philadelphia PA

Nauman, Donald O. (Erla) 31 Oakwood Ln, Manheim PA 17545, 717-665-3096 [LAN] IB3 [AC]

Nauman, Kenneth E. (Miriam W.) 922 W Hickory St, Arcadia FL 34266, 941-993-9353, KenMirNa@sunline.net [SE] IB2, IB3 [AC] Conference Minister, Southeast Mennonite Conference, Sarasota FL; District Minister, Southeast Mennonite Conference, Southwest District FL

Naylor, Ruth Eileen (Stanley Fred) 123 Villanova Dr, Bluffton OH 45817, 419-358-6309, snaylor@wcoil.com [CDC] [RE]

Neff, Clarence R., 249 Ebenshade Rd, Ronks PA 17572,

717-687-6406 [LAN] [AC]

Neff, Daniel W. (Carol) 465 Long Rd, Manheim PA 17545, 717-569-0812 [LAN] III [AC] Ordained Deacon, East Petersburg Menn Ch, East Petersburg PA

Neff, Earl L., 8 Stone Rd, Quarryville PA 17566, 717-786-3487 [LAN] III [AC]

Neff, L. Delmar (Nancy) 63 Christiana Pike, Christiana PA 17509, 610-593-5334 [LAN] [RE]

Neil, Marlin A. (Freda) 16062 Mountain Green Rd, Spring Run PA 17262, 717-349-7160, shadypine@juno.net [FRK] IIB1 [AC] Pastor, Shady Pine Menn Ch, Willow Hill PA

Neis Jr., Thomas A. (Patricia) 94 Fairfax Village North, Harrisburg PA 17112-9555, 717-540-5280 [LAN] [AW]

Nelson, Dawn Ruth (Paul Joseph) 318 W Broad St, Harleysville PA 19438, 215-256-9606 [FRC] IIB3a [AC] Chaplain, Indian Creek Foundation, Harleysville PA

Nelson, James H. (Odie) 3405 Corvair Ln, Saginaw MI 48602, 517-249-5894 [IM] IIA [AC] Pastor, Grace Chapel, Saginaw MI

Ness, Charles A. (Janet) PO Box 228, Skippack PA 19474, 610-584-6624, perkmc@juno.com [FRC] IIB1 [AC] Pastor, Perkiomenville Menn Ch, Perkiomenville PA

Neufeld, Bonnie Beth (Chuck) 3316 W 163rd, Markham IL 60426, 708-333-9827, chuckneufeld@compuserve.com [CDC, IL] IIB1 [AC] Co-Pastor, Community Menn Ch, Markham IL

Neufeld, Chuck T. (Bonnie) 3316 W 163rd St, Markham IL 60426, 708-333-9827, chuckneufeld@compuserve.com [CDC, IL] IIB1 [AC] Pastor, Community Menn Ch, Markham IL

Neufeld, Ernest Wiens (Lila) PO Box 53, Mt Lake MN 56159-2828, 507-427-2828 [CP] [RE]

Neufeld, Peter J., 312 Robert, Hutchinson KS 67502-0312, 620-663-2581 [WDC] [RE]

Neufeld, Walter P. (Frieda Braun Neufeld) 901 East Hoch, Moundridge KS 67107-7138, 620-345-2547 [WDC] [RE]

Newswanger, Carl K. (K. Louise Myers Newswanger) 1970 Engel Ct NW, Salem OR 97304, 503-391-2772, newswanger2@attbi.com [PNW] IIB1 [AC] Pastor, Salem Menn Ch, Salem OR

Newswanger, Ricky L. (Wilda) 3155 Rothsville Rd, Ephrata PA 17522, 717-859-1682 [LAN] IIC [AC] Youth Pastor, Hammer Creek Menn Ch, Lititz PA

Newton, Elbert Walker (Gloria Martyn Newton) 1041 N Altadena Dr, Pasadena CA 91107, 626-398-8224, pasamenno@aol.com [PSW] IIB2 [AC] Associate Pastor, Pasadena Menn Ch, Pasadena CA

Nice, Aaron D., 16270 Union St, Morrison IL 61270, 815-722-2541 [IL] [RE]

Nice, Evelyn Godshall (Frank Edward) 1161 Stuart St, Harrisonburg VA 22802, 540-434-4441 [VA] IC [AC]

Nice, Frank E. (Evelny) 1161 Stuart St, Harrisonburg VA 22802, 540-434-4441 [VA] IB3 [AC]

Nicholson, Ransford, 1806 N Euclid Ave, Sarasota FL 34237, 941-365-6878 [SE] [AW]

Nimon, James R. (Lydia) 273 Mount Airy Rd, New Providence PA 17560, 717-786-4583, Jimmy@ConsumingFireMinistries.org [LAN] IIB2 [AC] Associate Pastor, Living Stones Fell, Peach Bottom PA

Nisly, Paul W. (Laura) PO Box 262, Grantham PA 17027-0262, 717-766-4937 [LAN] IB3 [AC]

Nisly, Weldon D. (Margaret A.) 13773 30th Ave NE,

Seattle WA 98125-3509, 206-368-7529, weldonNisly@mennonite.net [PNW] IIB1 [AC] Pastor, Seattle Menn Ch, Seattle WA

Nissley, Addona H. (Mary Elizabeth) 1554 Park Rd, Harrisonburg VA 22802, 540-434-9427 [VA] [RE]

Nissley, Clair R. (Ruth) 1832 Pecks Rd, Middletown PA 17057-5349, 717-367-2033, crnissley@juno.com [LAN] III [AC] Ordained Deacon, Goods Menn Ch, Bainbridge PA

Nissley, D. Lowell (Miriam A. Brackbill Nissley) 811 Richardson Way, Sarasota FL 34232, 941-371-6230, nusslihaus@msn.com [SE] [RE]

Nissley, Darin, 227 Tyler Ave SE, Canton OH 44707, 330-452-2416, daratoma@netzero.net [OH] IIA [AC] Youth Pastor, First Menn Ch, Canton OH

Nissley, Elizabeth G. (Kenneth) 127 N Market St, Mount Joy PA 17552-1305, 717-653-2550, enissley@earthlink.net [LAN] IIC [AC]

Nissley, Jay W. (Elta) 1487 Breneman Rd, Manheim PA 17545, 717-665-7367, jayeltaniss@juno.com [LAN] IIB1 [AC] Associate Pastor, Kauffman Menn Ch, Manheim PA

Nissley, M. John (Lois C.) 430 Bright Rd, Findlay OH 45840-7043, 419-425-6708, teleios2@aol.com [LAN] IIB1 [AW]

Nitzsche, Mary Erb (Wayne Arthur) 917 Patrick Pl, Wooster OH 44691, 330-264-2470, menwan@juno.com [CDC, OH] IB3 [AC]

Nitzsche, Wayne A. (Mary Erb Nitzsche) 917 Patrick Pl, Wooster OH 44691, 330-264-1516, MENWAN@juno.com [OH] IB3 [AC] Regional Pastor, Ohio Conference of the Mennonite Church, Kidron OH

Nofziger, Donald D., 307 S Higbee St, Milford IN 46542, 574-658-3245 [CDC] [RE]

Nofziger, Pauline Ann, 8038 Witts Mill Ln, Cincinnati OH 45255, 513-474-0637 [CDC, OH] IIB1 [AC] Pastor, Cincinnati Menn Fell, Cincinnati OH

Nolt, M. Luke (Dorothy) 160 Forest Hill Rd, Leola PA 17540, 717-656-7817 [LAN] IIB2 [AC] Associate Pastor, Stumptown Menn Ch, Bird-in-Hand PA

Nolt, Robert E. (Anna) 1704 West 4th St, Newton KS 67114, 316-284-0218 [SC] IB2 [AC]

North, Wayne G. (Doris) 466 Eckert Cr, Harrisonburg VA 22801, 540-433-3538, wayne@lindale.org [VA] IB3 [AC] Interim Pastor, Lindale Menn Ch, Harrisonburg VA

Norton, Steve (Sharon) Beyschlag Strasse #17, Halle 06110, Germany, 011-49-345-1200820 [IM] IIB3b [AC] Missionary, Eastern Mennonite Missions, Halle Germany

Nowlin, Preston (Carolyn) 1915-B Old tavern Rd, Powhatan VA 23139, 804-598-7289 [VA] [RE]

Nunez, Andrew (Carmen) 1475 Popham Ave #1E, Bronx NY 10453, 718-716-6579, acnunez2001@yahoo.com [LAN] IIA [AC] Pastor, Believers Menn Garifuna Ministries, Brooklyn NY

Nussbaum, Delvin, 13877 Emerson Rd, Dalton OH 44618, 330-857-2463 [OH] [RE]

Nussbaum, Gary, 15511 Hackett Rd, Dalton OH 44618, 330-857-4392 [OH] IIB3a [AC]

Nussbaum, Gerald C. (Virginia Kay) 16055 CR 18, Goshen IN 46528, 574-533-1919 [CDC] IIB3a [AC]

Nussbaum, Harold Walden, 505 W Main St, Berne IN 46711, 260-589-2461, harold@firstmennonite.org [CDC] IIB2 [AC] Minister of Visitation, First Menn Ch, Berne IN

MINISTERS

6

Nussbaum, Irvin A. (Nelda) 23899 Banyan Cr, Elkhart IN 46516, 574-875-1324 [IM] [RE]

Nussbaum, Larry (Cheryl L.) 547 N Roosevelt, Wichita KS 67208-3723, 316-684-5448, lamcassocpastor@prodigy.net [WDC] IIA [AC] Associate Pastor, Lorraine Avenue Menn Ch, Wichita KS

Nwani, Clement (Evelyn) 2926 W Florence Ave, Los Angeles CA 90043, 323-778-4063, clevychic@yahoo.com [PSW] IIB1 [AC] Co-Pastor, Abundant Life Miracle Christian Center, Los Angeles CA

Nwani, Evelyn (Clement) 2926 W Florence Ave, Los Angeles CA 90043, 323-778-4063, clevychic@yahoo.com [PSW] IIB1 [AC] Co-Pastor, Abundant Life Miracle Christian Center, Los Angeles CA

Nyce, Cleon (Mari An) 515 Forest Rd, Chambersburg PA 17201, 717-261-1071, cnnyce@innernet.net [FRK] IIB1 [AC] Pastor, Marion Menn Ch, Chambersburg PA

Nyce, R. Keith (Yvonne) 736 Bob Bea Ln, Harleysville PA 19438, 215-256-0522, Knyce@cc-fellowship.org [FRC] IIB1 [AC] Co-Pastor, Covenant Community Fell, Lansdale PA

Nyce, Steven C., 19 S School Ln, Souderton PA 18964, 215-721-0167 [FRC] IIB1 [AC] Pastor, Towamencin Menn Ch, Kulpsville PA

O

Oberholtzer, Jay R. (Rhoda) PO Box 318, Lititz PA 17543, 717-626-5658 [LAN] [RE]

Oberholtzer, Kristin Renee (Trace) 1452 Romansville Rd, Coatesville PA 19320-4758 [LAN] IIC [AC] Missionary/Church Worker, EMM/VMBM, Italy

Oberholtzer, Leon H. (Leona) 2251 Creek Hill Rd, Lancaster PA 17601, 717-393-7747, mmc@proclaim.net [LAN] IIB2 [AC] Pastor, Mellinger Menn Ch, Lancaster PA

Oberholtzer, Trace (Kristin R.) 1452 Romansville Rd, Coatesville PA 19320-4758 [LAN] IIC [AC] Missionary/Church Worker, EMM, Italy

Oberholzer, Richard, 13315 Cearfoss Pike, Hagerstown MD 21740, 301-739-5036 [FRK] [RE]

Obold, Frederick J. (Ruth W.) 716 Lewis Dr, Hesston KS 67062, 620-327-4435 [WDC] IIB3a [AC] Chaplain, Reno County Hospice, Hutchinson KS

O'Brien, Margaret, 110 East Weaver Ave, Harrisonburg VA 22801, 540-434-0097, megobrien@ntelos.net [VA] IIB2 [AC] Co-Pastor, Community Menn Ch, Harrisonburg VA

O'Connell, Darwin, 989 W Tremont Ave, Lima OH 45801, 419-223-3266 [OH] [RE]

Oesch, H. Duane, 11161 Moss Ln, Nampa ID 83651, 208-466-1897 [PNW] [AW]

Onelangsy, Aaron S., 92 Greenwood Dr, New Cumberland PA 17070, 717-938-8552 [LAN] IIA [AC] Pastor, Lao Menn Fell/Slate Hill, Camp Hill PA

Ortiz, Henry, 1750 Skippack Pike, Blue Bell PA 19422-1339, 610-292-8243 [FRC] [RE]

Ontjes, Kenneth Loren (Alice Marie) Box 19, Bridgewater SD 57319-0019, 605-729-2745 [CP] IIB1 [AC] Pastor, Neu Hutterthal Menn Ch, Bridgewater SD

Opong, Charles, 5125 S Crenshaw Blvd, Los Angeles CA 90043, 323-291-2235 [PSW] IIA [AC] Pastor, All Souls Christian Center, Los Angeles CA

O'Reilly II, George Christopher II (Karen L.) 1217 9th Ave, Mt Lake MN 56159, 507-427-2002 [CP] IIB1 [AC]

Pastor, Bethel Menn Ch, Mountain Lake MN

Orr, David E. (Sharon Faye) 809 Wellmon St, Bedford OH 44146, 440-786-2401, friendmc@megsinet.net [OH] IIB1 [AC] Pastor, Friendship Menn Ch, Bedford Heights OH

Ortiz, Jose M. (Iraida) 21 Village Ln, New Holland PA 17557, 717-354-2601, jose_ortiz@mail.mcc.org [ACC] IIB3c [AC] Executive Director, MCC, US, Akron PA

Ortiz, Marquel (Charlotte) 41 James St, Bernville PA 19506-8617, newlifebernville@juno.com [ACC] IIB1 [AC] Pastor, New Life Christian Fell, Bernville PA

Osborne, Millard Edmond (Joyce Nyce Osborne) 3430 Dawn Dr, Harrisonburg VA 22801, 540-438-8390, mosborne001@sprintmail.com [VA] [RE]

Osinkosky, Claire J., PO Box 488, Harrisonburg VA 22803, 540-574-4730 [CDC] [AW]

Ostlund, James W., PO Box 942, Moundridge KS 67107, edenyouth@hotmail.com [WDC] IIA [AC] Associate Pastor, Eden Menn Ch, Moundridge KS

Oswald, Leland (Doretta) 537 West Gay St, Harrisonburg VA 22802, 540-432-0308 [VA] [RE]

Otto, Darrel D. (Ruth Ann) 4422 Zephyr St, Wheat Ridge CO 80033, 303-657-5908 [RM] [RE]

Otto, John D. (Edna) 406 East F Ave, South Hutchinson KS 67505, 620-665-8966 [SC] [RE]

Overholt, Lewis (Mary E. Mast) 510 E Church St, Americus GA 31709, 912-924-0652, Lewis_Overholt@buk.org [SE] IIB1 [AC] Pastor, Americus Menn Fell, Americus GA

Owolabi, Timothy, 3960 Steinwood, Dalton OH 44618, 330-857-1166 [OH] [AW]

Ozor, Chibuzor Vincent (Chima) 1455 Kelly Green Dr, Ann Arbor MI 48103-2614, 313-996-9198, ozotas@aol.com [CDC, IM] IIB1 [AC] Pastor, Ann Arbor Menn Ch, Ann Arbor MI

P

Pacheco, Reinaldo (Ray) (Ana) 1423 East 34th St, Brooklyn NY 11210, 718-253-7267, arpac@aol.com [ACC] IIB1 [AC] Pastor, First Menn Ch, Brooklyn NY

Paetkau, Brenda Sawatzky (Donald William Paetkau) 519 S 3rd St, Goshen IN 46526, 574-537-0116, dpaetkau@juno.com [CDC] IIB2 [AC] Associate Pastor, Eighth Street Menn Ch, Goshen IN

Pagan, Samuel (Mayra) c/o Ramsey Memorial Methodist Church, 5900 Hull St, Richmond VA 23244 [VA] IIB3b [AC]

Pam, Chuwang Rwang (Grace) 4541 August St, Los Angeles CA 90008, 323-299-1499, chuwang@webtv.net [PSW] IIA [AC] Pastor, Los Angeles Faith Chapel, Inglewood CA; Mission Associate, Center for Anabaptist Leadership; Staff Associate for African Ministries, Center for Anabaptist Leadership, Pasadena CA

Pannell, Richard Anthony, 352 E Rock St, Harrisonburg VA 22802, 540-607-0366 [VA] IIA [AC] Associate Pastor, Immanuel Menn Ch, Harrisonburg VA

Parks, Burt Preston (Melanie Dawn Miller Parks) 133 Carter Grove Ln, Smithville OH 44677, 330-669-9256, methonite@valkyrie.net [OH] IIB1 [AC] Pastor, Smithville Menn Ch, Smithville OH

Parks, Lynn S. (Vandy L.) 6269 Walker St, Philadelphia PA 19135, 215-333-5868, vparks1@juno.com [LAN] IIC [AC] Associate Pastor, Oxford Circle Menn Ch, Philadelphia PA

Parks, Vandy L. (Lynn) 6269 Walker St, Philadelphia PA 19135, 215-333-5868, vparks1@juno.com [LAN] IIB2 [AC] Associate Pastor, Oxford Circle Menn Ch, Philadelphia PA

Pascacio, Egbert, 7860 S Western Ave, Los Angeles CA 90047, 323-466-4117, ddbdor@aol.com [PSW] IIA [AC] Pastor, Miracle of Faith Menn Ch, Los Angeles CA

Patterson, Allan, 36 Morgan St, Oberlin OH 44074, 440-774-4675, pmcpastor@aol.com [OH] IIB1 [AC] Pastor, Peace Menn Ch, Elyria OH

Patterson, Donald A. (Sharlene) 231 F Pl, Kalona IA 52247, 319-656-2600, donpatt@kctc.net [CP] IIB1 [AC] Pastor, Lower Deer Creek Menn Ch, Kalona IA

Pauls, Jeffrey G. (Donna) 12 S Kinzer Rd, Kinzers PA 17535, 717-442-8008, jpdp@epix.net [LAN] IIA [AC] Associate Pastor, Kinzer Menn Ch, Kinzers PA

Peachey, B. Frank (Carol) 230 N Pine St, Lancaster PA 17603, 717-295-4535 [LAN] IIB2 [AC]

Peachey, C. David (Carol Ann) RR 3 Box 299, Mifflinburg PA 17844, 717-966-1458, pchykeen1@juno.com [LAN] IIB1 [AC] Associate Pastor, Buffalo Menn Ch, Mifflinburg PA

Peachey, Gerald, 162 N Kish St, Belleville PA 17004, 717-935-2583 [ALL] IIB1 [AC]

Peachey, John Stephen (Suzi Christina) 10 Highfield Oval, Harpenden, Herts AL5 4BX, England, johnpeachey@mail.com [SE] IIC [AC]

Peachey, Laban, 5235 Grist Mill Rd, Harrisonburg VA 22802, 540-833-5131 [VA] IB3 [AC]

Peachey, Mark E., 602 Eleanor Ave, Scottdale PA 15683, 724-806-9857 [ALL] IB3 [AC]

Peachey, Raymond S., 6671 St Rte 655, Belleville PA 17004, 717-667-3097 [ALL] [RE]

Peachey, Timothy R., 102 Poe St, Belleville PA 17004, 717-935-2763 [ALL] IB3 [AC]

Peachey, Urbane (Gwendolyn W.) 242 Cats Back Rd, Ephrata PA 17522, 717-354-7001, UPeach@aol.com [ACC] IB3 [AC] Individual and Family Counselor, Bethany Counseling Ministry, Ephrata PA

Peak, Michael Wayne (Joylyn June) 58073 Diener Dr, Goshen IN 46528, 574-875-4288, 4peaks@pkfamily.com [IM] IIB1 [AC] Associate Pastor, Pleasant View Menn Ch, Goshen IN

Pegarella, David A., 146 Main St, Mountaintop PA 18707, 717-474-2955, davidp@epix.net [LAN] IIB1 [AC] Pastor, Nanticoke Christian Fell, Nanticoke PA

Pellecer, Byron (Hildalejandra) 741 NW 45 Ave Apt 42, Miami FL 33122, 305-529-9244, BPellece@bellsouth.net [SE] IIB1 [AC] Pastor, Iglesia Menonita Encuentro de Renovacion, Miami-Dade FL; Tutor, IBA/USA & Guatemala, Miami FL; District Minister, Southeast Mennonite Conference, South Florida District FL

Pellman, Hubert R. (Mildred) 1307 Woodland Dr, Harrisonburg VA 22802, 540-434-5797 [VA] [RE]

Pendleton, Joe (Jean) 9785 S Bagley Rd, Ashley MI 48806, 517-838-2588, joe_pendleton@hotmail.com [IM] IIB1 [AC] Pastor, Bethel Menn Ch, Ashley MI

Penner, Bradley B. (Viola [Vi] K.) 330 E Washington, Kingman KS 67068, 620-532-5330, darev@websurf.net [WDC] IIB1 [AC] Pastor, Kingman Menn Ch, Kingman KS

Penner, Bruno (Julia) 1313 2nd Ave, Mt Lake MN 56159, 507-427-2030 [CP] [RE]

Penner, Don (Sandy Penner) 402 Willow, Rocky Ford CO 81067, 719-254-7590, sansuepen@juno.com [RM] IIA [AC] Pastor, Rocky Ford Menn Ch, Rocky Ford CO

Penner, Marvin Wesley (Sue) HC 30, Box 2071, Wolf Point MT 59201-9702, 406-392-5215, mspenner@juno.com [CP] IIB1 [AC] Pastor, Bethel Menn Ch, Wolf Point MT

Penner, Ruth (Marvin J.) 3890 Friar Lane, Wichita KS 67204, 316-832-0546 [WDC] IIA [AC]

Penner, Stephen J. (Glena Schroeter Penner) 195 Ponderosa, Reedley CA 93654, 559-638-5565, sngpenner@telis.org [PSW] IIA [AC] Associate Pastor, First Menn Ch, Reedley CA

Penner, Vicki Lynn (Richard Warren Minder) 1511 Rhode Island St, Lawrence KS 66044-4271, 785-830-9547, peacemennonite@msn.com [WDC] IIB1 [AC] Pastor, Peace Menn Ch, Lawrence KS

Perez, Gilberto (Elizabeth) 1385 S Tuttle Ave, Sarasota FL 34239 [SE] [AW]

Perez, Rafael (Xiomara) 1241 Church St, Reading PA 19601, 610-372-1812, rafucho74@hotmail.com [LAN] IIA [AC] Pastor, New Revival Menn Ch, Reading PA

Perri, Mark D. (Annabelle) 42-45 149th Pl, Flushing NY 11355, 718-539-6702, MPerri2804@aol.com [ACC] IIA [AC] Pastor, Immanuel Community Ch, Flushing NY

Peters, Jay M., 746 Hossler Rd, Manheim PA 17545, 717-664-2814 [LAN] IIB2 [AC] Associate Pastor, Hernley Menn Ch, Manheim PA

Petersheim, Isaac R., 957 Weaverland Rd, East Earl PA 17519, 717-354-7328 [LAN] III [AC] Ordained Deacon, Cambridge Menn Ch, Honey Brook PA

Petersheim, John R. (Ruby) 3475 Apple Tree Dr, Harrisonburg VA 22802, 540-867-5568, johnorruby@att.net [VA] [RE]

Petersheim, Oliver S., 4113 Coseytown Rd, Greencastle PA 17225, 717-597-7381 [FRK] [RE]

Petersheim, Robert L. (Cindy A.) 1543 Morgantown Road, Morgantown PA 19543, 610-913-7413, rlpckp@juno.com [ACC] IIB3b [AC] Interim Pastor, Rockhill Menn Ch, Telford PA

Peterson, Kenneth James (Carol J.) 213 W Willow Glen Lane, Hillsboro KS 67063, 620-947-2091, kosanke@southwind.net [WDC] IIB1 [AC] Pastor, First Menn Ch, Hillsboro KS

Peterson, Neville John, C-315 N Yellowstone, Bozeman MT 59718 [NC] [RE] Pastor, White Chapel Menn Ch, Glendive MT

Pham, Thanh Cong, 530 Main St, Apt E-507, Harleysville PA 19438-2246, 215-513-4117, tcpham1@netzero.net [FRC] IIB1 [AC] Pastor, Vietnamese Gospel Menn Ch, Souderton PA

Pham, Xuan (Lisa) **Huong** (Can Le) 3871 Scibilia Rd, Fairfax VA 22033, 703-802-0139, lpham@forministry.com [VA] IIB1 [AC] Pastor, Vietnamese Christian Fell, Fairfax VA

Pitts, Katherine Jameson (Kenneth Duane) 1851 Conestoga Dr, Lancaster PA 17602, 717-672-0645, kjpitts@mennonite.net [ACC] IIB1 [AC] Co-Pastor, Community Menn Ch of Lancaster, Lancaster PA

Poirot Sr, Clifford S. (Judy) PO Box 307, Lacey Springs VA 22833, 540-433-1367 [VA] IIB3b [AC]

Ponce, Teofilo, 707 N 6th St #A, Goshen IN 46526, 574-533-7267 [IM] [RE]

Porter, Ike, 58726 CR 657, Mattawan MI 49071, 269-

668-2562 [IM] IIB3a [AC] Chaplain, Mattawan MI

Porzelius, Ernest Eugene (Violet J.) 173 Albert St, Bluffton OH 45817-1401, 419-358-8481 [CDC] [RE]

Possinger, David (Glenda) 14634 St Paul Rd, Clear Spring MD 21722, 301-842-1279, dgp14634@intrepid.net [FRK] IIB2 [AC] Associate Pastor, Mercersburg Menn Ch, Mercersburg PA

Post, Stephen, PO Box 109, Grand Marais MI 49839, 906-494-2724, smpost@jamadots.com [IM] IIA [AC] Pastor, Grand Marais Menn Ch, Grand Marais MI

Powell, John H. (Shirley J.) 50 Allenhurst Rd, Buffalo NY 14214, 716-837-1751, fjPowell@aol.com [NY] IB3, IIB3c [AW]

Preheim, Lois Janzen (Lyle Orie) 44229 281st St, Freeman SD 57029, 605-925-7760 [CP] IIC [AC] Director, Victim Offender Reconciliation Program, Sioux Falls, SD

Preheim, Patrick (Patty Jo) 2211 28th Ave S, Minneapolis MN 55406, 612-724-0733 [CP] IIB1 [AC] Pastor, Faith Menn Ch, Minneapolis MN

Price, Brian (Becky) PO Box 43, Wolford ND 58353-0043, 701-583-2102 [NC] IIA, IIC [AC]

Prichard, George F. (June L.) 2921 Silk Oak Dr, Sarasota FL 34232-5403, 941-377-8051 [EDC] [RE]

Pride Jr, Ronnie Bernard (Louvenia) 1001 Tarboro St, Rocky Mount NC 27801, 919-977-1901 [VA] IIB1 [AC] Pastor, Fellowship of Christ, Rocky Mount NC

Providence, George, 714 Reba Pl, Evanston IL 60202-2617, 847-869-4307, ddarkmannn@netzero.net [IL] IIA [AC]

Q

Quackenbos, Gary (Vickie) PO Box 338, Hancock MD 21750, 301-678-6526 [FRK] IIB1 [AC] Pastor, Bethel Community Ch, Warfordsburg PA

Quackenbos, Robert A. (Phyllis J.) 414 Spring Lakes Blvd, Bradenton FL 34210, 941-756-3245 [SE] [AW]

Quintela, Helen Wells (Alberto Jr) 622 Bidwell St, St Paul MN 55107, 651-222-4863 [CP] IIB3a [AC]

Quintero, Ceferino, Shalom Mennonite (Spanish), Unknown, Venezuela [LAN] IIA [AC] Associate Pastor, Shalom Mennonite, Venezuela

R

Raab, Myra (Glenn) 1619 Bramoor Dr, Kokomo IN 46902, 317-963-2156 [IM] IIB3a [AC] Chaplain, Kokomo IN

Raber, Chester, 139 S Duke St, Lancaster PA 17603, 717-397-4596 [IM] [RE]

Raber, Daniel A., 4828 NE 12th St, Newton KS 67114, 316-283-4530 [WDC] [RE]

Rada, Cruz (Margarita) 122 Evergreen Ln, Fruitland IA 52749, 319-262-9670 [CP] IIB1 [AC] Pastor, Muscatine Menn Ch, Muscatine IA

Rahn, Ben P., 3012 Ivy Dr, North Newton KS 67117, 316-283-1943 [WDC] [RE]

Raid, Howard Daniel, 111 South Spring St, Bluffton OH 45817, 419-358-2580 [CDC] [RE]

Raines, William, PO Box 61, Huntertown IN 46748, 260-637-8807 [IM] [AW]

Ralph, James (Anna) 132 S Main St, Quakertown PA 18951-1120, ballypj@juno.com [FRC] IIB1 [AC] Pastor, Bally Menn Ch, Bally PA

Ramer, Milton D., 1053 S Trappe Rd, Collegeville PA

19426, 610-489-2336 [FRC] [RE]

Ramseyer, Alice Ruth (Robert Lewis) 107 Magnolia Lane, Bluffton OH 45817, 419-358-0835, ramseyer@wcoil.com [CDC] [RE]

Ramseyer, Robert Lewis (Alice Ruth) 107 Magnolia Ln, Bluffton OH 45817, 419-358-0835, ramseyer@wcoil.com [CDC] [RE]

Ranck, Edwin H. (Rosanna) 1127 White Oak Rd, Christiana PA 17509-9765, 610-593-6488, reranck2@juno.com [LAN] [RE]

Ranck, Jay L., 1950 Lancaster Pike, Peach Bottom PA 17563, 717-548-3155 [LAN] IIB1 [AC] Pastor, Mechanic Grove Menn Ch, Peach Bottom PA

Ratzlaff, Harold Cecil, 1116 E 7th St #6, Newton KS 67114-2818, 316-283-6169 [WDC] [RE]

Ratzlaff, Richard, 27606 S Halstead St, Pretty Prairie KS 67570, 620-459-6203 [WDC] [RE]

Ratzlaff, Steve C. (Lynette Friesen Ratzlaff) 12100 Adams, Lincoln NE 68527, 402-464-7840, ratzlaff@alltel.net [CP] IIB1 [AC] Pastor, First Menn Ch, Lincoln NE

Reber, Donald, 1506 Winsted Dr, Goshen IN 46526, 574-534-1783 [IM] [RE]

Rediger, Anita Pauline (Martin) 3077 W 950 S, Geneva IN 46740, 260-368-9143, redigerfarm@adamswells.com [CDC] IIB3a [AC]

Rediger, Terry Ray (Jerilee Anne) 1378 N Damon Rd, Ritzville WA 99169-8717, 509-659-0690, trediger@ritzcom.net [PNW] IIB1 [AC] Pastor, Menno Menn Ch, Ritzville WA

Reed, Harold E. (Barbara K.) 451 Delp Rd, Lancaster PA 17601, 717-560-2252, hereed@characterlink.net [LAN] IB3 [AC] Bishop, Lancaster (City) District, Lancaster PA

Reed, Harold S. (Ethel) 219 Lancaster Ave, PO Box 186, Terre Hill PA 17581, 717-445-6673 [LAN] IIB1 [AC] Associate Pastor, Goodville Menn Ch, Goodville PA

Reed, Marvin S., 309 W Maple Grove Rd, Denver PA 17517, 717-445-7276 [LAN] IIB3a [AC]

Reese, Richard, 2017 W 74th St, Los Angeles CA 90047, 213-758-0248 [PSW] IIB2 [AC] Associate Pastor, Calvary Christian Fell, Inglewood CA

Regier, Daniel George (Goldie Jane) 120 Estelle Ave, Newton KS 67114-3251, 316-283-2289 [WDC] [RE]

Regier, Harold Richard, 1404 Axtell Rd, Newton KS 67114-1327, 316-283-7991 [WDC] [RE]

Regier, Maeanna, 917 N River Park Rd, Burrton KS 67020 [WDC] IIA [AC] Associate Pastor, First Menn Ch, Halstead KS

Regier, Richard James, 10518 S Heinz Rd, Canby OR 97013, 503-651-2430 [PNW] IIB1 [AC]

Rehwalt, Daniel William (Charlotte Ann) 1138 SE Rummel St, McMinnville OR 97128, 503-434-6779 [PNW] IIB1 [AC] Interim Pastor, First Menn Ch, McMinnville OR

Reichenbach, Douglas Alan, 14275 92nd St SE, Freeport MI 49325, 616-765-3592 [CDC] IIB1 [AC] Pastor, Hope Church of the Brethren, Freeport MI

Reid, Kathryn Goering (Stephen Breck) 11004 S Bay Lane, Austin TX 78739, 512-288-7351, kathy@thn.org [WDC] IIB1 [AC] Pastor, Austin Menn Ch, Austin TX

Reimer, Raymond H. (Rosella E Epp) 3916 E Ronning Dr, Sioux Falls SD 57103-1152, 605-332-8964 [CP] IIB3d [AC]

Reinford, Daniel J., 304 Whitechapel Rd, Lancaster PA

17603, 717-399-8912 [LAN] [RE]

Reinford, Nelson L., 10 School House Rd, Souderton PA 18964, 215-723-4175 [FRC] [RE]

Reinford, Ralph, 1359 Oil City Rd, Wooster OH 44691, 330-264-1660, woostermc@sssnet.com [OH] IIB1 [AC] Pastor, Wooster Menn Ch, Wooster OH

Reitz, Raymond E. (Nancy) 67 Charlestown Rd, Washington Boro PA 17582, 717-684-7192, rayreitz@onemain.com [LAN] IIB1 [AC] Pastor, Mountville Menn Ch, Mountville PA

Rempel, Amanda J. (Clarence E.) 1004 W 10th St, Newton KS 67114, 316-284-0470 [WDC] IIB3a [AC] Chaplain, Kidron Bethel, North Newton KS

Rempel, Clarence E. (Amanda J.) 1004 West 10th St, Newton KS 67114, 316-284-0470, ClarenceR@southwind.net [WDC] IIB1 [AC] Pastor, First Menn Ch, Newton KS

Rempel, Edwin F. (Kathrine M.) 6610 S Williams Cr W, Centennial CO 80121-2739, 303-347-9266, edfrem@aol.com [RM] IB2 [AC]

Rempel, Erwin Henry (Angela Marie Albrecht) 342 Victoria Rd, Newton KS 67114, 316-283-6807, earempel@southwind.net [WDC] IIB3c [AC] Associate Director, Mennonite Mission Network

Rempel, John Donald, 332 E 19th St #14, New York NY 10003, 212-228-6355, unoffice@mcc.org [ACC] IIB3c [AC] Director, MCC United Nations Liaison Office, Manhattan NY

Rempel, Kathrine M. (Edwin F.) 6610 S Williams Cr W, Centennial CO 80121-2739, 303-347-9266, edfrem@aol.com [RM] IB2 [AC]

Rempel, Vernon K. (Marilyn Y.) 3319 S Lafayette St, Englewood CO 81110, 303-781-4481, YKWE@aol.com [RM] IIB1 [AC] Pastor, First Menn Ch of Denver, Denver CO

Rempel, Wendell, 1266 N Klein, Reedley CA 93654-2006, 559-637-1195 [PSW] IIB3c [AW]

Rendon, Simon, 115 NW 9th St, McMinnville OR 97128, 503-472-6264 [PNW] IIB1 [AC]

Rene, Bernard (Mariette) 280 Ogden St, Orange NJ 07050 [LAN] [AW]

Renno, Tom (Betty J.) 1437 Strada-D-Oro, Venice FL 34292, 941-412-9316, TRenno@juno.com [SE] [AW]

Resch, Miriam, 26067 Walnut Valley, Elkhart IN 46517, 574-294-4781, Miriam1220@juno.com [IM] IIB3a [AC] Dove Counseling, Elkhart IN

Ressler, Elvin J. (Melanie Joyce) 151 Bancroft Rd, Kennett Square PA 19348, 610-444-0547, ejressler@juno.com [LAN] IB3, IIB1 [AC]

Ressler, Jeffrey D. (Cynthia A.) 109 E Adams St, Washington IL 61571, 309-444-7553, ebassocpastor@earthlink.net [IL] IIB2 [AC] Associate Pastor, East Bend Menn Ch, Fisher IL

Ressler, Maynard B., 49 Ridgeway Dr, York PA 17404, 717-792-0289 [OH] [RE]

Reyes, Carlos (Constance) 15122 Mt Savage Rd NW, Mt Savage MD 21545, 301-264-3039 [ALL] IIA [AC] Pastor, Red Run Menn Ch, Mt Savage MD

Reyes, Wilson, 807 Raven Crossing #101, Altamonte Springs FL 32734, 407-774-0521 [SE] [AW]

Reynolds, Glenn R., 537 Howard Ave, New Haven CT 06519, 203-562-5590 [LAN] IIB1 [AC] Pastor, Menn Bible Fell, New Haven CT

Reynolds, John (Leacy) 23 Ogden St, West Haven CT 06516, 203-937-1419 [LAN] IIC [AC] Licensed Deacon, Menn Bible Fell, New Haven CT

Rheinheimer, Ben, 1006 Mervin Ave, Goshen IN 46526, 574-534-9984, benjirh@yahoo.com [IM] IIA [AC] Youth Pastor, Yellow Creek Menn Ch, Goshen IN

Rheinheimer, Don (Jan) 3285 Spaatz Rd, Monument CO 80132, 719-488-9051, mcmcpastordon@earthlink.net [RM, WDC] IIB1 [AC] Co-Pastor, Mountain Community Menn Ch, Palmer Lake CO

Rheinheimer, Jan Lynette (Donald Dean) 3285 Spaatz Rd, Monument CO 80132, 719-488-9051 [RM, WDC] IIB1 [AC] Co-Pastor, Mountain Community Menn Ch, Palmer Lake CO

Rhodes III, Raleigh D. (Patricia) 67 Saint Catherine Dr, Quarryville PA 17566, 717-786-4134 [LAN] [AW]

Rice, Howard H., PO Box 1214, Bethlehem PA 18016, 610-882-3503 [LAN] IIB3b [AC]

Rice, Jack, 951 Copella Rd, Bath PA 18014, 610-759-0211, bendersp@epix.net [LAN] IIB1 [AC] Pastor, Great Shepherd Christian Fell, Pen Argyl PA

Richard, Gary (Anne) 1706 Sheridan St, Warsaw IN 46580, 574-269-7745 [IM] [AW]

Richard, Glen (Margaret) 422 Becky Ln, Mount Pleasant IA 52641, 319-385-4962 [CP] [RE]

Richards, E. Joe (Emma E. Sommers Richards) 1502 Brookfield Ct, Goshen IN 46526, 574-534-6357 [IM] [RE]

Richards, Emma Elizabeth (E. Joe) 1502 Brookfield Ct, Goshen IN 46526, 574-534-6357 [IM] [RE]

Richards, George R. (Clemmie) 223 Peabody St NW, Washington DC 20011, 202-829-1940 [LAN] IIB1 [AC] Pastor, Peabody Street Menn Ch, Washington DC

Richer, Roger (Florence) 1364 Orchard Cr, Upland CA 91786, 909-981-4533 [PSW] IIB1 [AC] Pastor, Mountain View Menn Ch, Upland CA

Richert, Irvin E. (Shirley I.) 1019 Brookfield Cr, Quakertown PA 18951, 215-536-7725 [EDC] [RE]

Richter Sr, Gerald B. (Charlotte A.) 508 East Bacon St, Pottsville PA 17901, 717-622-8382, jerry01@dfnow.com [LAN] IIB1 [AC] Pastor, Palo Alto Menn Ch, Pottsville PA

Ring, Paul, 4275 Mount Tabor Rd, Vinton OH 45686, 740-388-9305 [OH] IIB1 [AC] Pastor, Fellowship Chapel, Vinton OH

Risser, Gerald E. (Joyce E.) 1246 Nissley Rd, Bainbridge PA 17502 [LAN] III [AC] Ordained Deacon, Goods Menn Ch, Bainbridge PA

Risser, Harold L. (Dorothy) 2368 Turnpike Rd, Elizabethtown PA 17022, 717-367-3198 [LAN] [RE]

Risser, Isaac M. (Mildred) 3363 Melody Ave, Roanoke VA 24018, 540-725-1184 [VA] [RE]

Rissler, Jason R., 428 Nectarine St, Harrisburg PA 17104, jasonrissler@juno.com [LAN] IIA [AC] Pastor, New Hope Community Ch, Harrisburg PA

Ritchie, Amy Suzanne Gall (Kurt) 15143 Featherstone Rd, Constantine MI 49042, 269-435-7732, amy.kurtritchie@juno.com [CDC] IIB1 [AC] Co-Pastor, Florence Church of the Brethren, Constantine MI

Ritchie, Kurt (Amy Gall Ritchie) 15143 Featherstone Rd, Constantine MI 49042, 269-435-7732, amy.kurtritchie@juno.com [CDC] [AW]

Rittenhouse, Mary Yunginger (Dennis) 6 Fairway Dr, Denver PA 17517, 717-445-6241, denmarrit@1usa,com [LAN] IIC [AC] Chaplain, Landis Homes, Lititz PA

Ritz, Lee Roy (Joyce) 1101 Schoffers Rd, Birdsboro PA 19508, 610-582-8915, his.servants7@juno.com [LAN]

MINISTERS

6

IIA [AC] Pastor, Hampden Menn Ch, Reading PA

Rivera, Juan Jose (Maria Elena) PO Box 50292, Sarasota FL 34278, 941-954-7189 [SE] IIB1 [AC] Pastor, Iglesia Seguidores de Cristo, Sarasota FL

Rivera, Oswaldo, 1885 S Dayton-Lakeview, New Carlisle OH 45344, 937-846-1356 [OH] IIA [AC] Spanish Pastor, Huber Menn Ch, New Carlisle OH

Robbins, Edward T. (Deborah R.) 1408 N Wabash Ave, Kokomo IN 46901, 765-868-2014, erobbins1@juno.com [IM] [AW]

Roberson, Ellis Wayne (Janice) 6005 Adamstown Rd, Adamstown MD 21710, 301-831-8812, pastor@dawsonvillechurch.org [LAN] IIB1 [AC] Pastor, Dawsonville Menn Ch, Poolesville MD

Roberts, Gary L. (Sue) 1 Lighthouse Dr, Kirkwood PA 17536, 717-529-6071, mtvernonmennonite@juno.com [LAN] IIB1 [AC] Pastor, Mt Vernon Menn Ch, Kirkwood PA

Robinson, Lindsey A., 226 Reily St, Harrisburg PA 17102, 717-232-6252, locustlanemenn@paoline.com [LAN] IB2, IIB1 [AC] Pastor, Locust Lane Menn Chapel, Harrisburg PA

Robles, Isaias, 8630 Fawn Creek Dr, Tampa FL 33626 [SE] IIA [AC] Pastor, North Tampa Christian Fell, Tampa FL

Rodman, Jerry (Carolyn) 1850 N State Rt 827, Angola IN 46703, 260-665-6364 [IM] [RE]

Rodriguez, Damian (Dilcia Matilde) 4308 Frank St, Dallas TX 75210, 214-428-7731, damian_rodriguez@msn.com [WDC] IIB1 [AC] Pastor, Comunidad de Esperanza, Dallas TX

Rodriguez, Herman, PO Box 566, Warden WA 98857, 509-349-7686 [PNW] IIA [AC] Pastor, Centro Cristiano Manantiales de Vida Eterna, Warden WA

Roeschley, Jane Thorley (Mark) 14524 N 800 East Rd, Graymont IL 61743, 815-743-5978, jroeschley.mcn@verizon.net [CDC, IL] IIA [AC] Associate Pastor, Menn Ch of Normal, Normal IL

Rogers, Terry (Karen S.) 508 N Main St, Morton IL 61550, 309-263-7407 [IL] [AW]

Rohrer, Larry D. (Sharon Jayne [Specht]) 66 N Cross St, Columbiana OH 44408, 330-482-3420 [OH] IIB1 [AC] Pastor, Midway Menn Ch, Columbiana OH

Rohrer, Raymond E. (Elizabeth) 105 Eastbrook Rd, Ronks PA 17572, 717-397-7044 [LAN] [RE]

Romain Jr, Victor H. (Oneisha) 52 Taylor Rd, Harrisburg PA 17103 [LAN] IIB1 [AC] Pastor, Steelton Menn Ch, Steelton PA

Roman, Carmen, 37 Reliance Rd, Souderton PA 18964, 215-721-7087 [FRC] IIA [AC] Associate Pastor, Norristown New Life Menn Ch, Norristown PA

Romero, Carlos (Celina) 61536 CR 35, Goshen IN 46528, 574-825-0808 [IM] IB1 [AC] staff, Mennonite Education Agency, Elkhart IN

Romero, Eugenio (Aurelia) PO Box 7438, Nogales AZ 85628-7438, 623-848-2583 [LAN] IIB3b [AC]

Ropp, Herman E. (Gladys) 1630 Park Rd, Harrisonburg VA 22802, 540-433-1780 [VA] [RE]

Ropp, Janice Kennel (Lonnie) 2325 W Weathersfield Way, Schaumburg IL 60193, 847-985-0178, lonnieropp@attbi.com [CDC, IL] IIC [AC] Minister of Counseling, Christ Community Menn Ch, Schaumburg IL

Ropp, Ronald David (Martha Jo Emerick Ropp) Rt 8

Box 73-A, Normal IL 61761-9725, 309-452-8534 [CDC, IL] IIB3a [AC]

Ropp, Steve A. (Cindy) 601 E Taylor, Bloomington IL 61701, 309-829-7428, steverym@juno.com [CDC, IL] IIB2, IIB3c [AC] Youth Pastor, Menn Ch of Normal, Normal IL

Rose, Carol Ann, 2043 Fairview, Wichita KS 67203, 316-264-9616, carolarose@juno.com [WDC] IIB1 [AC] Pastor, Menn Ch of the Servant, Wichita KS

Rosemberg, Rojas, 1601 W 4th St, Wilmington DE 19805, 302-654-3587 [LAN] IIB1 [AC] Pastor, Centro Evangelistico Cristiano, Wilmington DE

Rosenberger, Charlotte Graber (Henry L.) 1239 Route 113 Box 59, Blooming Glen PA 18911, CharlotteR@FMC-online.org [FRC] IC [AC]

Ross, Richard, 436 E Sassafras, Orrville OH 44667, 330-684-2573 [OH] IIB3a [AC]

Roth, Arnold C. (Lucille) 6402 Cedar Trail, South Bend IN 46614 [IM] [RE]

Roth, Arthur J. (Marjorie) 320 W 7th St, Julesburg CO 80737, 970-474-2580 [CP] IIB1 [AC] Pastor, Julesburg Menn Ch, Julesburg CO

Roth, Charlene, 1515 30th Ave, Greeley CO 80634, 970-304-0417, rcroth@juno.com [RM] IIB1 [AC] Pastor, Greeley Menn Ch, Greeley CO

Roth, Cloy (Ora) 200 Meadowbrook Dr, Hot Springs AR 71913, 501-624-8722 [CP] IIB1 [AC] Pastor, Wood River Menn Ch, Wood River NE

Roth, David Willis (Connie Sue) PO Box 803, Victoria Ln, Des Allemands LA 70030, 985-758-3927 [GS] IIA [AC] Pastor, Des Allemands Menn Ch, Des Allemands LA

Roth, Earl, 114 Hickory Cr, Elkhart IN 46517-9700, 574-294-5729 [CDC] [RE]

Roth, James L. (Ann Marie) 412 7th St NE, Hickory NC 28601, 828-328-4761, jimannroth@yahoo.com [VA] IIB1 [AC]

Roth, Jerry A. (Anna) PO Box 106, Marion PA 17235, 717-375-2037 [FRK] IIB1 [AC] Pastor, Chambersburg Menn Ch, Chambersburg PA

Roth, Lester, 203 Farmington Rd, Archbold OH 43502, 419-446-9477 [OH] [RE]

Roth, Mark Ray (Carol Lee) 11150 Rd 781, Philadelphia, MS 39350, 601-656-9302, croth@choctaw.org [GS] IIB2 [AC] Senior Pastor, Nanih Waiya Indian Menn Ch, Philadelphia MS

Roth, Nelson R. (Emma Jane [Byler]) 206 Mayluth Rd, Johnstown PA 15904-2635, 814-266-5000, NRothCCC@aol.com [ALL] IIB1 [AC] Pastor, Crossroads Community Ch, Johnstown PA

Roth, Oliver (Verda) RR 1, Milford NE 68405, 402-761-2065 [CP] [RE]

Roth, Randall J. (Mary) 3107 Madison Ave, Des Moines IA 50310, 515-255-9127, RRoth13@aol.com [CP] IIB1 [AC] Pastor, Des Moines Menn Ch, Des Moines IA

Roth, Ron, 1515 30th Ave, Greeley CO 80634, 970-304-0417, rcroth@juno.com [RM] IIB1 [AC] Pastor, Greeley Menn Ch, Greeley CO

Roth, Roy D., 2211 Oakway Rd, Eugene OR 97401, 541-344-8547 [PNW] [RE]

Roth, Willard Edward (Alice M.) 1077 Greenleaf Blvd #311, Elkhart IN 46514-3565, 574-266-7684, waroth@juno.com [CDC, IM] [RE]

Roth, Willis (Darlene) 7457 W Abbott Rd, Grand Island NE 68803, 308-382-8039 [CP] [RE]

Rowe, Robert C. (Naomi) 8614 Pine Tree Rd, Jessup MD 20794, 301-725-0540 [LAN] IIB1 [AC] Pastor, Guilford Road Menn Ch, Jessup MD

Roynon, James, V986 CR 20, Archbold OH 43502, 419-446-2967, wclinton@bright.net [OH] IIB1 [AC] Pastor, West Clinton Menn Ch, Wauseon OH

Royster, D. David (Pamela) 5635 Wyalusing Ave, Philadelphia PA 19131, 215-471-7994 [LAN] [AW]

Rudy, Carl J. (Ruth) 2021 College Dr, La Junta CO 81050, 719-384-9297, carlrudy@iguana.rural.net [RM] [RE]

Rudy, John H. (Lucy) 89 Linda Ave, Lancaster PA 17602, 717-299-6031 [ACC] [RE]

Ruffin, Jimmie (Kim) 1823 Woodhaven Dr, Fort Wayne IN 46819, 260-447-9566, kiji112464@msn.com [IM] IIA [AC] Pastor, Fairhaven Menn Ch, Fort Wayne IN

Rush, John L. (Esther) 638 Mountain View Rd, Reading PA 19607, 610-777-0171, rushjoes@aol.com [ACC] IIB3b [AC] Executive Director, Justice & Mercy Ministries, Reading PA

Rush, Paul D., 1419 Richland Town Pike, Quakertown PA 18951, 215-536-3103 [FRC] [RE]

Rust, C. Timothy (Janine J.) 55238 CR 31, Bristol IN 46507-9569, 574-825-1111, tim@rusthollar.com [IL] [AW]

Ruth, John L., 760 Salfordville Rd, Harleysville PA 19438, 610-287-5487 [FRC] [RE]

Ruth, Marvin L. (Lizzie) 595 N Mountain Rd, Newville PA 17241, 717-776-3084 [LAN] [RE]

Ruth, Winfield M., RR 152 Box 21 Apt 261, Sellersville PA 18960, 215-453-9675 [FRC] [RE]

Rutherford Jr, Richard E. (Dorothy E.) 272 Picture Mountain Dr, Martinsburg WV 25401-0660, 304-263-7850, pastor@blackoakmennonite.net [ACC] IIB1 [AC] Pastor, Black Oak Menn Ch, Warfordsburg PA

Ruth-Heffelbower, Clare Ann (Duane) 3198 E Menlo Ave, Fresno CA 93710, 559-287-4578 [PSW] IIB3b [AW]

Ruth-Heffelbower, Duane Fredric (Clare Ann) 3198 E Menlo Ave, Fresno CA 93710, 559-287-4578 [PSW] IIB3b [AW]

Rutt, Harry W. (Julia) 390 W Newport Rd, Ronks PA 17572-9718, 717-656-6244, harryrutt1@juno.com [LAN] [AW]

Rutter, Allen G., 21-377 CR H-50, Stryker OH 43557, 419-682-5096, alrutter@bright.net [OH] IIB1 [AC] Pastor, Lockport Menn Ch, Stryker OH

S

Sabatine, Leonard J. (Norma) 1740 Howell Rd RD1, Easton PA 18042-9221, 610-253-0086 [LAN] III [AC] Ordained Deacon, Maranatha Family Christian Fell, Nazareth PA

Sanchez, Moises (Stor Sanchez) 644 Franklin Ave, 2nd Floor, Brooklyn NY 11238, 718-399-1345 [ACC] IIA [AC] Assistant Pastor, First Menn Ch, Brooklyn NY

Saner, John R. (Virginia) HC Box 37, Mifflin PA 17058, 717-436-6621 [LAN] [RE]

Sangree, Paul C. (Patricia Thomas) 400 Owl Bridge Rd, Millersville PA 17551, 717-872-2590 [LAN] [RE]

Sangrey, Landis K. (Martha) 109 Turnbridge Dr, Lancaster PA 17603, 717-397-6053 [LAN] [RE]

Santiago, Jose A. (Agdelia) 511 Oak Grove Dr, Lancaster PA 17601, 717-656-9205, joses@emm.org [LAN] IB3 [AC] Pastor, Iglesia Menonita Roca de Salvacion, Lancaster PA; Supervisor, Spanish District, Lancaster PA

Santiago, Noel (Juanita) 210 S Main St, Sellersville PA 18960-2529, 215-257-1126, NoelS@FMC-online.org [FRC] IIB3c [AC]

Sarmiento, Luis D. (Patricia) A Apartado 43A, Charavalle, Venezula [LAN] IIB1 [AC]

Sauder, Bruce L. (Wanda) 409 Linden Rd, East Earl PA 17519, 717-445-9280, blwjsauder@hydrosoft.net [LAN] IIB2 [AC] Associate Pastor, Goodville Menn Ch, Goodville PA

Sauder, Donald M. (Myrtle) 5530 Levering Ave, Elkridge MD 21075, 410-796-5274 [LAN] III [AC] Licensed Deacon, Guilford Road Menn Ch, Jessup MD

Sauder, Eugene H. (Grace) 274 W Maple Grove Rd, Denver PA 17517-8929, 717-445-6119 [LAN] III [AC] Ordained Deacon, Lichty Menn Ch, New Holland PA

Sauder, Glenn E. (Brenda) 518 W Broad St, New Holland PA 17557, 717-354-9990, sauderspot@juno.com [LAN] IIA, IIB1 [AC] Pastor, Hinkletown Menn Ch, Ephrata PA

Sauder, James, 1225 Fern Ave, Reading PA 19607, 610-796-1528, jarhosa@juno.com [LAN] IIB1 [AC] Co-Pastor, Shiloh Menn Ch, Reading PA

Sauder, Joseph P. (Geneva) 5670-A Waterloo Rd, Columbia MD 21045, 410-465-1863, joe@sauder.org [LAN] III [RE]

Sauder, Marty (Jean) 1050 North Kiowa St, Allentown PA 18103, 610-770-1409, msauder@erols.com [FRC] IIB1 [AC] Pastor, Spruce Lake Fell, Canadensis PA

Sauder, Roy E., 600 Haven Dr, Archbold OH 43502, 419-446-2385 [OH] [RE]

Sauder, Steve (Anna) 809 Heritage Dr, Oakland MD 21550-1746, 301-334-7969, ssauder@pennswoods.net [ALL] IB3, IIB1 [AC] Pastor, Gortner Union Ch, Oakland MD

Sauder, Steven A. (Rebecca) 5755 Elkridge Heights Rd, Elkridge MD 21075, 410-579-8714, ssauder@ineva.com [LAN] IIA [AC] Associate Pastor, Guilford Road Menn Ch, Jessup MD

Savage, Regan (Janice Histand Savage) 35 Millstone Ct, Langhorne PA 19047, 215-757-3209 [FRC] IIB1 [AC] Pastor, MillCreek Community Ch, Langhorne PA

Sawatsky, Margaret, 2406 Roys Ave, Elkhart IN 46517, masawatsky@juno.com [CDC] IIA [AC] Chaplain

Sawatzky, Benjamin J. (Leona Elizabeth [Friesen]) 2904A Ivy Dr, North Newton KS 67117, 316-283-6107 [WDC] [RE]

Sawatzky, Erick (Beverley Ann) 405 Park West Dr, Goshen IN 46526, 574-533-1830, EBSawatzky@cs.com [CDC] IIB3d [RE] Prof of Pastoral Ministry/Dir of Field Education

Sawatzky, Sheldon Victor (Marietta G Landis) 2816 Goldenrod Rd, North Newton KS 67117, 316-283-2969 [WDC] IIB3c [AC] Associate Director, Mennonite Mission Network, Newton KS

Sawatzky, Walter (Joy) 222 West Broad St, Souderton PA 18964, 215-721-4776, WalterS@MRN.org [FRC] IC [AC]

Scaggs, Sam R. (Beverly) 441 Wenger Rd, Chesapeake VA 23322 [VA] [AW]

Scandrett, Kendrick J. (Catherine) 441 St Berndne St, Reading PA 19602, 610-796-7397, jclea7@juno.com [ACC] IIB1 [AC] Pastor, Hopewell Menn, Reading PA

Schaadt, Michael Alan, 819 Muschlitz St, Bethlehem PA 18015, 610-866-8433, pastormikeis@email.msn.com [EDC] [AW]

MINISTERS

6

Schanz, Philip (Barbara) 1470 Reiff Rd, Lansdale PA 19446, 215-855-4752 [EDC] III [AC]

Schertz, Dale E., 503 W Short St, Remington IN 47977-9801, 219-261-2731 [CDC] [RE]

Schertz, Vernon E. (Betty I.) 2010 Albany Dr SW, Atlanta GA 30311, 404-758-3096, verbetz@juno.com [SE] [AW]

Schildt, Kenneth E. (Charlene) 74 Engle Rd, Marietta PA 17545, 717-426-1579, schildts@paonline.com [LAN] IIC [AC] Licensed Deacon, Bossler Menn Ch, Elizabethtown PA

Schipani, Daniel, 57995 River Lake Ct, Elkhart IN 46516, 574-875-8913 [IM] IIB3d [AC] Staff, Associated Mennonite Biblical Seminary, Elkhart IN

Schlabach, Mark (Starla) 248 Meadow Ln, Conestoga PA 17516, 717-871-3002, mschlabach@lifeministries.com [LAN] IIA [AC] Pastor, Life Menn Fell, Conestoga PA

Schloneger, Enid Elaine (Robert) 822 Orchard Rd, Sellersville PA 18960, 215-257-6999 [FRC] IIB1 [AC] Lead Pastor, Blooming Glen Menn Ch, Blooming Glen PA

Schloneger, Florence Eileen (Weldon Ray) 1501 Bell St, Beatrice NE 68310, 402-223-2897 [WDC] IIB1 [AC] Co-Pastor, First Menn Ch, Beatrice NE

Schloneger, Robert (Enid Elaine) 822 Orchard Rd, Sellersville PA 18960, 215-257-6999 [FRC] IIB1 [AC] Lead Pastor, Blooming Glen Menn Ch, Blooming Glen PA

Schloneger, Weldon Ray (Florence Eileen) 1501 Bell St, Beatrice NE 68310, 402-223-2897 [WDC] IIB1 [AC] Co-Pastor, First Menn Ch, Beatrice NE

Schmell, Barry Lee (Deborah Lee) 6133 Cordava Ct, Fort Wayne IN 46815, 260-493-7867, bdschmell@aol.com [CDC] IIB1 [AC] Pastor, Maplewood Menn Ch, Fort Wayne IN

Schmell, Rodger K. (Diana) 31 Church Rd Apt #2, Hatfield PA 19440, 215-997-8175, rdschmell@juno.com [EDC] IIA [AC] Youth Pastor, Deep Run West Menn Ch, Perkasie PA

Schmidt, Debra Ann (Donald Ray) 901 S Pine, Newton KS 67114, 316-283-8186, fmchutch@southwind.net [WDC] IIB1 [AC] Pastor, First Menn Ch, Hutchinson KS

Schmidt, Dennis Gene, 525 N Jefferson St, Berne IN 46711-1517, 260-589-9877, dennis@firstmennonite.org [CDC, OH] IIB2 [AC] Pastor of Christian Education, First Menn Ch, Berne IN

Schmidt, Melvin D. (Charlotte) 4212 Longfellow St, Hyattsville MD 20781, 301-927-0420 [ALL] IB3, IIB1 [AC] Pastor, Hyattsville Menn Ch, Hyattsville MD

Schmidt, Steven Gary (Wanda Ream Schmidt) 10 Chaparral Ct, La Junta CO 81050-3803, 719-384-9359, pastor@emclj.org [RM] IIB1 [AC] Pastor, Emmanuel Menn Ch, La Junta CO

Schmidt, Vyron Lloyd, 906 Player Dr, Goshen IN 46526-2726, 574-533-0671 [IM] IIB3c [AC]

Schmitt, Howard S. (D. Jean) 1003 Willow Creek Dr, Plain City OH 43064, 614-873-0670, howjean@prodigy.net [OH] IIB1 [AC] Pastor, Sharon Menn Ch, Plain City OH

Schmucker, Eli S. (Myrtle) PO Box 257, New Paris IN 46553, 574-831-4432 [IM] IIB1 [AC] Pastor, Gospel Lighthouse, New Paris IN

Schmucker, Leonard E. (Lucille) 172 Beau Chemin, Louisville OH 44641, 330-875-0343,

lsch@accinternet.com [SC] [RE]

Schrag, Charlene, 25411 S Holman, Estacada OR 97023, 503-630-7216, pmcyouth@teleport.com [PNW] IIA [AC] Youth Pastor, Portland Menn Ch, Portland OR

Schrag, James Frederick (Judith A.) 3225 Southwood Ct, Newton KS 67114, 316-283-0608 [WDC] IB1 [AC] Executive Director, Mennonite Church USA, Newton KS

Schrag, Laverle (Ronald D.) 222 W 20, Hutchinson KS 67502, 620-663-4958, verls@midusa.net [WDC] IIB2 [AC] Associate Pastor, First Menn Ch, Hutchinson KS

Schrag, Myron Dave (Ericka Koop Schrag) 1201 S 14th St, Goshen IN 46526, 574-533-8366, schrags@npcc.net [CDC] [RE]

Schrag, Rhoda M., 1105 S 8th St, Goshen IN 46526, 574-534-7873, rmschrag@juno.com [CDC] IIB1 [AC] Pastor, Southside Fell, Elkhart IN

Schrag, Tim E. (Sue Hertzler Schrag) 105 Sandra Ln, Normal IL 61761, 309-862-1880, t.schrag@verizon.net [CDC, IL] IIB1 [AC] Pastor, Menn Ch of Normal, Normal IL

Schrag, Willard A., 113 West Lincoln, Moundridge KS 67107-9701, 620-345-6433 [WDC] [RE]

Schreiner, Sally, 6728 N Bosworth Ave #3N, Chicago IL 60626, 773-338-8569, sallylwcc@aol.com [IL] IIB1 [AC] Senior Pastor, Living Water Community Ch, Chicago IL

Schrock, Daniel P. (Jennifer Halteman Schrock) 64366 Meadow Ridge Dr, Goshen IN 46526, 574-533-1729, danschrock@juno.com [IM] IIB1 [AC] Pastor, Berkey Avenue Menn Fell, Goshen IN

Schrock, Elwood G. (Lorene) 166 N State Rd 40, Exeland WI 54835-2176, 715-943-2317 [NC] IIB1 [AC] Pastor, Exeland Menn Ch, Exeland WI

Schrock, Homer E. (Debbie) 10 Schapansky Rd, Cochranville PA 19330, 610-593-6462 [ALL] [RE]

Schrock, James A., PO Box 67, Pettisville OH 43553, 419-445-3311 [OH] IIC [AC]

Schrock, John L. (Melissa Kauffman Schrock) 192 Garmatter St, Bluffton OH 45817, 419-358-0958, FMC.john@bluffton.edu [CDC] IIB2 [AC] Associate Pastor, First Menn Ch, Bluffton OH

Schrock, Richard (Rosella) RR 2 Box 522, Garden City MO 64747, 816-862-6559 [SC] [RE]

Schrock, Thomas L. (Jeanette A.) RR 1 Box 23, Putnam IL 61560, 815-646-4678 [IL] IIB1 [AC] Pastor, Trinity New Life Menn Ch, Henry IL

Schrock-Hurst, Carmen (Luke) 640 Melbourne St, Pittsburgh PA 15217, 412-421-2933 [ALL] [AC]

Schrock-Hurst, Luke (Carmen) 640 Melbourne St, Pittsburgh PA 15217, 412-421-2933 [ALL] [AC]

Schroeder, Joel R. (Kay) 1180 10th St, PO Box 132, Henderson NE 68371, 402-723-4791, joelkay@telcoweb.net [CP] IIB2 [AC] Youth Pastor, Bethesda Menn Ch, Henderson NE

Schultz, Timothy J., 16 Maureen Ave, Clarence NY 14031, 716-759-1806, tim@buffalo.edu [NY] IIB1 [AC] Pastor, Harris Hill Menn Ch, Williamsville NY

Schulz, Eugene, PO Box 167, Walsenburg CO 81089, 719-738-2037 [RM] [RE]

Schumacher, Kevin John, 12642 S Hiefield Ct, Oregon City OR 97045, 503-722-2304 [PNW] IIA [AC] Pastor, Calvary Menn Ch, Aurora OR

Schumm, Clare, 609 Revere Dr, Goshen IN 46526, 574-534-2343 [IM] IIB3a [AC] Chaplain, Greencroft Inc, Goshen IN

Schwartz, Jacob P., 23641 Findley Rd, Sturgis MI 49091, 269-467-6253 [IM] IIB3a [AC] Jail Chaplain, St. Joseph County Jail, IN

Schwartz, Thomas (Leanell) 138 Keathly Dr, Battle Creek MI 49017, 616-964-9214 [IM] IIB1 [AC] Pastor, Pine Grove Menn Ch, Battle Creek MI

Schwartzentruber, Hubert (Mary Rittenhouse Schwartzentruber) 711 Rising Sun Rd, Telford PA 18969, 215-723-1460 [FRC] IIB3a [AC] Chaplain, Souderton Mennonite Homes, Souderton PA

Schweitzer, James Roland (Carol Ann) 2455 E Mountain View Dr SE, Albany OR 97322, 541-928-4304 [PNW] IIC [AC]

Scott Jr, William L. (Vivian) 2821 Chamber St, Saginaw MI 48601, 989-755-7159, billy.boy@juno.com [IM] IIB1 [AC] Pastor, Ninth Street Menn Ch, Saginaw MI

Scoville, Gordon, PO Box 417, Lowville NY 13367, 315-376-6379, nbmenno@northnet.org [CP] IIB1 [AC] Interim Pastor, First Menn Ch of New Bremen, Lowville NY

Sears, Earl (Jane) 7273 1575 E St, Tiskilwa IL 61368, 815-646-4497, esears@theramp.net [IL] [RE]

Seitz Jr, Kenneth L. (Kathryn F.) PO Box 971, Reedley CA 93654, 559-637-1017 [PSW] IIB1 [AC] Pastor, First Menn Ch, Reedley CA

Seitz Sr, Kenneth L. (Grace) 1285 Shank Dr, #125, Harrisonburg VA 22802, 540-564-6532 [VA] [RE]

Sell, Glen M. (Ethel) 677 Lititz Rd, Manheim PA 17545-9726, 717-626-1566, gmsell@juno.com [LAN] IB3 [AC] Interim Bishop/Overseer, LMC—Juniata District, PA

Sensenig, Craig G. (Denise) 122 W Main St, PO Box 644, Terre Hill PA 17581, 717-445-6916, cdsbrsen@epix.net [LAN] IIA [AC] Assistant Pastor, Groffdale Menn Ch, Leola PA

Sensenig, David E. (Marilyn) 103 Edgewood Dr, New Holland PA 17557 [LAN] IIB2 [AC] Associate Pastor, Martindale Menn Ch, Ephrata PA

Sensenig, Donald M. (Doris) 106 S 4th St, Akron PA 17501, 717-859-2940, dondors@juno.com [LAN] IIB1 [AC] Pastor, Stumptown Menn Ch, Bird-in-Hand PA

Sensenig, Gary (Joanne) Mennonite Guesthouse, PO Box 14646, Nairobi, Kenya [LAN] IIC [AC] Missionary/Church Worker, EMM, Nairobi Kenya, Africa

Sensenig, Jennifer Davis (Kent) 824 Main St Apt 3-D, Cedar Falls IA 50613, 319-277-5611, cfmcjds@cedarnet.org [CP] IIB1 [AC] Pastor, Cedar Falls Menn Ch, Cedar Falls IA

Sensenig, Joanne E. (Gary) Mennonite Guesthouse, PO Box 14646, Nairobi, Kenya, Africa, 717-354-0234 [LAN] IIC [AC] Missionary, Mennonite Guesthouse, Nairobi Kenya

Serrano, Ciro, 1701 S Main St, Goshen IN 46526, 574-537-8134, ciro@hertzler.com [IM] IIA [AC] Pastor, Iglesia Menonita del Buen Pastor, Goshen IN

Seville, D. C., 7108 W Cholla, Peoria AZ 85345, 602-486-9160 [PSW] IIB1 [AC] Pastor, Emmanuel Menn Ch, Surprise AZ

Shank, David A., 26430 Banker St Rd, Sturgis MI 49091, 269-659-4047 [IM] [RE]

Shank, Dorothy J. (Orval) 2272 Lake Terrace Dr, Harrisonburg VA 22802, 540-438-0866, dorvals@aol.com [VA] [RE]

Shank, Luke J., 1001 E Oregon Rd, Lititz PA 17543, 717-581-0297, lukejs@dejazzd.com [LAN] [RE]

Shank, Marlin W. (Beulah) 663 Overcash Rd, Chambersburg PA 17201, 717-375-2866 [FRK] III [AC]

Shank, Orval M. (Dorothy) 2272 Lake Terrace Dr, Harrisonburg VA 22802, 540-438-0866, dorvals@aol.com [VA] [RE]

Shank, Raymond W. (Gladys) 860A Hillside Ave, Harrisonburg VA 22802, 540-433-5495 [VA] IIB2 [AC] Associate Pastor, Lindale Menn Ch, Harrisonburg VA

Shank, Rowland (Thelma) 2967 Westwind Dr, Harrisonburg VA 22801, 540-564-0568 [VA] [RE]

Shantz, Kathy Keener (Stan R.) 4351 W Vista Ave, Glendale AZ 85301, 623-939-7773, KKShantz@aol.com [PSW] IIB2 [AC] Associate Pastor, Trinity Menn Ch, Glendale AZ

Shantz, Stan, 4334 W Vista Ave, Glendale AZ 85323, 623-939-7773, srshantz@aol.com [PSW] IIB1 [AC] Pastor, Trinity Menn Ch, Glendale AZ

Sharp, Donald D. (Loretta) 22 S 12th St, Akron PA 17501-1606 [ALL] [AW]

Sharp, Galen (Donna) 75 Allison Gap Rd, Belleville PA 17004, 717-483-6063 [ALL] IIB3a [AC]

Sharp, Harold E. (Vonnie) 102 Forest Ln, Belleville PA 17004, 717-483-6929 [ALL] IB3, IIB1 [AC]

Sharp, Harold R., 1411 N Abbe Rd, Fairview MI 48621, 517-848-5280 [IM] [RE]

Sharp, John E. (Michele Miller Sharp) 416 Marilyn Ave, Goshen IN 46526, 574-534-6685, johnes@goshen.edu [IM] IB3, IIB3c [AC] Overseer for North Main St Menn, Nappanee IN; Overseer for Assembly Menn, Goshen IN

Shaub, Andrew H. (Ruth C.) 529 Saratoga Rd, Lancaster PA 17603, 717-397-0424 [LAN] III [RE]

Shearer, Harold F. (Irene) 2361 Fairfield Ave, Sarasota FL 34232, 941-371-7649, hishearer@comcast.net [SE] IIB2 [AC] Minister of Visitation, Bahia Vista Menn Ch, Sarasota FL

Shearer, John (Vel) 1560 Jody Ave, Lebanon PA 17046, 717-270-5302 [ACC] IIB3a [AC]

Sheats, Earl (Pansy) 8610 Mennonite Church Rd, Westover MD 21871, 410-957-2097, epsheats@yahoo.com [ACC] [AW]

Sheeler, Timothy J. (Joyce) 4275 Enola Rd, Newville PA 17241, 717-776-6263, tjsheeler@excite.com [LAN] III [AC] Ordained Deacon, Diller Menn Ch, Newville PA

Sheller, Gayle, 952 C St, Springfield OR 97477, 541-726-9382, eugmenno@efn.org [PNW] IIB1 [AC] Pastor, Eugene Menn Ch, Eugene OR

Shelly, Eugene (Martine S.) 3234 Irwin Ave, Bronx NY 10463-3705, 718-549-1569, GShelly@aol.com [LAN] IIB3a [AC]

Shelly, Karl Schirch (Michelle Schirch Shelly) 605 N Greene Rd, Goshen IN 46526, 574-534-0185, kmshelly85@juno.com [CDC, IM] IIA [AC] Co-Pastor, Assembly Menn Ch, Goshen IN

Shelly, Maynard (Griselda Gehman Shelly) 3017 Ivy Ct, North Newton KS 67117-8072, 316-283-0518 [WDC] [RE]

Shelly, Patricia Joyce, 533 W Broadway, Newton KS 67114 [WDC] IIB3d [AC] Professor of Bible, Bethel College, North Newton KS

Shenk, Calvin E. (Marie) 965 S Dogwood Dr, Harrisonburg VA 22801, 540-433-8125, shenkc@emu.edu [LAN] IIB3d [AC]

Shenk, Charles B. (Ruth) 3505 Lindstrom Dr, Columbus OH 43228, 614-274-5552, CBShenk@aol.com [CDC, OH] [RE]

MINISTERS

6

Shenk, Charles E. (Marian) 206 Newcomer Dr, Scottdale PA 15683, 724-887-7641, shenk@westol.com [ALL] IB3 [AC] Interim Pastor, Menn Ch of Scottdale, Scottdale PA

Shenk, Clayton O. (Dorothy) 3346 Redbud Ln, Harrisonburg VA 22801-5313, 540-433-3296 [VA] [RE]

Shenk, Dale (Trish) 1505 S 8th St, Goshen IN 46526-4701, 574-534-3537, deshenk@bethanycs.net [IM] IB3, IIB3d [AC] Bible Teacher, Bethany Christian Schools, Goshen IN; Overseer for First Menn, Middlebury IN

Shenk, David W. (K. Grace) Lithuania Christian College, Malunininku 4, 5813 Klaipeda, Lithuania [LAN] IIB1 [AC]

Shenk, Donna Lois (James W.) 37 Third St, Akron PA 17501, 717-859-3512, jimshenk@juno.com [ACC] IIB3a [AC] Chaplain, Ephrata Community Hospital, Ephrata PA

Shenk, Edith N. (Joseph C.) 1240 Ivy Ln, Harrisonburg VA 22802, 540-433-3078, jesh@worldnet.att.com [VA] IIB1 [AC] Pastor, Weavers Menn Ch, Harrisonburg VA

Shenk, Evelyn Landis (John) 1560 College Ave, Harrisonburg VA 22802, 540-434-8220 [VA] IIB3a [AC]

Shenk, Ezra W. (Sara) 300 13th St, Wellman IA 52356, 319-648-4434 [CP] IIB1 [AC] Pastor, Daytonville Community Ch, Wellman IA

Shenk, Harold A. (Mary Grace) 13233 Glendale Dr, Hagerstown MD 21742, 301-797-5062, h-mgshenk@juno.com [ACC] IB3, IIB1 [AC] Co-Pastor, Hebron Menn Ch, Hagerstown MD

Shenk, Henry G. (Irene) 742 Bruce Ave, Mount Joy PA 17552, 717-653-5819 [LAN] [RE]

Shenk, J. B. (Betty) 1607 Kentfield Way, Goshen IN 46526, 574-534-8432 [IM] [RE]

Shenk, Jean Kraybill (Norman G.) 4050 Old Harrisburg Pike, Mount Joy PA 17552, 717-653-5256, normans@supernet.com [LAN] IIC [AC]

Shenk, John B. (Myrtle) 6138 Sundra Cr, East Petersburg PA 17520, 717-569-1589 [LAN] [RE]

Shenk, Joseph C. (Edith N.) 1240 Ivy Ln, Harrisonburg VA 22802, 540-433-3078, jesh@worldnet.att.com [VA] IIB1 [AC] Pastor, Weavers Menn Ch, Harrisonburg VA

Shenk, Mary Grace (Harold) 13233 Glendale Dr, Hagerstown MD 21742, 301-797-5062, h-mgshenk@juno.com [ACC] IB3, IIB1 [AC] Co-Pastor, Hebron Menn Ch, Hagerstown MD

Shenk, Nelson J. (June Yoder Shenk) 145 S 5th St, Bally PA 19503, 610-845-3240, ballyshenk@enter.net [FRC] IIB1 [AC] Pastor, Boyertown Menn Ch, Boyertown PA

Shenk, Norman G. (Jean Kraybill Shenk) 4050 Old Harrisburg Pike, Mount Joy PA 17552, 717-653-5256, normans@supernet.com [LAN] [RE]

Shenk, Philip L. 4650 Ridgewood Rd E, Springfield OH 45503, 937-399-9941 [OH] IIB3b [AC]

Shenk, Ruth F. (Charles B.) 3505 Lindstrom Dr, Columbus OH 43228, 614-274-5552, CBhenk@aol.com [CDC, OH] [RE]

Shenk, Stanley C. (Doris) 1406 S 12th St, Goshen IN 46526, 574-533-3511 [IM] [RE]

Shenk, Wilbert, 570 N Madison #6, Pasadena CA 91101, 626-683-3494 [IM] IIB3d [AC] Professor, Fuller Theological Seminary, Pasadena CA

Shenk II, H. Michael (Peggy Brackbill Shenk) 1345 Hillcrest Dr, Harrisonburg VA 22802, 540-434-0578 [VA] IB3, IIB1 [AC] Pastor, Valley View Menn Ch, Harrisonburg VA

Shenk III, H. Michael (Ramona) 5532 Greenhill Rd, Linville VA 22834, 540-833-4727 [VA] IIB2 [AC] Pastor, Valley View Menn Ch, Harrisonburg VA

Sherer, Joseph N. (Mary Lou) 26 Donegal Springs Rd, Mount Joy PA 17552, 717-653-1528, joesherer@mjmc.org [LAN] IIB1 [AC] Pastor, Mount Joy Menn Ch, Mount Joy PA

Sherrill, Mike (Teresa Thompson Sherrill) Higashi Moto Machi 2-2-10, Kokubunji, Tokyo 185-0022, Japan, 011-81-042-301-2911, journey@sherrill.com [PSW] IIB3b [AC]

Sherrill, Teresa Thompson (Mike) Higashi Moto Machi 2-2-10, Kokubunji, Tokyo 185-0022, Japan, 011-81-042-301-2911, journey@sherrill.com [PSW] IIB3b [AC]

Shertzer, W. Lynn (Dawn) 832 Fisher Rd, Mechanicsburg PA 17055-9601, 717-766-4142, shertzer@paonline.com [LAN] IIA [AC] Pastor, Slate Hill Menn Ch, Camp Hill PA

Shirk, Hazel (Mervin) 1019 Ponder Ave, Sarasota FL 34232, 941-371-2005 [SE] IIB2 [AC] Minister of Special Care, Bay Shore Menn Ch, Sarasota FL

Shirk, Leon R. (Henrietta) 663 N Railroad Ave, New Holland PA 17557, 717-354-8731, Bethanymc1@juno.com [ACC] IIB1 [AC] Pastor, Bethany Grace Fell, East Earl PA

Shirk, Stanley R. (Mary Jane) 3355 Dawn Dr, Harrisonburg VA 22801, 540-564-2663 [VA] IIB2 [AC]

Shisler, Barbara, 93 Klingerman Rd, Telford PA 18969, 215-723-9326 [FRC] IIB1 [AC] Pastor, Perkasie Menn Ch, Perkasie PA

Shonk, Roy Lee Kenneth (Pam) 290 Newberry Rd, Middletown PA 17057, 717-944-1520, RPShonk@juno.com [LAN] IIA [AC] Associate Pastor, Fountain of Life Ch, Middletown PA

Short, Reid, 408 High St, Archbold OH 43502, 419-445-5094, rshort7@fulton.net [OH] IIB1 [AC] Pastor, Emmanuel Menn Ch, Monclova OH

Short, Tim, 130 E Good Ave, Wadsworth OH 44281, 330-336-8467, tim19nov@hotmail.com [OH] IIB1 [AC] Pastor, Bethel Menn Ch, Rittman OH

Showalter, Ann, 321 E 12th St #105, Newton KS 67114-1972, asho@ourtownusa.net [WDC] [RE]

Showalter, Gerald W. (Evonne) 552 Harpersville Rd, Newport News VA 23601, 757-595-9221, gshowaltr@aol.com [VA] IIB2 [AC] Minister of Pastoral Care, Huntington Menn Ch, Newport News VA

Showalter, Glenn D. (Elinor) 5357 Little Cove Rd, Mercersburg PA 17236, 717-328-3059 [FRK] III [AC] Licensed Deacon, Rock Hill Menn Ch, Chambersburg PA

Showalter, Nathan D. (Christina Lee) 350 Locust Ln, Mount Joy PA 17552, 717-492-9534, nates@nni.com [LAN] IB3 [AC] Interim Bishop/Overseer, LMC - Manor District, PA; Co-Director Leadership Development, Lancaster Mennonite Conference, Lancaster PA

Showalter, Omar V. (Esther T.) 1631 Park Rd, Harrisonburg VA 22802-2465, 540-434-5181 [VA] [RE]

Showalter, Richard A. (Jewel Wenger Showalter) 150 James St, Landisville PA 17538, 717-898-5886 [LAN] IIB3c [AC]

Showalter,, Richard H. (Bertha) 3912 Stuarts Draft Hwy, Waynesboro VA 22980, 540-943-5827 [VA] IB3 [AC]

Shreiner, Mary Ann (Bob) 1407 Ashton Ct, Goshen IN 46526, 574-533-4546 [IM] IIC [AC] Minister of Senior Adults & Special Needs Persons, Clinton Frame Menn

Ch, Goshen IN

Shreiner, Robert L. (Mary Ann Hershey Shreiner) 1407 Ashton Ct, Goshen IN 46526, 574-533-4546 [IM] IIB1 [AC] Pastor, Clinton Frame Menn Ch, Goshen IN

Shrock Jr, Henry, 13820 Market Ave N, Hartville OH 44632, 330-877-6384, henrich98@aol.com [OH] IIB2 [AC] Associate Pastor, Hartville Menn Ch, Hartville OH

Shue, Terry W. (Kay Y.) 4000 Steinwood Dr, Dalton OH 44618, 330-857-8866, tkshue@bright.net [OH] IIB1 [AC] Pastor, Kidron Menn Ch, Kidron OH

Shuford, Robert Weir (Lois Farley Shuford) 943 Wesley Ave, Evanston IL 60202, 847-328-6312, blshuford@attbi.com [CDC, IL] IIB3a [AC] Chaplain, Our Lady of the Resurrection Medical Center, 5645 W. Addison, Chicago IL

Shull, Jeff (Melodi) 540 New St, Roaring Spring PA 16673, 814-224-9955, JMMSHULL@msn.com [ALL] IIB1 [AC] Pastor, Martinsburg Menn Ch, Martinsburg PA

Shull, Randall (Kristina [Kris]) 4117 Green Park Dr, Mount Joy PA 17552, 717-653-9340, randallshull@mjmc.org [LAN] IIB2 [AC] Associate Pastor, Mount Joy Menn Ch, Mount Joy PA

Shultz, Alma M. (Harold B.) 1967 Millport Rd, Lancaster PA 17602, 717-393-2376, hashultz@juno.com [LAN] IIC [AC] Licensed Deaconess, Sunnyside Menn Ch, Lancaster PA

Shutt, Joyce Musselman (Earl E.) 878 Mt Carmel Rd, Orrtanna PA 17353-9703, 717-642-5219, jms555@blazenet.net [EDC] IIB3a [AC]

Sider, Ronald J. (Arbutus) 312 W Logan St, Philadelphia PA 19144-4120, 215-844-1031, ronsider@esa-online.org [LAN] IIB2 [AC] Associate Pastor, Oxford Circle Menn Ch, Philadelphia PA

Sieber, Paul C. (Martha) 1642A CR 500 E, Champaign IL 61821, 217-863-2514 [CDC, IL] [RE]

Siegrist, Brian (Cheri Lyndaker Siegrist) 3010 Sumter Blvd, North Port FL 34287 [SE] IIC [AC] Pastor, Peace Christian Fell, North Port FL

Siegrist, David H. (Dorothy) 1166 West Penn Grant Rd, Lancaster PA 17603, 717-872-4085, ddsiegrist@juno.com [LAN] IIA [AC] Pastor, River Corner Menn Ch, Lancaster PA

Siegrist, E. Donald (Anne) 3465 State Rt 417, Jasper NY 14855, 607-792-3710, asiegrist@yahoo.com [NY] IB3, IIB1 [AC]

Siegrist, Wesley D. (Teresa) 885 Newport Rd, Manheim PA 17545, 717-665-7516 [LAN] IIB1 [AC] Pastor, Erb Menn Ch, Lititz PA

Simmons, Mary Lou E., 517 N Lafayette St, Allentown PA 18104, 610-782-0523, Loubeellens@aol.com [EDC] IIB3a [AC] Chaplain, Country Meadows Retirement Communities, Allentown PA

Simonsick, Robert (Patti) HC79 Box 192, Calico Rock AR 72519, 870-297-4345, bprabs@centurytel.net [SC] IIB1 [AC] Pastor, Calico Rock Menn Fell, Calico Rock AR

Sipes, Roger L., 27 Orchard Dr, Berkeley Springs WV 25411, 304-258-1139, rogerlsipes@hotmail.com [ACC] [AW]

Sirkel, Ronald Alfred, 1301 E Kansas, McPherson KS 67460, rsirkel@cox.net [WDC] IIC [AC] Pastor, Hopefield Menn Ch, Moundridge KS

Sitther, Thinager Paulraj, 3487 Beechwood Blvd, Pittsburgh PA 15217-2964, thinagars@yahoo.com [ALL] IIB1 [AC]

Slabach, Albert C., 1729 State Rt 643, Baltic OH 43804, 330-852-2216 [OH] [RE]

Slabach, Joe L. (Clara) 53805 CR 43, Middlebury IN 46540, 574-825-9135 [IM] [AW]

Slabaugh, Daniel (Ethel L.) 1212 N Holland-Sylvania Rd #112, Toledo OH 43615, 419-535-3142 [IM] [RE] Interim Pastor, Toledo Menn Ch, Sturgis MI

Slabaugh, Phil L. (Brenda) 207 W Front St, Wayland IA 52654, 319-256-6073, pslabaugh@farmtel.net [CP] IIB1 [AC] Pastor, Bethel Menn Ch, Wayland IA

Slagel, Dean, 605 Maple Crest Dr, Goshen IN 46526, 574-533-9915 [IM] [RE]

Slagel, Steve E. (Barbara Jean) 12924 CR 44, Millersburg IN 46543, 574-642-4554, steves@eastgoshenmc.org [IM] IIB1 [AC] Pastor, East Goshen Menn Ch, Goshen IN

Slaubaugh, Tobias, 4738 Banks Ln, Sarasota FL 34232, 941-377-9841 [IM] [RE]

Slough, Rebecca Jo, 7634 Morning Mist Cr, Trotwood OH 45426, 513-854-9222, rslough@ambs.edu [CDC] IIB3d [AC]

Smeltzer, Carl L., 103 Hillcrest Ave, Souderton PA 18964-1150 [FRC] IIB3a [AC] Chaplain

Smeltzer, Walter (Doris) 2026 W Kellogg St, Peoria IL 61604, 309-674-1777 [IL] IIB2 [AC] Associate Pastor, Living Love Ministries, Peoria IL

Smith, Cynthia Neufeld (Roger) 1331 SW Jewell, Topeka KS 66604, 785-232-5781, neufeldsmith@att.net [WDC] IIB1 [AC] Co-Pastor, Southern Hills Menn Ch, Topeka KS

Smith, Dale Wendell (Justina P.) 400 W 24th Apt #7, North Newton KS 67117, 316-282-0041 [WDC] [RE]

Smith, Duncan James (Charlene K. Epp) 1292 NW Fall Ave, Beaverton OR 97006-4031, 971-570-4216, duncansmithpnmc@cs.com [PNW] IB2 [AC] Conference Minister, Pacific Northwest Mennonite Conference, Portland OR

Smith, Gordon Louis (Mindy) 202 Windward Ct, Newton KS 67114, gosmith@sbcglobal.net [WDC] IIB1 [AC] Pastor, Faith Menn Ch, Newton KS

Smith, H. James (Phyllis) 19975 Peach Ridge Rd, Goshen IN 46526-9104 [IM] IIB3c [AC] Church Relations, Mennonite Mutual Aid, Goshen IN

Smith, James (Karla) c/o Roy Williams, 22642 Newfield Ct, Land O'lakes FL 34639, Jim_Smith@sil.org [SE] IIC [AC]

Smith, Jeffrey Wayne (Kathy Lynn) 205 Christine Dr, Archbold OH 43502, 419-445-0287 [OH] IIB2 [AC] Associate Pastor, Central Menn Ch, Archbold OH

Smith, Jonathan A. (Cindi) Jonathan A Smith, 315 Curtis St, Hutchinson KS 67502, 620-669-1455, jasmith@ourtownusa.net [SC] IIB1 [AC] Associate Pastor, South Hutchinson Menn Ch, South Hutchinson KS

Smith, Karla (James) c/o Roy Williams, 22642 Newfield Court, Land O'lakes FL 34639, Jim_Smith@sil.org [SE] IIC [AC]

Smith, Margaret Richer (Robert) 21 Wolf Brook Cr, Iowa City IA 52240, 319-338-7642 [CP] IIB1 [AC] Pastor, First Menn Ch of Iowa City, Iowa City IA

Smith, Norman, 3969 Sunnydale St, Elida OH 45807 [OH] [RE]

Smith, Randy W. (Ann Yoder Smith) 115 West 27th St, PO Box 1, North Newton KS 67117-0001, 316-283-

MINISTERS

6

0578 [WDC] IIB3a [AC] Campus Pastor, Bethel College, North Newton KS

Smith, Robert (Margaret) 21 Wolf Brook Cr, Iowa City IA 52240, 319-338-7642 [CP] IIB1 [AC] Pastor, First Menn Ch of Iowa City, Iowa City IA

Smith, Roger Neufeld (Cynthia) 1331 SW Jewell, Topeka KS 66604, 785-232-5781 [WDC] IIB1 [AC] Co-Pastor, Southern Hills Menn Ch, Topeka KS

Smoker, Kevin S. (Carol) 55 Whitehall Rd, Reinholds PA 17569, 717-733-0171 [LAN] IIB2 [AC] Associate Pastor, Blainsport Menn Ch, Stevens PA

Smoker Jr, Arthur E. (Nova Jean [Wingard]) 1304 S 15th St, Goshen IN 46526, 574-533-0968, AESmoker@aol.com [IM] IB3, IIB1 [AC] Pastor, North Goshen Menn Ch, Goshen IN

Smucker, Daniel M., 3515 Willow Run Rd, Harrisonburg VA 22802, 540-434-7944 [VA] [RE]

Smucker, Donovan Ebersole, 410 W Elm St, Bluffton OH 45817 [CDC] [RE]

Smucker, John I. (Irene) 149-03 Sanford Ave #1A, Flushing NY 11355, 718-961-1463 [ACC] [RE]

Smucker, John R. (Donna Louise Gerber) 2513 College Ave, Goshen IN 46526, 574-534-0841 [IM] [RE]

Smucker, Klaudia, 1006 Leroy, Goshen IN 46526, 574-534-8710, klaudia@collegemennonite.org [IM] IIB2 [AC] Pastor, College Menn Ch, Goshen IN

Smucker, Marcus G., 2747 Old Philadelphia Pike, Bird-in-Hand PA 17505-9707, 717-768-3064 [IM] [RE]

Smucker, Stan J. (Marlene Rufenacht Smucker) PO Box 93, North Newton KS 67117, 316-283-3750, smuckersm@juno.com [WDC] [RE]

Snader, Paul E. (Carolyn) 200 Weidmansville Rd, Ephrata PA 17522, 717-733-6718, psnader@juno.com [LAN] III [AC] Ordained Deacon, Indiantown Menn Ch, Ephrata PA

Snavely, Carl H. (Alma) 4295 Colebrook Rd, Hershey PA 17033, 717-367-3634 [LAN] III [AC] Ordained Deacon, Stauffer Menn Ch, Hershey PA

Snider, Howard Mervin, Box 332, North Newton KS 67117-0332, 316-283-2309 [WDC] [RE]

Snyder, James R. (Brenda) 487 Sportsman Club Rd, Nazareth PA 18064, 610-614-0371, jimbrensny@juno.com [LAN] IIB1 [AC] Pastor, Maranatha Family Christian Fell, Nazareth PA

So, Joshua, 2259 Kingston Ave, San Bruno CA 94066, 415-872-2563 [PSW] IIB1 [AC]

So, Lemuel (Leona) 169 W Chew Ave, Philadelphia PA 19120, 215-224-7622, lemuelso@netscape.net [LAN] IIB1 [AC] Pastor, Love Truth Chinese Menn Ch, Philadelphia PA

So, Sing Kin (Louisa) Box 25305, Tempe AZ 85285-5305, kinso@hotmail.com [LAN] [AW]

Sollenberger, Menno B. (Joyce) 4169 New Franklin Rd, Chambersburg PA 17201, 717-263-8336 [FRK] [AW]

Sollenberger, Samuel (Patricia) 1255 Candice Ln, Chambersburg PA 17201, 717-264-1125 [FRK] IIB1 [AC] Pastor, Rock Hill Menn Ch, Chambersburg PA

Solorzano, Oscar Javier, 1235 N Recreation #204, Fresno CA 93703, 559-252-6750 [PSW] IIB1 [AC] Pastor, Iglesia Amor Viviente, Fresno CA

Sommers, Clayton, 904 N Korby St, Kokomo IN 46901, 317-452-7109 [IM] [RE]

Sommers, Elvin J., 14242 State Rt 161, Plain City OH 43064, 614-873-8910 [OH] [RE]

Sommers, Michael Kent (Julia Gay) 23589 Allen Dr, Elkhart IN 46516, 574-875-5916, mjsommers@msn.com [CDC] IIB1 [AC] Pastor, Hively Avenue Menn Ch, Elkhart IN

Sosa, Rolando, 708 College Ave, Goshen IN 46526, rolandoas@goshen.edu [IM] IIA [AC] Pastor, Iglesia Menonita del Buen Pastor, Goshen IN

Souder, Eugene K. (Alice) 13241 Port Republic Rd, Grottoes VA 24441, 540-249-4368, eksouder@aol.com [VA] [RE]

Souders, Aaron H. (Mary) 3095 Miller Rd Apt A, Washington Boro PA 17582-9717, 717-872-8201 [LAN] [RE]

Spaulding, Randall L. (Laura) 3342 Glouster St, Sarasota FL 34235, 941-951-0743 [SE] IIC [AC] Minister of Music and Worship, Bahia Vista Menn Ch, Sarasota FL

Spayde, Robert J. (Karen) 108 West Broad St, Salunga PA 17538, 717-892-6943 [LAN] IIA [AC] Pastor, Stauffer Menn Ch, Hershey PA

Speigle, Donald E. (Grace) 5689 Somerset Pike, Boswell PA 15531, 814-629-5947 [ALL] IIB3b [AC]

Speigle, Wayne (Joanne Brenneman) 862 Hunsicker Rd, Telford PA 18969, 215-256-1995, wjspeigle@aol.com [EDC] IIB1 [AC] Pastor, West Swamp Menn Ch, Quakertown PA

Spires, Tammerie Brotzman (David B.) 1006 Cardinal Ln, Richardson TX 75080-4707, 972-783-0817, tbspires@attbi.com [WDC] IIA [AC] Co-Pastor, Many Peoples Menn Fell, Dallas TX; Associate Pastor, Peace Menn Ch, Dallas TX

Spory, Ron (Denise) 125 Noble Rd, Johnstown PA 15905, 814-288-5617 [ALL] IIC [AC] Pastor, New Life Menn Ch, Listie PA

Sprague, Jerry, PO Box 150777, Cape Coral FL 33915-0777, 239-772-5683, JerryCCFOffice@juno.com [SE] IIC [AC] Associate Pastor, Cape Christian Fell, Cape Coral FL

Springer, Ed M. (Esther) 1685 Saddlespur St, Florissant MO 63033, 314-839-4716 [CDC, IL] [RE]

Sprunger, Charles E. (Geraldine K .) 46 Marian Rd, Trappe PA 19426, 610-489-4688, chsprunger@yahoo.com [EDC] [RE]

Sprunger, John Walter (Deb) 401 S Grant St, Scottdale PA 15683, 724-887-5337 [ALL] IB3 [AC]

Sprunger, Lyman W., Rt 1, Box 66, Canton OK 73724-9801, 405-886-3398 [WDC] [RE]

Sprunger, Robert John, 1312 Daly Dr, New Haven IN 46774, 260-493-0244, bobgldc@fwi.com [CDC] IIB3b [AC]

Stackley, Muriel T., Box 236, Pawnee Rock KS 67567-0236, 620-982-4886, murielts@earthlink.net [WDC] [RE]

Stafford, Rodney Alan (Molly Susan Day) 2524 NE 42nd Ave, Portland OR 97213, 503-331-6993, pmcpastr@teleport.com [PNW] IIB1 [AC] Pastor, Portland Menn Ch, Portland OR

Stahl, Mark William (Karen Kay) 1434 Golfview Dr, Nappanee IN 46550, 574-773-3306, mwstahl@hoosierlink.net [CDC] IIB1 [AC] Pastor, First Menn Ch, Nappanee IN

Stahl-Wert, John (Milonica) 7215 Thomas Blvd, Pittsburgh PA 15208, 412-731-8014, stahlwert@plf.org [ALL] IB3 [AC] President, Pittsburgh Leadership

Foundation, Pittsburgh PA

Stair, Tim, 1900 S Main St, Goshen IN 46526, 574-535-7262, cmc@collegemennonite.org [IM] IIA [AC] Pastor, College Menn Ch, Goshen IN

Stalter, Edwin J. (Marcella R.) PO Box 576, Flanagan IL 61740, 815-796-2918 [IL] [RE]

Stambaugh, Carlton D. (Arlene) 1115 Moulstown Rd N, Hanover PA 17331-9424, 717-632-8641, card@superpa.net [LAN] IB3, IIB1 [AC] Bishop/Overseer, LAN - York-Adams District, PA; Bishop, Christian Community Fell, Manchester PA

Stauffer, Faye L. (Steven) 730 W Newport Rd, Lititz PA 17543, 717-665-3570 [LAN] IIC [AC] Chaplain, Lancaster County Prison, Lancaster PA

Stauffer, J. Mark, 101 Menno Village, Chambersburg PA 17201, 717-264-2543 [VA] [RE]

Stauffer, James K. (Ruth) 1250 Parkway Dr, Harrisonburg VA 22802, 540-574-6141 [VA] [RE]

Stauffer, Leon L. (Dolores) 60 Hospital RD, Wernersville PA 19565-9406, 610-927-4668, pastorleon@pro-usa.net [LAN] IIB1 [AC] Pastor, Green Terrace Menn Ch, Wernersville PA

Stauffer, P. Eugene (Mabel E.) 545 Indiantown Rd, Ephrata PA 17522, 717-733-7152 [LAN] III [AC] Licensed Deacon, Green Terrace Menn Ch, Wernersville PA

Stauffer, Steven B. (Faye L.) 730 W Newport Rd, Lititz PA 17543, 717-665-3570, sfstauffer@dejazzd.com [LAN] IIB2 [AC] Pastor, Kauffman Menn Ch, Manheim PA

Stauffer, Timothy T. (Robin) 1089 S Meadow Ln, Palmyra PA 17078, 717-469-1559 [LAN] IIB1 [AC] Pastor, East Hanover Menn Ch, Palmyra PA

Stauffer, William Henry, 5157 Troendly Rd SW, Stonecreek OH 43840, 216-897-7932 [CDC] [RE]

Steckly, Kenneth (Darlene) 91 Walnut St, Garden City MO 64747, 816-862-6477, kendars@casstel.net [SC] IIB1 [AC] Pastor, Sycamore Grove Menn Ch, Garden City MO

Steelberg, Donald R. (Elsie Enns Steelberg) 201 N Broadview, Wichita KS 67208, 316-681-3538 [WDC] [RE]

Steffen, Harlan (Evelyn) Rt 3 Box 46, Syracuse IN 46567, 574-457-4594 [IM] IIB1 [AC] Pastor, Wawasee Lakeside Chapel, Syracuse IN

Steffy, Jason J. (Maribelle) 299 E Main St, Leola PA 17540, 717-656-7506 [LAN] [RE]

Steffy, Karl E. (Ellen) 467 Fruitville Pike, Manheim PA 17545, 717-665-2611, kesteffy@dejazzd.com [LAN] IIB1 [AC] Pastor, East Petersburg Menn Ch, East Petersburg PA

Steffy, Roger L. (Carol A.) 205 E Keller St, Mechanicsburg PA 17055, 717-795-9106, randc.steffy@verizon.net [LAN] [AW]

Steiner, Elno, 14852 Wooster St NW, North Lawrence OH 44666, 330-837-4371 [OH] [RE]

Steiner, Glenn M., 2256 Cork Oak St W, Sarasota FL 34232-6810, glennbvmenno@comcast.net [SE] IIB1 [AC] Pastor, Bahia Vista Menn Ch, Sarasota FL

Stenson, Gary Gene (Elsie) 1101 Columbia Ave, Lansdale PA 19446, 215-362-2527, gstenson@gracemennonite.org [EDC] IIB1 [AC]

Stetler IV, Roy H. (Patricia) 27 Furman Rd, Dillsburg PA 17019, 717-432-0871, stetlers@juno.com [LAN] IIA

[AC] Associate Pastor, Slate Hill Menn Ch, Camp Hill PA

Stevens, David A. (Carole Diane Stevens) 174 Green St, Sellersville PA 18960, 215-257-5835 [FRC] IIB2 [AC] Pastor, Blooming Glen Menn Ch, Blooming Glen PA

Stevenson, Robert L., Cd Lopez Mateos, Edo de, CP 52901, Mexico, 525-686-5421 [FRC] IIB3b [AC]

Stillman, Roger (Karen) 1322 Susquehannock Dr, Drumore PA 17518, 717-284-4797, bettergetready2000@yahoo.com [LAN] IIA [AC] Associate Pastor, Living Stones Fell, Peach Bottom PA

Stobaugh, James Parris (Karen) 510 Swank Rd, Hollsopple PA 15935, 814-479-7710, JPStobaugh@aol.com [ALL] IIB3c [AC]

Stoll, Alvin E. (Rita Marie) N3455 Hwy 73, Glen Flora WI 54526, 715-668-5583, alvines@centurytel.net [NC] IIB1 [AC] Pastor, South Lawrence Menn Ch, Glen Flora WI

Stoll, Don (Mary) 2711 Stewart Rd, Midland MI 48640, 517-832-3303 [IM] [AW]

Stoll, Owen, 2265 Hazel St, Hartville OH 44632, 330-877-9217 [OH] [RE]

Stoltzfus, Dale W. (Doris) 270 Ivy Terrace, Lancaster PA 17601, 717-560-5696, dordalew@aol.com [LAN] IB1, IB3 [AC] Bishop/Overseer, LMC - Landisville District, PA; Co-Director, Office of Ministerial Leadership, Mennonite Church USA, Lancaster PA

Stoltzfus, Daniel H., 409 E Broadway, South Bend IN 46618, 574-288-8192 [IM] [RE]

Stoltzfus, David K. (Betty) 1102 Aspen Dr, Narvon PA 17555, 717-445-9315, dstoltz@ptdprolog.net [ACC] IB3, IIB2 [AC] Associate Pastor, Bethany Grace Fell, East Earl PA

Stoltzfus, Ed (Mildred) 255 Hartman Dr, Harrisonburg VA 22802, 540-434-9849 [VA] [RE]

Stoltzfus, George B. (Mae Mast) 3717 Crabtree Ln, Elkhart IN 46514, 574-266-4407, geobs@juno.com [IM] IIB3c [AC] Medical Ethics, Mennonite Agency Consortium Medical Ethics, Elkhart IN

Stoltzfus, Harvey Z. (Lillian) 158 Swamp Rd, Morgantown PA 19543-9476, 610-286-5914, beewatcher@juno.com [ACC] IB3, IIB1 [AC]

Stoltzfus, John M., 740 E North Broadway, Lombard IL 60148, 630-627-0817, jmstoltzfus@mennonite.net [IL] IIA [AC] Associate Pastor, Lombard Menn Ch, Lombard IL

Stoltzfus, Mervin R. (Janet E. [Mellinger]) 23 Carriage Dr, Gordonville PA 17529, 717-768-3116, woodray@aol.com [ACC] IIB3c [AC] Youth Ministry, Atlantic Coast Conference, Morgantown PA

Stoltzfus, Milton L., 282 Baumgardner Rd, Willow Street PA 17584, 717-464-9072 [LAN] IIB3a [AC] Chaplain, Friendship Community, Lititz PA

Stoltzfus, Nathan G. (Marian) PO Box 19, Morgantown PA 19543, 610-286-5080 [ACC] [RE]

Stoltzfus, Noah S. (Edith) 36 Fredericksville Rd, Mertztown PA 19539, 610-641-0543, noah.edie@juno.com [ACC] IIB1 [AC] Pastor, Zion Menn Ch, Birdsboro, Birdsboro PA

Stoltzfus, Regina Shands (Art) 808 Strong Ave, Elkhart IN 46517 [OH] IIB3c [AC] Assistant Campus Pastor, Goshen College, Goshen IN; Minister of Urban Ministries, Menn Mission Network, Elkhart IN

Stoltzfus, Ruth Brunk, 1111 Mount Clinton Pike, Harrisonburg VA 22802, 540-434-7705 [VA] [RE]

Stoltzfus, Sherman M. (Heather) 1013 Fern Ave,

Reading PA 19607-1626, 610-775-9970, smandhm@aol.com [LAN] IIA [AC] Pastor, Alsace Christian Fell, Temple PA

Stoltzfus, Victor, 607 College Ave, Goshen IN 46526, 574-533-4550 [IM] [RE]

Stoltzfus Jr, Amos K. (Rowena M.) 2575 Main St, Morgantown PA 19543, 610-286-5607, pastoramos@pkfamily.com [ACC] IB3, IIB1 [AC] Pastor, Rockville Menn Ch, Honey Brook PA

Stoner, Andre Gingerich (Cathy) 628 Cushing, South Bend IN 46616, 574-289-4623, andrekrmc@juno.com [IM] IIB1 [AC] Pastor, Kern Road Menn Ch, South Bend IN

Stoner, Barry Lee (Brenda) 1455 Hollywood Dr, Lancaster PA 17601, 717-291-1127, bstoner4@juno.com [LAN] IIA [AC] Associate Pastor, Mellinger Menn Ch, Lancaster PA

Stoner, John Andrew (Anita L. [Hoke]) 11026 Old Oak Trail, Ft Wayne IN 46845, 877-321-3289 pin 7093, rpandy@juno.com [CDC] IIB3a [AC]

Stoner, John David (Martha L.) 29 Mayfield Dr, Leola PA 17540, 717-656-7744 [LAN] [RE]

Stoudt, Curtis, 763 Ruth Rd, Telford PA 18969, 215-723-4637 [FRC] [RE]

Strite, Clarence B. (Mary Grace) 1561 Pin Oak Dr, Chambersburg PA 17201, 717-264-5798, cnmstrite@comcast.net [ACC] IIB1 [AC] Interim Pastor, Cedar Grove Menn Ch, Greencastle PA

Strite, James L. (Norma) 5975 Reeves Rd, East Petersburg PA 17520-1530, 717-569-1720, jlstrite@yahoo.com [LAN] III [AC] Ordained Deacon, Manheim Menn Ch, Manheim PA

Strunk, Stephen Carl (Naomi K.) 964 Holland Rd, Holland PA 18966, 216-355-5834, snstrunk@enter.net [EDC] IIB1 [AC] Pastor, Church of the Good Samaritans, Holland PA

Stuckey, Anne, 14277 Killybegs Lane, PO Box 175, Somerset MI 49281, annestuckey@bnnorth.net [OH] IIB2 [AC] Associate Pastor, Zion Menn Ch, Archbold OH

Stuckey, Earl, 18526 CR K, West Unity OH 43570, 419-924-2535 [OH] [RE]

Stuckey, Robert, 18540 CR O, Alvordton OH 43501, 419-924-2130, bobnem@williams-net.com [OH] IIA [AC] Preaching Minister, Salem Menn Ch, Waldron MI

Stuckey, Walter, 10334 CR 21N, West Unity OH 43570, 419-445-6225 [OH] [RE]

Stucky, Edwin R., 514 Spruce Ave, Moundridge KS 67107-9501, 620-345-2589 [WDC] [RE]

Stucky, Harley J., 2117 N Main, Box 394, North Newton KS 67117, 316-283-3029 [WDC] [RE]

Stucky, Nathan T. (Janel Denise) 7271 Boggs School House Rd, Westover MD 21871, 410-957-6857, natestucky@hotmail.com [ACC] IIA [AC] Youth Pastor, Holly Grove Menn Ch, Westover MD

Stucky, Willard L., 600 Bluestem, Box 55, North Newton KS 67117, 316-283-0648 [WDC] [RE]

Studer, Gerald C. (Marilyn) 1260 Orchard Ln, Lansdale PA 19446, 215-368-8455 [FRC] [RE]

Stutzman, Benjamin S. (Katrina Derstine Stutzman) Box 68, Blooming Glen PA 18911, 215-258-0338 [FRC] IIB2 [AC] Pastor, Blooming Glen Menn Ch, Blooming Glen PA

Stutzman, David J. (Donna P.) 1966 Wimbledon Ct, NW, Salem OR 97304, 503-581-3236, ddstutz@hotmail.com

[PNW] IIB1 [AC] Pastor, Western Menn Ch, Salem OR

Stutzman, Dennis (Ronda) 3605 E Longview Rd, Haven KS 67543, 620-663-2657, yoderchurch@ourtownusa.net [VA] IIB2 [AC] Pastor, Yoder Menn Ch, Haven KS

Stutzman, Ervin R. (Bonita) 1315 Harmony Dr, Harrisonburg VA 22802-5545, 540-442-8331, stutzerv@emu.edu [VA] IIB3d [AC] Associate Professor of Church Ministries, Eastern Mennonite Seminary, Harrisonburg VA

Stutzman, Kyle D. (Melodie) 714 King Ave, Waynesboro VA 22980, stutzmak@ntelos.net [VA] IIA [AC] Minister of Youth and Christian Education, Waynesboro Menn Ch, Waynesboro VA

Stutzman, Linford (Janet) 1083 Smith St, Harrisonburg VA 22802, 540-432-1714, stutzmal@emu.edu [VA] IIB3d [AC]

Stutzman, Marvin (Yvonne) 1285 Shank Dr #116, Harrisonburg VA 22802, 757-482-7023 [VA] [RE]

Stutzman, Roman, 6308 CR 189, Millersburg OH 44654, 330-674-1185 [OH] [RE]

Sutter, David L. (Janice Yordy Sutter) 233 E Irvington Ave, South Bend IN 46614, 574-288-5520, davekrmc@juno.com [IM] IB3, IIB1 [AC] Pastor, Kern Road Menn Ch, South Bend IN

Sutter, Janice Yordy (David) 233 E Irvington Ave, South Bend IN 46614, 574-288-5520, janicekrmc@juno.com [IM] IIB1 [AC] Pastor, Kern Road Menn Ch, South Bend IN

Sutter, Lester L. (Marietta) 6042 Westview Dr, Ferndale WA 98248-9214 [LAN] [RE]

Sutter, Stanley Ray (Catherine) 529 Greeley Ave, Staten Island NY 10306, 718-351-8163, Est1man@aol.com [LAN] IIA [AC] Pastor, Redeeming Grace Fell, Staten Island NY

Sutton, James, 62 Harmon Ave, Painesville OH 44077, 440-357-6040, jdsutt@ncweb.com [OH] IIB1 [AC] Pastor, New Mercies Community Ch, Burton OH

Sutton, Norma S., 5218 N Sawyer, Chicago IL 60625, 312-463-3044 [CDC, IL] IIB3d [AC] Other, North Park Theological Seminary, Chicago IL

Swarr, Paul L. (Bertha) 1311 Carlisle Ave, Richmond VA 23231, 804-222-4345 [VA] [RE]

Swartley, Willard M. (Mary) 57697 7th Street, Elkhart IN 46517, 574-522-0314, wswartley@ambus.edu [IM] IIB3c [AC] Staff, Associated Mennonite Biblical Seminary, Elkhart IN

Swartz, Delores, 58204 CR 23, Goshen IN 46528, 574-875-0098 [IM] IIB3a [AC] Chaplain, Greencroft Retirement Center, Goshen IN

Swartz, Joseph J., 4750 E CR 300 N, North Vernon IN 47265, 812-458-6323 [IM] [RE]

Swartz, Ronald Duane (Lucretia Ann) 66 W 6 Mile Rd, Sault Ste Marie MI 49783, 906-635-0459, rswartz@northernway.net [IM] IIB1 [AC] Pastor, Wayside Menn Ch, Sault Ste Marie MI

Swartz, Sam, PO Box 327, West Liberty OH 43357, 937-465-7867 [OH] [RE]

Swartzendruber, A. Lloyd, 1301 Virginia Ave, Harrisonburg VA 22802, 540433-2269 [VA] [RE]

Swartzendruber, Dean (Lois) 831 3rd Pl, Kalona IA, 319-656-2999 [CP] [RE]

Swartzendruber, Loren, PO Box 3000, Hesston KS 67062 [SC] IIB3c [AC] President, Hesston College,

Hesston KS

Swartzendruber, Scott (Jan) 918 10th St, Kalona IA 52247, 319-656-3945, kmcscott@kctc.net [CP] IIB1 [AC] Pastor, Kalona Menn Ch, Kalona IA

Swartzentruber, Clayton L., 209 Dock Dr, Lansdale PA 19446, 215-393-0955 [FRC] [RE]

Swihart, James, PO Box 579, Kalida OH 45853, 419-532-3598, kfoc@bright.net [OH] IIB1 [AC] Pastor, Kalida Family Outreach Center, Kalida OH

Swihart, Jason Allen (Tiffany Rose) 805 Peck, RR 3, Box 84, Hydro OK 73048, 405-663-2782 [WDC] [AW]

Swora, Mathew (Rebecca J.) 1024 Mercury Dr, W, Shoreview MN 55126, 651-482-9620, emmanuel@visi.com [CP] IIB1 [AC] Pastor, Emmanuel Menn Ch, Shoreview MN

T

Tadeo, Raul, 405 W Schultz Ave, Dalton OH 44618, 330-828-0040, rvtadeo1934@valkyrie.net [OH] IIB3b [AC] Hispanic Ministries Coordinator, Hispanic Ministries, Wooster

Tann, Herman, 307 Pringle St, Goshen IN 46526, 574-534-0133 [IM] [RE]

Taylor, Owen (Rosetta) 2201 Rebourde Dr, South Bend IN 46628, 574-273-0059 [CP] IIB1 [AC] Pastor, Northside Christian Family Center, Omaha NE

Teague, Norman (Fannie) 5191 Kratzer Rd, Linville VA 22834, 540-833-2402 [VA] [RE]

Temple, Kathleen J. (Theodore Grimsrud) 1150 Lincolnshire Dr, Harrisonburg VA 22802, 540-574-4311, templekj@emu.edu [VA] IIB3d [AC]

Thacker, John David, 2705 Arlington Dr, Anchorage AK 99517, 907-222-1381, johndavidthacker@hotmail.com [PNW] IIA [AC] Pastor, Prince of Peace Menn Ch, Anchorage AK

Thiessen-Nation, Mark, c/o Eastern Mennonite Seminary, 1200 Park Rd, Harrisonburg VA 22802 [PSW] IIB3b [AC]

Thieszen, Eugene Roy, Menn Ministries Maun Project, PO Box 20513, Maun, Botswana, 267-661-204 [CP] IIB3b [AC]

Thieszen, Harold Daniel (Esther M.) 606 Bluestem St, North Newton KS 67117-8020, 316-283-8623, haroldt@southwind.net [WDC] [RE]

Thomas, Aldine (Esther) 59456 CR 35, Middlebury IN 46540, 574-825-2506 [IM] IIC [AC] Minister of Visitation, Clinton Frame Menn Ch, Goshen IN

Thomas, Everett J. (Barbara Gunden Thomas) 1817 Woodgate Dr, Goshen IN 46526-6456, 574-533-6143, editor@themennonite.org [IM] IIB3c [AC] Editor, *The Mennonite,* Goshen IN

Thomas, J. Samuel (Marian J.) 1361 Nissley Rd, Landisville PA 17538, 717-898-8662, sthomas405@aol.com [LAN] IIB1 [AC] Pastor, Landisville Menn Ch, Landisville PA

Thomas, James (Sherry) 425 Moonshine Hollow Rd, Johnstown PA 15905, 814-288-5763 [ALL] IIB1 [AC]

Thomas, Marlin E. (Janice) PO Box 724 626 Park Ave, Milford NE 68405, 402-761-3731 [CP] IIB1 [AC] Interim pastor, James Street Menn Ch, Lancaster PA

Thomas, Melvin (Marie) 174S Bethlehem Pike Apt A-10, Ambler PA 19002, 215-540-0144, melthomas@erols.com [FRC] IIB1 [AW]

Thomas, Stephen B. (Linda) 1011 S 7th St, Goshen IN 46526, 574-534-7118, s-lthomas@juno.com [IM] IIB1 [AC] Pastor, Walnut Hill Menn Ch, Goshen IN

Thomas, Vincent J. (Martha) 4125 Board Rd, Manchester PA 17345, 717-266-4108 [LAN] [AW]

Thomas Jr, Jefferson, 338 Ferndale, Youngstown OH 44511, 330-788-9108 [OH] III [AC] Pastor, Berean Fell Ch, Youngstown OH

Thomassen, Donald L. (Barbara Norma) 659 Glen Eyrie Cr, Colorado Spring CO 80904, 719-471-4753, KTTPooh@aol.com [RM] IIB1 [AC] Pastor, First Menn Ch of Colorado Springs, Colorado Springs CO

Thompson, Kenneth Lee (Victoria) 2089 Ryer Ave, Bronx NY 10460, 718-733-6975, FCC2283@juno.com [ACC] IIB1 [AC] Pastor, Friendship Community Ch, Bronx NY

Thomsen, June E. (Ib) 4824 S Knox Ave, Chicago IL 60632, 773-767-1977, thomsen@avenew.com [CDC] IIB1 [AC] Pastor, Grace Community Ch, Chicago IL

Thornton, Jim (Kathy) 305 Moss Ave, Seaford VA 23696, 757-898-3970, kktjwt@aol.com [VA] IIA [AC] Minister of Preaching/Teaching, Huntington Menn Ch, Newport News VA

Tice, Ezra M. (Joan Van Antwerp Tice) 25 Vicki Cr, Gettysburg PA 17325, 717-334-5068, ezratice@supernet.com [ACC] IIB1 [AC] Pastor, Bethel Menn Ch, Gettysburg PA

Tijerina, David, 109 Pleasant St, Archbold OH 43502, 419-445-0016 [OH] IIB1 [AC] Pastor, Iglesia Menonita del Buen Pastor, Archbold OH

Tijerina, Guillermo G., 613 N Defiance, Archbold OH 43502, 419-445-6502 [OH] [RE]

Tippett, Thomas Arthur (Teresa Ann) 4505 S State Rd, Harbor Springs MI 49740, 616-526-6034 [IM] IIC [AC]

Tobin, George E. (Carol) 4 Prince Edward Ln, Media PA 19063, 610-566-1611 [LAN] IIC [AC] Missionary/Church Worker, Ubon Ratchathani Thailand

Todd, Jay (Ruth) 866 Quarry Rd, Manheim PA 17545, 717-569-1345 [LAN] III [AC] Ordained Deacon, East Petersburg Menn Ch, East Petersburg PA

Toews, Russell G., PO Box 711, Hotevilla AZ 86030, 520-734-6630 [PSW] IIA [AC] Pastor, Bacavi Menn Ch, Hotevilla AZ

Torres, Nestali, 184 Barton, Buffalo NY 14213, 716-883-7035, Nestali_Torres@msn.com [NY] IIB1 [AC] Pastor, Westside Menn Ch, Buffalo NY

Townsend, James D. (Debra) 834 High St, Alpha NJ 08865, 908-454-1314, alphamenno@juno.com [FRC] IIB1 [AC] Pastor, Alpha Menn Ch, Alpha NJ

Tran, Quang Xuan, 101 Powell Ln, Upper Darby PA 19082, 610-352-8689, msquang@go.com [LAN] IIB1 [AC] Pastor, Vietnamese Menn Ch, Philadelphia PA

Tribby, Phyllis Harden, 6047 Flower St, Arvada CO 80004, arvadamennonite1@yahoo.com [WDC] IIB1 [AC]

Troyer, James L. (Anna) 1671 River Rd, Manistique MI 49854, 906-341-5007 [IM] IB3, IIB1 [AC] Pastor, Cedar Grove Menn Ch, Manistique MI

Troyer, John L. (Maxine) W15537 Sandtown Rd, Engadine MI 49827, 906-586-6421 [IM] IIB1 [AC] Pastor, Wildwood Menn Ch, Engadine MI

Troyer, John M. (Sheila W.) 27077 Baker Dr, Sturgis MI 49091, john.troyer@lgrove.org [IM] IIA [AC] Pastor, Locust Grove Menn Ch, Burr Oak MI

Troyer, John M., 11947 CR 24, Middlebury IN 46540,

MINISTERS

6

574-825-5143 [IM] [RE]

Troyer, John V. (Ina May) 7321 Springfield Rd, Delavan IL 61734, 309-244-8674 [IL] [RE]

Troyer, Lowell Ovid, 2301 Morton Ave, Elkhart IN 46517, 574-294-6272 [CDC] [RE]

Troyer, Martin Bradley, 1001 Vine, Lebanon OR 97355, 541-258-1558, martytroyer@ptinet.net [PNW] IIA [AC] Associate Pastor, Lebanon Menn Ch, Lebanon OR

Troyer, Rick (Joanie) 705 S Forest Park Dr, Eureka IL 61530, 309-467-3787, rickrmc@mtco.com [IL] IIB1 [AC] Co-Pastor, Roanoke Menn Ch, Eureka IL

Troyer, Robert L. (Marcia) PO Box 583, Milford NE 68405, 402-761-3500 [CP] IIB3a [AC]

Troyer, Samuel J. (Betsy) 2440 McCleary Dr, Chambersburg PA 17201, 717-264-1366 [FRK] IIB3a [AC] Chaplain, Menno Haven, Chambersburg PA

Troyer, Stanley J. (Marilyn Ann) 7291 N Maple, Mancelona MI 49659, 616-587-0715, stroyer@freeway.net [IM] IB2 [AC] Missionary, Church Resource Ministries, Mancelona MI

Troyer, Willis C., 7475 E 100 S, Lagrange IN 46761, 260-463-2212 [IM] [RE]

Trupe, Robert L. (Sylvia) 958 Rettew Mill Rd, Ephrata PA 17522, 717-733-0291 [LAN] IIB1 [AC] Pastor, Martindale Menn Ch, Ephrata PA

Tsai, Caleb Tsan, 258 Chaumont Cr, Foothill Ranch CA 92610-2344 [PSW] [RE]

Tschetter, Peter William (Beulah) 701 2nd Ave, Mountain Lake MN, 507-427-3068 [CP] [RE]

Tschetter, Randall LaMont (Wanette) 2300 Carter Pl, Sioux Falls SD 57105, 605-331-5034 [CP] IIB1 [AC] Pastor, Bethany Menn Ch, Freeman SD

Tschetter, Richard Daniel, 3386 Road R, Pandora OH 45877-9779, 419-358-4593 [CDC] [RE]

Tu, Truong (Dorcas Hua) 738 Moore St, Philadelphia PA 19148, 215-271-5018, alcmc@juno.com [LAN] IIA [AC] Pastor, Abundant Life Chinese Menn Ch, Philadelphia PA

Turner, Jeffrey A. (Angela M.) 3079 N Presentation Ct, Sioux Falls SD 57104, 605-336-6230, jefturner@juno.com [CP] IIA [AC] Pastor, Good Shepherd Community Ch, Sioux Falls SD

Tyson, Warren L. (Linda A.) 66 Millstone Dr, PO Box 785, Brownstown PA 17508-0785, 717-661-7266, wltyson@yahoo.com [ACC] IIB2, IB3 [AC] Conference Minister, Eastern District Conference, Souderton PA; Conference Minister, Atlantic Coast Conference, Morgantown PA

U

Ulloa, Marco Antonia (Patricia) 111 School Ln, Landisville PA 17538-1247 [LAN] IIB3c [AC]

Ulrich, Wilfred D. (Betty S.) 504 Crestwood Dr, Eureka IL 61530, 309-467-2194 [CDC, IL] [RE]

Umble, Jeni Hiett (Arthur K.) 60251 Surrey Ln, Elkhart IN 46517, 574-875-5904, ajumble@juno.com [CDC, IM] IIB3b [AC] Church Community Service, Elkhart IN

Umble, Leroy D., 17 Strasburg Rd, Atglen PA 19310, 215-593-2943 [ACC] [RE]

Umble, R. Clair (Miriam) 46 Newlin Rd, Parkesburg PA 19365, 717-442-8667 [ACC] [RE]

Umble, Richard (Ruth) 530 Valley Ave, Atglen PA 19310, 610-593-2140, rrrumble@juno.com [ACC] IIB1 [AC] Interim Pastor, Media Menn Ch, Oxford PA

Unruh, Ervey A. (Norma J.) 831 South New York Ave, Liberal KS 67901, 620-624-6818, eunruh@swdtimes.com [WDC] IIB1 [AC] Pastor, Calvary Menn Ch, Liberal KS

Unruh, Raymond (DeMaris) RR 3 Box 84, Hydro OK 73048-9124 [WDC] IIB1 [AC] Pastor, Bethel Menn Ch, Hydro OK

Unruh, Verney, 1120 Harrison, Newton KS 67114, 316-283-2298 [WDC] [RE]

V

Van Voorhis, Laura, 6130 Carvel Ave Apt 17, Indianapolis IN 46220, 317-722-0715, vanvols@msn.com [IM] IIB2 [AC] Associate Pastor, First Menn Ch, Indianapolis IN

Vangore, Sanjeeva Rao B. (Surya Kumari) 1457 Autumn Rd, Rydal PA 19046, 215-885-9039 [LAN] IIA [AC]

Vanpelt, Steven C. (Joy) 234 Brenneman Rd, Lancaster PA 17603, 717-464-4283, svanpelt1@juno.com [LAN] IIB1 [AC] Pastor, Lyndon Menn Ch, Lancaster PA

Vargas, Blanca (Victor) 1710 Lynette #606, San Antonio TX 78209, blancavargas@prodigy.net [SC, WDC] IIA [AC] Pastor, Comunidad de Vida, San Antonio TX

Vargas, Victor M. (Virginia) 1225 Bair Rd NE, Keizer OR 97303, 503-390-1944, vvictormv@cs.com [PNW] IIB1 [AC] Pastor, Iglesia Menonita Pentecostes, Woodburn OR

Vasquez Jr, Pedro (Amy) 997 Birmingham St, Bridgeport CT 06606, 203-373-9714 [LAN] IIC [AC] Associate Pastor, Gospel Light Community Ch, Bridgeport CT

Vaughn, Jr, William (Irene) 6501 Pierce St, Norfolk VA 23513, 757-855-8822 [VA] IIB1 [AC] Pastor, Word of Life Menn Ch, Norfolk VA

Ventura, John, 94 S Xavier, Denver CO 80219, 303-935-0722 [RM] [RE]

Versluis, Paul (Joi) 1346 Ravenwood St, Ann Arbor MI 48103, 734-827-0741, PJVersluis@msn.com [CDC, IM] IIB1 [AC] Pastor, Shalom Community Ch, Ann Arbor MI

Vielman, Jorge, 1703 Lawndale Pl, Goshen IN 46526, jorgeev@juno.com [IM] IIA [AC] Pastor, Iglesia Menonita del Buen Pastor, Goshen IN

Villalobos Mora, Carlos L. (Nubia) 301 Carbonton Rd, Sanford NC 27330 [LAN] IIB1 [AC] Pastor, Iglesia Menonita Bethel Ch, Sanford NC

Vincent, Lorie L. (Mark LaVon) W325 S7418 Squire Ln, Mukwonago WI 53149, DesignForMinistry@prodigy.net [IM] [AC] Design for Ministry, Mukwonago WI

Vincent, Mark (Lorie) W325 S7418 Squire Ln, Mukwonago WI 53149, DesignForMinistry@prodigy.net [IM] IIB3c [AC] Lead Partner, Design for Ministry, Mukwonago WI

Vogt, Royce W. (Marla) 910 E 14th, Harper KS 67058, 620-896-2093 [SC] IIB1 [AC] Pastor, Pleasant Valley Menn Ch, Harper KS

Vogt, Virgil (Joan) 726 Monroe, Evanston IL 60202, 846-869-4599, vvvogt@ameritech.net [IL] IIB1 [AC] Pastor, Reba Place Ch, Evanston IL

Voran, Peter Willard, 3057 Ivy Ct, North Newton KS 67117, 316-284-2343 [WDC] [RE]

Voth, James Joel (Barbara Ruth) 1400 Westborough Dr, Newton KS 67114-1476, 316-283-2644, jvoth@cox.net [WDC] IIB1 [AC] Pastor, Grace Hill Menn Ch, Whitewater KS

Voth, John Wesley (Carolyn Ruth) 105 N Vann, PO Box 845, Chouteau OK 74337, 918-476-5166 [WDC] [RE]
Voth, Tom Edward (Pamela Joyce Penner) 37830 Bethel Church Rd, Fortuna MO 65034, 573-378-4878 [CDC] IIB1 [AC] Pastor, Bethel Menn Ch, Fortuna MO

W

Wade, Andrew Frost (Susan) c/o Hong Kong Menn Centre, 76 Waterloo Rd, 1/F, Kowloon, Hong Kong, 011-852-2714-2852 [PNW] IIB3b [AC]
Wadel, Mark N. (Betty Anne) PO Box 3, Westminster MD 21158, 410-876-2808 or 848-1500 [FRK] [AW]
Wagler, Howard L. (Cathy) 317 E Trails West Rd, South Hutchinson KS 67505, 620-663-5803, pastorhoward@shmc-online.net [SC] IIB1 [AC] Lead Pastor, South Hutchinson Menn Ch, South Hutchinson KS
Wagner, Dennis William Kinde, 1238 Chaucer Pl, Maineville OH 45039-9750, 513-677-2349, DWKWagner@aol.com [CDC] IIB3a [AC]
Waite, Phil (Elizabeth Bontrager) 1620 Wisconsin, Berwyn IL 60402, 708-484-6756, pwaite6116@aol.com [CDC, IL] IIB1 [AC] Pastor, Oak Park Menn Ch, Oak Park IL
Walcott, Carl A. (Annette) 4913 Headland Hills, Tampa FL 33624, 813-961-1114 [SE] IIC [AC] Minister of Visitation, College Hill Menn Ch, Tampa FL
Walker, Kurt (Marla) 1343 US Hwy 136, Armington IL 61721, 309-392-2460 [IL] IIA [AC] Associate Pastor, Hopedale Menn Ch, Hopedale IL
Walks Along Sr, Joe (Victoria) PPO Box 232, Lame Deer MT 59043, 406-477-8388 [CP] IIB1 [AC] Pastor, Lame Deer Menn Ch, Lame Deer MT
Wall, Elmer A. (Winifred E. [Mumaw]) 415 Fairview Dr, Goshen IN 46528, 574-534-1995, elwinwall@juno.com [CDC] [RE] Interim Pastor, Eighth Street Menn Ch, Goshen IN
Walls Jr, Wilbur Roy (Rose A.) 4049 S Nucla Way, Aurora CO 80013, 720-870-3875, roywalls1@attbi.com [RM, WDC] IIB1 [AC] Pastor, Peace Menn Community Ch, Aurora CO
Walters, Robert G., 2187 Skyline Dr, Bethleham PA 18105, 610-865-3316 [FRC] [RE]
Walters Sr, Robert G. (Lois A.) 2270 SR 49, Westfield PA 16950, 814-334-5640 [NY] IIA [AC] Co-Pastor, West Union Menn Ch, Rexville NY
Waltner, Erland (Winifred Schlosser Waltner) 2806 Benham Ave, Elkhart IN 46517-1950, 574-522-6042 [CDC] [RE]
Waltner, Harris H. (Christine M. [Duerksen]) 3053 Ivy Court, North Newton KS 67117 [WDC] [RE]
Waltner, James H., 1717 Mayflower Pl, Goshen IN 46526, 574-534-5474, jwaltner@tln.net [IM] IB3 [AC] Overseer for East Goshen Menn, Goshen IN; Overseer for North Goshen Menn, Goshen IN; Overseer for Belmont Menn Ch, Elkhart IN; Overseer for Kern Road Menn, South Bend IN
Waltner, John Harris, 15350 NE 202nd St, Woodinville WA 98072, 425-482-9738, Jnhwaltner@aol.com [PNW] [AW]
Walton, Robin W., 5233 Hitesman Way, Columbus OH 43214, 614-431-5233 [CDC, OH] IIB3a [AC]
Ward, Frank Gene, 95223 Ainakuai Pl, Miliana HI 96789, 808-626-0350 [WDC] [RE]

Warner, Edward (Mary) RR 2 Lightfoot Rd, Harbor Springs MI 49740, 616-526-6971 [IM] IIB1 [AC] Pastor, Stutsmanville Chapel, Harbor Springs MI
Weaver, A. Richard (Ruth) 230 Penn Ave, Ephrata PA 17522, 717-733-1891, arweaver@ptd.net [LAN] IIB2 [AC] Pastor, New Holland Menn Ch, New Holland PA
Weaver, Christopher Z. (Sheri Lynn) 348 Arrowhead Rd, Inman KS 67546 [WDC] IIA [AC] Associate Pastor, Bethel Menn Ch, Inman KS
Weaver, Clair H. (Betsy J.) 538 Waterside Cr, Lebanon PA 17042-9487, 717-273-9710, cweaver705@aol.com [LAN] IIB1 [AC] Associate Pastor, Lebanon Christian Fell, Lebanon PA
Weaver, David L. (Dawn) 1944 Hemlock Rd, Lancaster PA 17603, 717-399-7354, davidweaver@juno.com [LAN] IIB1 [AC] Pastor, Rohrerstown Menn Ch, Lancaster PA
Weaver, David M. (Esther) RR 1 Box 122, Roaring Branch PA 17765, 717-673-5083 [LAN] [RE]
Weaver, David W. (Pauline) RD 1 Box 600, McAlisterville PA 17049-9606, 717-463-2672 [LAN] [RE]
Weaver, Deborah (Dan) 5312 S Dorchester Ave #1, Chicago IL 60615, 717-363-0232, deboral.weaver@excite.com [CDC, IL] IIA [AC] Pastoral Counselor, MidWest Resources for Counseling and Psychotherapy
Weaver, Delmar R. (Linda) 19 Buch Mill Rd, Lititz PA 17543, 717-733-6574 [LAN] IIB2 [AC] Associate Pastor, Millport Menn Ch, Leola PA
Weaver, Don R. (Linda) 607 Gault Rd, New Holland PA 17557-9007, 717-354-5001, DLHGRDW@aol.com [LAN] IIB1 [AC] Pastor, Weaverland Menn Ch, East Earl PA
Weaver, Dorothy Jean, 1514 College Ave, Harrisonburg VA 22802, 540-433-3336 [VA] IIB3d [AC]
Weaver, Earl S. (Marilyn) 224 White Oak Rd, New Holland PA 17557, 717-354-7510, esweaver@juno.com [LAN] IIC [AC] Associate Pastor, Weaverland Menn Ch, East Earl PA
Weaver, Eugene Z., PO Box 156 Tikini Rd, Cherry Creek SD 57622 [LAN] IIB1 [AC]
Weaver, Harold K., 527 Dock Dr, Lansdale PA 19446, 215-368-5783 [FRC] [RE]
Weaver, Irvin D., 6322 Acker Ln, Linville VA 22834, 540-833-4232 [VA] [RE]
Weaver, Ivan K., 1501 Dogwood Ct, Goshen IN 46526, 574-534-0726 [IM] [RE]
Weaver, Jay S. (Shirley A.) 195 Speedwell Forge Rd, Lititz PA 17543, 717-626-4314, jsw195@dejazzd.com [LAN] IIB2 [AC] Associate Pastor, Indiantown Menn Ch, Ephrata PA
Weaver, Jerry, 8157 Kline St, Arvada CO 80005, 303-420-4417 [RM] [AW]
Weaver, Kenneth, PO Box 15402, Fort Wayne IN 46885 [IM] IIB3a [AC]
Weaver, L. Keith (JoAnne), 115 Swamp Church Rd, Reinholds PA 17569, 717-336-5253, keith@lanmenconf.org [LAN] IB3 [AC] Bishop/Overseer-LAN-Ephrata District; Conference Moderator—Lancaster
Weaver, Marion C. (Jean) 539 Augusta Farms Rd, Waynesboro VA 22980, 540-337-2639 [VA] [RE]
Weaver, Marvin L. (Lois H.) 145 Rose Dr, Lancaster PA 17602, 717-397-7279 [LAN] IIB3a [AC] Chaplain, Auntie Anne's Pretzels, Inc, Lancaster PA

MINISTERS

6

Weaver, Paul G. (Shirley A.) 9 Shupp Ln, Denver PA 17517, 717-484-4899 [LAN] IIB1 [AC] Pastor, Red Run Menn Ch, Denver PA

Weaver, Paul H., 1001 E Oregon Rd G 13, Lititz PA 17543, 717-560-7809 [LAN] [RE]

Weaver, Richard S. (Virginia) 3842 Rawley Pike, Harrisonburg VA 22801, 540-867-5600 [VA] [RE]

Weaver, Samuel O. (Sarah) 1550 N College Ave, Harrisonburg VA 22802, 540-434-2985, weaverso@emu.edu [VA] IB3 [AC]

Weaver, Stanley (Arlie Virginia) 10607 N 9th Dr, Phoenix AZ 85029, 602-906-0512 [PSW] IIB2 [AC]

Weaver, Stephen Souder (Ann) 180 Cherry Hill Rd, Ronks PA 17572, 717 687-6982, ssweaver@paonline.com [LAN] [AW]

Weaver, Timothy D. (Juanita) 421 Campus Dr, Perkasie PA 18944, 215-453-0554 [FRC] IIB1 [AC] Pastor, Deep Run Menn Ch East, Perkasie PA

Weaver, Victor R., 681 Meadow Dr, Honey Brook PA 19344, 610-273-3010 [LAN] IIB1 [AC] Associate Pastor, Cambridge Menn Ch, Honey Brook PA

Weaver, Wayne S. (Edna G.) 155 Weidmansville Rd, Ephrata PA 17522, 717-733-3323 [LAN] [RE]

Weaver, William M. (Viola) 957 Camp Hebron Rd, Halifax PA 17032, 717-896-8714 [LAN] [RE]

Weaver Jr, David W. (Sue) 21170 D'Herde Rd, Gulfport MS 39503, 228-832-0661, dave@starvisionsat.com [GS] IIB2 [AC] Assistant Pastor, Gulfhaven Menn Ch, Gulfport MS

Weaver Jr, M. Lloyd (Sarah Marie Yoder Weaver) 198 Colony Rd, Newport News VA 23602, 757-877-1925, LWeaver10@AOL [VA] [RE]

Weber, Floyd S. (Salinda) 287 Panorama Dr, Denver PA 17517, 717-445-5805 [LAN] III [RE]

Weber, George G. (Gladys) 123 Farm Crest Dr, Ephrata PA 17522, 717-351-0834 [LAN] [RE]

Weber, Larry H. (Sandra) 368 Boulder Hill Rd, Mohnton PA 19540-9425, 717-445-5229, laweb@juno.com [LAN] IIC [AC] Associate Pastor, Bowmansville Menn Ch, Bowmansville PA

Weber, Linford R. (Flo G.) 270 Hoch Rd, Fleetwood PA 19522, 610-944-9236, lrweber@juno.com [ACC] IIB3a [AC] Caseworker, Berks County Children and Youth Services, Reading PA

Wehibe, Shawlee (Mary Jane) 18 Parkview Dr, Elizabethtown PA 17022, 717-367-0497, swehibe@pol.net [LAN] IIC [AC] Licensed Deacon, Bossler Menn Ch, Elizabethtown PA

Weidner, Mark L. (Susan Ann) 2812 S 6th St, Elkhart IN 46517, 574-389-9009, mweidner@ambs.edu [CDC, OH] IIB3c [AC]

Welty, Lavon Jerry (Carol Ann) 211 Devonshire Ave, Lima OH 45804-3319, 419-222-6102, lavonw@wcoil.com [CDC, OH] IB2, IIB1 [AC] Conference Minister, Central District Conference, Ohio and Michigan, Lima OH

Welty, Merritt (Linda) 30269 CR KK, La Junta CO 81050, 719-853-6444, mlwelty@rural-com.com [RM] IIB1 [AC] Pastor, East Holbrook Menn Ch, Cheraw CO

Welty, Russell Ralph (Ellen L.) 264 Acacia Dr, Stockbridge GA 30281, 770-389-4316 [CDC] [RE]

Wendland, Wolfgang (Sarah Rebecca) 1124 Arcadia St, Bethlehem PA 18018-3002, 610-861-4409, wkwendland@netcarrier.com [LAN] IIB1 [AC] Pastor,

Bethlehem Community Fell, Bethlehem PA

Wenger, Alma E. (Nelson H.) 690 Earhart Rd, Manheim PA 17545, 717-665-7233, wenger690@redrose.net [LAN] IIC [AC] Licensed Deaconess, Erisman Menn Ch, Manheim PA

Wenger, Chester L. (Sara Jane) 2186 Old Phila Pike, Lancaster PA 17602, 717-397-3065, clwsjw@juno.com [LAN] [RE]

Wenger, Earl Malcolm (Esther Elizabeth Boehr Wenger) 3049 Ivy Court, North Newton KS 67117-8072, 316-283-2903 [WDC] [RE]

Wenger, Edward J. (Lynn) 128 Morrison Ave, Jackson MN 56143-1354, 507-847-2609, ewenger@rconnect.com [CP] IIB1 [AC] Pastor, Hilltop Community Ch, Jackson MN

Wenger, Esther Elizabeth, 3049 Ivy Ct, North Newton KS 67117-8072, 316-283-2903 [WDC] [RE]

Wenger, Harold (Christine Headings Wenger) CP 27, Beira, Mozambique, 258-3-326417, mccmoz@teledata.mz [LAN] IIB3b [AC] Co-Country Representative, Mennonite Central Committee, Maputo/Beira Mozambique

Wenger, Harold Paul, 4670 Elk Creek Rd, Middletown OH 45042-9659, 513-988-9080, halois@siscom.net [CDC] [RE]

Wenger, James Rodney (Faith Ann) 5805 Berkeley Ave, Baltimore MD 21215, jaswenger@aol.com [ACC] IB3, IIB1 [AC] Pastor, North Baltimore Menn Ch, Baltimore MD

Wenger, Kathryn W. (Mark) 177 Nottingham Ln, Waynesboro VA 22980, 540-943-5970, sprngdle@intelos.net [VA] IIB1 [AC] Co-Pastor, Springdale Menn Ch, Waynesboro VA

Wenger, L. Larry (RaeDella A.) 1036 Edgemoor Ct, Lancaster PA 17601, 717-392-3589, larry.wenger@juno.com [LAN] III [AC] Ordained Deacon, James Street Menn Ch, Lancaster PA

Wenger, Linden M. (Esther) 1285 Shank Dr Apt 319, Harrisonburg VA 22802, 540-564-3745 [VA] [RE]

Wenger, Mark R. (Kathy Weaver Wenger) 177 Nottingham Ln, Waynesboro VA 22980, 540-943-5970, sprngdle@intelos.net [VA] IIB1 [AC] Co-Pastor, Springdale Menn Ch, Waynesboro VA

Wenger, Michael W. (Donna) 126 Bomberger Rd, Akron PA 17501, 717-859-1671, mwenger@ptd.net [LAN] IIC [AC] Youth Pastor, Hinkletown Menn Ch, Ephrata PA

Wenger, Nelson H. (Alma E.) 690 Earhart Rd, Manheim PA 17545, 717-665-7233, wenger690@redrose.net [LAN] IIC [AC] Licensed Deacon, Erisman Menn Ch, Manheim PA

Wenger, Robert G. (Lois) HC 70 Box 67A, Harman WV 26270, 304-227-3647, rolowenger@juno.com [VA] IIB1 [AC] Pastor, Riverside Menn Ch, Harman WV

Wenger, Ruth Yoder (David A.) 3304 Steuben Ave, Bronx NY 10467-3006, 718-882-8924, wengermail@aol.com [LAN] IIC [AC] Pastor, North Bronx Menn Ch, Bronx NY

Wenger, Tonya Ramer (Jonathan) 1805 Frisch Rd, Madison WI 53711-3248, 608-276-9311, tramer@prairienet.org [CDC, IL] IIB1 [AC] Pastor, Madison Menn Ch, Madison WI

Wenger Jr, James L. (Melani) 63 Poplar St, Penns Grove NJ 08069, 856-299-4385, jamesnmel@aol.com [LAN] IIB1 [AC] Pastor, Friendship Menn Chapel, Carney's Point NJ

Wenger, Warren M., 52C Fairview Ave, Perkasie PA 18944, 215-453-9286 [FRC] [RE]

Wengerd, Robert D., 7852 Glenwood Ave, Boardman OH 44512, 330-758-2597, bobwengerd@aol.com [OH] IIB1 [AC] Pastor, North Lima Menn Ch, North Lima OH

Wentland, Theodore (Frieda Marie Herbstreit Wentland) 411 N 3rd, Fisher IL 61843, 217-897-1577, tedwent@juno.com [IL] IIB1 [AC] Pastor, Fullerton Presbyterian, Farmer City IL

Wero, George, 1111 James Cr, Bloomfield NM 87413, 505-632-1380 [RM] IIB1 [AC] Pastor, Light of Life Menn Ch, Farmington NM

Wert, Boyd M. (Martha R.) 1001 E. Oregon Rd, Litiz PA 17453, 717-591-2605 [LAN] III [RE]

Wert, Charles W. (Mildred [Millie]) 84 Quarry Rd, Leola PA 17540, 717-656-8546 [LAN] [RE] Bishop/Overseer, LAN - Groffdale District, PA

Westmoreland Jr, James M., 991 Olive St, Coatesville PA 19320, 610-383-6695 [LAN] IIB2 [AC] Associate Pastor, Newlinville Menn Ch, Coatesville PA

Whaley, Alan Howard, 3502 W Lamar Rd, Phoenix AZ 85019, 602-841-8044, menn1ofphx@aol.com [PSW] IB2, IIB1 [AC] Pastor, First Menn Ch of Phoenix, Phoenix AZ; Area Minister, Pacific Southwest Mennonite Conference, AZ

Whigham Jr, Ertell M., 977 Trinity Ln, Gulph Mills PA 19406, 610-834-1024, NNLErtell1@juno.com [FRC] IIB1 [AC] Associate Pastor, Norristown New Life Menn Ch, Norristown PA

White, Richard (Betty) HC 68, Box 209, Bowden WV 26254, 304-636-8667 [VA] IIB2 [AC] Associate Pastor, Lambert Menn Ch, Belington WV

Whitehead, Grace E., 1515 W Havens, Kokomo IN 46901, 317-452-1130, rewgew@aol.com [IM] IIB3b [AC] Restoration Ministries, Kokomo IN

Whitemore, David Malcolm, 2951 N Governeour Unit 206, Wichita KS 67226, 316-683-2963 [WDC] [RE]

Whitman, Alice W. (Vincent) 1417 Brunnerville Rd, Lititz PA 17543, 717-626-9130, vawhitman@yahoo.com [LAN] IIC [AC] Licensed Deaconess, Crossroads Menn, Lancaster PA

Whitman, Vincent (Alice W.) 1417 Brunnerville Rd, Lititz PA 17543, 717-626-9130, vawhitman@yahoo.com [LAN] IIB1 [AC] Pastor, Crossroads Menn, Lancaster PA

Wickey, William (Florence Edna) 28314 Findley Rd, Burr Oak MI 49030, 574-646-2545 [IM] [RE]

Wideman, Louise Renee, 3003 Benham Ave, Elkhart IN 46517 [SC] IIB1 [AC]

Widmer, Rosemary (David) 23238 CR 32, Goshen IN 46526, 574-875-1009, rose@collegemennonite.org [IM] IIB2 [AC] Pastor, College Menn Ch, Goshen IN

Widrick, Kyle Wayne (Tammy Z.) 12373 County Route 66, Adams Center NY 14806, 315-583-5973, kwidrick@msn.com [NY] IIB1 [AC] Pastor, Woodville Menn Ch, Adams NY

Widrick, Loren J. (Marilyn Z.) 10657 CR 77, Adams NY 13605, 315-232-4797, lorenw@gisco.net [NY] IIB1 [AC] Pastor, Woodville Menn Ch, Adams NY

Wiebe, Carl, 6009 County Rd 203, Millersburg OH 44654, 330-674-0189, carl@mcmc.org [OH] IIB1 [AC] Pastor, Martins Creek Menn Ch, Millersburg OH

Wiebe, Edward J. (Velma) 2328 23rd St, Rockford IL 61108, 815-397-7946 [CDC] [RE]

Wiebe, Gordon Wayne, Rt 1 Box 59, Doland SD 57436, 605-266-2588 [CP] IIB1 [AC] Pastor, Emmanuel Menn Ch, Doland SD

Wiebe, Leonard C., 2701 Goldenrod Rd, North Newton KS 67117, 316-283-4711, leonardw@southwind.net [WDC] [RE] Interim Pastor, Whitestone Menn Ch, Hesston KS

Wiebe, Peter B. (Rheta Mae) 4436 W Vista Ave, Glendale AZ 85301, 623-842-1145, PWiebe@meda.org [PSW] IIB3c [AW]

Wiebe-Johnson, Stephen Michael, 08 BP 2120, Abidjan 08, Cote d'Ivoire, West Africa [IM] IIB3b [AC] Missionary, Mennonite Mission Agency, Benin West Africa

Wiens, Mark Allen (Gayle Ann) PO Box 256, Goessel KS 67053-0256, 620-367-2528, wiensmg@mtelco.net [WDC] IIB2 [AC] Associate Pastor, Alexanderwohl Menn Ch, Goessel KS

Wikerd, Paul H. (Loretta M.) 253 State St, Hamburg PA 19526, 610-562-3936, pwikerd@enter.net [EDC] [RE]

Willems, Frank J. (Velma Elsie) 303 S Birch, Hillsboro KS 67063, 620-947-2543 [SC] [RE]

Willems, John (Dora E.) 2796 Goldfinch Loop SE, Albany OR 97322, 541-926-2006 [PNW] [RE]

Williams, Dean E. (Cindy) 20721 Lower Highland, Bergton VA 22811, 540-852-3241 [VA] IIB1 [AC] Pastor, Mathias Menn Ch, Bergton VA

Williams, Nan (Robert) 5 Wentworth Pl, Hampton VA 23666, 757-826-4224 [VA] IIA [AC] Associate Pastor, Calvary Community Ch, Hampton VA

Williams, Robert (Nan) 5 Wentworth Pl, Hampton VA 23666, 757-826-4224 [VA] IIA [AC] Associate Pastor, Calvary Community Ch, Hampton VA

Williams, Roy W. (Ruth) 22642 Newfield Ct, Land O Lakes FL 34639, 813-996-4244, RRRSJW@aol.com [SE] IB3, IIB1 [AC] Pastor, College Hill Menn Ch, Tampa FL; District Minister, Southeast Mennonite Conference, Tampa FL

Williams, Sharon K. (James P.) 153 Green St, Souderton PA 18964, 215-721-9268 [FRC] IIB3c [AC]

Wilson, Larry J. (L. Jane) 1398 E CR 2250 N, White Heath IL 61884, 217-687-4132, ljwilson@net66.com [CDC, IL] IIB1 [AC] Pastor, First Menn Ch of Champaign-Urbana, Urbana IL

Wilson, Mike, 318 1/2 Petoskey Street Apt 5, Petoskey MI 49770, 231-487-1658, michael_ray_wilson@yahoo.com [IM] IIC [AC] Chaplain, Petoskey MI

Wilson, Samuel A. (Jackie) 5285 Balfour, Detroit MI 48224, 313-885-1485 [IM] IIB1 [AC] Pastor, Community Christian Fell, Detroit MI

Wilson, Scot (Sharon) 7023 Clabeusch St, Pigeon MI 48755, 517-453-3632, mamc@avci.net [IM] IIB1 [AC] Pastor, Michigan Avenue Menn Ch, Pigeon MI

Wineland, Richard Kevin (Machelle) 708 Garber St, Hollidaysburg PA 16648 [IM] [AW]

Wingard, Aldus, 4480 Egypt Rd, Smithville OH 44677, 330-669-2110 [ALL] [RE]

Winslow, Mark Howard, 9025 E Rainsage St, Tucson AZ 85747, 520-574-7755 [PSW] IIB3a [AC]

Wintermote, Jeffrey Dale (Tamara Jean [Vogt]) 23698 CR B-C, Archbold OH 43502, 419-445-0154, jeffmote@yahoo.com [OH] IIB2 [AC] Youth Pastor, Zion Menn Ch, Archbold OH

MINISTERS

6

Winters, John W. (Ida E.) 1001 E Oregon Rd, Lititz PA 17543, 717-569-7790 [LAN] [RE]

Wise, Arthur C. (Betty J.) 5520 Antoinette St, Sarasota FL 34232, 941-377-3104 [SE] IIB3a [AC] Executive Director/Chaplain, Sunnyside Retirement Village, Sarasota FL

Wise, Glenn D., 12864 Path Valley Rd, Willow Hill PA 17271, 717-349-7061, [FRK] III, [AC] Ordained Deacon, Shady Pine Menn Ch, Willow Hill PA

Witmer, Dale E. (Jeanne M.) 6109 Geneva Dr, East Petersburg PA 17520-1240, 717-569-5247 [LAN] IIC [AC] Licensed Deacon, Erisman Menn Ch, Manheim PA

Witmer, E. Ray (Meredyth) 1729 Lincoln Hwy E, Lancaster PA 17602, 717-393-9800, rmwitmer@juno.com [LAN] III [AC] Licensed Deacon, Crossroads Menn, Lancaster PA

Witmer, H. Howard (Miriam) 274 S Erisman Rd, Manheim PA 17545, 717-653-4723, hhwitmer@juno.com [LAN] [RE] Bishop/Overseer, LAN - Manheim District, PA

Witmer, Irwin L. (Mary) 1318 Mount Gretna Rd, Elizabethtown PA 17022, 717-367-3037 [LAN] III [RE]

Witmer, Jeanne M. (Dale E.) 6109 Geneva Dr, East Petersburg PA 17520-1240, 717-569-5247 [LAN] IIC [AC] Licensed Deacon, Erisman Menn Ch, Manheim PA

Witmer, John E. (Evelyn) 1067 Hearthstone Rd, Lancaster PA 17603-9452, 717-871-0686 [LAN] [RE]

Witmer, Kenneth R. (Lorraine) PO Box 363, Bowmansville PA 17507, 717-445-7458, krwitmer@juno.com [LAN] IIB2 [AC] Pastor, Bowmansville Menn Ch, Bowmansville PA

Witmer, Meredyth Ann (E. Ray) 1729 Lincoln Hwy E, Lancaster PA 17602, 717-393-9800, rmwitmer@juno.com [LAN] IIC [AC] Licensed Deaconess, Crossroads Menn, Lancaster PA

Witmer, Paul M. (Mary K.) 5033 Martin Dr, East Petersburg PA 17520, 717-581-7805 [LAN] [RE]

Witmer, Randall L. (Lorretta) 235 Hershey Ave, Lancaster PA 17603, 717-393-5840, rlwitmer@dejazzd.com [LAN] IIB1 [AC] Pastor, Laurel Street Menn Ch, Lancaster PA

Wittrig, Jerry (Ruth Ann) 1008 N Indiana Ave, Goshen IN 46526, 574-533-2408, jwtrg@aol.com [IM] IIB2 [AC] Co-Pastor, North Goshen Menn Ch, Goshen IN

Woelk, Frank, 241 Bergen Rd, Newport WA 99156, 509-447-2224, fwoelk@juno,com [PNW] IIB1 [AC] Pastor, Spring Valley Menn Ch, Newport WA

Woelk, Sampson (Maria) 61399 CR 3, Elkhart IN 46517, 574-293-4455, omc_Sam@juno.com [IM] IIA [AC] Associate Pastor, Olive Menn Ch, Elkhart IN

Woldeabe, Mulugeta Abate (Tihute Yohannes) 1687 Castle Hill Ave Apt 3, Bronx NY 10462-4249, 718-246-7263, abatem@worldnet.att.net [LAN] IIB1 [AC] Pastor, Emmanuel Worship Center, Bronx NY

Wolgemuth, Herbert R. (Kathleen M.) RR 1 Box 202-A, Covington PA 16917, 570-659-5479, herbw@ticopa.quik.com [LAN] [AW]

Wong, Tim (Teresa) 612 Watertown St, Newtonville MA 02460, 617-965-0703, ttwong@integrity.com [LAN] IIA [AC] Pastor, Boston Chinese Ch of Saving Grace, Newton MA

Wood, Joseph A. (Janace) RR 1 Box 152B, Hydro OK 73048, 405-663-2703 [SC] IIB1 [AC] Pastor, Pleasant View Menn Ch, Hydro OK

Wright, Chris (Lori) 356 E Edgewood, Morton IL 61550, 309-266-7038 [IL] IIB2 [AC] Youth Pastor, First Menn Ch of Morton, Morton IL

Wright, Jeff (Debra Yvonne Thesman Wright) Box CAL, 1539 E Howard St, Pasadena CA 91104, 626-720-8100, wrightstuff@pacificsouthwest.org [PSW] IB2, IIB1, IIB3b [AC] Preaching Minister, First Menn Ch, Upland CA; Executive Director, Center for Anabaptist Leadership, Pasadena CA; Area Minister for Southern California, Pacific Southwest Mennonite Conference, Pasadena CA

Wright, Timothy Lee (Linda Lou) 1704 Empire Blvd Apt #10, Rochester NY 14580, 716-670-9987, channels@frontiernet.net [NY] IIB1 [AC] Pastor, Jesus Ch, Webster NY

Wyatt Jr, Boyd (Shirley) RR 3 Box 70, Belington WV 26250, 304-823-1466 [VA] IIB1 [AC] Pastor, Lambert Menn Ch, Belington WV

Wyse, Dale, 30 Willow Way, Archbold OH 43502, 419-445-2765 [OH] [RE]

Wyse, Don, 5384 Olentangy River Rd, Columbus OH 43235-3442, 614-451-9169 [CDC] [RE]

Wyse, Elmer J. (Deloris J.) 115 N Creamery St, Eureka IL 61530, 309-467-4645, ewyse@mtco.com [IL] IIB1 [AC] Co-Pastor, Roanoke Menn Ch, Eureka IL

Wyse, Joyce M., 5384 Olentangy River Rd, Columbus OH 43235-3442, 614-451-9169, wyse.5@osu.edu [CDC] [RE] Interim Pastor, Columbus Menn Ch, Columbus OH

Wyse, Ned, 11080 Frontier Rd, Camden MI 49232, 517-254-4552, nlwyse@dmci.net [OH] IIB2 [AC] Preaching Minister, Salem Menn Ch, Waldron MI

Y

Yates, Bob, 413 N Defiance, PO Box 290, Stryker OH 43557, 419-682-1023, revbob98@yahoo.com. [OH] IIB1 [AC] Pastor, Pine Grove Menn Ch, Stryker OH

Yeager, Fred E., 408 Twin Bridge Rd, Chambersburg PA 17201, 717-369-2156 [FRK] [RE]

Yeakey II, Michael Aaron (Kathleen Faye Nofziger) 6085S 1000W, Topeka IN 46571, 260-593-2594 [CDC] IIC [AW]

Yoder, Aden J., 1006 Mervin Ave, Goshen IN 46526, 574-534-5573 [IM] [RE]

Yoder, Alvin, 321 Linden St, West Liberty OH 43357, 937-465-2263, ayoder@logan.net [OH] IIB1 [AC] Pastor, Bethel Menn Ch, West Liberty OH

Yoder, Amzie (Elena) 1605 Westridge, Carlsbad NM 88220, 505-887-7658, amziey@cavemen.net [RM] IIB1 [AC] Pastor, Carlsbad Menn Ch, Carlsbad NM

Yoder, Arlin David (Mary Lou) 8203 W 17th St N, Wichita KS 67212, 316-721-3762 [CP] [AW]

Yoder, Beth Ranck (Jerold) 1209 Telegraph Rd, Perkasie PA 18944, 215-257-1850, jyoder@enter.net [FRC] IIB1 [AC] Pastor, Perkasie Menn Ch, Perkasie PA

Yoder, Brenda J., 706 C St, Springfield OR 97477, 541-726-4478 [PNW] IIB3a [AC]

Yoder, Calvin L. (Lorie B.) 24 Diane Ave, Lititz PA 17543, 717-626-9364, calyoder@foresthillschurch.org [ACC] IIB1 [AC] Pastor, Forest Hills Menn Ch, Leola PA

Yoder, Carl V., 402 Walnut St, Archbold OH 43502, 419-445-4676 [OH] [RE]

Yoder, Chester E. (Sandra) 214 Spruce St, Denver PA 17517, 717-445-4782, yoder214@juno.com [LAN] IIB1 [AC] Associate Pastor, Bowmansville Menn Ch,

Bowmansville PA

Yoder, Daniel J. (Lois Beachy Yoder) 8301 Nathanael Greene, Charlotte NC 28227, 704-531-6010 [VA] [AW]

Yoder, David D. (Shirley) 1539 Hillcrest Dr, Harrisonburg VA 22802, 540-434-4776 [VA] IIB3c [AW]

Yoder, Delmar (Tammy) R1 Box 88, Ogema MN 56569, 218-983-3490 [NC] IIB1 [AC] Pastor, Strawberry Lake Menn Ch, Ogema MN

Yoder, Duane Allen (Barbara Jill) 4629 Hamlet's Grove Dr, Sarasota FL 34235, 941-358-2236, DuaneYoder@juno.com [SE] IIB1 [AC] Pastor, Bay Shore Menn Ch, Sarasota FL

Yoder, Earl A., PO Box 275, Springs PA 15562, 814-662-2210 [ALL] IB3 [AC]

Yoder, Edwin M., RR 4 Box 10, Harrisonburg VA 22801 [OH] [RE]

Yoder, Elena, 1605 Westridge, Carlsbad NM 88220, 505-887-7658 [RM] IIC [AW] Hospice Counselor, Carlsbad Hospital, Carlsbad NM US

Yoder, Elwin D. (Coleen) RR 2 Box 243, Warsaw MO 65355, 816-438-6084 [SC] IIB1 [AC] Pastor, Evening Shade Menn Ch, Warsaw MO

Yoder, Earl D., 530 Noble St Apt 1D, Souderton PA 18964, 215-721-4614 [FRC] [RE]

Yoder, Evan M., 1368 Georgetown Rd, Quarryville PA 17566-9468, 717-786-7413 [ACC] [AW]

Yoder, Glen (Lois) 336 Robin, Waverly OH 45690 [OH] [RE]

Yoder, Glen J. (Ellen) 321 Primrose Ln, Mountville PA 17554, 717-285-3906 [LAN] [AW]

Yoder, Harold, 1310 S 14th St, Goshen IN 46526, 574-825-2701 [IM] [RE]

Yoder, Harold J. (Ruth Anne) 26175 Woodridge Dr, Elkhart IN 46517, 574-293-5080 [IM] IIB2 [AC] Pastor, Yellow Creek Menn Ch, Goshen IN

Yoder, Harry (Jean M. Martin) Mennonite Memorial Home, 410 W Elm St, Bluffton OH 45817 [CDC] [RE]

Yoder, Harvey (Alma Jean) 1135 Hamlet Dr, Harrisonburg VA 22802, 540-432-1593, harvyoder@aol.com [VA] IIB1 [AC] Pastor, Family of Hope, Harrisonburg VA

Yoder, Helen, 5465 Black Hawk Ave SW, Wellman IA 52356, 319-646-6835, wyoder@yahoo.com [CP] IIA [AC] Staff Deacon, West Union Menn Ch, Parnell IA

Yoder, Herbert L. (Dorothy) 1435 Angle Rd SW, Kalona IA 52247, 319-656-2317 [CP] [RE]

Yoder, Irvin C., 1312 Copley Ct, Goshen IN 46526, 574-533-9084 [IM] [RE]

Yoder, J. David (Nancy) 2280 Lake Terrace Dr, Harrisonburg VA 22802-6193, 540-434-4769 [VA] IIB3c [AC]

Yoder, John O. (Arlene) PO Box 326, Maytown PA 17550, 717-426-1560, joytwo@paonline.com [LAN] IIB1 [AC] Pastor, Erisman Menn Ch, Manheim PA

Yoder, Jon, 5902 S Whiskey Hill Rd, Hubbard OR 97032, 503-651-2743, jzyoder@web-ster.com [PNW] IIA [AC] Pastor, Pacific Covenant Menn Ch, Canby OR

Yoder, Joshua, 1619 Benham Ave, Elkhart IN 46516, 574-295-1488, joshuapyoder@juno.com [IM] IIA [AC] Pastor, Fellowship of Hope Menn Ch, Elkhart IN

Yoder, Juel M., 3053 Sunnyview Rd NE, Salem OR 97303, 541-588-2567, captwc@hotmail.com [PNW] [AW]

Yoder, June Alliman, 200 Westwood Rd, Goshen IN

46526, 574-533-4943 [IM] IIB3d [AC] Professor, Associated Mennonite Biblical Seminary, Elkhart IN

Yoder, Kevin (Sharon) 60790 CR 101, Elkhart IN 46517 [IM] IIA [AC] Missionary, Eastern Mennonite Missions, Kenya Africa

Yoder, Lawrence M. (Shirlee K.) 1301 Mount Clinton Pike, Harrisonburg VA 22802, 540-434-1058, yoderlm@emu.edu [VA] IIB3d [AC]

Yoder, Leanne, Shalom Mennonite Fellowship, 6044 E 30th St, Tucson AZ 85711, eyoder@gci-net.com [PSW] IIC [AC] Co-Pastor, Shalom Menn Fell, Tucson AZ

Yoder, Lonnie D. (Teresa Boshart Yoder) 1066 Smith Ave, Harrisonburg VA 22802, 540-432-6467 [VA] IIB3d [AC]

Yoder, M. Leon (Sara) 521 State Route 103 N, Lewistown PA 17044, 717-899-6347 [ALL] [AC]

Yoder, Mark (Alice) 2726 Conestoga Creek Rd, Morgantown PA 19543, 610-286-9445 [LAN] III [RE]

Yoder, Marvin D. (Rachel) 61205 CR 17, Goshen IN 46526, 574-875-7850 [IM] [RE]

Yoder, Marvin K. (Neta Faye) 104 Fairview Dr PO Box 166, Wellman IA 52356, 319-646-2451 [CP] [RE]

Yoder, Mary Lehman (Michael) 216 Gorham Rd, Goshen IN 46526, 574-534-3741, mmyoder1@cs.com [CDC, IM] IIB1 [AC] Co-Pastor, Assembly Menn Ch, Goshen IN

Yoder, Monroe J. (Rachel) 268 Van Cortlandt Ave E Apt 2, Bronx NY 10467-3008, 718-652-2307, myrybronx@earthlink.net [LAN] IB3 [AC] Pastor, Seventh Avenue Menn Ch, New York NY; Bishop/Overseer, LAN - New York City District, New York NY

Yoder, Nathan E. (Miriam Grace) 1545 Shank Dr, Harrisonburg VA 22802, 540-432-9326, yoderne@emu.edu [VA] IIB3d [AC]

Yoder, Nelson S. (Pat) 5948 Michele Dr, Narvon PA 17555, 717-355-9130, npyoder1@juno.com [ACC] IIA [AC] Associate Pastor, Conestoga Menn Ch, Morgantown PA; Mental Health Therapist, Philhaven, Mt Gretna PA

Yoder, Ottis (Violet) 32553 County Hwy 34, Ogema MN 56569-9605, 218-983-3477 [NC] IB3 [AC] Bishop, Strawberry Lake Menn Ch, Ogema MN

Yoder, Pamela (Bob) 19321 Yoder Dr, Goshen IN 46528, 574-875-1862, pamela@firstmennonite.net [IM] IIA [AC] Pastoral Care Coordinator, First Menn Ch, Middlebury IN

Yoder, Paul E. M. (Helen) 1009 9th Ave, Wellman IA 52356, 319-646-2316 [CP] [RE]

Yoder, Paul T. (Daisy) 1588 Pine Ct, Harrisonburg VA 22802, 540-432-7200, twopilgrims49@aol.com [VA] [RE] Pastor, Greenmonte Menn Ch, Stuarts Draft VA

Yoder, Philip W., 1313 Kinzy St, Elkhart IN 46516, 574-294-2033 [IM] [AW]

Yoder, Ray K. (Edna) 794 Moccasin Dr, Harleysville PA 19438, 215-256-6356, rayyoder@excelonline.com [FRC] IIB1 [AC] Interim Pastor, Ephrata Menn Ch, Ephrata PA

Yoder, Richard W. (Barbara A.) 1410 Pembroke Cr #3, Goshen IN 46526, 574-534-0287, richard@im.mennonite.net [IM] IB2 [RE] Interim Regional Conference Minister, Indiana-Michigan Mennonite Conference, MI

Yoder, Robert D. (Vickie Dee) 14201 Germantown Rd, Columbiana OH 44408, 330-482-2123, bc958@cboss.com [OH] IIB1 [AC] Pastor, Leetonia

Menn Ch, Leetonia OH

Yoder, Robert E. (Pamela Sue) 19321 Yoder Dr, Goshen IN 46528, 574-875-1862, bob@im.mennonite.net [IM] IB2 [AC] Conference Minister of Youth & Young Adults, Indiana-Michigan & Central District Conferences, Goshen IN

Yoder, Robert K. (Elvira) 903 K Ave, Kalona IA 52247, 319-656-3910 [CP] [RE]

Yoder, Roy K. (Sandra Fay) PO Box 33 560 Kulps Rd, Bally PA 19503, 610-845-3650, rsyoder@excelonline.com [FRC] IIB3b [AC]

Yoder, Ruth Anne, 59193 Green Valley Parkway, Elkhart IN 46517-3427, 574-875-4512 [IM] IIB1 [AC] Pastor, Union Center Church of the Brethren, Nappanee IN

Yoder, Samuel J. (Mary Ann) RR 1 Box 73, Mifflinburg PA 17844, 717-966-2392 [ALL] IIB1 [AC] Pastor, Boyer Menn Ch, Mifflinburg PA

Yoder, Sanford K. (Barb) 202 Elm Cr, Eureka IL 61530, 309-467-4172 [IL] [AW]

Yoder, Sharon (Kevin) 60790 CR 101, Elkhart IN 46517 [IM] IIA [AC] Missionary, Eastern Mennonite Missions, Kenya Africa

Yoder, Shirlee K. (Lawrence M.) 1301 Mount Clinton Pike, Harrisonburg VA 22802, 540-434-1058 [VA] IIB3a [AC]

Yoder, Steven J. (Janet J. [Jantzi]) 107 W 24th St, Box 21, North Newton KS 67117, 316-283-6034, sjyoder@southwind.net [WDC] IIB2 [AC] Associate Pastor, Bethel College Menn Ch, North Newton KS

Yoder, Thomas L. (Karen) 859 Hillside Ave, Harrisonburg VA 22802, 540-434-9522 [VA] [AW]

Yoder, Vickie (Robert D.) 14201 Germantown Rd, Columbiana OH 44408, 330-482-2123, bc958@cboss.com [OH] IIB3a [AC]

Yoder, W. Harvey (Karen S.) 311 Jensen St, Macon MS 39341, 662-726-2542, whyksy@crawdat.com [GS] IIA [AC] Assistant Pastor, Nanih Waiya Indian Menn Ch, Philadelphia MS

Yoder, Wes P. (Jill R.) 66829 CR 11, Goshen IN 46526, 574-862-4246, wjyoder@npcc.net [IM] IIA [AC] Pastor, Forks Menn Ch, Middlebury IN

Yoder Sr, Paul R. (Grace W.) 1591 Pine Ct, Harrisonburg VA 22802, 540-438-4260, yowing819@cs.com [VA] [RE]

Yoder-Schrock, John Lamar (Marcia A.) PO Box 722, Moundridge KS 67107, 620-345-8141, westzionmc@wwwebservice.net [WDC] IIB1 [AC] Co-Pastor, West Zion Menn Ch, Moundridge KS

Yoder-Schrock, Marcia Ann (John L.) 1281 16th St, PO Box 69, Henderson NE 68371, 402-723-5300 [WDC] IIB1 [AC] Pastor, West Zion Menn Ch, Moundridge KS

Yordy, Maurice J. (Pat) RR 2 Box 175, Eureka IL 61530, 309-467-3109 [IL] IIB1 [AC] Pastor, East Peoria Menn Ch, Eureka IL

Yost, Burton George, 184 Garmatter St, Bluffton OH 45817-1165, 419-358-9495 [CDC] [RE]

Yovanovich, William Z. (Ruth B. Brubaker) 405 College Ave, Elizabethtown PA 17022, 717-367-3713 [LAN] [RE]

Yusavitz, Carl Raphael (Mary R.) 7128 Crittenden St, Philadelphia PA 19119-1214, 215-742-2065, cyusavitz@netscape.net [EDC, FRC] IIB3a [AC] Director of Pastoral Services, Penn Foundation, Sellersville PA

Yutzy, Homer E., 13169 CR 16, Wauseon OH 43567,

419-452-6756 [OH] [RE]

Yutzy, Melvin E., 8740 PC Georgesville Rd, Plain City OH 43064, 614-873-4144 [OH] [RE]

Yutzy, Oliver (Miriam) 2220 N 675 W, Shipshewana IN 46565, 260-768-4238 [IM] IIB3c [RE] Manager, Menno-Hof, Shipshewana IN

Z

Zabriskie, Kristin Klompeen (W. Tyler) 2067 Meridian Ave #2, South Pasadena CA 91030, 323-982-9028, kristizab@aol.com [PSW] IIA [AC] Associate Pastor, Pasadena Menn Ch, Pasadena CA

Zeager, J. Frank (Rhoda) 2405 Colebrook Rd, Middletown PA 17057, 717-944-5008 [LAN] IIB2 [AC] Associate Pastor, Stauffer Menn Ch, Hershey PA

Zehr, Calvin Dean (Carol) RR 1 Box 9C, Tiskilwa IL 61368, 815-646-4819 [IL] IIB1 [AC] Pastor, Willow Springs Menn Ch, Tiskilwa IL

Zehr, Douglas J. (Miriam R.) PO Box 281, Leo IN 46765, 260-627-5867 [IM] IIB1 [AC] Pastor, North Leo Menn Ch, Leo IN

Zehr, Evan (Amy Lynn [Brown]) 5574 Highland Ave, Lowville NY 13367, 315-376-3082, eazehr@northnet.org [NY] IIB1 [AC] Pastor, Lowville Menn Ch, Lowville NY

Zehr, Keith, 11500 Clarence Center Rd, Akron NY 14001, 716-542-9927, CCAM9927@aol.com [NY] IIB1 [AC] Pastor, Clarence Center-Akron Menn Ch, Akron NY

Zehr, Loren (Ethel M.) 1918 SE 40th Terrace, Cape Coral FL 33904, 239-772-5683, Lzehr@juno.com [SE] IIC [AC] Minister of Nurture, Cape Christian Fell, Cape Coral FL

Zehr, Marvin Jay (Jeannie K.) 824 Trinity Dr, Newton KS 67114, 316-283-8308 [WDC] IB2 [AC] Conference Minister, Western District Conference, North Newton KS

Zehr, Michael M. (Lois Shenk Zehr) 19839 Peach Ridge Rd, Goshen IN 46526, 574-534-2453 [IM] [RE]

Zehr, Michael Ray, 310 Enterprise Ave, Wauseon OH 43567, 419-337-6797, michael.zehr@northclinton.org [OH] IIB2 [AC] Associate Pastor, North Clinton Menn Ch, Wauseon OH

Zehr, Milton J. (Dorothy Leora) PO Box C, Alger Rd, Martinsburg NY 13404, 315-376-3734, dotconf@northnet.org [NY] IB2, IB3 [AC] Conference Minister, New York Mennonite Conference, Martinsburg NY

Zehr, Nathan (Ruth) 8343 VanAmber Rd, Castorland NY 13620, 315-376-2593, nrzehr@hotmail.com [NY] IIB1 [AC] Pastor, Pine Grove Menn Ch, Castorland NY

Zehr, Paul M. (Mary Martin Zehr) 209 Henrietta Ave, Lancaster PA 17602, 717-299-6104, zehrpm@emu.edu [LAN] IB3 [AC]

Zehr, Robert O. (Vivian Margaret Guengerich Zehr) 134 Maloney Rd, Des Allemands LA 70030, 985-758-2974, bobzehr@cox.net [GS] IB3, IIB1 [AC] Interim Pastor, Open Door Menn Ch, Jackson MS

Zehr, Terry, 3017 Pleasant Plain, Elkhart IN 46517, 574-522-6972, sunnysidemc@juno.com [IM] IIB1 [AC] Pastor, Sunnyside Menn Ch, Elkhart IN

Zehr, Terry J. (Lisa R.) Rt 1 Box 5, Lowville NY 13367, 315-376-5514, zehrtj@northnet.org [NY] IIB1 [AC] Pastor, Watertown Menn Ch, Watertown NY

Zehr Jr, Vernon, 2721 Skylark Rd, Wilmington DE 19808, 302-994-8698 [LAN] IIB2 [AC] Associate Pastor, Frazer Menn Ch, Frazer PA

Zeiset, Nelson B. (Esther) 111 Hopeland Rd,

Newmanstown PA 17073, 717-949-2478 [LAN] IIB2, IIB3a [AC] Associate Pastor, Green Terrace Menn Ch, Wernersville PA; Chaplain, Prison Ministry, PA

Zeiset, Samuel W., 420 Radcliff Rd, Willow Street PA 17584, 717-464-3340 [LAN] IIB3a [AC]

Zewdie, Kinfe (Adanech) 7432 Maury Rd, Baltimore MD 21244, 410-298-6053 [LAN] [AW]

Ziegler, Ralph (Osie) 9638 Mount Zion Rd, Linville VA 22834, 540-833-6440 [VA] [RE]

Ziemer, Richard Carl (Adella W.) 325 Cedar Crest Dr, Quakertown PA 18951, 215-536-8895 [EDC] [AW]

Zimmerman, Earl S. (Ruth Hoover Zimmerman) 1181 Lincolnshire Dr, Harrisonburg VA 22802, 540-433-5227, eszimmerman@aol.com [VA] IIB1 [AC] Co-Pastor, Shalom Menn Congregation, Harrisonburg VA

Zimmerman, George L. (Lois) 20 Evergreen St, Thompsontown PA 17094-9733, 717-535-9941, georgelois@jc-net.com [LAN] IIB1 [AC] Pastor, Krall Menn Ch, Lebanon PA

Zimmerman, Ivan R. (Vera Mae) 85 Millstone Dr, Denver PA 17517, 717-445-8297 [LAN] [RE]

Zimmerman, Lester L. (Thelma) 1407 Brunnerville Rd, Lititz PA 17543, 717-626-2641 [LAN] [RE]

Zimmerman, M. Craig (Grace) 966 Lower Bodiness Rd, Trout Run PA 17771, 570-995-9171 [LAN] IIA [AC] Pastor, Mountain View Fell, Trout Run PA

Zimmerman, Marlin M. (Bonnie) 708 E Linden St, Richland PA 17087, 717-866-5323, zimmb@ptd.net [LAN] III [AC] Ordained Deacon, Schubert Menn Ch, Bethel PA

Zimmerman, Michael S. (Marlene Faye) 528 E 28th Division Hwy, Lititz PA 17543, 717-627-2461 [LAN] IIB2 [AC] Associate Pastor, Erb Menn Ch, Lititz PA

Zimmerman, Norman L. (Betty) 524 Appalachian Ave, Mechanicsburg PA 17055, 717-766-0536 [LAN] [RE]

Zimmerman, R. Eugene, 315 E Wesner Rd, Blandon PA 19510, 610-926-4074 [LAN] IIB1 [AC]

Zimmerman II, John Charles, 56 Market St, Myerstown PA 17067, 717-933-5235 [LAN] IIC [AC] Associate Pastor, Schubert Menn Ch, Bethel PA

Zoll, David Eugene (Florence) 1715 Swamp Bridge Rd, Stevens PA 17578, 717-336-3369, zoll@ptdprolog.net [LAN] IIB2 [AC] Associate Pastor, Metzler Menn Ch, Akron PA

Zook, Darrell E. (Patricia Ann) 3284 CR 230, Palmyra MO 63461-2331, mtpisgah4@juno.com [SC] IIB1 [AC] Pastor, Pea Ridge Menn Ch, Palmyra MO; Pastor, Mount Pisgah Menn Ch, Leonard MO

Zook, Gary L. (Teresa) 11842 Williamsport Pike, Greencastle PA 17225, 717-597-3294 [FRK] IIB1 [AC] Pastor, North Side Menn Ch, Hagerstown MD

Zook, Gordon D. (Bonnie) 156 Robinhood Ln, Newport News VA 23602, 757-877-4247 [VA] IIB3d [AC]

Zook, Herbert, Wild Cherry Rd, New Castle PA 16101, 724-652-5436 [OH] [RE]

Zook, Lester L. (Grace E.) PO Box 302, 315 South Ash St, Pretty Prairie KS 67570-0302, 620-459-7389, lzook@southwind.net [WDC] IIB1 [AC] Pastor, First Menn Ch, Pretty Prairie KS

Zook, Robert G. (Ethel [Yoder]) 223 Howard Ave, Lancaster PA 17602, 717-393-2867, BobZook@lgms.pvt.k12.pa.us [LAN] IIB1 [AC] Pastor, Mt Pleasant Menn Ch, Paradise PA

Congregations by location

7

This section lists all congregations by location that are affiliated with area conferences relating to Mennonite Church USA (all congregations listed in section 2). In addition to congregations in the United States, you will note 20 congregations in Brazil, Canada, Mexico, Paraguay and Uruguay.

Congregations are in state/city order. Included with the name of the congregation are the congregational ID number, the area conference affiliation, and the page number where more details about the congregation can be found in section 2.

United States

ALABAMA
Atmore
Native Christian Fell (11140) (GS) 58
Poarch Community Ch (16535) (GS) 58

ALASKA
Anchorage
Prince of Peace Menn Ch (10051) (PNW) 94

ARIZONA
Chandler
Koinonia Menn Ch (23044) (PSW) 98
Glendale
Trinity Menn Ch (18333) (PSW) 98
Phoenix
First Menn Ch of Phoenix (5312) (PSW) 97
Sunnyslope Menn Ch (18317) (PSW) 98
Surprise
Emmanuel Menn Ch (18325) (PSW) 97
Tucson
Shalom Menn Fell (22418) (PSW) 98

ARKANSAS
Calico Rock
Calico Rock Menn Fell (17855) (SC) 102
El Dorado
First Menn Ch (10777) (GS) 58
Pea Ridge
Rogers Menn/Ch of the Brethren (29745) (SC) . . .103

CALIFORNIA
Chino
Jemaat Kristen Indonesia Hosana (10282) (PSW) . .98
Claremont
Peace House Fell (10027) (PSW) 98
Cupertino
Cupertino Menn Ch (5697) (PSW) 97
Downey
Faith Menn Ch (18259) (PSW) 97
Jemaat Kristen Indonesia Imanuel (10309) (PSW) . .98
Fresno
Hmong Community Ch (10247) (PSW) 97
Menn Community Ch (28373) (PSW) 98
Inglewood
Calvary Christian Fell (18242) (PSW) 97
Great Commission Deliverance Ch (11172) (PSW) . .97
Los Angeles Faith Chapel (11088) (PSW) 98
Irvine
Trinity Chinese Menn Ch (5183) (PSW) 98
La Mirada
Gereja Kristen Injili Indonesia Zion (10311) (PSW) .97
La Puente
House of the Lord Fell (24885) (PSW) 97
Los Angeles
Abundant Life Miracle Christian Center (11318)
(PSW) 96
All Souls Christian Center (11583) (PSW) 96
Faith and Love Christian Center (11584) (PSW) 97
Family Menn Ch (11109) (PSW) 97
Hollywood Christian Center (11586) (PSW) 97
Labor for Christ Ministry (11269) (PSW) 98
Miracle of Faith Menn Ch (24612) (PSW) 98
Prince of Peace Anabaptist Fell (18267) (PSW) 98
Royal Dominion Family Chapel (11319) (PSW) 98
Pasadena
Jemaat Kristen Indonesia Anugrah (10289) (PSW) . .97
Pasadena Menn Ch (28142) (PSW) 98

Paso Robles
First Menn Ch (5409) (PSW) 97
Reedley
First Menn Ch (5321) (PSW) 97
Reseda
Jemaat Kristen Indonesia Maranatha (10259) (PSW) 98
San Diego
Casa de Oracion Menonita (24604) (PSW) 97
San Diego Menn Ch (10001) (PSW) 98
San Francisco
First Menn Ch of San Francisco (23226) (PSW) 97
San Francisco Chinese Menn Ch (5692) (PSW) 98
Santa Fe Springs
Bethel Community Ch (5075) (PSW) 96
South Gate
Iglesia Monte Sinai (24232) (PSW) 97
Sun Valley
Iglesia Evangelica Bethel (25429) (PSW) 97
Upland
First Menn Ch (5330) (PSW) 97
Mountain View Menn Ch (18309) (PSW) 98

COLORADO
Arvada
Arvada Menn Ch (6020) (WDC) 114
Hmong Menn Ch (11119) (RM, WDC) 100, 116
Aurora
Peace Menn Community Ch (28605) (RM,
WDC) 100, 117
Boulder
Boulder Menn Ch (6153) (WDC) 114
Cheraw
East Holbrook Menn Ch (20834) (RM) 99
Colorado Springs
Beth-El Menn Ch (20792) (RM) 99
First Menn Ch of Colorado Springs (20867) (RM) . .99
Denver
First Menn Ch of Denver (20859) (RM) 100
Fort Collins
Fort Collins Menn Fell (24687) (RM, WDC) . . .100, 115
Glenwood Springs
Glenwood Menn Ch (20891) (RM) 100
Greeley
Greeley Menn Ch (20917) (RM) 100
Julesburg
Julesburg Menn Ch (13300) (CP) 47
La Jara
Menn Ch of La Jara (20925) (RM) 100
La Junta
Emmanuel Menn Ch (20842) (RM) 99
Lakewood
Glennon Heights Menn Ch (20883) (RM) 100
Palmer Lake
Mountain Community Menn Ch (25247)
(RM, WDC) 100, 116
Pueblo
Pueblo Menn Ch (21774) (RM) 100
Rocky Ford
Rocky Ford Menn Ch (20966) (RM) 100
Walsenburg
Walsenburg Menn Ch (20982) (RM) 100

CONNECTICUT
New Haven
Menn Bible Fell (13581) (LAN) 78

DELAWARE
Greenwood
Tressler Menn Ch (10462) (ALL) 37
Wilmington
Centro Evangelistico Cristiano (26724) (LAN) 72

DISTRICT OF COLUMBIA
Washington
Christian Conquest Fell (10010) (VA) 109
Iglesia del Evangelio Completo Alpha y O (23465)
(VA) 110
Peabody Street Menn Ch (14993) (LAN) 79
Washington Community Fell (24778) (VA) 112

FLORIDA
Apopka
Ebenezer Christian Ch (25049) (SE) 107
Arcadia
Pine Creek Chapel (22376) (SE) 107
Blountstown
Oak Terrace Menn Ch (12823) (SE) 107
Cape Coral
Cape Christian Fell (28175) (SE) 106
Fort Myers
Iglesia Menonita Arca de Salvacion (27904) (SE) . .107
Gainesville
Emmanuel Menn Ch (25080) (SE) 107
Homestead
Homestead Menn Ch (14332) (SE) 107
Immokalee
Assemblee de la Grace (11299) (SE) 106
Lakeland
Luz y Verdad (10212) (SE) 107
Lauderdale Lakes
Evangelical Garifuna Ch (12051) (SE) 107
Laurel
Laurel Worship Center (10281) (SE) 107
Miami
Eglise du Nouveau Testament (28449) (SE) 107
Good Shepherd Evangelical (10972) (SE) 107
Unity Pentecostal Ch of God (11153) (SE) 107
Miami-Dade
Iglesia Menonita Encuentro de Renovacion (10284)
(SE) 107
Tabernacle of Bethlehem (10253) (SE) 107
North Port
Peace Christian Fell (10241) (SE) 107
Sarasota
Ashton Menn Ch (13524) (SE) 106
Bahia Vista Menn Ch (18903) (SE) 106
Bay Shore Menn Ch (15693) (SE) 106
Covenant Menn Fell (12196) (SE) 107
Iglesia Seguidores de Cristo (25072) (SE) 107
Newtown Gospel Chapel (18762) (SE) 107
St Petersburg
New Beginning Community Ch (19531) (SE) 107
Tamarac
Iglesia Amor Viviente/Ft Lauderdale (11161) (SE) .107
Tampa
College Hill Menn Ch (13797) (SE) 107
North Tampa Christian Fell (14886) (SE) 107

GEORGIA
Americus
Americus Menn Fell (10067) (SE) 106

Atlanta
Atlanta Menn Fell (10291) 34
Berea Menn Ch (13565) (SE) 106

HAWAII
Honolulu
New Life Christian Fell (29157) (LAN) 79
Vietnamese Christian Fell (29215) (LAN) 81

IDAHO
Aberdeen
First Menn Ch (5335) (PNW) 94
Boise
Hyde Park Menn Fell (23663) (PNW) 94
Filer
Filer Menn Ch (17525) (PNW) 94
Nampa
First Menn Ch (17533) (PNW) 94

ILLINOIS
Arthur
Arthur Menn Ch (11817) (IL) 60
Carlock
Carlock Menn Ch (2195) (CDC) 42
Chenoa
Meadows Menn Ch (2540) (CDC) 43
Chicago
Bethel Menn Community Ch (11825) (IL) 60
Englewood Menn Ch (11882) (IL) 61
First Menn Ch (2359) (CDC) 43
Grace Community Ch (2400) (CDC) 43
Lawndale Menn Ch (11973) (IL) 61
Living Water Community Ch (11151) (IL) 61
Cicero
Centro Cristiano Vida Abundante (28928) (IL) 60
Sonido de Alabanza (23432) (IL) 62
Danvers
North Danvers Menn Ch (2620) (CDC) 44
Delavan
Menn Ch of Dillon (11866) (IL) 62
Eureka
East Peoria Menn Ch (11940) (IL) 61
Maple Lawn Fell (10049) (IL) 62
Roanoke Menn Ch (12070) (IL) 62
Evanston
Evanston Menn Ch (11890) (CDC, IL) 42, 62
Reba Place Ch (22343) (IL) 61
Fisher
East Bend Menn Ch (11874) (IL) 61
Flanagan
Prairieview Menn Ch (12138) (CDC, IL) 44, 62
Freeport
Freeport Menn Ch (11932) (IL) 61
Henry
Trinity New Life Menn Ch (26732) (IL) 62
Hopedale
Boynton Menn Ch (2160) (CDC) 42
Hopedale Menn Ch (11957) (IL) 61
Lombard
Lombard Menn Ch (11981) (IL) 61
Markham
Community Menn Ch (28332) (CDC, IL) 42, 61
Metamora
Metamora Menn Ch (12013) (IL) 62

Moline
Templo Alabanza Menonita (13284) (CP) 48
Morton
First Menn Ch of Morton (11908) (IL) 61
Trinity Menn Ch (23549) (IL) 62
Mundelein
North Suburban Menn Ch (27557) (CDC, IL) . . .44, 62
Normal
Menn Ch of Normal (11833) (CDC, IL) 44, 62
Oak Park
Oak Park Menn Ch (24653) (CDC, IL) 44, 62
Pekin
Bethel Menn Ch (2125) (CDC) 42
Peoria
First Norwood Menn Ch (11916) (IL) 61
Joy Fell Menn Ch (27391) (CDC, IL) 43, 61
Living Love Ministries (11096) (CDC, IL) 43, 61
Roanoke
Cazenovia Menn Ch (11841) (IL) 60
Schaumburg
Christ Community Menn Ch (29397) (CDC, IL) . .42, 60
Iglesia Menonita Comunidad de Fe (2207) (CDC) . .43
St Anne
Rehoboth Menn Ch (12062) (IL) 62
Sterling
Science Ridge Menn Ch (12104) (IL) 62
Summit Argo
Iglesia Cristiana Peniel (11097) (IL) 61
Tiskilwa
Plow Creek Menn Ch (22335) (CDC, IL) 44, 62
Willow Springs Menn Ch (12146) (IL) 62
Urbana
First Menn Ch of Champaign-Urbana (11924)
(CDC, IL) 43, 61
Washington
Calvary Menn Ch (2190) (CDC) 42
West Chicago
Berhane Wongel Ethiopian Ch (11025) (IL) 60

INDIANA
Berne
First Menn Ch (2344) (CDC) 42
Bloomington
Menn Fell of Bloomington (11426) (IM) 66
Bristol
Bonneyville Menn Ch (12245) (IM) 64
Elkhart
Belmont Menn Ch (12187) (IM) 64
Church Without Walls (10244) (IM) 64
Fellowship of Hope Menn Ch (22210) (IM) 65
Hively Avenue Menn Ch (2455) (CDC) 43
House of Power (10961) (IM) 66
Olive Menn Ch (21758) (IM) 67
Prairie Street Menn Ch (12880) (IM) 67
Roselawn Menn Ch (12914) (IM) 67
Southside Fell (12930) (CDC, IM) 44, 68
Sunnyside Menn Ch (12997) (IM) 68
Fort Wayne
Carroll Community Worship Center (12153) (IM) . . .64
Fairhaven Menn Ch (12435) (IM) 65
First Menn Ch (12476) (IM) 65
Maplewood Menn Ch (2530) (CDC) 43

CONGREGATIONS BY LOCATION

7

Goshen
Assembly Menn Ch (22582) (CDC, IM) 42, 64
Benton Menn Ch (12195) (IM) 64
Berkey Avenue Menn Fell (24323) (IM) 64
Clinton Brick Menn Ch (12336) (IM) 64
Clinton Frame Menn Ch (12328) (IM) 64
College Menn Ch (12518) (IM) 65
Communion Fell (26997) (IM) 65
East Goshen Menn Ch (12393) (IM) 65
Eighth Street Menn Ch (2270) (CDC) 42
Faith Menn Ch (10127) (CDC, IM) 42, 65
Iglesia Menonita del Buen Pastor (12377) (IM) 66
North Goshen Menn Ch (21998) (IM) 67
Pleasant View Menn Ch (12872) (IM) 67
Silverwood Menn Ch (2715) (CDC) 44
Walnut Hill Menn Ch (13045) (IM) 68
Waterford Menn Ch (13060) (IM) 68
Yellow Creek Menn Ch (13128) (IM) 68
Indianapolis
First Menn Ch (12450) (IM) 65
Shalom Menn Ch (10196) (IM) 67
Kokomo
Howard-Miami Menn Ch (12583) (IM) 66
Parkview Menn Ch (12849) (IM) 67
Kouts
Hopewell Menn Ch (12575) (IM) 66
Lafayette
Lafayette Menn Fell (26021) (CDC, IM) 43, 66
LaGrange
Plato Menn Ch (12864) (IM) 67
Leo
North Leo Menn Ch (12773) (IM) 67
Loogootee
Berea Menn Ch (12203) (IM) 64
Middlebury
First Menn Ch (12468) (IM) 65
Forks Menn Ch (12492) (IM) 65
Pleasant Oaks Menn Ch (2645) (CDC) 44
Montgomery
Providence Menn Ch (12898) (IM) 67
Morgantown
Bean Blossom Menn Ch (12179) (IM) 64
Muncie
Morning Star Ch (29652) (CDC, IM) 44, 66
Nappanee
First Menn Ch (2401) (CDC) 43
Maranatha Menn Chapel (24737) (IM) 66
North Main Street Menn Ch (12781) (IM) 67
New Carlisle
Hudson Lake Menn Ch (12591) (IM) 66
New Paris
Gospel Lighthouse (12526) (IM) 65
Paoli
Paoli Menn Fell (22624) (CDC, IM) 44, 67
Rensselaer
Burr Oak Menn Ch (12278) (IM) 64
Rome City
Lake Bethel Menn Ch (12625) (IM) 66
Shipshewana
Marion Menn Ch (12708) (IM) 66
Shore Menn Ch (12963) (IM) 68
South Bend
Kern Road Menn Ch (12617) (IM) 66
Restoration Menn (10245) (IM) 67

Syracuse
Wawasee Lakeside Chapel (13078) (IM) 68
Topeka
Emma Menn Ch (12419) (IM) 65
Topeka Menn Ch (2775) (CDC) 44
Valparaiso
Valparaiso Menn Ch (13037) (IM) 68
Wakarusa
Holdeman Menn Ch (12567) (IM) 66
Warsaw
Menn Ch of Warsaw (10007) (IM) 66

IOWA
Ames
Ames Menn Ch (23424) (CDC) 42
Burlington
Peace Menn Ch (28787) (CP) 47
Cedar Falls
Cedar Falls Menn Ch (24935) (CP) 46
Des Moines
Des Moines Menn Ch (13219) (CP) 46
Donnellson
Zion Menn Ch (2860) (CP) 48
Fort Dodge
Evangelical Menn Ch (13250) (CP) 46
Iowa City
First Menn Ch of Iowa City (13276) (CP) 46
Kalona
East Union Menn Ch (13243) (CP) 46
Kalona Menn Ch (13318) (CP) 47
Lower Deer Creek Menn Ch (13334) (CP) 47
Manson
Manson Menn Ch (13342) (CP) 47
Mount Pleasant
Pleasant View Menn Ch (13425) (CP) 47
Muscatine
Muscatine Menn Ch (13375) (CP) 47
Parnell
West Union Menn Ch (13474) (CP) 48
Pulaski
Pulaski Menn Ch (2650) (CP) 47
Washington
Washington Menn Ch (13458) (CP) 48
Wayland
Bethel Menn Ch (13177) (CP) 46
Eicher Emmanuel Menn Ch (2265) (CP) 46
Sugar Creek Menn Ch (13441) (CP) 48
Wayland Menn Ch (2815) (CP) 48
Wellman
Daytonville Community Ch (13201) (CP) 46
Wellman Menn Ch (13466) (CP) 48

KANSAS
Buhler
Buhler Menn Ch (6165) (WDC) 114
Burrton
Burrton Menn Ch (6170) (WDC) 114
Canton
Spring Valley Menn Ch (18127) (SC) 104
Dodge City
Faith Menn Ch (27425) (SC, WDC) 102, 115
Elbing
Zion Menn Ch (6865) (WDC) 117

Goessel
  Alexanderwohl Menn Ch (6005) (WDC) 114
  Goessel Menn Ch (6370) (WDC) 115
Greensburg
  Greensburg Menn Ch (17939) (SC) 102
Halstead
  First Menn Ch (6374) (WDC) 115
Hanston
  Hanston Menn Ch (6430) (WDC) 115
Harper
  Crystal Springs Menn Ch (17889) (SC) 102
  Pleasant Valley Menn Ch (18051) (SC) 103
Haven
  Yoder Menn Ch (18192) (SC) 104
Hesston
  Central Heights Menn Ch (6196) (WDC) 114
  Hesston Inter-Menn Fell (17970) (SC, WDC) . .102, 116
  Hesston Menn Ch (17962) (SC) 102
  Whitestone Menn Ch (18184) (SC, WDC) 104, 117
Hillsboro
  First Menn Ch (6376) (WDC) 115
  Trinity Menn Ch (6780) (WDC) 117
Hutchinson
  First Menn Ch (6382) (WDC) 115
Inman
  Bethel Menn Ch (6095) (WDC) 114
  Hoffnungsau Menn Ch (6460) (WDC) 116
  Inman Menn Ch (6505) (WDC) 116
Kansas City
  Argentine Menn Ch (17798) (SC) 102
  Rainbow Menn Ch (18093) (WDC) 117
Kingman
  Kingman Menn Ch (6511) (WDC) 116
Lawrence
  Peace Menn Ch (23853) (SC, WDC) 103, 117
Liberal
  Calvary Menn Ch (6185) (WDC) 114
Manhattan
  Manhattan Menn Ch (24174) (SC, WDC) 103, 116
McPherson
  First Menn Ch (6391) (WDC) 115
Moundridge
  Eden Menn Ch (6255) (WDC) 115
  First Menn Ch of Christian (6330) (WDC) 115
  Hopefield Menn Ch (6470) (WDC) 116
  West Zion Menn Ch (6830) (WDC) 117
Newton
  Faith Menn Ch (6325) (WDC) 115
  First Menn Ch (6403) (WDC) 115
  New Creation Fell (6596) (WDC) 116
  Shalom Menn Ch (10130) (SC, WDC) 103, 117
  Tabor Menn Ch (6765) (WDC) 117
North Newton
  Bethel College Menn Ch (6070) (WDC) 114
Pawnee Rock
  Bergthal Menn Ch (6045) (WDC) 114
Pretty Prairie
  First Menn Ch (6315) (WDC) 115
Protection
  Protection Menn Ch (18085) (SC) 103
Ransom
  First Menn Ch (6318) (WDC) 115
Salina
  Salina Menn Ch (6691) (WDC) 117

South Hutchinson
  Faith Menn Ch (24356) (SC) 102
  South Hutchinson Menn Ch (18101) (SC) 103
Topeka
  Southern Hills Menn Ch (6740) (SC, WDC) . . .104, 117
Whitewater
  Grace Hill Menn Ch (6390) (WDC) 115
Wichita
  Hope Menn Ch (6468) (WDC) 116
  Lorraine Avenue Menn Ch (6525) (WDC) 116
  Menn Ch of the Servant (23317) (SC, WDC) . .103, 116

KENTUCKY
Ages-Brookside
  Harlan Menn Fell (23333) (IM) 65
Morgantown
  Ridgeview Menn Ch (12740) (IM) 67
Talcum
  Talcum Menn Ch (13003) (IM) 68
West Liberty
  West Liberty Menn Ch (18457) (VA) 112

LOUISIANA
Buras
  Lighthouse Fell (25403) (GS) 58
Des Allemands
  Des Allemands Menn Ch (17897) (GS) 58
Metairie
  Iglesia Amor Viviente (28258) (GS) 58

MAINE
Farmingdale
  Kennebec Menn Ch (22889) (LAN) 76

MARYLAND
Accident
  Glade Menn Ch (10231) (ALL) 36
Baltimore
  Ethiopian Evangelical Ch of Baltimore (11108)
    (LAN) 74
  North Baltimore Menn Ch (27920) (ACC) 40
  Wilkens Avenue Menn Ch (15081) (LAN) 81
Boonsboro
  Mount Zion Menn Ch (14746) (FRK) 56
Ellicott City
  First Menn Ch of Columbia (14027) (LAN) 74
Grantsville
  Oak Grove Menn Ch (10348) (ALL) 36
Hagerstown
  Community Menn Ch (14738) (FRK) 55
  Hebron Menn Ch (23572) (ACC) 39
  North Side Menn Ch (16345) (FRK) 56
Hyattsville
  Hyattsville Menn Ch (10223) (ALL) 36
Jessup
  Guilford Road Menn Ch (14209) (LAN) 74
Laurel
  Capital Christian Fell (13805) (LAN) 72
Mount Airy
  Mount Airy Menn Ch (14753) (LAN) 78
Mt Savage
  Red Run Menn Ch (10397) (ALL) 37
Oakland
  Gortner Union Ch (22632) (ALL) 36

CONGREGATIONS BY LOCATION

7

Ocean City
Ocean City Menn Christian Fell (26476) (ACC) 40
Pinto
Pinto Menn Ch (10363) (ALL) 37
Poolesville
Dawsonville Menn Ch (13847) (LAN) 73
Swanton
Meadow Mountain Menn Ch (10322) (ALL) 36
Walkersville
Faith Community Menn Ch (11309) (FRK) 55
Westover
Holly Grove Menn Ch (16089) (ACC) 39

MASSACHUSETTS
Dorchester
Boston Bethel Missionary Ch (11433) (LAN) 71
Malden
Chinese Christian Ch of Malden (10743) (LAN) 72
Needham
Good Shepherd Christian Fell (25817) (LAN) 74
Newton
Boston Chinese Ch of Saving Grace (27722)
(LAN) 71
Somerville
Menn Congregation of Boston (16246)
(ACC, EDC) 40, 50

MICHIGAN
Ann Arbor
Ann Arbor Menn Ch (13508) (CDC, IM) 42, 64
Shalom Community Ch (23242) (CDC, IM) 44, 67
Ashley
Bethel Menn Ch (12237) (IM) 64
Battle Creek
Pine Grove Menn Ch (12559) (IM) 67
Brutus
Maple River Menn Ch (12682) (IM) 66
Burr Oak
Locust Grove Menn Ch (12666) (IM) 66
Centreville
Wasepi Menn Chapel (13052) (IM) 68
Comins
Comins Menn Ch (2205) (CDC) 42
Concord
Liberty Menn Ch (12641) (IM) 66
Constantine
Florence Church of the Brethren (11315) (CDC) . . .43
Detroit
Community Christian Fell (10243) (IM) 65
Peace Community Menn Ch (12385) (IM) 67
East Lansing
MSU Menn Fell (12757) (CDC, IM) 44, 67
Engadine
Wildwood Menn Ch (13110) (IM) 68
Escanaba
Soo Hill Community Ch (12971) (IM) 68
Germfask
Germfask Menn Ch (12500) (IM) 65
Grand Marais
Grand Marais Menn Ch (12542) (IM) 65
Gulliver
Maple Grove Menn Ch (12690) (IM) 66
Harbor Springs
Stutsmanville Chapel (12989) (IM) 68

Kalkaska
Coldsprings Menn Ch (12344) (IM) 65
Manistique
Cedar Grove Menn Ch (12302) (IM) 64
Menominee
Menominee River Fell (10135) (IL) 62
Midland
Midland Menn Ch (12724) (IM) 66
Naubinway
Naubinway Menn Ch (12807) (IM) 67
Rexton Menn Ch (12906) (IM) 67
Petoskey
Hilltop Menn Fell (12856) (IM) 66
Pigeon
Michigan Avenue Menn Ch (12716) (IM) 66
Pinckney
Good News Community Chapel (12286) (IM) 65
Saginaw
Grace Chapel (12534) (IM) 65
Ninth Street Menn Ch (12815) (IM) 67
Sault Ste Marie
Wayside Menn Ch (13086) (IM) 68
Sturgis
Christian Fell Center (28951) (IM) 64
Toledo Menn Ch (15685) (OH) 91
Waldron
Salem Menn Ch (16618) (OH) 91

MINNESOTA
Frazee
Lake Region Menn Ch (15578) (NC) 85
International Falls
Point of Pines Menn Ch (15610) (NC) 85
Jackson
Hilltop Community Ch (13136) (CP) 47
Minneapolis
Faith Menn Ch (23127) (CP) 46
Mountain Lake
Bethel Menn Ch (4120) (CP) 46
First Menn Ch (4397) (CP) 46
Lao Christian Fell (4496) (CP) 47
Ogema
Strawberry Lake Menn Ch (15644) (NC) 85
Rochester
Rochester Menn Ch (4667) (CP) 47
Shoreview
Emmanuel Menn Ch (11125) (CP) 46
St Paul
St Paul Menn Fell (28555) (CP) 48
United Hmong Menn Ch (4480) (CP) 48

MISSISSIPPI
Gulfport
Gulfhaven Menn Ch (17947) (GS) 58
Jackson
Open Door Menn Ch (22046) (GS) 58
Macon
Choctaw Christian Ch (15891) (GS) 58
Cornerstone Community Ch (16212) (GS) 58
Meridian
Jubilee Menn Ch (24547) (GS) 58
Philadelphia
Nanih Waiya Indian Menn Ch (16352) (GS) 58
Pearl River Menn Ch (21790) (GS) 58

Quitman
Grace Menn Christian Fell (11144) (GS) 58

MISSOURI
Birch Tree
Berea Menn Community Ch (17806) (SC) 102
Garden City
Sycamore Grove Menn Ch (18135) (SC) 104
Leonard
Mount Pisgah Menn Ch (18002) (SC) 103
Palmyra
Pea Ridge Menn Ch (18044) (SC) 103
St Louis
Bethesda Menn Ch (17814) (IL) 60
St Louis Menn Fell (24182) (CDC, IL) 44, 62
Warsaw
Evening Shade Menn Ch (17913) (SC) 102

MONTANA
Bloomfield
Bethlehem Menn Ch (4145) (NC) 84
Red Top Menn Ch (15628) (NC) 85
Busby
White River Cheyenne Menn Ch (4171) (CP) 48
Colstrip
Ashland Christian Fell (4025) (CP) 46
Dagmar
Coalridge Menn Ch (15529) (NC) 84
Glendive
White Chapel Menn Ch (15594) (CP) 48
Kalispell
Mountain View Menn Ch (10082) (NWMC, PNW) . .44
Lame Deer
Lame Deer Menn Ch (4635) (CP) 47
Wolf Point
Bethel Menn Ch (4130) (CP) 46

NEBRASKA
Beatrice
Beatrice Menn Ch (6030) (WDC) 114
First Menn Ch (6341) (WDC) 115
Beemer
Beemer Menn Ch (13144) (CP) 46
Henderson
Bethesda Menn Ch (4135) (CP) 46
Lincoln
First Menn Ch (13268) (CP) 46
Milford
Bellwood Menn Ch (13151) (CP) 46
Beth-El Menn Ch (13169) (CP) 46
Milford Menn Ch (13367) (CP) 47
Omaha
New Hope Menn Ch (10992) (CP) 47
Northside Christian Family Center (24166) (CP) 47
Shickley
Salem Menn Ch (13433) (CP) 47
Wood River
Wood River Menn Ch (13482) (CP) 48

NEW JERSEY
Alpha
Alpha Menn Ch (23051) (FRC) 52
Camden
Iglesia Manantial de Vida (29116) (LAN) 75

Carney's Point
Friendship Menn Chapel* (15008) (LAN) 74
New Song Congregation (11581) (LAN) 79
Dover
Garden Chapel (11544) (FRC) 52
Marlton
Crossroads Christian Community (10631) (LAN) . . .73
Norma
Norma Menn Ch (14860) (LAN) 79
Trenton
Iglesia Menonita Puerta de Sion (22897) (LAN) 75
Nueva Vida en Cristo (11436) (LAN) 79
Vineland
Faro Ardiente (22111) (LAN) 74

NEW MEXICO
Albuquerque
Albuquerque Menn Ch (11311) (RM) 99
Carlsbad
Carlsbad Menn Ch (20818) (RM) 99
Farmington
Light of Life Menn Ch (10656) (RM) 100

NEW YORK
Akron
Clarence Center-Akron Menn Ch (16980) (NY) 83
Alden
Alden Menn Ch (10496) (NY) 83
Bolivar
Kossuth Community Chapel (25395) (LAN) 76
Bronx
Emmanuel Worship Center (10016) (LAN) 73
Evangelical Garifuna (29660) (LAN) 74
Friendship Community Ch (16253) (ACC) 39
Iglesia Evangelica Menonita Eben-Ezer (28589)
(ACC) 40
King of Glory Tabernacle (14043) (LAN) 76
North Bronx Menn Ch (29561) (LAN) 79
Brooklyn
Believers Menn Garifuna Ministries (27599)
(LAN) 71
First Menn Ch (15958) (ACC) 39
Iglesia Christiana Valle de Jesus (25338) (LAN) 75
Iglesia Unida de Avivamiento (22350) (LAN) 75
International Christian Community Ch (11123)
(LAN) 76
Menn Evangelical Tabernacle (26849) (LAN) 78
Buffalo
Westside Menn Ch (10068) (NY) 83
Castorland
Pine Grove Menn Ch (11072) (NY) 83
Corning
Community Menn Fell of Corning (23614) (NY) 83
Flushing
Immanuel Community Ch (26468) (ACC) 40
Hammondsport
Pleasant Valley Menn Ch (15057) (NY) 83
Jamaica
Ephesians Menn Ch (23762) (ACC) 39
Lowville
First Menn Ch of New Bremen (21964) (NY) 83
Lowville Menn Ch (10892) (NY) 83
New York
Manhattan Menn Fell (3602) (ACC) 40
Seventh Avenue Menn Ch (15198) (LAN) 80

Penfield
Rochester Area Menn Fell (21956) (NY) 83
Rexville
West Union Menn Ch (15412) (NY) 83
Rochester
Bethsaida Evangelical Ch (11118) (NY) 83
Schoharie
Grace Fell (11170) (NY) .83
Staten Island
Redeeming Grace Fell (24588) (LAN) 80
Watertown
Watertown Menn Ch (21980) (NY) 83
Webster
Jesus Ch (10138) (NY) 83
Wellsville
Independence Gospel Fell Menn (14357) (NY) 83
Yorks Corners Menn Ch (15487) (NY) 83
Williamsville
Harris Hill Menn Ch (10504) (NY) 83

NORTH CAROLINA
Asheville
Asheville Menn Ch (24281) (VA) 109
Durham
Durham Menn Ch (18481) (VA) 110
Greensboro
Greensboro Menn Fell (29744) (VA) 110
Hickory
Hickory Menn Ch (18580) (VA) 110
Mountain View Menn Ch (18713) (VA) 111
Raleigh
Raleigh Menn Ch (28266) (VA) 111
Robbins
Iglesia el Verbo (11571) (LAN) 75
Rocky Mount
Fellowship of Christ (23473) (VA) 110
Sanford
Iglesia Menonita Bethel Ch (11435) (LAN) 75

NORTH DAKOTA
Alsen
Swiss Menn Ch (4755) (CP) 48
Casselton
Casselton Menn Ch (15511) (NC) 84
Surrey
Prairie Peace Fell (15545) (NC) 85
Wolford
Lakeview Menn Ch (15586) (NC) 85

OHIO
Archbold
Central Menn Ch (15842) (OH) 88
Iglesia Menonita del Buen Pastor (16022) (OH) 89
Zion Menn Ch (16873) (OH) 92
Aurora
Aurora Menn Ch (15677) (OH) 88
Barberton
Summit Menn Ch (16741) (OH) 91
Bedford Heights
Friendship Menn Ch (16006) (OH) 89
University Euclid Christ New Testament (16774)
(OH) 91
Bellefontaine
Jubilee Menn Ch (11111) (CDC, OH) 43, 89

Berlin
Berlin Menn Ch (15727) (OH) 88
Bluffton
First Menn Ch (2347) (CDC) 43
Burton
New Mercies Community Ch (10899) (OH) 90
Canton
First Menn Ch (15982) (OH) 89
Chesterville
Gilead Menn Ch (16014) (OH) 89
Cincinnati
Cincinnati Menn Fell (23325) (CDC, OH) 42, 88
Springdale Chapel (16717) (OH) 91
Cleveland
Lee Heights Community Ch (16139) (OH) 89
Columbiana
Midway Menn Ch (16261) (OH) 90
Columbus
Agora Christian Fell (11103) (CDC, OH) 42, 88
Columbus Menn Ch (16378) (CDC, OH) 42, 88
Defiance
Primera Iglesia Menonita (15974) (OH) 91
Dover
Dover Christian Fell (10709) (CDC, OH) 42, 89
Elida
Pike Menn Ch (16469) (OH) 90
Salem Menn Ch (16634) (OH) 91
Elyria
Peace Menn Ch (25825) (OH) 90
Fairpoint
Fairpoint Menn Ch (15925) (OH) 89
Hartville
Hartville Menn Ch (16048) (OH) 89
Helena
Primera Iglesia Menonita (24695) (OH) 91
Jackson
Hillside Chapel (16071) (OH) 89
Kalida
Kalida Family Outreach Center (16311) (OH) 89
Kidron
Kidron Menn Ch (16113) (OH) 89
Salem Menn Ch (2680) (CDC) 44
Sonnenberg Menn Ch (18846) (OH) 91
Leetonia
Leetonia Menn Ch (16147) (OH) 89
Lima
Lima Menn Ch (16402) (CDC, OH) 43, 89
Logan
St Johns Menn Chapel (16725) (OH) 91
Louisville
Beech Menn Ch (15701) (OH) 88
Stoner Heights Menn Ch (16733) (OH) 91
Lucasville
Owl Creek Menn Ch (16451) (OH) 90
Millersburg
Martins Creek Menn Ch (16196) (OH) 90
Millersburg Menn Ch (16279) (OH) 90
Moorhead Menn Ch (16295) (OH) 90
Monclova
Emmanuel Menn Ch (10037) (OH) 89
New Carlisle
Huber Menn Ch (16097) (OH) 89
North Canton
Dayspring Christian Fell (27334) (OH) 89

North Lawrence
Pleasant View Menn Ch (16527) (OH) 90
North Lima
North Lima Menn Ch (16337) (OH) 90
Orrville
Chestnut Ridge Menn Ch (18416) (VA) 109
Martins Menn Ch (16204) (OH) 90
Orrville Menn Ch (16444) (OH) 90
Pandora
Grace Menn Ch (2420) (CDC) 43
St John Menn Ch (2670) (CDC) 44
Pedro
Wayside Chapel (16816) (OH) 92
Plain City
Cornerstone Menn Fell (28225) (OH) 88
Sharon Menn Ch (16659) (OH) 91
Rittman
Bethel Menn Ch (15768) (OH) 88
Crown Hill Menn Ch (15883) (OH) 88
Smithville
Oak Grove Menn Ch (16428) (CDC, OH) 44, 90
Smithville Menn Ch (16667) (OH) 91
Springfield
Southside Christian Fell (24034) (OH) 91
Stryker
Lockport Menn Ch (16154) (OH) 90
Pine Grove Menn Ch (16477) (OH) 90
Sugarcreek
First Menn Ch (2324) (CDC) 43
Thurman
Community Christian Fell (16485) (OH) 88
Toledo
Toledo Menn Ch (15685) (OH, AAMA) 91
Trenton
Trenton Menn Ch (2779) (CDC) 44
Vinton
Fellowship Chapel (11308) (OH) 89
Wadsworth
First Menn Ch (2333) (CDC) 43
Walnut Creek
Walnut Creek Menn Ch (16808) (OH) 91
Wauseon
Inlet Menn Ch (16105) (OH) 89
North Clinton Menn Ch (16329) (OH) 90
Tedrow Menn Ch (16766) (OH) 91
West Clinton Menn Ch (16824) (OH) 92
West Lafayette
Lafayette Christian Fell (28191) (OH) 89
West Liberty
Bethel Menn Ch (15750) (OH) 88
Oak Grove Menn Ch (16410) (OH) 90
South Union Menn Ch (16683) (OH) 91
Winesburg
Longenecker Menn Ch (16162) (OH) 90
Wooster
Salem Menn Ch (16626) (OH) 91
Wooster Menn Ch (16840) (OH) 92
Youngstown
Berean Fell Ch (15719) (OH) 88

OKLAHOMA
Canton
Zion Menn Ch (6845) .115

Clinton
First Menn Ch (6362) (WDC) 115
Koinonia Menn Ch (6575) (WDC) 116
Cordell
Herold Menn Ch (6445) (WDC) 115
Deer Creek
Deer Creek Menn Ch (6230) (WDC) 114
Enid
Grace Menn Ch (6410) (WDC) 115
Ft Cobb
Greenfield Menn Ch (6425) (WDC) 115
Hammon
Bethel Menn Ch (6085) (WDC) 114
Hydro
Bethel Menn Ch (6090) (WDC) 114
Pleasant View Menn Ch (18069) (SC) 103
Inola
Eden Menn Ch (6250) (WDC) 115
Seiling
Menn Indian Ch (6558) (WDC) 116
Spencer
Joy Menn Ch (6642) (WDC) 116
Turpin
Turpin Menn Ch (6785) (WDC) 117

OREGON
Albany
Albany Menn Ch (17434) (PNW) 93
Plainview Menn Ch (17590) (PNW) 94
Aurora
Calvary Menn Ch (5180) (PNW) 93
Canby
Pacific Covenant Menn Ch (10142) (PNW) 94
Corvallis
Corvallis Menn Fell (10141) (PNW) 94
Prince of Peace Menn Ch (17509) (PNW) 95
Eugene
Eugene Menn Ch (17517) (PNW) 94
Hubbard
Zion Menn Ch (17640) (PNW) 95
Lebanon
Lebanon Menn Ch (17574) (PNW) 94
Logsden
Logsden Neighborhood Ch (17582) (PNW) 94
McMinnville
First Menn Ch (10278) (PNW) 94
Oak Grove
Ministerios Restauracion (11073) (PNW) 94
Portland
Peace Menn Ch (24380) (PNW) 94
Portland Menn Ch (17608) (PNW) 94
Salem
Jerusalem Iglesia (28315) (PNW) 94
Salem Menn Ch (17616) (PNW) 95
Western Menn Ch (17632) (PNW) 95
Sweet Home
River of Life Fell (10270) (PNW) 95
Woodburn
Comunidad Cristiana de Vida Nueva (11533)
(PNW) 94
Iglesia Menonita Pentecostes (23556) (PNW) 94

CONGREGATIONS BY LOCATION

7

PENNSYLVANIA

Adamstown
Gehman Menn Ch (14100) (LAN) 74

Akron
Akron Menn Ch (15651) (ACC) 39
Metzler Menn Ch (14613) (LAN) 78
Pilgrims Menn Ch (24513) (LAN) 79

Allentown
First Menn Ch (3338) (EDC) 50

Altoona
Canan Station Menn Ch (10173) (ALL) 36
Mill Run Chapel (10330) (ALL) 36

Ambler
Ambler Menn Ch (11353) (FRC) 52

Atglen
Maple Grove Menn Ch of Atglen (16188) (ACC) . . .40

Athens
New Life Menn Ch (10013) (FRC) 53

Bainbridge
Goods Menn Ch (14142) (LAN) 74

Bally
Bally Menn Ch (11361) (FRC) 52

Beaver Springs
Manbeck Menn Ch (10280) (ALL) 36

Belleville
Maple Grove Menn Ch (21931) (ALL) 36
Rockville Menn Ch (10405) (ALL) 37

Bernville
New Life Christian Fell (29249) (ACC) 40

Bethel
Meckville Menn Ch (14597) (LAN) 78
Schubert Menn Ch (15180) (LAN) 80

Bethlehem
Bethlehem Community Fell (29124) (LAN) 71
Steel City Menn Ch (11759) (FRC) 53

Bird-in-Hand
Stumptown Menn Ch (15297) (LAN) 80

Birdsboro
Zion Menn Ch?Birdsboro (16865) (ACC) 40

Blooming Glen
Blooming Glen Menn Ch (11403) (FRC) 52

Bowmansville
Bowmansville Menn Ch (13623) (LAN) 71

Boyertown
Ark Bible Chapel (15669) (ACC) 39
Boyertown Menn Ch (11411) (FRC) 52

Bristol
New Beginnings Community Ch (11429) (FRC) 53

Camp Hill
Lao Menn Fell/Slate Hill (11560) (LAN) 76
Slate Hill Menn Ch (15206) (LAN) 80

Canadensis
Spruce Lake Fell (26203) (FRC) 53

Canton
Canton Menn Ch* (25098) (LAN) 72
Wheelerville Menn Ch (15453) (LAN) 81

Chambersburg
Cedar Street Menn Ch (19000) (FRK) 55
Chambersburg Menn Ch (19018) (FRK) 55
Marion Menn Ch (19034) (FRK) 56
Pleasant View Menn Ch (19042) (FRK) 56
Pond Bank Menn Ch (19059) (FRK) 56
Rock Hill Menn Ch (19067) (FRK) 56

Chester
Way Through Christ (10073) (LAN) 81

Christiana
Andrews Bridge Christian Fell (11428) (ACC) 39

Coatesville
Coatesville Menn Ch (13755) (LAN) 72
Newlinville Menn Ch (14845) (LAN) 79
Sandy Hill Menn Ch (16642) (ACC) 40

Collegeville
Providence Menn Ch (11668) (FRC) 53

Columbia
Chestnut Hill Menn Ch (13714) (LAN) 72
Columbia Menn Ch* (13771) (LAN) 72

Conestoga
Life Menn Fell* (11294) (LAN) 77

Conneaut Lake
Sunnyside Menn Ch (16758) (OH) 91

Corry
Beaverdam Menn Ch (22004) (OH) 88

Davidsville
Carpenter Park Menn Ch (10181) (ALL) 36
Kaufman Menn Ch (10256) (ALL) 36

Denver
Red Run Menn Ch (15115) (LAN) 80

Downingtown
Cornerstone CELLebration Ch and Ministries (10650)
(LAN) 72
Downing Hills Christian Fell (13896) (LAN) 73

Doylestown
Doylestown Menn Ch (11445) (FRC) 52

Duncansville
Roaring Spring Menn Ch (3665) (EDC) 50

East Earl
Bethany Grace Fell (15735) (ACC) 39
Churchtown Menn Ch* (13748) (LAN) 72
Weaverland Menn Ch* (15420) (LAN) 81

East Petersburg
East Petersburg Menn Ch (13946) (LAN) 73

Easton
River of God Fell (11452) (FRC) 53

Elizabethtown
Bossler Menn Ch (13615) (LAN) 71
Cedar Hill Community Ch (13706) (LAN) 72
Elizabethtown Menn Ch (13953) (LAN) 73
Risser Menn Ch (15123) (LAN) 80

Ephrata
Ephrata Menn Ch (13961) (LAN) 73
Hinkletown Menn Ch* (14316) (LAN) 75
Indiantown Menn Ch* (14365) (LAN) 76
Martindale Menn Ch* (14548) (LAN) 77
New Life Fell (27052) (LAN) 79

Fairfield
Fairfield Menn Ch (3300) (EDC) 50

Fleetwood
Hope Community Ch (10039) (ACC) 39

Folcraft
Delaware County Fell (11562) (LAN) 73

Franconia
Franconia Menn Ch (11502) (FRC) 52

Frazer
Frazer Menn Ch (14050) (LAN) 74

Frederick
Frederick Menn Ch (11528) (FRC) 52

Gap
Old Road Menn Ch (14928) (LAN) 79
Gettysburg
Bethel Menn Ch (15743) (ACC) 39
Goodville
Goodville Menn Ch (14159) (LAN) 74
Gordonville
Ridgeview Menn Ch (16576) (ACC) 40
Greencastle
Cedar Grove Menn Ch (15834) (ACC) 39
Salem Ridge Menn Ch (19075) (FRK) 56
Halifax
Halifax Community Fell (27060) (LAN) 75
Harleysville
Salford Menn Ch (11718) (FRC) 53
Harrisburg
Herr Street Menn Ch (14266) (LAN) 75
Locust Lane Menn Chapel* (14498) (LAN) 77
New Hope Community Ch (11561) (LAN) 79
Peace Chapel (25353) (LAN) 79
Hatfield
Plains Menn Ch (11643) (FRC) 53
Havertown
Kapatiran Christian Ch (11102) (LAN) 76
Hershey
Stauffer Menn Ch (15230) (LAN) 80
Holland
Church of the Good Samaritans (3200) (EDC) 50
Hollidaysburg
Cornerstone Fell Menn Ch (29942) (ALL) 36
Hollsopple
Blough Menn Ch (10157) (ALL) 35
Living Way Fell (11434) (ALL) 36
Thomas Menn Ch (10454) (ALL) 37
Honey Brook
Cambridge Menn Ch* (13680) (LAN) 72
Rockville Menn Ch (16600) (ACC) 40
Huntingdon Valley
Grace Bible Fell of Huntingdon Valley (3379) (EDC) .50
Jersey Shore
Praise Center (24844) (LAN) 79
Johnstown
Crossroads Community Ch (10488) (ALL) 36
First Menn Ch (10215) (ALL) 36
Stahl Menn Ch (10447) (ALL) 37
Kennett Square
Kennett Square Menn Ch* (14381) (LAN) 76
Kinzers
Hershey Menn Ch* (14282) (LAN) 75
Kinzer Menn Ch (14399) (LAN) 76
Meadville Menn Ch (14571) (LAN) 77
Millwood Menn Ch* (14654) (LAN) 78
Kirkwood
Mount Vernon Menn Ch* (14720) (LAN) 78
Kulpsville
Towamencin Menn Ch (11783) (FRC) 54
Lancaster
ACTS Covenant Fell (28969) (LAN) 71
Bethel Menn Ch of Lancaster (3100) (EDC) 50
Blossom Hill Menn Ch (14795) (LAN) 71
Christ the King Community Ch* (27730) (LAN) 72
Community Menn Ch of Lancaster (27441) (ACC) . .39
Covenant Menn Ch (10055) (LAN) 73
Crossroads Menn (15172) (LAN) 73

East Chestnut Street Menn Ch (13912) (LAN) 73
El Buen Pastor (14167) (LAN) 73
First Deaf Menn Ch (14019) (LAN) 74
Habecker Menn Ch (14217) (LAN) 75
Iglesia Menonita Roca de Salvacion (11301)
(LAN) 75
James Street Menn Ch (15396) (LAN) 76
Lancaster Anabaptist Fell (11302) (LAN) 76
Landis Valley Menn Ch (14431) (LAN) 76
Laurel Street Menn Ch (14449) (LAN) 76
Lyndon Menn Ch (14514) (LAN) 77
Mellinger Menn Ch (14605) (LAN) 78
Neffsville Menn Ch (16360) (ACC) 40
New Danville Menn Ch (14837) (LAN) 78
River Corner Menn Ch (15131) (LAN) 80
Rohrerstown Menn Ch (15156) (LAN) 80
Rossmere Menn Ch (15164) (LAN) 80
Sunnyside Menn Ch (15305) (LAN) 80
Tinsae Kristos Evangelical Ch (11566) (LAN) 81
West End Menn Fell (11174) (LAN) 81
Witmer Heights Menn Ch (11120) (LAN) 81
Landisville
Landisville Menn Ch (14423) (LAN) 76
Langhorne
MillCreek Community Ch (29348) (FRC) 52
Lansdale
Covenant Community Fell (29306) (FRC) 52
Grace Menn Ch (3415) (EDC) 50
Lebanon
Cristo es la Respuesta (10342) (LAN) 73
Freedom in Christ Fell (11563) (LAN) 74
Gingrichs Menn Ch (14118) (LAN) 74
Krall Menn Ch (14407) (LAN) 76
Lebanon Christian Fell (24562) (LAN) 76
Luz de Salvacion (26716) (LAN) 77
Leola
Forest Hills Menn Ch (16287) (ACC) 39
Groffdale Menn Ch (14191) (LAN) 75
Millport Menn Ch (14621) (LAN) 78
Line Lexington
Line Lexington Menn Ch (11593) (FRC) 52
Listie
New Life Menn Ch (10740) (ALL) 36
Lititz
Derry Menn Ch (13862) (LAN) 73
Erb Menn Ch (13979) (LAN) 73
Hammer Creek Menn Ch* (14233) (LAN) 75
Hess Menn Ch (14308) (LAN) 75
Lititz Menn Ch (14480) (LAN) 77
Manchester
Christian Community Fell (25304) (LAN) 72
Manheim
Erisman Menn Ch (13987) (LAN) 74
Grace Community Fell (14084) (LAN) 74
Hernley Menn Ch (14290) (LAN) 75
Kauffman Menn Ch (14373) (LAN) 76
Manheim Menn Ch* (14530) (LAN) 77
Marietta
Marietta Community Chapel (24224) (LAN) 77
Martinsburg
Martinsburg Menn Ch (10298) (ALL) 36
Masontown
Masontown Menn Ch (10306) (ALL) 36
Mercersburg
Mercersburg Menn Ch (19109) (FRK) 56

CONGREGATIONS BY LOCATION

7

Middletown
Fountain of Life Ch (25320) (LAN) 74
Mifflin
Living Water Christian Fell (11567) (LAN) 77
Mifflinburg
Boyer Menn Ch (10165) (ALL) 36
Buffalo Menn Ch* (13631) (LAN) 71
Mifflintown
Cornerstone Community Menn Ch (3543) (EDC) . . .50
Lost Creek Menn Ch* (14506) (LAN) 77
Millersville
Millersville Menn Ch (14639) (LAN) 78
Milton
Community Menn Fell (13540) (LAN) 72
Monroeton
West Franklin Menn Ch (15404) (LAN) 81
Morgantown
Conestoga Menn Ch (15875) (ACC) 39
Morris
Menn Bible Fell (11619) (FRC) 52
Morris Run
Calvary Menn Fell (14670) (LAN) 71
Mount Joy
Mount Joy Menn Ch (14688) (LAN) 78
Mount Union
Otelia Menn Ch (10355) (ALL) 36
Mountain Top
Cornerstone Christian Fell (27193) (LAN) 72
Mountville
Mountville Menn Ch* (14696) (LAN) 78
Mt Pleasant Mills
Susquehanna Menn Ch* (15313) (LAN) 81
Nanticoke
Nanticoke Christian Fell (25809) (LAN) 78
Nazareth
Maranatha Family Christian Fell (10119) (LAN) 77
New Castle
Maple Grove Menn Ch (16170) (OH) 90
New Holland
Lichty Menn Ch* (14464) (LAN) 77
New Holland Menn Ch (14811) (LAN) 78
New Holland Spanish Menn (14704) (LAN) 78
Village Chapel Menn Ch (22491) (LAN) 81
Welsh Mountain Menn Ch (22061) (LAN) 81
New Providence
New Providence Menn Ch (14829) (LAN) 79
Newville
Diller Menn Ch (13888) (LAN) 73
Norristown
Methacton Menn Ch (11601) (FRC) 52
Norristown New Life Menn Ch (10125) (FRC) 53
Oley
Oley Menn Ch (16436) (ACC) 40
Oxford
Media Menn Ch (16238) (ACC) 40
Palmyra
East Hanover Menn Ch (13938) (LAN) 73
Paradise
Mt Pleasant Menn Ch (14712) (LAN) 78
Parkesburg
Parkesburg Menn Ch (14985) (LAN) 79
Peach Bottom
Living Stones Fell* (10155) (LAN) 77
Mechanic Grove Menn Ch* (14589) (LAN) 77

Pen Argyl
Great Shepherd Christian Fell (13557) (LAN) 74
Pennsburg
Finland Menn Ch (11486) (FRC) 52
Shalom Christian Fell (10018) (FRC) 53
Perkasie
Deep Run Menn Ch East (11437) (FRC) 52
Deep Run West Menn Ch (3225) (EDC) 50
Perkasie Menn Ch (11627) (FRC) 53
Perkiomenville
Perkiomenville Menn Ch (11635) (FRC) 53
Philadelphia
Abundant Life Chinese Menn Ch* (10102) (LAN) . .71
Arca de Salvacion (22459) (LAN) 71
Christian Life Menn Fell (10122) (LAN) 72
Comunidad de Amor (3212) (EDC) 50
Diamond Street Menn Ch (13870) (LAN) 73
Germantown Menn Ch (22079) (EDC) 50
Indonesian Fell (11568) (LAN) 76
Love Truth Chinese Menn Ch (27995) (LAN) 77
New Mercies Menn Ch (10293) (LAN) 79
Oxford Circle Menn Ch (14951) (LAN) 79
Philadelphia Cambodian Menn Ch (10075) (LAN) . .79
Vietnamese Menn Ch (27045) (LAN) 81
West Philadelphia Menn Fell (27276) (FRC) 54
Phoenixville
Hope Community Fell (11579) (ACC) 39
Pine Grove
Roedersville Menn Ch (15149) (LAN) 80
Pittsburgh
Pittsburgh Menn Ch (10371) (ALL) 37
Port Allegany
Birch Grove Menn Ch (15792) (ACC) 39
Pottsville
Palo Alto Menn Ch (14969) (LAN) 79
Quakertown
Rocky Ridge Menn Ch (11684) (FRC) 53
Salem Menn Ch (11700) (FRC) 53
Swamp Menn Ch (11767) (FRC) 53
West Swamp Menn Ch (3825) (EDC) 50
Quarryville
Quarryville Community Fell (11104) (ACC) 40
Reading
Hampden Menn Ch (15354) (LAN) 75
Hopewell MennReading (25999) (ACC) 39
Luz Verdadera (15107) (LAN) 77
New Revival Menn Ch (11570) (LAN) 79
Shiloh Menn Ch* (10765) (LAN) 80
South Seventh Street Menn Ch (15222) (LAN) 80
Reedsville
Barrville Menn Ch (10140) (ALL) 35
Reinholds
Emmanuel Menn Ch (3285) (EDC) 50
Richfield
Lauver Menn Ch* (14456) (LAN) 76
Schwenksville
Hersteins Menn Ch (11569) (FRC) 52
New Eden Fell (3260) (EDC) 50
Scottdale
Kingview Menn Ch (10264) (ALL) 36
Menn Ch of Scottdale (10413) (ALL) 36
Skippack
Wellspring Ch of Skippack (11726) (FRC) 54

Souderton
  Souderton Menn Ch (11734) (FRC) 53
  Vietnamese Gospel Menn Ch (11128) (FRC) 54
  Zion Menn Ch (3880) (EDC) 50
Spartansburg
  Valley View Menn Ch (16782) (OH) 91
Spring City
  Vincent Menn Ch (11809) (FRC) 54
Spring Mount
  Spring Mount Menn Ch (11742) (FRC) 53
Springs
  Springs Menn Ch (10439) (ALL) 37
State College
  University Menn Ch (10470) (ALL) 37
Steelton
  Steelton Menn Ch (15248) (LAN) 80
Stevens
  Blainsport Menn Ch (13607) (LAN) 71
Strasburg
  Strasburg Menn Ch* (15271) (LAN) 80
Susquehanna
  Lakeview Menn Ch (11577) (FRC) 52
Talmage
  Carpenter Community Ch (13698) (LAN) 72
Telford
  Rockhill Menn Ch (11692) (FRC) 53
Temple
  Alsace Christian Fell (13490) (LAN) 71
Terre Hill
  Cedar Lane Chapel (11580) (LAN) 72
Thompsontown
  Delaware Menn Ch* (13854) (LAN) 73
Trout Run
  Mountain View Fell (29975) (LAN) 78
Upper Darby
  Ethiopian Evangelical Ch of Philadelphia
  (10194) (LAN) 74
Warfordsburg
  Bethel Community Ch (18994) (FRK) 55
  Black Oak Menn Ch (15800) (ACC) 39
Washington Boro
  Masonville Menn Ch (14562) (LAN) 77
Watsontown
  Beaver Run Menn Ch (10236) (LAN) 71
Wernersville
  Green Terrace Menn Ch (14183) (LAN) 74
Whitehall
  Whitehall Menn Ch (10114) (FRC) 54
Williamsport
  Agape Fell* (15016) (LAN) 71
Willow Hill
  Shady Pine Menn Ch (19083) (FRK) 56
Willow Street
  Byerland Menn Ch (13656) (LAN) 71
  University Christian Fell* (10188) (LAN) 81
  Willow Street Menn Ch (15461) (LAN) 81
Wyncote
  Salam Menn Fell (11099) (LAN) 80
Yorkanna
  Stony Brook Menn Ch (15255) (LAN) 80
Zionsville
  Upper Milford Menn Ch (3800) (EDC) 50

SOUTH DAKOTA
Avon
  Friedensberg Bible Ch (4350) (CP) 46
Bridgewater
  Neu Hutterthal Menn Ch (4610) (CP) 47
  Zion Menn Ch (4855) (CP) 48
Doland
  Emmanuel Menn Ch (4275) (CP) 46
Freeman
  Bethany Menn Ch (4055) (CP) 46
  Hutterthal Menn Ch (4490) (CP) 47
  Salem Menn Ch (4675) (CP) 47
  Salem-Zion Menn Ch (4690) (CP) 47
Sioux Falls
  Good Shepherd Community Ch (4375) (CP) 47
  Sermon on the Mount Menn Ch (24018) (CP) 47

TENNESSEE
Antioch
  Harmony Christian Fell (28035) (IM) 65
Knoxville
  Concord Menn Ch (18424) (VA) 109
  Knoxville Menn Ch (18622) (VA) 110

TEXAS
Alamo
  Casa de Oracion (26971) (SC) 102
Austin
  Austin Menn Ch (28761) (SC, WDC) 102, 114
Brownsville
  Iglesia Menonita del Cordero (17830) (SC) 103
  Iglesia Menonita Rey de Gloria (27111) (SC) 103
Corpus Christi
  Prince of Peace Menn Ch (18077) (SC) 103
Dallas
  Comunidad de Esperanza (6240) (SC, WDC) .102, 114
  Iglesia Cristiana Menonita de Dallas (11273)
  (SC, WDC) 102, 116
  Iglesia Menonita Luz del Evangelio (6512)
  (SC, WDC) 103, 116
  Peace Menn Ch (17921) (SC, WDC) 103, 116
Houston
  Houston Menn Ch (23184) (SC, WDC) 102, 116
Mathis
  Calvary Menn Ch (17863) (SC) 102
  Tabernaculo de Fe (28316) (SC) 104
Perryton
  Perryton Menn Ch (20958) (RM) 100
Premont
  United Menn Ch (18168) (SC, USMBC) 104
San Antonio
  Comunidad de Vida (27410) (WDC) 114
  San Antonio Menn Ch (25239) (SC, WDC) . . .103, 117
San Benito
  New Life Christian Center (29546) (SC) 103
San Juan
  Iglesia Menonita Buenas Nuevas (28001) (SC) . . .103
Waco
  Hope Fell (10012) (SC, WDC) 102, 116

VERMONT
Bridgewater Corners
  Bethany Menn Ch (11387) (FRC) 52

CONGREGATIONS
BY LOCATION

7

Taftsville
Taftsville Chapel Menn Fell (11775) (FRC) 54

VIRGINIA
Arlington
Buenas Nuevas (10732) (LAN) 71
Bergton
Mathias Menn Ch (18689) (VA) 111
Bridgewater
New Beginnings Ch (27517) (VA) 111
Broadway
Crossroads Menn Ch (18465) (VA) 110
Trissels Menn Ch (18895) (VA) 112
Zion Menn Ch (18978) (VA) 112
Burke
Iglesia Menonita Hispana Vida Nueva (11572)
(LAN) 75
Charlottesville
Charlottesville Menn Ch (18408) (VA) 109
Chesapeake
Mount Pleasant Menn Ch (18747) (VA) 111
Christiansburg
Christiansburg Menn Fell (25296) (VA) 109
Edinburg
Woodland Menn Ch (18960) (VA) 112
Fairfax
Northern Virginia Menn Ch (23457) (VA) 111
Vietnamese Christian Fell (10104) (VA) 112
Fulks Run
Hebron Menn Ch (18572) (VA) 110
Grottoes
Mount Vernon Menn Ch (18754) (VA) 111
Hampton
Calvary Community Ch (27409) (VA) 109
Harrisonburg
Broad Street Menn Ch (18382) (VA) 109
Community Menn Ch (22178) (VA) 109
Family of Hope (29900) (VA) 110
Gospel Hill Menn Ch (18549) (VA) 110
Harrisonburg Menn Ch (18564) (VA) 110
Immanuel Menn Ch (10144) (VA) 110
Lindale Menn Ch (18655) (VA) 111
Mount Clinton Menn Ch (18721) (VA) 111
Park View Menn Ch (18788) (VA) 111
Ridgeway Menn Ch (18812) (VA) 111
Shalom Menn Congregation (29009) (VA) 111
Valley View Menn Ch (18911) (VA) 112
Weavers Menn Ch (18937) (VA) 112
Lacey Spring
Grace Menn Fell (11158) (VA) 110
Linville
Beldor Menn Ch (18341) (VA) 109
Luray
Big Spring Menn Ch (18374) (VA) 109
Lyndhurst
Lynside Menn Ch (18671) (VA) 111
Mountain View Menn Ch (18705) (VA) 111
Newport News
Huntington Menn Ch (18614) (VA) 110
Providence Menn Ch (16550) (VA) 111
Warwick River Menn Ch (18929) (VA) 112
Norfolk
Word of Life Menn Ch (18770) (VA) 112

Powhatan
Powhatan Menn Ch (18804) (VA) 111
Richmond
First Menn Ch of Richmond (18523) (VA) 110
Richmond Menn Fell (10042) 34
Singers Glen
Zion Hill Menn Ch (18986) (VA) 112
Staunton
Staunton Menn Ch (18861) (VA) 111
Stephens City
Stephens City Menn Ch (18879) (VA) 111
Stuarts Draft
Greenmonte Menn Ch (18556) (VA) 110
Stuarts Draft Menn Ch (18887) (VA) 112
Virginia Beach
Landstown Community Ch (24349) (VA) 110
Waynesboro
Springdale Menn Ch (18853) (VA) 111
Waynesboro Menn Ch (24760) (VA) 112
Williamsburg
Williamsburg Menn Ch (23135) (VA) 112

WASHINGTON
Bellevue
Evergreen Menn Ch (10145) (PNW) 94
Newport
Spring Valley Menn Ch (5730) (PNW) 95
Ritzville
Menno Menn Ch (5550) (PNW) 94
Seattle
Seattle Menn Ch (28381) (PNW) 95
Spokane
Shalom Ch (5723) (PNW) 95
Warden
Warden Menn Ch (5810) (PNW) 95

WEST VIRGINIA
Belington
Lambert Menn Ch (18630) (VA) 110
Fort Seybert
Pleasant Grove Menn Ch (18796) (VA) 111
Harman
Riverside Menn Ch (18820) (VA) 111
Morgantown
Morgantown Ch of the Brethren (27300) (ALL) 36
Philippi
Philippi Menn Ch (26500) (ALL) 37
Wardensville
Crest Hill Community Ch (18432) (VA) 110

WISCONSIN
Exeland
Exeland Menn Ch (15537) (NC) 85
Glen Flora
South Lawrence Menn Ch (15636) (NC) 85
Madison
Madison Menn Ch (10078) (CDC, IL) 43, 61
Stone Lake
Sand Lake Menn Chapel (24620) (NC) 85
Waukesha
Maple Avenue Menn Ch (23697) (CDC, IL) 43, 61

Canada

ONTARIO
Sleeman
Morson Community Bible Fell (15495) (NC) 85

Brazil

PARANA
Curitiba
Igreja Evangelica Menonita (11274) (SA) 118
Igreja Menonita de Vila Guaira (11275) (SA) 118
Palmeria
Igreja Evangelica Menonita de Witmarsum
(11276) (SA) 118
Segunda Igreja Evangelica Menonita de Witmarsum
(11277) (SA) 118

Mexico

TAMAULIPAS
Cd Reynosa
Iglesia Ebenezer (27600) (SC) 102
H Matamoros
Iglesia Evangelica Menonita Gethsemani (27602)
(SC) 102
H Matamoros
Iglesia Menonita Getsemani (10638) (IL) 61
Iglesia Menonita Rios de Agua Viva (10681) (SC) .103
Matamoros
Nueva Jerusalem (27605) (SC) 103

Reynosa
Iglesia Evangelica Galilea (27604) (SC) 102

VERACRUZ
Cd Boca del Rio
Centro Cristiano Menonita Jerusalem (27601)
(SC) 102

Paraguay

ASUNCIÓN
Mennoniten Gemeinde Asuncion (11278) (SA) ...118
Mennoniten Gemeinde Fernheim (11279) (SA) ...118
Mennoniten Gemeinde Neuland (11281) (SA) 118
Mennoniten Gemeinde zu Friesland (11280) (SA) .118
Puerto Mbopicua
Mennoniten Gemeinde Volendam (11282) (SA) ...118

Uruguay

Montevideo
Mennoniten Gemeinde Montevideo (11284) (SA) .118
Paullier
Mennoniten Gemeinde Delta (11283) (SA) 118
Rio Negro
Mennoniten Gemeinde Gartental (11286) (SA) ...118

CONGREGATIONS BY LOCATION

7

Congregations and membership by state

Country	State	Congregations	Membership
Brazil		4	985
Canada	Ontario	1	27
Mexico		7	23
Paraguay		5	2,353
Uruguay		3	381
USA	Alabama	2	50
USA	Alaska	1	18
USA	Arizona	6	666
USA	Arkansas	3	78
USA	California	36	2,630
USA	Colorado	19	1,457
USA	Connecticut	1	60
USA	Delaware	2	158
USA	District of Columbia	4	211
USA	Florida	27	2,345
USA	Georgia	3	125
USA	Hawaii	2	78
USA	Idaho	4	466
USA	Illinois	48	6,897
USA	Indiana	67	11,523
USA	Iowa	22	3,134
USA	Kansas	52	11,492
USA	Kentucky	4	86
USA	Louisiana	3	222
USA	Maine	1	34
USA	Maryland	22	1,299
USA	Massachusetts	5	317
USA	Michigan	33	1,687
USA	Minnesota	12	1,008
USA	Mississippi	8	376
USA	Missouri	7	454
USA	Montana	9	437
USA	Nebraska	12	2,613
USA	New Jersey	10	334
USA	New Mexico	3	132
USA	New York	35	2,346
USA	North Carolina	9	642
USA	North Dakota	4	171
USA	Ohio	80	12,528
USA	Oklahoma	14	1,041
USA	Oregon	20	1,787
USA	Pennsylvania	281	35,962
USA	South Dakota	10	1,655
USA	Tennessee	3	75
USA	Texas	19	858
USA	Vermont	2	97
USA	Virginia	50	7,811
USA	Washington	6	471
USA	West Virginia	6	184
USA	Wisconsin	5	251

Mennonite Church U

Every congregation and all parts of

Executive Board
Jim Schrag, executive director
J. Ron Byler, associate executive director

Executive Director's Office
Susan Mark Landis, peace advocate
John Sharp, historical committee director

Office of Congregational Life
Marlene Kropf, director

Office of Cross-Cultural Relations
Kenyetta Aduma, director

Office of Ministerial Leadership
Keith Harder and Dale Stoltzfus, directors

Office of Convention Planning
Jorge Vallejos, director

Office of Communications
Cindy Snider, director

Office of Administration
Ted Stuckey, director

Mennonite Publishing House
Joint with Mennonite Church Canada
Phil Bontrager, interim CEO

Faith & Life Resources

Herald Press
Levi Miller, director

Provident Bookstores
Ken Reinford, director

Mennonite
Carlos Romero, ex
Lisa Heinz, associa
J. David Joder, asse

For e-mail ac

Executive Board o
Mennonite Mission Net
Mennonite Publishing H
Mennonite Education Ag
MMA (Mennonite Mutua

urchwide Agencies
rch fully engaged in God's mission

Mennonite Mission Network
Stanley W. Green, executive director

Missional Church Advancement
Peter Graber, senior executive

Global Ministries
James R. Krabill, senior executive

Mission Network Services
Erwin Rempel, senior executive

Mennonite Media
Burton Buller, director

ite

Access:
6-866-2872
niteUSA.org
niteUSA.org

MMA (Mennonite Mutual Aid)
Howard Brenneman, president/CEO

Roy Bergey, vice president
Great Lakes Region

David Gautsche, vice president
Central Region

Leon Hoover, vice president
Pennsylvania Region

Glen Kauffman, vice president
Mid-Atlantic Region

Phil Mason, vice president
Midwest Region

Stanley Schrock, vice president
Western Region

gency

lastinitial@mennoniteusa.org
lastinitial@mennonitemission.net
lastinitial@mph.org
lastinitial@mea.mennonite.net
.lastname@mma-online.org

October 9, 2002

Mennonite Directory Advertisers

Ads for Mennonite-related agencies appear on the following pages.

We thank these agencies for helping to make the Mennonite Church USA 2003 Directory possible and we encourage you to support them.

"800" toll-free number - Pages 14, 279
Advancement Associates - Page 17
AMBS - Page 12
Amigo Center - Page 148
Atlanta 2003 - Pages 173, 279
Bethel College - Page 183
Dock Woods Community - Page 34
Eastern Mennonite Seminary - inside front cover
Eastern Mennonite University - Pages 37, 92, 133, 148
Good Books - Pages 135, 196, 264
Goodville Mutual - Page 104
Greencroft Retirement Communities - Page 37
Hesston College - Page 56
Lancaster Mennonite School - Page 85
Landis Homes Retirement Community - Page 117
Mennonite Central Committee - Page 48
Mennonite Education Agency - Page 17

Mennonite Financial Federal Credit Union - Page 158
Mennonite Health Services - Page 92
Mennonite Information Center - Page 100
Mennonite Media - Page 199
Mennonite Medical Association - Page 26
Mennonite Mission Network - Pages 5, 23, 29
Mennonite Mutual Aid - Pages 27, 281
Mennonite Nurses Association - Page 58
Mennonite Publishing House - Pages 15, 22, 26, 175, 281, outside back cover
Mennonite Village - Page 95
Mennonite Weekly Review - Page 171
Mennonite Your Way - Page 172
MRN Ministry Resources - Page 174
Mutual Aid Exchange - Page 6
New York Mennonite Agency, Inc. - Page 118
Oaklawn - Page 163
Park View Federal Credit Union - Page 158
Rockhill Mennonite Community - Page 112
Spruce Lake Retreat - Page 147
Sunnyside Village Retirement Community - Page 163
The Mennonite - inside back cover
Together - Page 263
Visual Identity - Page 54, 284
Williamsburg Christian Retreat Center - Page 148

Quickfind

NAME AND ADDRESS	TELEPHONE	FAX	E-MAIL AND WEBSITE
African American Mennonite Association (AAMA) 2311 Tower Place, Hampton VA 23666	757-262-0128	757-825-8771	aama_org@yahoo.com www.ammaorg.org
Allegheny Mennonite Conference PO Box 12, 111 E Main St, Somerset PA 15501-0012	814-443-2007	814-445-3418	officeamc@cs.com
Archives of Mennonite Church USA Goshen: 1700 S Main St, Goshen IN 46526-4794 North Newton: 300 East 27th St, North Newton KS 67117-0531	574-535-7477 316-284-5360	574-535-7756	archives@goshen.edu www.goshen.edu/mcarchives mla@bethelks.edu www.bethelks.edu/services/mla
Associated Mennonite Biblical Seminary 3003 Benham Ave, Elkhart IN 46517-1999	574-295-3726	574-295-0092	rreschly@ambs.edu www.ambs.edu
Atlantic Coast Mennonite Conference PO Box 737, 2791 Best Road, Morgantown PA 19543	800-238-0126 610-286-7517	none	atlanticcoast@juno.com
Bethel College 300 East 27th St, North Newton KS 67117	316-283-2500	316-284-5286	webmaster@bethelks.edu www.bethelks.edu
Buffton College 280 W College Ave, Bluffton OH 45817-1196	800-488-3257 419-358-3000	419-358-3323	webmaster@bluffton.edu www.bluffton.edu
Brethren in Christ General Conference (North America) 431 Grantham Rd, PO Box A, Grantham PA 17027	717-697-2634	717-691-7714	bic@messiah.edu www.bic-church.org
Canadian Mennonite 490 Dutton Dr, Unit C5, Waterloo ON N2L 6H7	519-884-3810	519-884-3331	editor@canadianmennonite.org www.canadianmennonite.org
Central District Conference 1015 Division St, Goshen IN 46528-2000	574-534-1485	574-534-8654	cdcoffice@hoosierlink.net
Central Plains Mennonite Conference PO Box 101, 121 E Third St, Freeman SD 57029	605-925-4463	605-925-7293	cpmcsd@gwtc.net
Church of the Brethren 1451 Dundee Ave, Elgin IL 60120	800-323-8039 847-742-5100	847-742-6103	info@brethren.org www.brethren.org
Christian Peacemaker Teams PO Box 6508, Chicago IL 60680-6508	773-277-0253	773-277-0291	cpt@igc.org www.cpt.org

NAME AND ADDRESS	TELEPHONE	FAX	E-MAIL AND WEBSITE
Conservative Mennonite Conference 9910 Rosedale Milford Center Rd, Irwin OH 43029	740-857-1234	740-857-1605	cmcrosedale@juno.com www.cmcrosedale.org
Eastern District Conference 711 Route 113, Souderton PA 18964	215-723-5513	215-723-1211	info@fmc-online.org www.fmc-online.org
Eastern Mennonite Missions 53 West Brandt Blvd, PO Box 458, Salunga PA 17538-0458	717-898-2251	717-898-8092	info@emm.org www.emm.org
Eastern Mennonite Seminary 1200 Park Rd, Harrisonburg VA 22802	540-432-4260	540-432-4444	info@emu.edu www.emu.edu
Eastern Mennonite University 1200 Park Rd, Harrisonburg VA 22802	540-432-4000	540-432-4444	info@emu.edu www.emu.edu
Franconia Conference of the Mennonite Church 771 Route 113, Souderton PA 18964-1000	215-723-5513	215-723-1211	info@fmc-online.org www.fmc-online.org
Franklin Mennonite Conference 4856 Molly Pitcher Hwy S, Chambersburg PA 17201	717-375-4544	717-375-2136	fmcmb@cvn.net
Goshen College 1700 S Main St, Goshen IN 46526	800-348-7422 574-535-7000	574-535-7660	info@goshen.edu www.goshen.edu
Gulf States Mennonite Conference 315 Northwood Dr, Philadelphia MS 39350	662-726-2542	662-726-2542	gsmc@pngusa.com
Hesston College 325 S College, PO Box 3000, Hesston KS 67062-2093	866-437-7866 620-327-4221	620-327-8300	admissions@hesston.edu www.Hesston.edu
Iglesia Hispana Menonita 1208 "L" St, Box 111, Reedley CA 93654	(iglesia) 559-638-7723 (casa) 559-637-9787	559-637-8826	jvmontes@juno.com
Illinois Mennonite Conference 104 E South St, PO Box 3, Tremont IL 61568	309-925-2111	309-346-5904	ilconinfo@earthlink.net
Indiana-Michigan Mennonite Conference 212 S Main St, Goshen IN 46526	800-288-8486 574-534-4006	574-533-5676	imoffice@im.mennonite.net www.im.mennonite.net
Lancaster Mennonite Conference 2160 Lincoln Hwy E #5, Lancaster PA 17602	800-216-7249 717-293-5246	717-431-1987	lmccenter@lanmenconf.org www.lanmenconf.org
Lao Mennonite Ministries 71 Lakeshore Dr, St Catharines ON L2N 2T3 Canada	905-646-3651	905-646-3651	kuayingt@mennomission.net
Mennonite Brethren Churches, U.S. Conference 315 S Lincoln St, PO Box V, Hillsboro KS 67063-0155	620-947-3151	620-947-3266	usconf@southwind.net www.usmb.org
Mennonite Central Committee 21 S 12th St, PO Box 500, Akron PA 17501-0500 U.S. - 21 S 12th St, PO Box 500, Akron PA 17501-0500	888-563-4676 717-859-1151 717-859-3889	 717-859-2171 717-859-3875	 mailbox@mcc.org, www.mcc.org mailbox@mcc.org, www.mcc.org
Mennonite Church Canada 600 Shaftesbury Blvd, Winnipeg MB R3P 0M4, Canada	866-888-6785 204-888-6781	204-831-5675	office@mennonitechurch.ca www.mennonitechurch.ca
Mennonite Church USA Executive Board Great Lakes: 500 S Main St, PO Box 1245, Elkhart IN 46515-1245 Great Plains: 722 Main St, PO Box 347, Newton KS 67114-0347	866-866-2872 574-294-7523 316-283-5100	 574-293-1892 316-283-0454	www.mennoniteusa.org elkhart@mennoniteusa.org newton@mennoniteusa.org

NAME AND ADDRESS	TELEPHONE	FAX	E-MAIL AND WEBSITE
Mennonite Disaster Service 1018 Main St, Akron PA 17501	717-859-2210	717-859-4910	mds@mdsbinat.org www.mds.mennonite.net
Mennonite Economic Development Associates (MEDA) 302-280 Smith St, Winnipeg MB R3C 1K2, Canada	800-665-7026	204-942-4001	meda@meda.org www.meda.org
Mennonite Education Agency 63846 County Rd 35 Suite 1, Goshen IN 46528-9621	866-866-2872 574-642-3164	574-642-4863	info@mea.mennonite.net www.mcusa.mennonite.net/agency_mea
Mennonite Health Services 234 S Main St, Suite 1, Goshen IN 46526	800-611-4007 574-534-9689	574-534-3254	info@mhsonline.org www.mhsonline.org
Mennonite Indian Leaders Council (MILC) 722 Main St, PO Box 347, Newton KS 67114-0347 500 S Main St, PO Box 370, Elkhart IN 46515-0370	316-283-5100 574-294-7523	316-283-0454 574-294-8669	milc@mennonitemission.net
Mennonite Media 1251 Virginia Ave, Harrisonburg VA 22802-2497	800-999-3534 540-434-6701	540-434-5556	info@mennomedia.org www.mennonitemission.net
Mennonite Men 722 Main St, PO Box 347, Newton KS 67114-0347	316-283-5100	316-283-0454	jimg@mennoniteusa.org www.mennonitemen.org
Mennonite Mission Network Great Lakes: 500 S Main St, PO Box 370, Elkhart IN 46515-0370 Great Plains: 722 Main St, PO Box 347, Newton KS 67114-0347	866-866-2872 574-294-7523 316-283-5100	574-294-8669 316-283-0454	www.mennonitemission.net info@mennonitemission.net info@mennonitemission.net
Mennonite Mutual Aid 1110 N Main St, PO Box 483, Goshen IN 46527-0483	800-348-7468 574-533-9511	574-533-5264	mma@mma-online.org www.mma-online.org
Mennonite Publishing House, Inc. 616 Walnut Ave, Scottdale PA 15683 718 Main St, PO Box 347, Newton KS 67114-0347	866-866-2872 724-887-8500 316-283-5100	724-887-3111 316-283-0454	www.mph.org info@mph.org flp@ph.org
Mennonite Women USA 722 Main St, PO Box 347, Newton KS 67114-0347	316-283-5100	316-283-0454	mwusa@mennonitewomenusa.org
Mennonite World Conference 8 rue du Fosse des Treize, 67000 Strasbourg, France 50 Kent Ave, Kitchener ON N2G 3R1, Canada	(33)388-15-27-50 519-571-0060	(33)388-15-27-51 519-571-1980	www.mwc-cmm.org strasbourgh@mwc-cmm.org kitcheners@mwc-cmm.org
New York Mennonite Conference PO Box C, 5546 Alger Road, Martinsburg NY 13404	315-376-3734	315-376-3071	dotconf@northnet.org www.bfn.org/~nymennon
North American Vietnamese Mennonite Fel. 7155 Sherbrook St, Vancouver BC V5X 4E3, Canada	604-324-1200	none	nhienp@hotmail.com
North Central Conference of the Mennonite Church 166 N State Rd 40, Exeland WI 54835-2176	715-943-2317	none	egschrock@juno.com
Ohio Conference of the Mennonite Church 13363 Jericho Rd, PO Box 210, Kidron OH 44636	330-857-5421	330-857-5485	ohmc@zoominternet.net www.ohio.mennonite.net
Pacific Northwest Mennonite Conference 2102 N 20th St, Boise ID 83702	208-336-5646	none	lhauder@earthlink.net www.pnmc.org
Pacific Southwest Mennonite Conference Box CAL, 1539 E Howard St, Pasadena CA 91104	626-720-8100	626-720-8101	admin@pacificsouthwest.org www.pacificsouthwest.org

NAME AND ADDRESS	TELEPHONE	FAX	E-MAIL AND WEBSITE
Provident Bookstores 616 Walnut Ave, Scottdale PA 15683	800-759-4447 724-887-8500	724-887-3111	pbs@mph.org www.providentbookstores.com
Rocky Mountain Mennonite Conference 6610 S Williams Circle W, Centennial CO 80121	303-795-0090	303-795-0090	rmmc@rmmc.org www.rmmc.org
South Central Mennonite Conference 2517 N Main, PO Box 448, North Newton KS 67117	316-283-7080	316-283-0620	scc@mennoscc.org
Southeast Mennonite Conference 1004 Ponder Ave, Sarasota FL 34232-6633	941-342-9959	941-342-0318	smc5245@juno.com
Ten Thousand Villages 704 Main St, PO Box 500, Akron PA 17501-0500	717-859-8100	717-859-2622	inquiry@villages-mcc.org www.tenthousandvillages.org
The Mennonite Editor, 1700 S Main St, Goshen IN 46526 Newton: 722 Main St, Newton KS 67114	800-790-2498 574-535-0651 316-283-5155	574-535-6050 316-283-0454	www.themennonite.org editor@themennonite.org editor@themennonite.org
United Native Ministries 2121 Hawthorne Dr, Elkhart IN 46517	574-295-8530	574-293-1892	no e-mail
Virginia Mennonite Board of Missions 901 Parkwood Dr, Harrisonburg VA 22802	800-707-5535 540-434-9727	540-434-7627	info@wmbm.org www.vmbm.org
Virginia Mennonite Conference 901 Parkwood Dr, Harrisonburg VA 22802	800-707-5535 540-434-9727	540-434-7627	info@vmconf.org www.vmconf.org
Western District Conference 2517 N Main, PO Box 306, North Newton KS 67117	316-283-6300	316-283-0620	wdc@mennowdc.org www.mennowdc.org